D1281065

LOGIC, METHODOLOGY AND PHILOSOPHY OF SCIENCE III

This research has been sponsored in part by the
Mathematics Branch, Office of Naval Research through
the European Office of Aerospace Research, OAR,
United States Air Force under Grant AF EOAR 67-55.

STUDIES IN LOGIC

AND

THE FOUNDATIONS OF MATHEMATICS

Editors

A. HEYTING, *Amsterdam*

A. MOSTOWSKI, *Warszawa*

A. ROBINSON, *New Haven*

P. SUPPES, *Stanford*

Advisory Editorial Board

Y. BAR-HILLEL, *Jerusalem*

K. L. DE BOUVÈRE, *Santa Clara*

H. HERMES, *Freiburg i.Br.*

J. HINTIKKA, *Helsinki*

J. C. SHEPHERDSON, *Bristol*

E. P. SPECKER, *Zürich*

NORTH-HOLLAND PUBLISHING COMPANY

AMSTERDAM

LOGIC, METHODOLOGY AND PHILOSOPHY OF SCIENCE III

PROCEEDINGS OF THE THIRD INTERNATIONAL CONGRESS
FOR LOGIC, METHODOLOGY AND PHILOSOPHY OF SCIENCE,
AMSTERDAM 1967

Edited by

B. VAN ROOTSELAAR

Agricultural University, Wageningen, The Netherlands

and

J. F. STAAL

University of California, Berkeley, USA

1968

NORTH-HOLLAND PUBLISHING COMPANY
AMSTERDAM

North-Holland Publishing Company - Amsterdam - 1968

*No part of this book may be reproduced in any form
by print, photoprint, microfilm or any other means
without written permission from the publisher*

Library of Congress Catalog Card Number: 68-29768

PRINTED IN THE NETHERLANDS

Q
175
I535
1967

CONTENTS

1. MATHEMATICAL LOGIC

2. FOUNDATIONS OF MATHEMATICAL THEORIES

3. AUTOMATA AND PROGRAMMING LANGUAGES

317906

11. HISTORY OF LOGIC, METHODOLOGY AND PHILOSOPHY OF SCIENCE

PREFACE

This volume constitutes the Proceedings of the Third International Congress for Logic, Methodology and Philosophy of Science. The Congress was held at the Grand Hotel Krasnapolsky, Amsterdam, from August 25 to September 2, 1967, under the joint of the Division of Logic, Methodology and Philosophy of Science of the International Union of History and Philosophy of Science. The Congress took place in the Netherlands at the invitation of the *Nederlandse Vereniging voor Logica en Wijsbegeerte der Exacte Wetenschappen*.

The Congress was organized by an executive committee consisting of J. Ch. Boland (treasurer), K. L. de Bouvère, Haskell B. Curry, A. Heyting (chairman), B. van Rootselaar (secretary), J. F. Staal (secretary). The technical organization was entrusted to the Holland Organizing Centre, the Hague.

The Congress was divided into eleven sections and there were three symposia. The program for each section was drawn up by the following advisory committees in cooperation with the executive committee.

1. *Mathematical Logic:*
   K. L. de Bouvère, H. B. Curry, R. M. Montague, P. S. Novikov,
   J. Hintikka, J. Łos, A. Tarski.

2. *Foundations of Mathematical Theories:*
   S. Feferman, A. Heyting, S. C. Kleene, G. Kreisel, A. Mostowski,
   B. van Rootselaar, K. Schütte, A. Tarski.

3. *Automata and Programming Languages:*
   E. W. Dijkstra, S. Gorn, A. van Wijngaarden, H. Zemanek.

4. *Philosophy of Logic and Mathematics:*
   C. D. Parsons, B. Dreben, P. Lorenzen.

5. *General Problems of Methodology and Philosophy of Science:*
   A. G. M. van Melsen, G. Nuchelmans.

6. *Methodology and Philosophy of Physical Sciences:*
   P. G. Bergmann, H. Groenewold, G. Holton, H. Putnam,
   B. van Rootselaar, L. Rosenfeld.

7. *Methodology and Philosophy of Biological Sciences:*
   M. A. Bouman, M. T. Jansen, M. Jeuken, J. Lever, C. P. Raven,
   H. P. Wolvekamp.

8. *Methodology and Philosophy of Psychological Sciences:*
   A. Bresson, J. J. Gibson, P. Suppes, J. G. Taylor.
9. *Methodology and Philosophy of Social Sciences:*
   I. Gadourek.
10. *Methodology and Philosophy of Linguistics:*
    Y. Bar-Hillel, N. Chomsky, J. F. Staal, A. van Wijngaarden.
11. *History of Logic, Methodology and Philosophy of Science:*
    L. M. de Rijk, J. F. Staal.

There was an intersectional symposium on "The role of formal logic in the evaluation of argumentation in natural languages". Parts of the discussion, which was chaired by Y. Bar-Hillel, are expected to be published.

In section 2 a symposium on "Foundations of intuitionism" was organized by A. Heyting. The invited addresses by S. C. Kleene, G. Kreisel, J. Myhill, W. W. Tait, A. S. Troelstra are included in these proceedings. The address by Myhill, who was unable to attend, was read by P. G. Gilmore. A symposium on "Parenthemes" was organized by H. Hiż in section 3. Invited participants were A. Grzegorczyk and Z. Pawlak.

These proceedings comprise the texts, sometimes revised, of most of the addresses presented by invited speakers. Abstracts of many of these addresses and of many of the contributed papers were issued to members at the beginning of the Congress. The titles of all papers are listed in the scientific program which is published at the end of this volume. The editors regret that they did not succeed in collecting the texts of all the invited addresses. Accordingly, these proceedings do not include the addresses by M. Dummett, D. Finkelstein, H. Gaifman*, R. O. Gandy, S. A. Kripke, D. S. Scott, P. Vopenka.

On behalf of the Executive Committee and on behalf of the *Nederlandse Vereniging voor Logica en Wijsbegeerte der Exacte Wetenschappen*, the editors wish to thank all those who made the organization of the Congress possible. Thanks are due in particular to His Royal Highness the Prince of the Netherlands, who accepted the patronage of the Congress; to the members of the Committee of Honour and of the Ladies' Committee; and to the institutions and firms that contributed to the Congress.

Landbouwhogeschool, Wageningen   The Editors
University of California, Berkeley

---

* Professor Gaifman's paper entitled *The structure of models of Peano's arithmetic* will appear in The Pacific Journal of Mathematics.

LIST OF DONORS

Ministry of Education and Science of the Netherlands
Municipality of Amsterdam
Division of Logic, Methodology and Philosophy of Science of the International Union of History and Philosophy of Science
Office of Naval Research, Washington, USA
United States National Committee for the Division of Logic, Methodology and Philosophy of Science
Prins Bernhard Fonds
Landbouwhogeschool, Wageningen
Wiskundig Genootschap, Amsterdam
Internationale Bedrijfsmachine Maatschappij N.V. (IBM Nederland), Amsterdam
N.V. Philips, Eindhoven
Shell Internationale Research Maatschappij N.V., 's Gravenhage
Unilever N.V., Rotterdam
Nationale Nederlanden N.V., Rotterdam
Koninklijke Zout-Ketjen N.V., Hengelo
N.V. Hollandse Signaalapparaten, Hengelo
Algemeen Rekencentrum N.V., Amsterdam
Koninklijke Nederlandse Vliegtuigfabriek Fokker N.V., Amsterdam
Nederlandse Vereniging voor Logica en Wijsbegeerte der Exacte Wetenschappen

Speech by Professor A. Heyting,

president of the congress, at the opening session on august 25

Ladies and Gentlemen,

In the name of the Organizing Committee of this Congress I welcome you to the Netherlands, to the city of Amsterdam and to the Congress. It makes us happy that so many scholars from countries all over the world have come together here to exchange information, to renew and strengthen old connections and to form new ones.

A special word of welcome is due to Mr. Nittel, who will officially open the Congress in the name of the Minister of Education and Sciences, to Professor Bar-Hillel, president of the Division for LMPS of the IUHPS, to Miss Hersch, professor in the University of Geneva, who will speak in the name of Mr. Maheu, Director-general of UNESCO, to the members of the Committee of Honour, and last but not least to the ladies who so kindly consented to add lustre to this meeting by a musical performance, Mrs. de Smidt and Mrs. Valkhoff.

With grief I mention those whom I cannot welcome here because they died in the interval between the Congress in Jerusalem and this one. Among them are no less than three of our invited speakers.

Norwood Russell Hanson died, 43 years old, on April 18 of this year in an airplane crash. He was professor of philosophy at Yale University. The organizing committee had invited him for a lecture in section 5, General problems of Methodology and Philosophy of Science.

Uriel Weinreich, professor of Yiddish at Columbia University, New York, died on March 30 of this year, 40 years old. He had been invited for a lecture in section 10, Methodology and Philosophy of Linguistics.

A. I. Malcev, professor of mathematics at the University of Nowosibirsk, member of the Academy of Sciences of the USSR, a leading Russian mathematician and logician, died in July of this year, about 60 years old. He was invited for a lecture in a plenary meeting of the Congress, organized by section 1, Mathematical Logic.

On December 2, 1966, Luitzen Egbertus Jan Brouwer died, 85 years old, by a traffic accident. It is unnecessary to dwell here upon his pioneer work in mathematics and its foundations. The symposium on the foundations of intuitionism, which will be held in this Congress, was planned long before his death; it has now assumed the character of a posthumous homage.

Another pioneer, Abraham Adolf Fraenkel, died on October 15, 1965. He was 74 years old. After a professorate at Marburg, Germany, he had been for many years professor of mathematics at Jerusalem. He was one of the founders of the axiomatical set theory and much of the work that is done nowadays in this field would have been impossible without the foundations he laid. It may be said at this place that he had very special connections with the Netherlands; I salute here Mrs. Fraenkel, who is Dutch by birth.

Another pioneer, but in a slightly different sense, was Mrs. S. A. Janowska, professor of logic in the University of Moscow, who died in November 1966 in the age of 70. She deserves our thanks for encouraging and furthering the study of symbolic logic in the USSR.

It was further brought to my attention that Stanislaw Jaskowski, professor of mathematics at the University of Toruń, Poland, and a wellknown logician, died on November 16, 1965.

Professor John Lemmon died on July 29, 1966. He was only 36 years old and had just begun a promising career by his appointment as a professor of philosophy at the University of California.

Though he died before the Jerusalem Congress, I must mention here Evert Willem Beth, because if he had lived, he would have taken an important part in the organization of this congress. The organizing committee painfully missed him for his extensive knowledge and for his deliberate judgment. We are grateful that Mrs. Beth accepted to preside over the ladies' committee and that she is present here.

I beg you to commemorate these scholars and the many others whom I could not mention by a few moments of silence.

A congress like this one oscillates, so to say, between two poles, the mathematical and the philosophical. In other words, it oscillates between communication of results and defense of opinions. Fortunately, these two aspects are not separated. Often results give rise to discussion on their interpretation, and conversely philosophical opinions inspire mathematical results. In both cases discussion is essential. Let me end, in this context, with a short anecdote. A visitor from abroad came to Amsterdam this spring because he had been told we would have a hot summer here. He was very much disappointed when he realized that this had only been a weather forecast.

I take it that he found what he looked for in other parts of the world. What is the connection with this Congress? Simply this that I hope that it will become a hot congress, and then not in the meteorological sense, and that, as the French proverb says, from the clash of opinions sparks of truth will spring up.

Thank you.

Speech by Professor A. Heyting,

at the closing session on September 2

I wish to thank all those who contributed to the success of this Congress: First of all His Royal Highness the Prince of the Netherlands, who accepted the patronage of the Congress. Further the members of the Committee of Honour, the Government of the Netherlands and the Municipality of the city of Amsterdam, who offered us a reception, and the Division of Logic and Philosophy of Science of the International Union of History and Philosophy of Science which accepted the invitation of the Netherlands to organize the Congress. The direction and collaborators of the Holland Organizing Centre firmly kept the material organization in their hands; among them the ladies behind the counter deserve special mentioning for their kind and efficient help to anybody who needed it. Those who read papers and those who participated in discussions really made the Congress deserve this name. The ladies' committee organized excursions, thereby serving two purposes, the first one direct, namely to be agreeable to the associate members (which is an unelegant name for the lady visitors), the second indirect, namely to keep the ladies from making their husbands play truant from the lectures. Finally I thank all those who by assisting to the sessions positively contributed to the success of the Congress, the Division which I mentioned a few moments before, the United States National Committee for this Division, the Office of Naval Research in the U.S.A., the Dutch Prins Bernhard Fonds, which supports cultural efforts, the Wiskundig Genootschap at Amsterdam and several industrial firms which understand that even abstract scientific research is in the long run favourable to industrial development, and therefore are willing to support it.

It was an agreeable experience that we met in this Congress many young scientists also from countries which used to send delegates consisting only of people who had reached the top of their career. I am convinced that contacts between young men of different countries will essentially contribute to the progress of science.

Let me end by expressing the hope that this Congress has been useful in the first place for the advancement of science, but in addition by bringing together people from all over the world.

In Memoriam A. I. Malcev

On the night of the 6th of August professor A. Malcev suddenly died in Novosibirsk. That was an unexpected blow for all those who knew him, but this is also an important loss for the world of mathematics.

Malcev was a great mathematician and made fundamental scientific discoveries in the fields of algebra and mathematical logics. His first printed work, in 1936, was on mathematical logic, where he proved the compactness theorem and indicated its applications for model theory. This theorem brought him later the world fame. The next years Malcev made deep investigations in group theory, Lie-algebras and topological algebras. He not only founded the fundamental theorems, as for instance the known Levi-Malcev theorem in the theory of Lie-algebras, but also found an interesting direction for research. These are, for example, study of finite approximations (residual finiteness) for groups and algebraic systems. Malcev also developed completely new methods. He was a pioneer in using methods of mathematical logic and universal algebra for results on such topics as group theory. Here one can remember Malcev's famous work of 1941 (on new tools for studying local theorems in group theory) which even on the first reading surprises by its clearness and strength. It was mentioned by professor A. Robinson at the last ICLMPS.

Later on Malcev worked in the model theory and decidability where he found many important results, for instance, undecidability of the elementary theory of finite groups. Malcev also was among the first logicians to study enumerated algebras. The last years he studied varieties and quasivarieties of universal algebras.

Apart from his own scientific work and discoveries he always gave much of his time and attention to the life of algebra and mathematical logic in the Soviet Union. The seminar Algebra & Logic created by him in Novosibirsk is now well-known in the world since it is the scientific school he created there.

Malcev was also original as a philosopher and we deeply regret that he never published his philosophical thoughts. Being born in a modest family of a glass-blower, he loved nature and music and was a very charming person.

Even a short acquaintance or a simple conversation with him was always rewarding.

The memory of him as a man will remain among his students and all those who knew him. And his scientific work leaves such a strong impression that one can not realize all its consequences now.

Yu. L. Ershov

Section 1

Mathematical Logic

INFINITARY PROPERTIES OF MODELS
GENERATED FROM INDISCERNIBLES

C. C. CHANG*

University of California, Los Angeles, USA

1. Introduction

Let $\mathfrak{A} = \langle A, \ldots \rangle$ be a model of a theory T in a first-order language L with identity. We suppose that L has enough function symbols and T has enough axioms to assure that all Skolem functions are present. Let X be a subset of A simply ordered by the relation $\leqslant$. X is said to be *a set of indiscernibles in* $\mathfrak{A}$ if for any two finite strictly increasing sequences $x_1 < x_2 < \cdots < x_n$ and $y_1 < y_2 < \cdots < y_n$ of elements of X the models $(\mathfrak{A}, x_1, \ldots, x_n)$ and $(\mathfrak{A}, y_1, \ldots, y_n)$ are elementarily equivalent. A fundamental existence theorem due to EHREN-FEUCHT and MOSTOWSKI [1956] states that: If a theory T has infinite models, then given any order type τ, T has a model $\mathfrak{A}$ with a set of indiscernibles X of type τ. Assume now X is a set of indiscernibles in $\mathfrak{A}$. Let $H(X)$ be the Skolem hull of X in $\mathfrak{A}$, and let $\mathfrak{H}(X)$ be the submodel of $\mathfrak{A}$ determined by $H(X)$. It is well known that:

(A) $\mathfrak{H}(X)$ is an elementary submodel of $\mathfrak{A}$.

(B) X is a set of indiscernibles in $\mathfrak{H}(X)$ with respect to the same ordering $\leqslant$.

(C) If Y is a subset of X with the natural ordering induced on it, then $\mathfrak{H}(Y)$ is an elementary submodel of $\mathfrak{H}(X)$ and Y is a set of indiscernibles in $\mathfrak{H}(Y)$.

If we introduce the notation $\subset$ for submodels and $\prec$ for elementary submodels, then (C) can be written more compactly as

(D) If $(Y, \leqslant) \subset (X, \leqslant)$, then $\mathfrak{H}(Y) \prec \mathfrak{H}(X)$.

A fortiori it follows that

(E) If $(Y, \leqslant) \prec (X, \leqslant)$, then $\mathfrak{H}(Y) \prec \mathfrak{H}(X)$.

---

* The preparation of this paper was partially supported by NSF Grant 5600 and partially by a Fulbright grant.

The main idea of this paper consists of the observation (Proposition 1) that (E) remains true if the symbol $\prec$ is replaced in both the hypothesis and the conclusion by the symbol $\prec_{\lambda\kappa}$ which expresses the elementary submodel relation for certain infinitary languages $L_{\lambda\kappa}$. Thus $L_{\lambda\kappa}$ properties of Y and X are reflected up to $L_{\lambda\kappa}$ properties of $\mathfrak{H}(Y)$ and $\mathfrak{H}(X)$. In general, for (E) to hold for these more general languages some restrictions must be placed on λ and κ. If no restrictions are placed on λ and κ, a version of (E) will still hold under a further broadening of the language (as will be explained below). It turns out that this simple observation has many interesting consequences. For example, in Theorem 2 we give an improvement of a result of SILVER [1966] (this result goes back to SCOTT [1961], ROWBOTTOM [1964] and GAIFMAN [1964]). Theorem 3 contains a (poor man's) version of the upward Löwenheim-Skolem theorem for $L_{\kappa\kappa}$ and Theorem 4 shows the existence of models $\mathfrak{A}$ with an ordered set X of $L_{\kappa\kappa}$-indiscernible elements in $\mathfrak{A}$. Thus our observation shed more light on the model theory of infinitary languages.

2. Infinitary languages

Throughout κ shall be an infinite regular cardinal. Some of our results can be restated for singular cardinals, however not much will be gained by putting in this complication. Small greek letters $\lambda, \mu, \ldots$ shall denote ordinals or cardinals. The classical infinitary languages $L_{\lambda\kappa}$ where λ is a cardinal has besides the symbols of L the following additional symbols:

> individual variables v_ξ, $\xi < \kappa$;
> infinite conjunction $\bigwedge$ and disjunction $\bigvee$ over fewer than λ formulas;
> infinite universal $\forall$ and existential $\exists$ quantifiers over sequences of variables of length less than κ.

The notions of atomic formulas, formulas, subformulas, free and bound occurrences of variables, and sentences of $L_{\lambda\kappa}$ are defined as usual. Because κ is regular any sentence of $L_{\lambda\kappa}$ contains only subformulas with fewer than κ free variables. The quantifier rank of a formula is introduced by induction as usual. That is, the quantifier rank of φ is the sup of the quantifier ranks of all subformulas of φ if φ is a negation, conjunction, or disjunction; otherwise the quantifier rank of φ is one more than the quantifier rank of ψ if $\varphi = \forall x \psi$ or $\varphi = \exists x \psi$. Notice that every formula whose rank is a limit ordinal is a boolean combination of subformulas of smaller rank. If λ is regular then every formula of $L_{\lambda\kappa}$ has quantifier rank less than λ. The standard notion of satisfaction is assumed. We write $\mathfrak{A} \equiv_{\lambda\kappa} \mathfrak{B}$ if $\mathfrak{A}$ and $\mathfrak{B}$ are $L_{\lambda\kappa}$-elementarily equivalent and $\mathfrak{A} \prec_{\lambda\kappa} \mathfrak{B}$ if $\mathfrak{A}$ is an $L_{\lambda\kappa}$-elementary submodel of $\mathfrak{B}$. It is quite clear that $L_{\omega\omega}$ is just the ordinary language L.

We now consider a broader class of infinitary languages $L'_{\lambda\kappa}$ where λ is an ordinal. The new symbols of $L'_{\lambda\kappa}$ are:

individual variables v_ξ, $\xi < \kappa$;
infinite conjunction $\bigwedge$ and infinite disjunction $\bigvee$ over *arbitrary* sets of formulas;
infinite universal $\forall$ and existential $\exists$ quantifiers over sequences of variables of length less than κ.

We retain all the formation rules as in the case of $L_{\lambda\kappa}$, however the formulas of $L'_{\lambda\kappa}$ are restricted by the following two conditions:

each formula of $L'_{\lambda\kappa}$ has fewer than κ free variables,
each formula of $L'_{\lambda\kappa}$ has quantifier rank at most λ.

These restrictions are very natural and will make the formulas of $L'_{\lambda\kappa}$ into a set. Satisfaction is defined as usual and we introduce the corresponding notions $\mathfrak{A} \equiv'_{\lambda\kappa} \mathfrak{B}$ and $\mathfrak{A} \prec'_{\lambda\kappa} \mathfrak{B}$. We can verify that $L'_{\omega\omega}$ is not L. Indeed, if λ is a regular cardinal then every formula of $L_{\lambda\kappa}$ is a formula of $L'_{\lambda\kappa}$ but the converse is not true. We point out that if L is fixed and κ is fixed, then one can easily find cardinals λ such that (for all practical purposes) the two languages $L_{\lambda\kappa}$ and $L'_{\lambda\kappa}$ differ only by those formulas whose rank is λ. The cardinal λ has to be large enough so that conjunction and disjunction over arbitrary sets of formulas is equivalent to conjunction and disjunction over fewer than λ formulas.

As an example for gaining an understanding of $L'_{\lambda\kappa}$, we state and prove the following simple result:

(I) Suppose that $\mathfrak{A}$ and $\mathfrak{B}$ are elementarily equivalent κ-saturated models (not necessarily of power κ). Then $\mathfrak{A} \equiv'_{\lambda\kappa} \mathfrak{B}$ for every ordinal λ. If, in addition $\mathfrak{A} \prec \mathfrak{B}$, then $\mathfrak{A} \prec'_{\lambda\kappa} \mathfrak{B}$ for all λ.

PROOF: We only prove the first part; the second part follows easily. We prove the following by induction on the ordinal λ:

If $\mathfrak{A}$ and $\mathfrak{B}$ are κ-saturated elementarily equivalent models, then $\mathfrak{A} \equiv'_{\lambda\kappa} \mathfrak{B}$.

When $\lambda = 0$, every sentence of $L'_{0\kappa}$ is a boolean combination of atomic sentences. Thus the assertion follows. If λ is a limit ordinal, then every sentence of $L'_{\lambda\kappa}$ is a boolean combination of sentences of rank less than λ. Again the assertion follows. Suppose φ is a sentence of rank $\lambda + 1$, then φ

is a boolean combination of sentences of form $\exists \bar{x} \psi$ where ψ is a formula of rank at most λ and $\bar{x}$ is a sequence of variables of length less than κ. We may assume that $\varphi = \exists \bar{x} \psi$. Suppose $\mathfrak{A} \vDash \varphi$. Then there is a sequence $\bar{a}$ of elements of A of length less than κ such that $\mathfrak{A} \vDash \psi [\bar{a}]$. Since $\mathfrak{B}$ is κ-saturated, there is a sequence $\bar{b}$ of elements of B such that $(\mathfrak{A}, \bar{a}) \equiv (\mathfrak{B}, \bar{b})$. As $(\mathfrak{A}, \bar{a})$ and $(\mathfrak{B}, \bar{b})$ are still κ-saturated, we apply the induction hypothesis and get $(\mathfrak{A}, \bar{a}) \equiv'_{\lambda\kappa} (\mathfrak{B}, \bar{b})$. Thus $\mathfrak{B} \vDash \psi [\bar{b}]$ and $\mathfrak{B} \vDash \varphi$. The converse is proved in an entirely similar manner. So $\mathfrak{A} \equiv'_{(\lambda+1)\kappa} \mathfrak{B}$ and the induction is complete.

It follows easily from (I) and standard results in model theory that if a countable theory T has infinite models then T has models of power at most 2^{λ} which have arbitrarily large $L_{\lambda^+\lambda^+}$-elementary extensions. If we assume the generalized continuum hypothesis then T has models of power κ which have arbitrarily large $L_{\kappa\kappa}$-elementary extensions. We shall see later, in (III), that the generalized continuum hypothesis is not needed for this result. We might mention that these arbitrarily large extensions can be made to be $L_{\mu\lambda^+}$-elementary and $L_{\mu\kappa}$-elementary extensions for arbitrarily large μ. Apparently, we can not prove these last results without the generalized continuum hypothesis.

3. The main proposition

Let X be a set of indiscernibles in $\mathfrak{A}$. In view of (A) and (B), we may as well assume that $\mathfrak{A} = \mathfrak{H}(X)$. Let Y be a subset of X carrying the natural order $\leqslant$ from X. We suppose for simplicity that the symbol $\leqslant$ is among those of L. Clearly each element a of $H(X)$ is obtained from a finite number of elements of X by a (Skolem) term t, i.e. $a = t(x_1 \ldots x_n)$.

PROPOSITION 1.
(i) For any ordinal λ, if $(Y, \leqslant) \prec'_{\lambda\kappa} (X, \leqslant)$, then $\mathfrak{H}(Y) \prec'_{\lambda\kappa} \mathfrak{H}(X)$.
(ii) Let λ be a cardinal such that $\|L\|^{\alpha} < \lambda$ for each cardinal $\alpha < \kappa$. If $(Y, \leqslant) \prec_{\lambda\kappa} (X, \leqslant)$, then $\mathfrak{H}(Y) \prec_{\lambda\kappa} \mathfrak{H}(X)$. ($\|L\|$ is the number of symbols in L.)

We shall first give the proof of (i). The proof of (ii) will then follow from some additional remarks. We need several lemmas.

LEMMA A. Let θ be any formula of $L'_{\lambda\kappa}$. There is a formula $\tilde{\theta}$ of $L'_{\lambda\kappa}$ with exactly the same free variables as θ such that given any eventually constant κ-termed sequence s of elements of $H(X)$,

$$\mathfrak{H}(X) \vDash \theta [s] \quad \text{if and only if} \quad \mathfrak{H}(X) \vDash \tilde{\theta}^{(X)} [s].$$

PROOF: ($\tilde{\theta}^{(X)}$ is the relativization of $\tilde{\theta}$ to X.) We define $\tilde{\theta}$ by induction on θ:

if θ is an atomic formula, $\tilde{\theta} = \theta$;

if $\theta = \bigwedge_{i \in I} \theta_i$, $\tilde{\theta} = \bigwedge_{i \in I} \tilde{\theta}_i$; similarly for W;

if $\theta = \forall x \varphi$ where x is a μ-termed sequence of variables, let $\tilde{\theta} = \bigwedge_{f \in F} \forall x_f \varphi_f$, where F is the set of all μ-termed sequences f of terms of L and for each such sequence f, φ_f is obtained from φ by putting in the term $f_\xi(y_\xi)$ for all free occurrences of the variable x_ξ. Each y_ξ is a finite sequence of new variables appropriate to the term f_ξ, and x_f is the sequence obtained from the y_ξ's by piecing them together;

if $\theta = \exists x \varphi$, $\tilde{\theta} = W_{f \in F} \exists x_f \varphi_f$.

We easily verify that $\tilde{\theta}$ is a formula of $L'_{\lambda\kappa}$ with exactly the same free variables and quantifier rank as θ. Since every element of $H(X)$ is a term of elements from X, a universal quantification over $H(X)$ amounts to conjunction of all terms $t(x_1 \ldots x_n)$ followed by universal quantification of $x_1, \ldots, x_n$ over X. From this remark the conclusion of the lemma can be proved by an easy induction.

LEMMA B. Given the formula $\tilde{\theta}$ as in Lemma A. Let s be an eventually constant κ-termed sequence of elements of $H(X)$. Each element s_ξ, $\xi < \kappa$, of the sequence is $t_\xi(\bar{s}_\xi)$ when t_ξ is a term and $\bar{s}_\xi$ is an appropriate finite sequence of elements of X. Let $\tilde{\theta}_s$ be obtained from $\tilde{\theta}$ by replacing each free v_ξ by $t_\xi(y_\xi)$ and let $\bar{s}$ be an eventually constant κ-termed sequence obtained from $\bar{s}_\xi$ by an appropriate piecing together. Then $\tilde{\theta}_s$ has the same quantifier rank as $\tilde{\theta}$, and

$$\mathfrak{H}(X) \vDash \tilde{\theta}^{(X)}[s] \quad \text{if and only if} \quad \mathfrak{H}(X) \vDash \tilde{\theta}_s^{(X)}[\bar{s}].$$

PROOF: Obvious.

LEMMA C. Let θ be any formula of $L'_{\lambda\kappa}$. Then there is a formula θ^* of $L'_{\lambda\kappa}$ containing only the symbols $\leqslant$ and $=$ with the same quantifier rank and free variables as θ such that for any eventually constant κ-termed sequence s of X,

$$\mathfrak{H}(X) \vDash \theta^{(X)}[s] \quad \text{if and only if} \quad (X, \leqslant) \vDash \theta^*[s].$$

PROOF: We obtain θ^* from θ by systematically replacing each atomic formula $\varphi(x_1 \ldots x_n)$ of θ by an atomic formula $\varphi^*(x_1 \ldots x_n)$ containing only the predicate symbols $\leqslant$ and $=$. Suppose $x_1, \ldots, x_n$ are the free variables of φ. Consider all possible ways of linearly ordering $x_1, \ldots, x_n$, including possible identifications of x_i with x_j. For each such linear ordering, call it $\leqslant_p$, let $x_{i_1} <_p x_{i_2} <_p \cdots <_p x_{i_m}$, $m \leqslant n$, be a sublist of the variables $x_1, \ldots, x_n$

arranged in increasing $<_p$ order and such that each x_j, $1 \leqslant j \leqslant n$, is equal to some x_{i_k}, $1 \leqslant k \leqslant m$. Let $\varphi_p(x_{i_1} \ldots x_{i_m})$ be obtained from $\varphi(x_1 \ldots x_n)$ by replacing each x_j by the x_{i_k} such that $x_j = x_{i_k}$. Since the set X is indiscernible in $\mathfrak{H}(X)$, we have either

    (i) for all $a_1 < \cdots < a_m$ of X, $\mathfrak{H}(X) \vDash \varphi_p[a_1 \ldots a_m]$,

or

    (ii) for all $a_1 < \cdots < a_m$ of X, $\mathfrak{H}(X) \vDash \neg \varphi_p[a_1 \ldots a_m]$.

Let $\sigma_p(x_1 \ldots x_n)$ be the $\leqslant_p$-diagram of the set $\{x_1 \ldots x_n\}$; σ_p contains only the predicate symbols $\leqslant$ and $=$, and it has $x_1, \ldots, x_n$ as free variables. Let φ^* be the disjunction of all σ_p such that case (i) above holds for φ_p. We now claim that for any elements $a_1, \ldots, a_n$ of X, in any order and not necessarily distinct,

$$\mathfrak{H}(X) \vDash \varphi[a_1 \ldots a_n] \quad \text{if and only if} \quad (X, \leqslant) \vDash \varphi^*[a_1 \ldots a_n]. \tag{1}$$

We argue as follows. The elements $a_1, \ldots, a_n$ are ordered by $\leqslant$ on X in some way, say $\leqslant_p$. For the formula φ_p we have

$$\mathfrak{H}(X) \vDash \varphi[a_1 \ldots a_n] \quad \text{if and only if} \quad \mathfrak{H}(X) \vDash \varphi_p[a_{i_1} \ldots a_{i_m}].$$

If $\mathfrak{H}(X) \vDash \varphi[a_1 \ldots a_n]$, then $\mathfrak{H}(X) \vDash \varphi_p[a_{i_1} \ldots a_{i_m}]$. Since $a_{i_1} < \cdots < a_{i_m}$ and X is indiscernible, case (i) must hold. So σ_p is a part of φ^*, and since $(X, \leqslant) \vDash \sigma_p[a_1 \ldots a_n]$, we have $(X, \leqslant) \vDash \varphi^*[a_1 \ldots a_n]$. On the other hand, if not $\mathfrak{H}(X) \vDash \varphi[a_1 \ldots a_n]$, then not $\mathfrak{H}(X) \vDash \varphi_p[a_{i_1} \ldots a_{i_m}]$. So case (ii) will hold and σ_p is not a part of φ^*. Since each σ_p is a complete description of the ordering $\leqslant_p$, we see that $(X, \leqslant) \vDash \neg \varphi^*[a_1 \ldots a_n]$. So (i) is proved. Now replace each atomic φ in θ by φ^*. Clearly θ^* is a formula of $L'_{\lambda\kappa}$ with the same quantifier rank and free variables as θ but containing only the symbols $\leqslant$ and $=$. A simple induction based on (1) will prove the lemma.

    PROOF of Proposition 1. Since $Y \subset X$, $\mathfrak{H}(Y) \prec \mathfrak{H}(X)$, and Y is a set of indiscernibles in both $\mathfrak{H}(X)$ and $\mathfrak{H}(Y)$, we see that Lemmas A, B, C hold with X replaced everywhere by Y. That is to say, the transformations θ to $\tilde{\theta}$ to $\tilde{\theta}_s$ and θ to θ^* do not depend on X but only depend on the set of formulas satisfied by increasing sequences from X. Now suppose $(Y, \leqslant) \prec'_{\lambda\kappa} (X, \leqslant)$. Let θ be a formula of $L'_{\lambda\kappa}$ and let s be an eventually constant sequence of elements of $H(Y)$. Using Lemmas A, B, C we get $\tilde{\theta}$, $\tilde{\theta}_s$ and $(\tilde{\theta}_s)^*$, and the auxiliary eventually constant sequence $\bar{s}$ of elements of Y. The following statements are equivalent:

$$\mathfrak{H}(Y) \vDash \theta[s],$$
$$\mathfrak{H}(Y) \vDash \tilde{\theta}_s^{(Y)}[\bar{s}],$$
$$(Y, \leqslant) \vDash (\tilde{\theta}_s)^*[\bar{s}],$$

$$(X, \leqslant) \vDash (\tilde{\theta}_s)^* [\bar{s}],$$
$$\mathfrak{H}(X) \vDash \tilde{\theta}_s^{(X)} [\bar{s}],$$
$$\mathfrak{H}(X) \vDash \theta [s].$$

So part (i) of the proposition is proved. To prove (ii) we need to make only one observation. We have to show that if λ satisfies the hypothesis of (ii), then the formulas of $L_{\lambda\kappa}$ are closed under the transformations $\tilde{\theta}, \tilde{\theta}_s$ and $(\tilde{\theta}_s)^*$. The only possible difficulty occurs in the definition of $\tilde{\theta}$ and in particular in the inductive definitions of $\tilde{\theta}$ when $\theta = \forall x\varphi$ or $\theta = \exists x\varphi$. Referring to the relevant part of Lemma A, notice that $\mu < \kappa$ and the total number of terms of L is $\|L\|$. Whence $|F| \leqslant \|L\|^{|\mu|} < \lambda$. So the conjunction $\bigwedge_{f \in F} \forall x_f \varphi_f$ and disjunction $\bigvee_{f \in F} \exists x_f \varphi_f$ are permitted in $L_{\lambda\kappa}$. The proposition is proved.

Combining Proposition 1 with our previous result (I) we have:

(II) Every countable theory T with infinite models has a countable model which has arbitrarily large $L_{\kappa\omega}$-elementary extensions.

PROOF: Let $\mathfrak{A}$ be a countable model of T with a set of indiscernibles X of order type of the rationals. We may assume that $\mathfrak{A} = \mathfrak{H}(X)$. It is easy to find arbitrarily large ordered sets Y such that $(X, \leqslant) \prec (Y, \leqslant)$, Y is ω-saturated, Y is indiscernible in $\mathfrak{H}(Y)$, and $\mathfrak{H}(X) \prec \mathfrak{H}(Y)$. By (I) we have $(X, \leqslant) \prec'_{\kappa\omega} (Y, \leqslant)$, and by Proposition 1 we get $\mathfrak{H}(X) \prec_{\kappa\omega} \mathfrak{H}(Y)$. Since κ is regular, this easily leads to $\mathfrak{H}(X) \prec_{\kappa\omega} \mathfrak{H}(Y)$.

4. Remarks on infinitary properties of well-orderings

In this section all exponentiation of ordinals or cardinals are taken in the ordinal sense. We identify an ordinal λ with the model $\langle \lambda, \leqslant \rangle$ where $\leqslant$ is the natural ordering on the elements of λ. For purposes of the following discussion we let OR denote the class of all ordinals and $\leqslant$ the natural ordering of ordinals. The first result we mention is due to MOSTOWSKI and TARSKI [1949] (for a reference see the report by FEFERMAN [1957]):

(i)$_\omega$ $\langle \omega^\omega, \leqslant \rangle \prec \langle OR, \leqslant \rangle$.

With the help of an observation due to Ehrenfeucht, they also obtained:

(ii)$_\omega$ $\langle \omega^{\omega^\omega}, \leqslant, + \rangle \prec \langle OR, \leqslant, + \rangle$,

and

(iii)$_\omega$ $\langle \omega^{\omega^{\omega^\omega}}, \leqslant, +, \cdot \rangle \prec \langle OR, \leqslant, +, \cdot \rangle$.

In each case they can prove that the ordinals occurring on the left are smallest possible by showing that all smaller ordinals are definable in the appropriate languages. In the course of investigation for this paper I proved (in November 1966) the following Proposition 2. After I found the proof I discovered in the September 1966 Journal of Symbolic Logic an article by KINO [1966] in which she proved a part of Proposition 2. (See remark (d) below for a more precise statement.) Thus a part of the credit for Proposition 2 is due to Kino.

PROPOSITION 2. Suppose $\kappa \leqslant \lambda < \mu$ are cardinals and $cf(\lambda) \geqslant \kappa$, $cf(\mu) \geqslant \kappa$. Then

$$\langle \kappa^\lambda, \leqslant \rangle \prec'_{\lambda\kappa} \langle \mu, \leqslant \rangle.$$

Furthermore each ordinal smaller than κ^λ is definable in $L'_{\lambda\kappa}$.

Remarks. (a) Let $\kappa = \lambda = \omega$ and let μ run through all infinite cardinals, then we have

(i')$_\omega$ $\langle \omega^\omega, \leqslant \rangle \prec'_{\omega\omega} \langle \mathrm{OR}, \leqslant \rangle.$

This is stronger than the result (i)$_\omega$ and is, incidentally, precisely the observation of Ehrenfeucht with the aid of which (ii)$_\omega$ and (iii)$_\omega$ were proved. Actually one can also obtain the stronger forms (ii')$_\omega$ and (iii')$_\omega$ analogous to (i')$_\omega$.

(b) In general, let $\kappa = \lambda$ and let μ run through all cardinals with cofinality at least κ, we get:

(i')$_\kappa$ $\langle \kappa^\kappa, \leqslant \rangle \prec'_{\kappa\kappa} \langle \mathrm{OR}, \leqslant \rangle,$

and, by using the same idea of Ehrenfeucht:

(ii')$_\kappa$ $\langle \kappa^{\kappa^\kappa}, \leqslant, + \rangle \prec'_{\kappa\kappa} \langle \mathrm{OR}, \leqslant, + \rangle,$

(iii')$_\kappa$ $\langle \kappa^{\kappa^{\kappa^\kappa}}, \leqslant, +, \cdot \rangle \prec'_{\kappa\kappa} \langle \mathrm{OR}, \leqslant, +, \cdot \rangle.$

In each case, every ordinal smaller than the corresponding power of κ is definable in $L'_{\kappa\kappa}$.

(c) Suppose that $\kappa < \lambda < \mu$. Then $\kappa^\lambda = \lambda$, so we have the simple results

$$\langle \lambda, \leqslant \rangle \prec'_{\lambda\kappa} \langle \mu, \leqslant \rangle$$

and

$$\langle \lambda, \leqslant \rangle \prec'_{\lambda\kappa} \langle \mathrm{OR}, \leqslant \rangle.$$

If λ is also regular, then we may of course remove the primes and get

$$\langle \lambda, \leqslant \rangle \prec_{\lambda\kappa} \langle \mu, \leqslant \rangle$$

and
$$\langle \lambda, \leqslant \rangle \prec_{\lambda\kappa} \langle OR, \leqslant \rangle.$$

If, in addition, $\kappa = \omega$, then we have new results for the infinitary languages $L_{\lambda\omega}$.

(d) The results of Kino mentioned earlier are (at least in the case of regular cardinals, for singular cardinals see KINO [1966]) the following:

(i)$_\kappa$ $\begin{cases} \langle \kappa^\kappa, \leqslant \rangle \prec_{\kappa\kappa} \langle OR, \leqslant \rangle & \text{if} \quad \kappa = \lambda^+ \quad \text{or} \quad \kappa = \omega, \\ \langle \kappa, \leqslant \rangle \prec_{\kappa\kappa} \langle OR, \leqslant \rangle & \text{if} \quad \kappa \quad \text{is a limit regular cardinal}. \end{cases}$

This curious difference between κ a successor or limit cardinal (see (i')$_\kappa$) is due to the fact that $L_{\kappa\kappa}$ is really weaker than $L'_{\kappa\kappa}$ if κ is a limit cardinal. After reading her proof of (i)$_\kappa$, I was convinced that Kino could have easily obtained the full force of Proposition 2 if she knew of the language $L'_{\lambda\kappa}$ or if she realized the consequences of Proposition 1. The required extensions to the arguments in KINO [1966] are almost trivial.

For reasons given in the last remark, we shall not give a proof of Proposition 2 here. We shall however indicate briefly in what follows the main steps which led us to the proof.

LEMMA 1. If $\mu = \sigma + 1$ or if μ is a limit ordinal and $cf(\mu) \geqslant \kappa$, then

$$\langle \kappa^{\lambda+1}, \leqslant \rangle \prec'_{\lambda\kappa} \langle \kappa^{\lambda+1} \cdot \mu, \leqslant \rangle.$$

PROOF: By induction on the ordinal λ. The proof is rather tedious, but straightforward.

LEMMA 2. If $\mu = \sigma + 1$ or if μ is a limit ordinal and $cf(\mu) \geqslant \kappa$, and if λ is a limit ordinal and $cf(\lambda) \geqslant \kappa$, then

$$\langle \kappa^\lambda, \leqslant \rangle \prec'_{\lambda\kappa} \langle \kappa^\lambda \cdot \mu, \leqslant \rangle.$$

PROOF: We use the fact that $\kappa^\lambda = \bigcup_{\eta < \lambda} \kappa^{\eta+1}$ and $\kappa^\lambda \cdot \mu = \kappa^{\eta+1} \cdot \mu'$ for each $\eta < \lambda$. Then by Lemma 1,

$$\langle \kappa^{\eta+1}, \leqslant \rangle \prec'_{\eta\kappa} \langle \kappa^{\eta+1} \cdot \mu', \leqslant \rangle$$

for all $\eta < \lambda$. Whence by an argument involving unions of elementary chains we get the conclusion.

The proof of Proposition 2 follows from Lemma 2 by putting in the appropriate values for λ and μ.

5. Applications

We state our results for countable theories, although it is clear how to state them if L is not countable.

THEOREM 1. Let T be a countable theory with infinite models. Then there exists an elementary tower $\mathfrak{A}_\lambda$, λ an ordinal, of models of T such that:

(i) each $\mathfrak{A}_\lambda = \mathfrak{H}(X_\lambda)$ where X_λ is a set of indiscernibles in $\mathfrak{A}_\lambda$ of order type λ;

(ii) $\|\mathfrak{A}_\lambda\| = |\lambda|$ for each λ;

(iii) if $\lambda < \mu$, then X_λ is an initial segment of X_μ and $\mathfrak{A}_\lambda \prec \mathfrak{A}_\mu$;

(iv) the tower of models $\mathfrak{A}_\lambda$ have exactly the same infinitary properties as the tower of ordinals $\langle \lambda, \leqslant \rangle$.

PROOF: The construction of the tower so that (i)–(iii) are satisfied is easy. To show (iv), suppose $\lambda < \mu$ and ρ is an arbitrary ordinal such that

$$\langle \lambda, \leqslant \rangle \prec'_{\rho\kappa} \langle \mu, \leqslant \rangle.$$

Then it follows from Proposition 1 that $\mathfrak{A}_\lambda \prec'_{\rho\kappa} \mathfrak{A}_\mu$, and this is the meaning of (iv).

The following is a corollary of Theorem 1. Compare with results (I) and (II).

(III) Let T be a countable theory with infinite models. Then in each infinite power κ, T has a model of power κ which has arbitrarily large $L_{\kappa\kappa}$-elementary extensions.

PROOF: Consider the model $\mathfrak{A}_\lambda$ of Theorem 1 where $\lambda = \kappa^\kappa$ (ordinal exponentiation). Proposition 2 shows that there are arbitrarily large cardinals μ such that

$$\langle \lambda, \leqslant \rangle \prec'_{\kappa\kappa} \langle \mu, \leqslant \rangle.$$

Whence by Theorem 1 there are arbitrarily large $\mathfrak{A}_\mu$ such that $\mathfrak{A}_\lambda \prec_{\kappa\kappa} \mathfrak{A}_\mu$.

Returning to the remark following (I), we see that the proof of (III) does not yield arbitrarily large $L_{\mu\kappa}$-elementary extensions. If we assume the generalized continuum hypothesis then extensions of the stronger sort can be found either directly by (I) or by using the η_κ-sets of Hausdorff and the methods of (II).

For the terminology needed for the next theorem see SILVER [1966].

THEOREM 2. Suppose there exists a cardinal ρ satisfying the partition property $\rho \to (\omega_1)^{<\omega}$. Let $\kappa < \lambda < \mu$ be cardinals such that $cf(\lambda) \geqslant \kappa$ and $cf(\mu)$

$\geqslant \kappa$. Then

$$\langle F''\lambda, \varepsilon \rangle \prec'_{\lambda\kappa} \langle F''\mu, \varepsilon \rangle ,$$

where F is the Gödel function enumerating all the constructible sets.

PROOF: It is proved in SILVER [1966] that (under the given hypothesis) for each cardinal $\lambda > \omega$, the model $\langle F''\lambda, \varepsilon \rangle$ is the Skolem hull of a set X_λ of indiscernibles with order type λ. Furthermore, if $\omega < \lambda < \mu$ (cardinals), then X_λ is an initial segment of X_μ and $\langle F''\lambda, \varepsilon \rangle \prec \langle F''\mu, \varepsilon \rangle$. From Proposition 2 we have

$$\langle X_\lambda, \leqslant \rangle \prec'_{\lambda\kappa} \langle X_\mu, \leqslant \rangle .$$

Whence the conclusion follows from Proposition 1.

Some special cases of Theorem 2 are worthwhile stating. Let Δ denote the constructible universe, then

(*) $\langle F''\omega_1, \varepsilon \rangle \prec_{\omega_1\omega} \Delta ,$

and

(**) $\langle F''\omega_2, \varepsilon \rangle \prec_{\omega_2\omega_1} \Delta .$

(*) improves the previously known result $\langle F''\omega_1, \varepsilon \rangle \prec \Delta$, and (**) yields $\langle F''\omega_2, \varepsilon \rangle \prec_{\omega_1\omega_1} \Delta$. At the moment we do not know any interesting meta-mathematical consequences of (*) or (**). Whether (**) really gives more information about the constructible universe Δ (supposing that $\rho \rightarrow (\omega_1)^{<\omega}$ exists) is not completely clear. (The interested reader may wish to see CHANG [1967] for some other problems.)

THEOREM 3. (Poor man's upward Löwenheim-Skolem theorem for $L_{\kappa\kappa}$.) Suppose that L is countable and ρ is a cardinal such that $\rho \rightarrow (\kappa^\kappa)^{<\omega}$ (ordinal exponentiation). Then every model $\mathfrak{A}$ of power ρ has an $L_{\omega\omega}$-elementary submodel $\mathfrak{B}$ of power κ and the model $\mathfrak{B}$ has arbitrarily large $L_{\kappa\kappa}$-elementary extensions.

PROOF: Using the trick first discovered by ROWBOTTOM [1964], we can find a set X of indiscernibles of $\mathfrak{A}$ with $(X, \leqslant)$ having order type κ^κ. Let $\mathfrak{B}$ be the Skolem hull of X in $\mathfrak{A}$. Then $\|\mathfrak{B}\| = \kappa$ and $\mathfrak{B} \prec \mathfrak{A}$. Let μ be any infinite cardinal such that $cf(\mu) \geqslant \kappa$. Find a set Y ordered of type μ such that X is an initial segment of Y and Y is a set of indiscernibles in $\mathfrak{H}(Y)$ and $\mathfrak{H}(X) \prec \mathfrak{H}(Y)$. A combination of Propositions 1 and 2 shows that $\mathfrak{B} \prec_{\kappa\kappa} \mathfrak{H}(Y)$. Clearly $\|\mathfrak{H}(Y)\| = \mu$.

An ordered subset X of A is said to be $L_{\kappa\kappa}$-indiscernible if for any ordinal $\lambda < \kappa$ and any two λ-termed strictly increasing sequences x and y of elements of X, we have

$$(\mathfrak{A}, x) \equiv_{\kappa\kappa} (\mathfrak{A}, y).$$

THEOREM 4. Let T be a countable theory with infinite models, and let μ be any ordinal. Then T has a model $\mathfrak{A}$ of power $\max(\kappa, |\mu|)$ which has a set X of $L_{\kappa\kappa}$-indiscernible elements with order type μ.

PROOF: We construct a model $\mathfrak{A}$ of T of power $\max(\kappa, |\mu|)$ with a well-ordered set Y of indiscernibles of type $\kappa^\kappa \cdot (\mu + 1)$. We may assume that $\mathfrak{A} = \mathfrak{H}(Y)$. Let X be a subset of Y defined by

$$X = \{ y(\kappa^\kappa \cdot (\rho + 1)): \rho < \mu \},$$

where $y(\eta)$ is the ηth element of Y. X has type μ, and the elements of X are separated in Y by at least a segment of type κ^κ. We can now appeal to Lemmas 1 and 2 (the proof is easy and uses some simple properties of well-ordered sums of ordinals) and show that for any $\lambda < \kappa$ and any two λ-termed strictly increasing sequences x and y from X, we have

$$(Y, \leqslant, x) \equiv'_{\kappa\kappa} (Y, \leqslant, y).$$

Since $\mathfrak{A} = \mathfrak{H}(Y)$, we use Proposition 1 to get $(\mathfrak{A}, x) \equiv'_{\kappa\kappa} (\mathfrak{A}, y)$, which gives the desired conclusion.

Theorem 4 shows that there are models with well-ordered sets of $L_{\kappa\kappa}$-indiscernibles. One could not hope to establish this by a direct application of the Ehrenfeucht-Mostowski result, as one can show that no infinite cardinal has the partition property with an infinite exponent. I do not know if one can construct models with $L_{\kappa\kappa}$-indiscernibles of any given order type. An even more specific open problem is to find a set Σ of $L_{\omega_1\omega_1}$-types of T of power ω_1 such that T has arbitrarily large models realizing only $L_{\omega_1\omega_1}$-types of Σ. Using a slightly different approach, I can show that there is a set Σ of $L_{\omega_1\omega}$-types of T of power ω_1 such that T has arbitrarily large models realizing only $L_{\omega_1\omega}$-types in Σ.

References

CHANG, C. C., Sets constructible using $L_{\kappa\kappa}$, Amer. Math. Soc. Summer Inst. in Axiomatic Set Theory at UCLA, 1967, Proceedings, IVE 1–12.

EHRENFEUCHT, A. and A. MOSTOWSKI, Models of axiomatic theories admitting automorphisms, Fund. Math. **43** (1956) 50–68.

FEFERMAN, S., Some recent work of Ehrenfeucht and Fraïssé, Summary of talks at AMS Summer Inst. in Logic at Cornell, 1957, pp. 201–209.

GAIFMAN, H., Measurable cardinals and constructible sets, Amer. Math. Soc. Notices **11** (1964) 771.

KINO, A., On definability of ordinals in logic with infinitely long expressions, J. Symb. Logic **31** (1966) 365–375. See also correction: J. Symb. Logic **32** (1967) 343.

MOSTOWSKI, A. and A. TARSKI, Arithmetical classes and types of well-ordered systems, Bull. Amer. Math. Soc. **55** (1949) 65.

ROWBOTTOM, F., Large cardinals and small constructible sets, Doctoral dissertation, Univ. of Wisconsin 1964.

SCOTT, D., Measurable cardinals and constructible sets, Bull. Acad. Polon. Sci. Ser. des Sci. Math., Astr. et Phys. **7** (1961) 145–149.

SILVER, J., Some applications of model theory in set theory, Doctoral dissertation, Univ. of California, Berkeley, 1966.

TWO COMPLETE ALGEBRAIC THEORIES OF LOGIC

W. CRAIG

University of California, Berkeley, California, USA

The purpose of this paper is to present two complete and sound algebraic theories of logic. They are algebraic theories in the sense that each theorem is an equality between two terms, each of which is formed by means of function symbols and by means of variables all of which belong to the same kind. They are theories of logic because, roughly speaking, one is able to express and prove in them everything that can be expressed or, respectively, proved in first-order logic with a symbol for identity. They are sound in the sense that only those equalities between terms can be derived which are valid, i.e., hold under all the intended interpretations. Finally, they are complete in the sense that all those equalities between terms which are valid can be derived. Our proof of their completeness is quite long. We shall only present an outline.

The two theories are closely related. Both use the same terms, but differ with respect to their interpretation. One theory is based on a language which, roughly speaking, results from the language for ω-dimensional cylindric set algebras by adding symbols for a certain projection operation P and its conjugate Q. By changing from operations on sets of sequences of length ω to operations on sets of sequences of arbitrary finite length we obtain the language for the other theory. Our axioms for the latter theory were discovered by asking what was needed to make Q a suitable neat embedding so that the neat embedding theorem from the theory of cylindric algebras could be applied. For the former theory we then added those axioms which were needed to exploit the completeness of the latter theory.

Algebraic theories of logic have certain advantages over the usual theories for first-order logic with identity. All variables are of one kind, and there are no variable-binding operators. Also, since in each case the problem is to derive an equality from axioms which are themselves equalities, one can always proceed linearly, considering throughout the operation being denoted by each of the two terms of the equality to be derived.

1. An algebraic language

An ordinal shall be the set of its predecessors, $\alpha, \beta, \ldots$ shall be ordinals, and $i, j, \ldots$ finite ordinals. The set of all finite ordinals shall be ω. For each α and each set U, $^{\alpha}U$ shall be the set of functions f whose domain dom f is α and whose range ran f is a subset of U. In other words, $^{\alpha}U$ is the set of sequences f of order type α such that each term $f_{\beta} = f(\beta)$ of the sequence is an element of U, $\beta < \alpha$. We let $^{\varphi}U = \bigcup_{n<\omega} {}^{n}U$. Thus $^{\varphi}U$ is the set of finite sequences of elements of U. The only element of ^{0}U and, if $U = \emptyset$, the only element of $^{\varphi}U$ is the function whose domain is empty, i.e., the empty set or sequence $\emptyset$. When U is understood, we let $^{\frown}$ be the operation of concatenating with a sequence $g \in {}^{\varphi}U$ a sequence $h \in {}^{\varphi}U \cup {}^{\varphi}U$. An *operation* on a set A shall be a function which, for some m, $0 \leqslant m < \omega$, takes the m-tuples of elements of A as arguments and which for each argument yields a value belonging to A.

For any set U, we now introduce the following operations on $\{X : X \subseteq {}^{\varphi}U\}$, taking 0, 0, 1, 1, 1 arguments respectively.

$\mathit{1} = {}^{\varphi}U$.

$D = \{f : f \in \mathit{1}, \{0, 1\} \subseteq \mathrm{dom} f, f_0 = f_1\}$.

$C_i X = \{f : f \in \mathit{1}$ and, for some $g \in X$, $\mathrm{dom} f = \mathrm{dom} g$ and $f_j = g_j$ for each $j \neq i$ such that $j \in \mathrm{dom} f\}$.

$PX = \{f : \text{for some } u \in U \text{ and } g \in X, g = \langle u \rangle^{\frown} f\}$.

$QX = \{f : \text{for some } u \in U \text{ and } g \in X, f = \langle u \rangle^{\frown} g\}$.

By letting $\mathit{1} = {}^{\omega}U$, one obtains corresponding operations on $\{X : X \subseteq {}^{\omega}U\}$. For these we shall use the same symbols. We let $\cap, \cup, \sim$ be the operation of intersection, union, or complementation respectively on either $\{X : X \subseteq {}^{\varphi}U\}$ or $\{X : X \subseteq {}^{\omega}U\}$. In each case, either it will appear from the context which U and whether $\{X : X \subseteq {}^{\varphi}U\}$ or $\{X : X \subseteq {}^{\omega}U\}$ is intended, or else this does not matter.

We let $Q^0 X = X$ and $Q^{i+1}X = QQ^i X$. For $i < j$, we let $D_{ij} = D_{ji} = C_{i+1} \cdots$ $\cdots C_{j-1}(Q^i D \cap Q^{i+1}D \cap \cdots \cap Q^{j-1}D)$ and we let $D_{ii} = Q^{i+1}\mathit{1}$. In particular, $D_{01} = D$, $D_{i(i+1)} = Q^i D$, and $D_{00} = Q\mathit{1}$. Then, as an operation on $\{X : X \subseteq {}^{\omega}U\}$, D_{ij} is $\{f : f \in {}^{\omega}U, f_i = f_j\}$. Thus the operations on $\{X : X \subseteq {}^{\omega}U\}$ we are considering are those that can be defined (by means of a term) by adding P and Q to those operations on $\{X : X \subseteq {}^{\omega}U\}$ which are considered in the theory of cylindric algebras.

As an operation on $\{X : X \subseteq {}^{\varphi}U\}$, $Q\mathit{1}$ is $\bigcup_{1 \leqslant n < \omega} {}^{n}U$ and more generally $Q^m \mathit{1}$ is $\bigcup_{m \leqslant n < \omega} {}^{n}U$, which is the set of finite sequences of elements of U such that the length of the sequence is at least m. Hence $Q^m \mathit{1} \cap \sim Q^{m+1}\mathit{1} = {}^{m}U$.

We now construct a language L_{pq} for these operations. The *variables* shall be $x_0, \ldots, x_k, \ldots, k < \omega$. For readability we let $x = x_0$ and $y = x_1$. The *function symbols*, with 2, 2, 1, 0, 0, 1, 1, 1 places respectively, shall be $+, \cdot, -, \mathbf{1}, d,$ c_i, p, q, where $0 \leqslant i < \omega$. From the 0-placed function symbols and the variables we form the *terms* by adding 1-placed function symbols to the left of terms and by inserting 2-placed function symbols between terms, enclosing the resulting expression by a pair of parentheses. Henceforth, $\rho, \sigma, \tau, \ldots$ shall always be terms. An *equality* shall be any expression $\sigma \doteq \tau$. We let L_q be the sublanguage of L_{pq} which results when one refrains from using p.

Juxtaposition of names of symbols is used to indicate juxtaposition of the symbols named. We let $\mathbf{0}$ be the term $-\mathbf{1}$. We let q^0 be the empty string of symbols, and q^{i+1} the string qq^i. Parentheses are used autonymously. Names for outermost pairs or for pairs associating to the right are sometimes suppressed.

It should be clear what is meant by the *value* of τ for a set U and a sequence $\langle X_0, X_1, \ldots \rangle$ of subsets of $^\wp U$. The value is determined by assigning to each x_k in τ the set $X_k \subseteq {}^\wp U$ and to each function symbol in τ the corresponding operation on $\{X : X \subseteq {}^\wp U\}$. The value of τ for a set U and a sequence $\langle X_0, X_1, \ldots \rangle$ of subsets of $^\omega U$ is determined analogously.

We let $\vDash^\cup \sigma \doteq \tau$ if and only if σ and τ have the same value for each *nonempty* U and each sequence $\langle X_0, X_1, \ldots \rangle$ of subsets of $^\wp U$. Note that $\vDash^\cup pqx \doteq x$, but that for $U = \emptyset$ and $\mathbf{1} = {}^\wp U = \{\emptyset\}$ one has $PQ\mathbf{1} = P\emptyset = \emptyset \neq \mathbf{1}$. We let $\vDash \sigma \doteq \tau$ if and only if σ and τ have the same value for each U (or, equivalently, for each nonempty U) and each sequence $\langle X_0, X_1, \ldots \rangle$ of subsets of $^\omega U$.

2. Two equational theories

We now present two sets of equalities, $E_{pq}^\cup$ and E_{pq}. One can verify that $\vDash^\cup \sigma \doteq \tau$ for each $\sigma \doteq \tau$ in $E_{pq}^\cup$ and that $\vDash \sigma \doteq \tau$ for each $\sigma \doteq \tau$ in E_{pq}. Thus $E_{pq}^\cup$ and E_{pq} are *sound* for their intended interpretation.

The Boolean part of $E_{pq}^\cup$ shall be a set of equational axioms for the theory of Boolean algebras, such that $+, \cdot, -, \mathbf{1}$ but no other function symbols are used. The remaining part of $E_{pq}^\cup$ shall consist of the following unbracketed equalities 1(a), ..., 3(c), where $0 \leqslant i < \omega$ and $0 \leqslant j < \omega$. We let E_{pq} be the set consisting of the equalities in $E_{pq}^\cup$ together with the two bracketed equalities 2(a') and 3(d). In 3(c) we use $d_{i(i+1)}$ and $d_{(i+1)i}$ for the term $q^i d$, and $d_{i(i+2)}$ and $d_{(i+2)i}$ for the term $c_{i+1}(q^i d \cdot q^{i+1} d)$.

1. (a) $c_i 0 \doteq 0$.
   (b) $x \cdot c_i x \doteq x$.
   (c) $c_i(x \cdot c_i y) \doteq c_i x \cdot c_i y$.

   (d) $c_i c_j x \simeq c_j c_i x.$

2. (a) $q0 \simeq 0.$

  [(a′) $q1 \simeq 1.$]

   (b) $q(x+y) \simeq qx + qy.$

   (c) $q(x \cdot y) \simeq qx \cdot qy.$

   (d) $qc_i x \simeq c_{i+1} qx.$

   (e) $c_i(-q^{i+1} 1 \cdot x) \simeq -q^{i+1} 1 \cdot x.$

   (f) $qpx \simeq c_0(q1 \cdot x).$

   (g) $pqx \simeq x.$

3. (a) $c_0 d \simeq q^2 1.$

  (a′) $c_1 d \simeq q^2 1.$

   (b) $c_{i+2} d \simeq d.$

   (c) $d_{ij} \cdot c_i(d_{ij} \cdot x) \simeq d_{ij} \cdot x$ for $i \neq j$ and $-2 \leqslant i - j \leqslant 2.$

  [(d) $-c_0 - d \cdot qx \simeq -c_0 - d \cdot x.$]

The following changes applied to E_{pq} yield a set from which, in a sense to be made precise in a moment, the same equalities can be derived: Omit 2(e), replace 2(a), 2(a′) and 2(b) by $q - x \simeq -qx$, in 2(f) replace $q1 \cdot x$ by x, and in 3(a) and 3(a′) replace $q^2 1$ by 1.

Given any set E of equalities, an *E-path from τ to τ'*, or also a *derivation based on E of $\tau \simeq \tau'$*, shall be a finite sequence $\langle \tau_0, \ldots, \tau_t \rangle$ of terms such that τ_0 is τ, τ_t is τ' and, for each $i < t$, either τ_{i+1} is τ_i or τ_{i+1} results from τ_i by the replacement of an occurrence of a term σ by the occurrence of a term σ' such that either $\sigma \simeq \sigma'$ or $\sigma' \simeq \sigma$ is obtained by substituting terms for variables throughout some equality in E. We let $E \vdash \tau \simeq \tau'$ if and only if there is a derivation based on E of $\tau \simeq \tau'$. As is well-known, $E \vdash \tau \simeq \tau'$ if and only if, in the usual semantical sense, $\tau \simeq \tau'$ is a consequence of the set of expressions $\forall_{x_{i_0}} \ldots \forall_{x_{i_k}} (\rho \simeq \rho')$ such that $\rho \simeq \rho'$ is in E.

We now state our main result, the *completeness* of $E_{pq}^{\cup}$ and of E_{pq} for their intended interpretation.

THEOREM 1. (a) If $\vdash^{\cup} \tau \tau'$, then $E_{pq}^{\cup} \vdash \tau \simeq \tau'$.

         (b) If $\vdash \tau \simeq \tau'$, then $E_{pq} \vdash \tau \simeq \tau'$.

From the soundness and completeness of $E_{pq}^{\cup}$ for its intended interpretation it follows that $\vdash^{\cup} \tau \simeq \tau'$ if and only if there is an $E_{pq}^{\cup}$-path $\langle \tau_0, \ldots, \tau_t \rangle$ from τ to τ'. One may therefore think of $E_{pq}^{\cup}$ as a sound and complete set of one-premise rules with each premise τ_i and conclusion τ_{i+1} denoting for each $U \neq \emptyset$ the same operation on $\{X : X \subseteq {}^\varphi U\}$. Unless τ_i is τ_{i+1}, premise and conclusion indicate a different mode of determining the value of the operation for given arguments. For example, $q(x \cdot y)$ indicates that one first forms the intersection of the two arguments and then applies Q, while $qx \cdot qy$ indicates that one first applies Q to each argument and then forms the intersection. Yet, by our choice of $E_{pq}^{\cup}$, the difference between the two modes is small. Hence any two modes which can be indicated in L_{pq} of determining the value of an operation on $\{X : X \subseteq {}^{\omega}U\}$ can be transformed into one another by a sequence of small changes, none of which affects the operation itself. Similar remarks apply to E_{pq}.

Under either of the two interpretations, L_{pq} is *adequate* for first-order language with identity in a sense which we now sketch. For each formula ψ of first-order language with identity we can find some n and some formula φ such that φ is provably equivalent to ψ and such that (i) no individual variable v_i with $i \geqslant n$ occurs in φ, (ii) if x_j is any predicate symbol other than $\simeq$ and if x_j is r_j-placed, then the only atomic formula containing x_j and occurring in φ is $x_j(v_{n-r_j}, v_{n-r_j+1}, \ldots, v_{n-2}, v_{n-1})$, and (iii) for convenience, the only atomic formulas containing $\simeq$ and occurring in φ are of the form $v_i \simeq v_{i+1}$, and the only connectives occurring in ψ are $\neg$, $\wedge$, and quantifiers $\exists_{v_i}$. Let $\mathrm{tm}\,\varphi$ be the term obtained from φ by replacing each $x_j(v_{n-r_j}, v_{n-r_j+1}, \ldots, v_{n-2}, v_{n-1})$ by $q^{n-r_j}x_j$, each $v_i \simeq v_{i+1}$ by $q^i d$, each $\neg$ by $-$, each $\wedge$ by $\cdot$, and each $\exists_{v_i}$ by c_i. Then for any nonempty U and any sequence $\langle X_0, X_1, \ldots \rangle$ of subsets of ${}^{\omega}U$, the value of $q^n 1 \cdot - q^{n+1} 1 \cdot \mathrm{tm}\,\varphi$ is the set of those $g \in {}^n U$ such that some $g^{\frown}h$ satisfies in the usual sense φ in $\langle U, {}^{r_0}U \cap X_0, {}^{r_1}U \cap X_1, \ldots \rangle$. When the function symbols of L_{pq} are interpreted as operations on $\{X : X \subseteq {}^{\omega}U\}$ then satisfaction of φ is related to the values of $\mathrm{tm}\,\varphi$ in a more complex way. However, φ is valid if and only if $\mathrm{tm}\,\varphi$ has the value ${}^{\omega}U$ for each U and each sequence $\langle X_0, X_1, \ldots \rangle$ of subsets of ${}^{\omega}U$.

The completeness and soundness of $E_{pq}^{\cup}$ under the intended interpretation, together with this adequacy of L_{pq}, allow us to formulate problems concerning proofs in first-order logic with identity as problems concerning $E_{pq}^{\cup}$-paths. Similarly for E_{pq}. This reformulation may have advantages.

3. Outline of proof

The completeness of E_{pq} is derived from that of $E_{pq}^{\cup}$. To prove the completeness of $E_{pq}^{\cup}$ we consider the set $E_q^{\cup}$ of equalities of L_q which is obtained from $E_{pq}^{\cup}$ by removing 2(g) and by replacing 2(f) by the following equality:

2(f)$_q$ $qx \simeq c_0 qx$.

The completeness of $E_{pq}^{\cup}$ is derived from the following result, a *quasi-completeness* of $E_q^{\cup}$ for the intended interpretation.

THEOREM 2. *If* $\vDash^{\cup} \tau \simeq \tau'$ *and if* τ *and* τ' *are terms of* L_q, *then there is some* m *such that* $E_q^{\cup} \vdash q^m \tau \simeq q^m \tau'$.

We call τ *normal* if and only if τ is some $p^j\sigma$ such that (1) no p occurs in σ, and (2) each subterm $q\rho$ of σ is either some q^ix_j or some q^id or some q^i1. Thus, roughly speaking, τ is normal if all occurrences of p are outermost and all occurrences of q innermost. We call σ *weakly k-normal* if and only if σ satisfies (1), (2) and the following four conditions: (3) if q^i1 occurs in σ then $i \leqslant k$, (4) if q^ix_j occurs in σ, then $i \leqslant k$, (5) if q^id occurs in σ, then $i < k-1$, and (6) if c_i occurs in σ, then $i < k$. (If, in addition, 1 does not occur in σ then we call σ *k-normal*. However, we do not use k-normality here.)

Lemmas 3(b), 4 and 5 are used in proving Lemma 6 below. Lemma 3(a) is useful in deriving Theorem 1 from Theorem 2. These lemmas also throw light on the expressive power of L_q and of L_{pq}.

LEMMA 3. (a) For any τ one can find some normal τ' such that $E_{pq}^{\cup} \vdash \tau \simeq \tau'$. (b) For any term τ of L_q one can find some normal term τ' of L_q such that $E_q^{\cup} \vdash \tau \simeq \tau'$.

LEMMA 4. For any term τ of L_q and any m, $E_q^{\cup} \vdash \tau \simeq (q^01 \cdot - q^11 \cdot \tau) + \cdots + (q^{m-1}1 \cdot - q^m1 \cdot \tau) + (q^m1 \cdot \tau)$.

LEMMA 5. For any normal term τ of L_q and any k one can find some weakly k-normal term τ' of L_q such that $E_q^{\cup} \vdash q^k1 \cdot - q^{k+1}1 \cdot \tau \simeq q^k1 \cdot - q^{k+1}1 \cdot \tau'$.

LEMMA 6. Assume that Theorem 2 holds whenever τ' is 0 and τ is $q^k1 \cdot c_0 \ldots c_{k-1}\rho$ for some $k < \omega$ and some weakly k-normal ρ. Then Theorem 2 holds for any τ and τ'.

Consider now an arbitrary k and an arbitrary weakly k-normal ρ such that, for no m, $E_q^{\cup} \vdash q^m(q^k1 \cdot c_0 \ldots c_{k-1}\rho) \simeq q^m0$. By Lemma 6, to prove Theorem 2 it suffices to construct some U and some sequence $\langle X_0, X_1, \ldots \rangle$ of subsets of $^\omega U$ for which the value of $q^k1 \cdot c_0 \ldots c_{k-1}\rho$ is a nonempty set. We use a Henkin-type construction. Let $a_1, a_2, \ldots$ be individual constants not present in a given first-order language and let χ be a sentence of the given language which contains no individual variables other than $v_0, v_1, \ldots, v_{k-1}$. If χ has a model, then to construct a model of χ by Henkin's method it suffices to consider those formulas φ which contain no individual variables other than $v_0, v_1, \ldots, v_{k-1}$. One forms for any such φ and any $r_0, r_1, \ldots, r_{k-1} > 0$ the sentence $\varphi[a_{r_0}, a_{r_1}, \ldots, a_{r_{k-1}}]$ which results from φ by substitution of a_{r_0}, $a_{r_1}, \ldots, a_{r_{k-1}}$ for the free occurrences, if any, in φ of $v_0, v_1, \ldots, v_{k-1}$ respectively. One then forms a certain maximal consistent set of such $\varphi[a_{r_0}, a_{r_1}, \ldots, a_{r_{k-1}}]$.

To adapt this construction, we let d_{ji} be the term $c_{i+1}...c_{j-1}(q^i d \cdot q^{i+1} d \cdot$
$\cdots \cdot q^{j-1} d)$ and $s_i^j \tau$ the term $c_j(d_{ji} \cdot \tau)$ for any $j > i$ and any τ. For each
$m > \max(r_0, r_1, ..., r_{k-1})$ and each weakly k-normal τ we let $\tau[m; r_0, ..., r_{k-1}]$
be the term $s_{m-r_0}^m s_{m-r_1}^{m+1} ... s_{m-r_{k-1}}^{m+k-1} q^m \tau$. Otherwise $\tau[m; r_0, ..., r_{k-1}]$ will be
undefined. We think of *each* $\tau[m; r_0, ..., r_{k-1}]$ as related to τ in the same
way in which the single sentence $\varphi[a_{r_0}, ..., a_{r_{k-1}}]$ is related to φ. Speaking
very roughly, applying q^m to τ converts the first m places of sequences into
a "working space" which application of $s_{m-r_0}^m s_{m-r_1}^{m+1} ... s_{m-r_{k-1}}^{m+k-1}$ uses to
"mimick" substitution of $a_{r_0}, a_{r_1}, ..., a_{r_{k-1}}$.

We form a sequence $\langle \sigma_1, \sigma_2, ... \rangle$ such that (1) σ_1 is $c_0...c_{k-1} \rho[1; 1, 1,$
$..., 1]$, (2) each σ_m is some $\tau[m; r_0, ..., r_{k-1}]$, (3) for each $\tau[n; r_0, ..., r_{k-1}]$
there is some $m > n$ such that $\sigma_m = \tau[m; r_0, ..., r_{k-1}]$ and (4) if σ_m is $c_j \tau'[m;$
$r_0, ... r_{j-1}, r_j, r_{j+1}, ..., r_{k-1}]$, then σ_{m+1} is $\tau'[m+1; r_0, ..., r_{j-1}, m+1, r_{j+1},$
$..., r_{k-1}]$.

A set of terms shall be *consistent* if and only if it contains no $\rho_0', ..., \rho_{r-1}'$
such that $E_q^{\cup} \vdash \rho_0' \cdot \cdots \cdot \rho_{r-1}' \cong 0$. We let $V_1 = \{\sigma_1\}$. For $1 < m < \omega$, we let
$V_m = \{\sigma_m\} \cup \{\tau[m; r_0, ..., r_{k-1}] : \tau[m-1; r_0, ..., r_k] \in V_{m-1}\}$ if, for each n,
$\{q^{k+m+n} 1\} \cup \{q^n \sigma_m\} \cup \{q^{n+1} \rho' : \rho' \in V_{m-1}\}$ is consistent, and we let $V_m =$
$= \{\tau[m; r_0, ..., r_{k-1}] : \tau[m-1; r_0, ..., r_{k-1}] \in V_{m-1}\}$ otherwise.

One can show* that the positive integers r can be partitioned into equivalence classes $\bar{r}$ such that r_0 and r_1 belong to the same class if and only if, for
some m and $r_2, ..., r_{k-1}$, $d[m; r_0, r_1, r_2, ..., r_{k-1}]$ is in V_m. We let U be the set
of $\bar{r}$. One can also show* that for each j there is a set $X_j \subseteq {}^\omega U$ such that for
each $s \leqslant k$, $\langle \bar{r}_s, \bar{r}_{s+1}, ..., \bar{r}_{k-1} \rangle \in X_j$ if and only if, for some m and some $r_0, ...,$
r_{s-1}, $q^s x_j[m; r_0, ..., r_{s-1}, r_s, ..., r_{k-1}]$ is in V_m. By induction on the number
of function symbols in τ one then shows that if $f = \langle f_0, f_1, ..., f_{m+k-1} \rangle \in {}^{k+m}U$
and $f_{m-r_0} = \bar{r}_0, f_{m-r_1} = \bar{r}_1, ..., f_{m-r_{k-1}} = \bar{r}_{k-1}$, then f belongs to the value of
$\tau[m; r_0, ..., r_{k-1}]$ for U and $\langle X_0, X_1, ... \rangle$ if and only if, for some n, $\tau[n; r_0,$
$..., r_{k-1}]$ is in V_n. It follows that $\langle \bar{1}, ..., \bar{1} \rangle \in {}^k U$ belongs to the value of
$c_0...c_{k-1} \rho$ for U and $\langle X_0, X_1, ... \rangle$. This concludes the sketch of our proof.

---

* Membership of 2(e) in $E_q^{\cup}$ is not required for this, it is only needed for Lemmas 5 and 6.

NUMBERED FIELDS

YU. L. ERSHOV

Mathematical Institute, Novosibirsk, USSR

General definitions of the theory of numbered algebras may be found in MALCEV [1961]. The special theory of numbered fields was considered in works of FRÖLICH and SHEPHERDSON [1958], MOSCHOVAKIS [1965] and RABIN [1960]. NERODE [1963] used numbered fields for constructing an algorithm for p-adic integral zeros of diophantine equations. A construction of complicated algorithms for solving diophantine problems, as for example the algorithm in AX [1967], calls for a systematic development of the general theory of numbered fields. The use of this theory is a new powerful tool for solving such problems, I think.

In this communication I will talk about a new aspect of the general theory of numbered fields. I do not use a general definition of a numbered field as Malcev or Moschovakis do, but use the following definitions:

Let F be a field. A map $\varphi: N \to F$ from the set of natural numbers on F is called a numbering of the field F if φ is a one-one map of N on F, and sum and product operations are recursive – that is to say: functions $f_+(x, y)$ and $f_.(x, y)$ such that $\forall xy(\varphi(f_+(x, y)) = \varphi(x) + \varphi(y))$ and $\forall xy(\varphi(f_.(x, y)) = \varphi(x) \cdot \varphi(y))$ are recursive.

If I have the numbering of the field F, I shall speak about the numbered field F.*) If $i: F_1 \to F_2$ is an isomorphism from F_1 to F_2 and the fields F_1 and F_2 are numbered fields $(\varphi_1: N \to F_1; \varphi_2: N \to F_2)$ I say that i is a constructive map if the function $f^i(x)$ – such that $\forall x(i(\varphi_1(x)) = \varphi_2(f^i(x)))$ is recursive.

If F is a numbered field $(\varphi: N \to F$ its numbering) I say that a subfield $F_1 \subset F$ is a constructive subfield iff $\varphi^{-1}(F_1)$ is a recursively enumerable set.

1. Let $F_0 \subset F_1$ be two fields and $\varphi_0: N \to F_0$ and $\varphi_1: N \to F_1$ the numberings of these fields, such that the immersion $i: F_0 \to F_1$ is a constructive map.

---

*) This restricted notion of a numbered field equals to RABIN'S [1960] notion of a computable field.

Using some results of the theory of recursively ennumerable classes we have without serious difficulties:

a) *There exists a recursively enumerable numbering of all intermediate constructive (or all finitely generated) fields.* (F_2 is an intermediate field between F_0 and F_1 if $F_0 \subseteq F_2 \subseteq F_1$ and F_2 is a constructive subfield of F_1.)

This statement is equivalent to the following:

There is a recursive relation $R(x, y, z)$ such that if x is fixed, the set $F_{(x)} = \varphi_1(\{y | \exists z R(x, y, z)\})$ is a subfield (clearly constructive) *of the field F_1 and this subfield contains the field F_0;* and moreover *for any constructive subfield F_2 of the field F_1 which contains F_0 there is x such that $F_{(x)} = F_2$.*

For numberings which satisfy a) it is possible to define reducibility. Then the following is true:

b) *There exists a numbering which satisfies* a) *to which all numberings verifying* a) *are reducable.* In other words there exists a principal (or Gödel's) numbering. And any two such numberings are isomorphic.

If we are interested in one-one (or Fiedberg's) numberings the following is true:

c) *If the problem of equalities for finitely generated intermediate fields between F_0 and F_1 is decidable, in other words if the relation $R(\langle n_1, ..., n_k \rangle, \langle m_1, ..., m_l \rangle) \Leftrightarrow F_0(\varphi_1(n_1), ..., \varphi_1(n_k)) = F_0(\varphi_1(m_1), ..., \varphi_1(m_l))$ is recursive then there is a one-one numbering which satisfies* a).

2. Using results from sec. 1, I may present constructive definitions for some classical notions.

Let F_0 be a prime field and $F^* = F_0(x_0, ... , x_n, ...)$ be a pure transcendental extension of F_0 with ω independent variables, and F_1 be the algebraic closure of F^*. We may introduce a numbering of the field F_1 using Rabin's result that the immersion $F_0 \rightarrow F_1$ is constructive if F_0 is numbered in a natural way. Then the numbering of F_1 and the numbering of all finitely generated subfields of F_1 are constructive definitions for the notion of universal domain in algebraic geometry.

Such a construction may be carried out for any numbered field.

If we assume this definition then some algorithm problems arise for standard constructions in algebraic geometry. For example, does there exist an algorithm for finding definition fields of algebraic varieties defined by polynomials?

The numbering of the algebraic closure of the field of rational numbers and the numberings of all fields of algebraic numbers are natural objects for constructivising Galois theory, class field theory and so on. The results of

Ax's work [1967] and its proofs are naturally stated for these constructive objects.

3. I will say something about relations between the theory of numbered fields and decision problems for elementary theories. The main statement which I shall formulate now, may be known but it has not been printed in explicit form. Some results which I shall state later in this section are found among Malcev's ideas.

THEOREM. If $\mathscr{F}$ is an AC_A-class of fields which has a decidable elementary theory, then there exists a numbered field $F \in \mathscr{F}$ such that there exists a recursive map from the recursive set $\text{Th}(F)$ – set of all sentences that are true in F – to recursive functions which are Skolem functions for correspondent sentences. Moreover there are many such fields: there exists a recursively enumerable class $\mathscr{F}_0$ of numbered fields that satisfy conditions for field F with recursive enumeration of recursive maps from the sets of sentences to correspondent recursive Skolem functions and $\text{Th}(\mathscr{F}_0) = \text{Th}(\mathscr{F})$.

Remark. This theorem is true not only for classes of fields but for any class of algebras or models if we use the right notion of a numbered algebra or a numbered model (relational system).

Using this theorem one gets a new proof of Rabin's theorem about the existence of a numbering for the algebraic closure of a numbered field and a proof for his theorem on the characterization of fields with a splitting algorithm. These new proofs use the relative model completeness and decidability of the theory of algebraically closed fields. The same ideas may be used for proving that numbered ordered fields have constructive immersions in their algebraic real-closed extensions. Such results may be proved for some normed fields.

The theorem may be used for the proofs of existence of numberings for some fields. For example, numberings for the field of all algebraic numbers, the field of all real algebraic numbers, the field of all p-adic algebraic numbers may be constructed in this way. It is easy to prove that any two numberings for one of these fields are isomorphic. Nerode's result about existence of a numbering for the field of all algebraic p-adic numbers is proved in such a way.

4. I should like to mention one problem about numeration. It relates to the theorems in the first section.

Does there exist a recursively enumerable class of all constructive extensions for a fixed numbered field, such that any other recursively enumurable class of some constructive extensions of this field reduces to the first one?

I note that this problem is not very clear. One has to find reasonable definitions for all concepts involved.

I think that the answer will be negative.

References

Ax, J., Solving diophantine problems modulo every prime, Ann. of Math. **85** (1967) 161–183.

Frölich, A. and J. C. Shepherdson, Effective procedures in field theory, Phil. Trans. Roy. Soc. London, Ser A. **248** (1958) 407–432.

Malcev, A. I., Constructive algebra I, Usp. Math. Nauk **166**, No. 3 (1961) 3–60.

Moschovakis, Y. N., Notation system and recursive ordered fields, Compositio Math. **17** (1965) 40–71.

Nerode, A., A decision method for p-adic integral zeros of diophantine equations, Bull. Am. Math. Soc. **69** (1963) 513–517.

Rabin, M. O., Computable algebra general theory and theory of computable fields, Trans. Am. Math. Soc. **95** (1960) 341–360.

MODELS WITH ORDERINGS

H.J. KEISLER

University of Wisconsin, Madison, Wisconsin, USA

By an *ordered model* we mean a relational structure

$$\mathfrak{A} = \langle A, L, R_0, R_1, \ldots \rangle$$

for a countable language $\mathscr{L}$, such that L is a binary relation which linearly orders the set A. A linearly ordered structure $\langle A, L \rangle$ is said to be κ-like if A has power κ but each element $a \in A$ has fewer than κ predecessors with respect to L. $\mathfrak{A}$ is said to be a κ-like model if $\mathfrak{A}$ is an ordered model and $\langle A, L \rangle$ is κ-like.

This paper concerns the following problem of MOSTOWSKI [1957] and FUHRKEN [1965] (see also VAUGHT [1965]):

Which pairs of cardinals κ, λ have the property that for every κ-like model $\mathfrak{A}$ there exists a λ-like model $\mathfrak{B}$ which is elementarily equivalent to $\mathfrak{A}$?

Let $\kappa \rightarrow \lambda$ mean that the pair of cardinals κ, λ has the above property. Our main theorem is the following.

THEOREM 2.1. Suppose κ is a strong limit cardinal (that is, $\mu < \kappa$ implies $2^\mu < \kappa$), and λ is a singular cardinal. Then $\kappa \rightarrow \lambda$.

It follows that if κ and λ are both singular strong limit cardinals, then $\kappa \leftrightarrow \lambda$.

The solutions of several other cases of the problem are known from the literature. We list them here. Assume that κ, λ are infinite cardinals.

1. $\omega \rightarrow \lambda$ (SPECKER and MACDOWELL [1961]).
2. $\kappa^+ \rightarrow \omega^+$ (Vaught; see MORLEY and VAUGHT [1962]).
3 (GCH). If λ is regular, then $\kappa^+ \rightarrow \lambda^+$ (CHANG [1965]).
4. If κ is weakly inaccessible and λ is regular, then $\kappa \rightarrow \lambda^+$ (GCH when $\lambda > \omega$) (FUHRKEN [1964]).
5. If κ is strongly inaccessible and λ is singular, then $\kappa \rightarrow \lambda$ (SILVER [unpublished]).
6. If κ is weakly compact and $\lambda > \omega$, then $\kappa \rightarrow \lambda$ (HELLING [1966]).

Simple counterexamples show the following negative results (see FUHRKEN [1964]):

7. If $\kappa > \omega$, then $\kappa \nleftrightarrow \omega$.

8. If κ is singular and λ is regular, then $\kappa \nleftrightarrow \lambda$.

9. If λ is a limit cardinal, then $\kappa^+ \nleftrightarrow \lambda$.

Without the GCH, there is no hope of proving that $\kappa \leftrightarrow \lambda$ for all singular cardinals κ and λ, because an obvious example shows:

10. If κ is not a strong limit cardinal and λ is a strong limit cardinal, then $\kappa \nleftrightarrow \lambda$.

If we assume the GCH, then the present situation can be summarized in the table below (using 1–10 and Theorem 2.1). The question mark in the table indicates the main problem which remains open. (Helling's result 6 above is a partial solution.) Theorem 2.1 filled in the singular→singular position in the table. A yes with an asterisk, yes *, indicates that the answer is yes if λ is the successor of a regular cardinal, and is open if λ is the successor of a singular cardinal.

		λ			
$\kappa \to \lambda$		ω	successor	singular	inaccessible
	ω	yes	yes	yes	yes
	successor	no	yes *	no	no
κ	singular	no	no	yes	no
	inaccessible	no	yes *	yes	?

Notice that Theorem 2.1 implies the unpublished result 5 above of Silver, since all strongly inaccessible cardinals are strong limit cardinals. Silver's proof used ultraproducts, and seems quite different from the proof of Theorem 2.1 in this paper.

The proof of Theorem 2.1, like the proofs of several of the earlier results 1–6, has the following plan. We introduce a particular set Σ of sentences which involve extra function symbols and, in this case, a doubly indexed sequence of new constant symbols c_{ij}. We then show (in Lemmas 2.3 and 2.5): (I) If the theory of a model $\mathfrak{A}$ is consistent with Σ, and if λ is a singular cardinal, then there is a λ-like model $\mathfrak{B}$ which is elementarily equivalent to $\mathfrak{A}$. (II) If $\mathfrak{A}$ is κ-like where κ is a strong limit cardinal, then the theory of $\mathfrak{A}$ is consistent with Σ.

To prove (I) we replace the constants c_{ij} in Σ by $c_{\alpha\beta}$, where α ranges over

$\mathrm{cf}(\lambda)$ and β ranges over cardinals μ_α which approach λ. Then we use the compactness theorem to get a λ-like model.

The proof of (II) depends on the *polarized partition relations* of ERDÖS and RADO [1956], and uses the results of that paper. Partition theorems have been applied in model theory several times before. For instance, see EHREN-FEUCHT and MOSTOWSKI [1956], MORLEY [1965], [1965a], ROWBOTTOM [1964] and SILVER [1966]. It appears that polarized partition relations have not been used in model theory before, however. They arise here because, to show that Σ is consistent with the theory of $\mathfrak{A}$, we need to consider doubly indexed sequences of elements corresponding to the constants c_{ij}.

In Section 1 we introduce a notion concerning partitions, that of a "large" set, and we prove some lemmas about large sets which we shall use later. In Section 2 we prove the main result 2.1. In Section 3 we obtain a number of related results which follow from the proof. For example, if λ is a strong limit cardinal, then we have a compactness theorem (Corollary 3.2) and a completeness theorem (Corollary 3.3) for λ-like models. These answer questions raised in MOSTOWSKI [1957] and VAUGHT [1965]. Using general results of FUHRKEN [1964], [1965], our results translate at once into new theorems about the quantifier "there exist at least λ". We also modify our proofs to show that, if λ is singular, then every complete extension of Zermelo set theory with a choice function has a λ-like model (Theorem 3.8).

The results of this paper were first announced in an abstract, KEISLER [1967]. This work was supported in part by National Science Foundation Grant GP-5913. The author is a fellow of the Alfred E. Sloan Foundation.

1. Some lemmas in partition theory

Let us fix our set-theoretic notation. We always assume the axiom of choice. We shall identify cardinals with initial ordinals. The letters κ, λ, μ will be used for cardinals, sometimes with subscripts. We use α, β, γ, δ for ordinals. Ordinals are defined so that $\alpha = \{\beta : \beta < \alpha\}$. The iterated power of 2, denoted by $2(\kappa, \alpha)$, is defined recursively as follows:

$$2(\kappa, 0) = \kappa; \quad 2(\kappa, \alpha) = \sup_{\beta < \alpha} 2^{2(\kappa, \beta)}, \quad \text{when} \quad \alpha > 0.$$

The power, or cardinality, of a set X is denoted by $|X|$. The cardinal successor of κ is denoted by κ^+. The cofinality of a cardinal κ is denoted by $\mathrm{cf}(\kappa)$. We assume a knowledge of the arithmetic of cardinals. The notation $f: X \to Y$ means that f is a function on X into Y. If f is a function $f: X \to Y$, then $f|Z$ denotes the restriction of f to Z, and for each $y \in Y$, $f^{-1}(y) = \{x : f(x) = y\}$.

If X is linearly ordered by a binary relation L, a subset $Y \subset X$ is said to be *cofinal* in $\langle X, L \rangle$ iff for all $x \in X$ there exists $y \in Y$ such that $L(x, y)$.

We shall use some special notation from ERDÖS and RADO [1956] concerning partition relations. We denote by $[X]^\kappa$ the set of all subsets of X of power exactly κ. Thus $[X]^\kappa \neq 0$ iff $|X| \geqslant \kappa$. Let r be a natural number. The expression

$$\kappa \to (\lambda)^r_\mu$$

means that for any partition of κ into μ parts, there is a set $X \in [\kappa]^\lambda$ such that $[X]^r$ lies entirely in one part of the partition. The above expression is called a *partition relation*.

THEOREM 1.1 (Ramsey). For any positive $r, a, b < \omega$,

$$\omega \to (a)^r_b.$$

Moreover, there exists $c < \omega$ such that

$$c \to (a)^r_b.$$

THEOREM 1.2 (ERDÖS and RADO [1956]). For any infinite cardinal κ and any $r < \omega$,

$$2(\kappa, r)^+ \to (\kappa^+)^{r+1}_\kappa.$$

We now introduce the *polarized partition relations* of ERDÖS and RADO [1956]. Let r, s be positive integers. The expression

$$(\kappa_1, ..., \kappa_s) \to (\lambda_1, ..., \lambda_s)^r_\mu$$

means that for any partition of the set

$$[\kappa_1]^r \times \cdots \times [\kappa_s]^r$$

into μ parts, there exist sets

$$X_1 \in [\kappa_1]^{\lambda_1}, ..., X_s \in [\kappa_s]^{\lambda_s}$$

such that the set

$$[X_1]^r \times \cdots \times [X_s]^r$$

lies entirely within one part of the partition. (Erdös and Rado used vertical columns of κ's and λ's for the polarized partition relations, and used the above row notation for a quite different kind of partition relation. We use rows instead of columns here to save space.)

THEOREM 1.3 (ERDÖS and RADO [1956]). Suppose that

$$(\kappa_1, ..., \kappa_s) \to (\lambda_1, ..., \lambda_s)_\mu^r \quad \text{and} \quad \kappa_{s+1} \to (\lambda_{s+1})_{\mu'}^r,$$

where $\mu' \geqslant \mu^{\kappa_1 \cdots \kappa_s}$. Then

$$(\kappa_1, ..., \kappa_{s+1}) \to (\lambda_1, ..., \lambda_{s+1})_\mu^r.$$

The last two theorems have an immediate consequence, which is a polarized partition relation useful in this paper.

COROLLARY 1.4. Suppose that for $1 \leqslant t \leqslant s$, κ_t, λ_t are infinite cardinals and

$$\kappa_t > 2(\lambda_t, r - 1), \qquad \lambda_{t+1} \geqslant 2^{\kappa_t}.$$

Then

$$(\kappa_1, ..., \kappa_s) \to (\lambda_1^+, ..., \lambda_s^+)_{\lambda_1}^r.$$

PROOF: By Theorem 1.2 we have

$$\kappa_t \to (\lambda_t^+)_{\lambda_t}^r, \qquad 1 \leqslant t \leqslant s.$$

Also,

$$\lambda_{t+1} \geqslant 2^{\kappa_t} = \kappa_t^{(\kappa_t)} \geqslant \lambda_1^{\kappa_1 \cdots \kappa_t}.$$

The result now follows from Theorem 1.3 by induction on t.

If $F : X \to \lambda$, then the set $\{F^{-1}(\alpha) : \alpha < \lambda\}$ forms a partition of X into at most λ parts. Any partition of X into at most λ parts can be represented by a function $F : X \to \lambda$ in this way. The partition we get from F also has an order structure inherited from the natural ordering of λ. We shall now study the partition which comes from F.

Let r, s be positive integers and let $F : X \to \lambda$. We shall often consider sequences x of length s, each term being a set of power r. For such sequences, we write

$$x = \langle x_1, ..., x_s \rangle = \langle \{x_{11}, ..., x_{1r}\}, ..., \{x_{s1}, ..., x_{sr}\} \rangle,$$

with single subscripts for terms of x and double subscripts for elements of terms of x. We define $[F]^{r,s}$ to be the set of all s-tuples x of elements of $[X]^r$ such that

$$F(x_{ij}) = F(x_{il}), \qquad i = 1, ..., s \quad \text{and} \quad j, l = 1, ..., r,$$

and

$$F(x_{11}) < F(x_{21}) < \cdots < F(x_{s1}).$$

More concisely,

$$[F]^{r,s} = \bigcup \{[F^{-1}(\alpha_1)]^r \times \cdots \times [F^{-1}(\alpha_s)]^r : \alpha_1 < \cdots < \alpha_s < \lambda\}.$$

We now come to the main notion which we shall use, the notion of a "large" set. Suppose $F: \kappa \to \lambda$ and $S \subset [F]^{r,s}$. For each positive integer p, we consider a game $G(S, p)$ between two players, I and II. In this game each player has p moves. Player I moves first, and for his first move he chooses a cardinal $\mu_1 < \kappa$. Then II chooses an ordinal $\beta_1 < \lambda$. Then I chooses $\mu_2 < \kappa$ and then II chooses $\beta_2 < \lambda$, and so on. The player II *wins* the game $G(S, p)$ iff $\beta_1 < \beta_2 < \cdots < \beta_p$ and there exist sets

$$Y_1 \in [F^{-1}(\beta_1)]^{\mu_1}, \ldots, Y_p \in [F^{-1}(\beta_p)]^{\mu_p}$$

such that

$$[F|(Y_1 \cup \cdots \cup Y_p)]^{r,s} \subset S.$$

Otherwise I wins.

Since p is finite, it is clear that exactly one player has a winning strategy for the game $G(S, p)$. By a winning strategy for I we mean a sequence of functions,

$$\mu_1, \mu_2(\beta_1), \ldots, \mu_p(\beta_1, \ldots, \beta_{p-1})$$

such that for any play of II, $\beta_1, \ldots, \beta_p$, the game is won by I. Similarly, a winning strategy for II is a sequence of functions

$$\beta_1(\mu_1), \beta_2(\mu_1, \mu_2), \ldots, \beta_p(\mu_1, \ldots, \mu_p)$$

which guarantees a win for II.

We shall say that a set $S \subset [F]^{r,s}$ is *large* iff for every positive integer p, the player II has a winning strategy for the game $G(S, p)$.

If $F: X \to \lambda$ and $|X| = \kappa$, then all the above definitions still make sense, and in this case we shall also use the notion of a large set $S \subset [F]^{r,s}$.

The name "large" is motivated by the following trivial lemma.

LEMMA 1.5. Suppose $F: \kappa \to \lambda$, $\kappa > 1$, $S \subset [F]^{r,s}$, and S is large. Then S is non-empty, and any subset of $[F]^{r,s}$ which includes S is also large.

The next two lemmas will be used in the proof of our theorem in the next section, and are harder.

LEMMA 1.6. Suppose κ is a strong limit cardinal (that is $\mu < \kappa$ implies $2^\mu < \kappa$), and let $\lambda = \mathrm{cf}(\kappa)$. Let $F: \kappa \to \lambda$ be such that for each $\mu < \kappa$, there exist arbitrarily large $\beta < \lambda$ with $|F^{-1}(\beta)| \geq \mu$. Let r, s be positive integers with $s > 1$, and let $f: [F]^{r,s-1} \to \lambda$. Then the set

$$S = \{x \in [F]^{r,s} : f(x_1, \ldots, x_{s-1}) < F(x_{s1})\}$$

is large.

PROOF: We wish to show that for each positive integer p, II has a winning strategy for the game $G(S, p)$. For $1 \leqslant p < s$, all II has to do to win the game is to choose $\beta_1 < \cdots < \beta_p$ such that

$$|F^{-1}(\beta_1)| \geqslant \mu_1, ..., |F^{-1}(\beta_p)| \geqslant \mu_p,$$

because the set

$$[F|(F^{-1}(\beta_1) \cup \cdots \cup F^{-1}(\beta_p))]^{r,s}$$

is empty and thus trivially included in S. Hence in this case the fact that II has a winning strategy follows from our assumption that for each $\mu < \kappa$ there are arbitrarily large $\beta < \lambda$ with $|F^{-1}(\beta)| \geqslant \mu$.

In case $\kappa = \lambda$ (whence κ is strongly inaccessible), we easily see that II has a winning strategy for each p. We may assume without loss of generality that $|F^{-1}(\beta)| < \kappa$ for each $\beta < \lambda$, because there is a subset $X \subset \kappa$ of power κ such that $F|X$ has that property. At each move $t \leqslant p$, II chooses β_t such that $|F^{-1}(\beta_t)| \geqslant \mu_t$, $\beta_{t-1} < \beta_t < \lambda$, and β_t is an upper bound for the set

$$\{f(x): x \in [F|(F^{-1}(\beta_1) \cup \cdots \cup F^{-1}(\beta_{t-1}))]^{r,s-1}\}.$$

This set has an upper bound because it is a subset of κ of power $< \kappa$. Then we have

$$[F|(F^{-1}(\beta_1) \cup \cdots \cup F^{-1}(\beta_p))]^{r,s} \subset S,$$

so II wins the game $G(S, p)$.

Assume now that $\kappa > \lambda$ (whence κ is a singular strong limit cardinal). We argue by induction on p. Let $p \geqslant s$ and suppose II has a winning strategy

$$\beta_1(\mu_1), ..., \beta_{p-1}(\mu_1, ..., \mu_{p-1})$$

for the game $G(S, p-1)$. We shall describe a winning strategy

$$\gamma_1(\mu_1), ..., \gamma_p(\mu_1, ..., \mu_p) \tag{1}$$

for II in the game $G(S, p)$. Let $\lambda_1 = \lambda + \mu_1$, and for $1 \leqslant t < p$,

$$\kappa_t = 2(\lambda_t, r), \qquad \lambda_{t+1} = 2^{\kappa_t} + \mu_t.$$

Thus κ_t, λ_t depend only on $\mu_1, ..., \mu_t$, and since κ is a strong limit cardinal, each $\kappa_t < \kappa$. We define the first $p-1$ moves in the strategy (1) by

$$\gamma_t(\mu_1, ..., \mu_t) = \beta_t(\kappa_1, ..., \kappa_t), \qquad 1 \leqslant t < p.$$

We now construct the last move. Since $\kappa_t > 2(\lambda_t, r-1)$, we may apply Corollary 1.4 and we have

$$(\kappa_1, ..., \kappa_{p-1}) \to (\lambda_1^+, ..., \lambda_{p-1}^+)_{\lambda_1}^r.$$

This partition relation obviously remains true when we make the numbers on the right side smaller, so

$$(\kappa_1, \ldots, \kappa_{p-1}) \to (\mu_1, \ldots, \mu_{p-1})_\lambda^r. \qquad (2)$$

For brevity let

$$\gamma_1 = \gamma_1(\mu_1), \ldots, \gamma_{p-1} = \gamma_{p-1}(\mu_1, \ldots, \mu_{p-1}).$$

From the definition of the γ's and the assumption that the β's are a winning strategy for II in the game $G(S, p-1)$, we see that there are sets

$$Y_1 \in [F^{-1}(\gamma_1)]^{\kappa_1}, \ldots, Y_{p-1} \in [F^{-1}(\gamma_{p-1})]^{\kappa_{p-1}}$$

such that

$$[F|(Y_1 \cup \cdots \cup Y_{p-1})]^{r,s} \subset S.$$

Consider the partition P of the set

$$[Y_1]^r \times \cdots \times [Y_{p-1}]^r$$

such that two elements

$$x = \langle x_1, \ldots, x_{p-1} \rangle, \qquad y = \langle y_1, \ldots, y_{p-1} \rangle$$

of this set are in the same partition class iff for all increasing sequences $i_1 < \cdots < i_{s-1} < p$, we have

$$f(x_{i_1}, \ldots, x_{i_{s-1}}) = f(y_{i_1}, \ldots, y_{i_{s-1}}).$$

There are at most λ partition classes. Therefore, by (2), there exist sets

$$Z_1 \in [Y_1]^{\mu_1}, \ldots, Z_{p-1} \in [Y_{p-1}]^{\mu_{p-1}}$$

such that the set

$$[Z_1]^r \times \cdots \times [Z_{p-1}]^r$$

lies entirely in one partition class. This implies that the set

$$\{f(z) : z \in [F|(Z_1 \cup \cdots \cup Z_{p-1})]^{r,s-1}\}$$

is finite. Hence it has an upper bound, say α, and $\alpha < \lambda$.

We now define the last move for II, $\gamma_p(\mu_1, \ldots, \mu_p)$, to be the least ordinal $\gamma < \lambda$ such that $\alpha < \gamma$, $\gamma_{p-1} < \gamma$, and $|F^{-1}(\gamma)| \geq \mu_p$. Let $Z_p \in [F^{-1}(\gamma)]^{\mu_p}.$ We then have

$$f(z_1, \ldots, z_{s-1}) \leq \alpha < F(z_{s1})$$

for all

$$z \in [F|(Z_1 \cup \cdots \cup Z_p)]^{r,s}$$

and hence II wins the game $G(S, p)$. Our proof is complete.

LEMMA 1.7. Suppose κ is a strong limit cardinal, and let $\lambda = \mathrm{cf}(\kappa)$. Let r, s be positive integers, let $F: \kappa \to \lambda$ and suppose that $S \subset [F]^{r,s}$ is large. Then for any partition

$$S = S_1 \cup \cdots \cup S_m$$

of S into finitely many parts, at least one of the parts S_i is large.

PROOF: We give the proof only for $\kappa > \omega$. The proof for $\kappa = \omega$ is similar. It suffices to prove the lemma for the case $m = 2$, for the result for arbitrary m then follows at once by induction.

Suppose $S = S_1 \cup S_2$ is large but S_1 and S_2 are both small. Then for some positive integers p_1 and p_2, the player I has winning strategies for the games $G(S_1, p_1)$ and $G(S_2, p_2)$. Let p be the greater of p_1, p_2. Then I has winning strategies for both of the games $G(S_1, p)$ and $G(S_2, p)$, because making p larger only makes the game easier for I. Notice that the set of all plays

$$\mu_1, \ldots, \mu_p, \beta_1, \ldots, \beta_p$$

for which I wins the game $G(S_i, p)$ is closed under enlarging the μ's. It follows that by taking the maximum of a pair of winning strategies for I in the games $G(S_1, p)$ and $G(S_2, p)$, we get a single strategy which is a winning strategy for I in both of the games. Let such a strategy be

$$\mu_1, \mu_2(\beta_1), \ldots, \mu_p(\beta_1, \ldots, \beta_{p-1}). \tag{1}$$

For each $\beta < \lambda$, define

$$H(\beta) = \sup\{\mu_j(\beta_1, \ldots, \beta_{j-1}): 1 \leqslant j \leqslant p \quad \text{and} \quad \beta_1, \ldots, \beta_{j-1} \leqslant \beta\}.$$

Since $H(\beta)$ is the supremum of fewer than $\lambda = \mathrm{cf}(\kappa)$ cardinals less than κ, we have $H(\beta) < \kappa$.

By Ramsey's Theorem (Theorem 1.1 above), there exists $q < \omega$ such that

$$q \to (p)_2^s. \tag{2}$$

Let us define simultaneously for $t = 1, \ldots, q-1$:

$$L_1 = \omega + \mu_1, \qquad L_{t+1}(\beta_1, \ldots, \beta_t) = H(\beta_t) + 2^{K_t(\beta_1, \ldots, \beta_{t-1})},$$

$$K_1 = 2(L_1, r), \qquad K_{t+1}(\beta_1, \ldots, \beta_t) = 2(L_{t+1}(\beta_1, \ldots, \beta_t), r).$$

Since κ is a strong limit cardinal and we have assumed at the beginning that $\kappa > \omega$, all the K's and L's are infinite cardinals less than κ. Because $2(\mu, r) > 2(\mu, r-1)$ for any cardinal μ, we may apply Corollary 1.4. We obtain for all $\beta_1, \ldots, \beta_{q-1} < \lambda$, the partition relation

$$(K_1, K_2(\beta_1), \ldots, K_q(\beta_1, \ldots, \beta_{q-1})) \to (L_1^+, L_2(\beta_1)^+, \ldots, L_q(\beta_1, \ldots, \beta_{q-1})^+)_{L_1}^r.$$

This partition relation certainly remains true if we make the numbers on the right side smaller. Therefore

$$(K_1, K_2(\beta_1), ..., K_q(\beta_1, ..., \beta_{q-1})) \to (\mu_1, H(\beta_1), ..., H(\beta_{q-1}))^r_\omega. \quad (3)$$

Since the set S is large, the strategy

$$K_1, K_2(\beta_1), ..., K_q(\beta_1, ..., \beta_{q-1})$$

is not a winning strategy for the player I in the game $G(S, q)$. Therefore there exist $\beta_1 < \cdots < \beta_q < \lambda$ and

$$X_1 \in [F^{-1}(\beta_1)]^{K_1}, ..., X_q \in [F^{-1}(\beta_q)]^{K_q(\beta_1, ..., \beta_{q-1})}$$

such that

$$[F|(X_1 \cup \cdots \cup X_q)]^{r,s} \subset S. \quad (4)$$

We shall define a certain partition P on the set

$$[X_1]^r \times \cdots \times [X_q]^r \quad (5)$$

into finitely many parts. Since each set X_j has power $K_j(\beta_1, ..., \beta_{j-1})$, we will then be in a position to use the partition relation (3). Let x, y be any two elements of the set (5) above. We shall put x and y into the same partition class of P iff for all increasing sequences $j_1 < \cdots < j_s \leqslant q$, the elements

$$\langle x_{j_1}, ..., x_{j_s} \rangle, \langle y_{j_1}, ..., y_{j_s} \rangle$$

of $[F|X_1 \cup \cdots \cup X_q]^{r,s}$ are either both elements of S_1 or are both elements of S_2. Because of (4), they are both elements of $S = S_1 \cup S_2$.

The partition P we have just defined partitions the set (5) into finitely many partition classes, in fact at most 2^n where n is the power of the set $[q]^s$. By (3), there exist sets

$$Y_1 \in [X_1]^{\mu_1}, \quad Y_2 \in [X_2]^{H(\beta_1)}, ..., Y_q \in [X_q]^{H(\beta_{q-1})}$$

such that the set

$$[Y_1]^r \times \cdots \times [Y_q]^r \quad (6)$$

lies entirely within one partition class of P.

We shall next use the partition relation (2). We define a partition Q of the set $[q]^s$ into two parts. Consider an arbitrary element

$$\{j_1, ..., j_s\} \in [q]^s,$$

where the elements j_t are listed in increasing order. Since the set (6) lies within a single part of the partition P, we have one of the following:

$$[Y_{j_1}]^r \times \cdots \times [Y_{j_s}]^r \subset S_1, \tag{7}$$

$$[Y_{j_1}]^r \times \cdots \times [Y_{j_s}]^r \subset S_2. \tag{8}$$

Let us define the partition Q so that all the elements of $[q]^s$ satisfying (7) are in one class, and all those satisfying (8) are in the other class. Then by (2), there is a set

$$\{k_1, \ldots, k_p\} \in [q]^p$$

such that $[\{k_1, \ldots, k_p\}]^s$ is entirely within one partition class of Q, say the one for which (7) holds. Arrange the k's in increasing order, $k_1 < \cdots < k_p$.

Now define

$$\gamma_1 = \beta_{k_1}, \ldots, \gamma_p = \beta_{k_p}.$$

We shall show that if the player II plays $\gamma_1, \ldots, \gamma_p$, and if I plays the strategy (1), then II will win the game $G(S_1, p)$. This will contradict our assumption that (1) is a winning strategy for I in the game $G(S_1, p)$, and thus our proof will be complete.

Since $\beta_1 < \cdots < \beta_q$ and $k_1 < \cdots < k_p$, we have $\gamma_1 < \cdots < \gamma_p$. Moreover, for all $i < p$, we have $\gamma_i \leqslant \beta_{k_i - 1}$. The function $H(\beta)$ is monotone relative to β, that is,

$$\beta \leqslant \beta' \quad \text{implies} \quad H(\beta) \leqslant H(\beta').$$

Therefore, for $1 < t \leqslant p$,

$$|Y_{k_t}| \geqslant H(\beta_{k_t - 1}) \geqslant H(\gamma_{t-1}) \geqslant \mu_t(\gamma_1, \ldots, \gamma_{t-1}).$$

It follows that we may choose sets Z_t, $1 \leqslant t \leqslant p$, such that

$$Z_t \subset Y_{k_t} \quad \text{and} \quad |Z_t| = \mu_t(\gamma_1, \ldots, \gamma_{t-1}).$$

Since $Y_j \subset X_j \subset F^{-1}(\beta_j)$ for $1 \leqslant j \leqslant q$, we have

$$Z_1 \in [F^{-1}(\gamma_1)]^{\mu_1}, \ldots, Z_p \in [F^{-1}(\gamma_p)]^{\mu_p(\gamma_1, \ldots, \gamma_{p-1})}.$$

Moreover, since (7) holds for all increasing s-tuples in $\{k_1, \ldots, k_p\}$,

$$[F|(Z_1 \cup \cdots \cup Z_p)]^{r,s} \subset S_1.$$

Therefore the player II wins the game $G(S_1, p)$. Our proof is complete. The proof in the case $\kappa = \omega$ uses a finite analogue of Corollary 1.4 which follows from Theorem 1.1 instead of 1.2.

2. The main theorem

We consider a countable first order predicate logic $\mathscr{L}$ which has an identity symbol, a binary predicate symbol $P_<$, and other predicate or function symbols $P_0, P_1, \ldots$. Let the individual variables of $\mathscr{L}$ be $v_1, v_2, v_3, \ldots$. For the basic model-theoretic notions taken for granted here see TARSKI and VAUGHT [1957].

The notion of a κ-like model for $\mathscr{L}$ was defined in the introduction. In this section we shall prove our main theorem about κ-like models:

THEOREM 2.1. Suppose κ is a strong limit cardinal and λ is a singular cardinal. Then for every κ-like model $\mathfrak{A}$, there is a λ-like model $\mathfrak{B}$ which is elementarily equivalent to $\mathfrak{A}$.

In the proof of this theorem we shall use the classical result that, given a countable language $\mathscr{L}$, we can effectively expand $\mathscr{L}$ to a countable language $\mathscr{L}^*$ (by adding "Skolem functions", or "Hilbert ε-functions" to $\mathscr{L}$), and find a theory T_{Skolem} in $\mathscr{L}^*$ such that:

(i) Every model for $\mathscr{L}$ can be expanded to a model of T_{Skolem} by some interpretation of the new symbols of $\mathscr{L}^*$.

(ii) T_{Skolem} is model-complete (see ROBINSON [1963]).

(iii) Every submodel of a model of T_{Skolem} is also a model of T_{Skolem}.

From (ii) and (iii) it follows that:

(iv) If $\mathfrak{A}^*$ is a model of T_{Skolem}, then every submodel of $\mathfrak{A}^*$ is an elementary submodel of $\mathfrak{A}^*$.

We now expand the language $\mathscr{L}^*$ still further, forming $\mathscr{L}^{**}$, by adding to $\mathscr{L}^*$ a countable doubly indexed sequence of constants c_{ij}, where i and j range over the positive integers. We shall order the pairs $\langle i, j \rangle$ lexicographically, that is,

$$\langle i, j \rangle < \langle k, l \rangle \quad \text{iff either} \quad i < k, \quad \text{or} \quad i = k \quad \text{and} \quad j < l.$$

Let us say that an n-tuple of constants

$$\langle c_{i_1 j_1}, \ldots, c_{i_n j_n} \rangle$$

is *increasing* iff their subscripts form a strictly increasing n-tuple.

DEFINITION 2.2. Let Σ be the set of all sentences of $\mathscr{L}^{**}$ of the types (a)–(d) below:

(a) The axioms for simple order in the symbol $P_<$, and the set of axioms of the theory T_{Skolem}.

(b) $P_<(c_{ij}, c_{kl})$, where $\langle i, j \rangle < \langle k, l \rangle$.

(c) $P_<(\tau(c_{i_1 j_1}, ..., c_{i_n j_n}), c_{ij})$, where $\tau(v_1, ..., v_n)$ is a term of $\mathscr{L}^*$ and $i_1, ..., i_n < i$.

(d) $P_<(\tau(c_{i_1 j_1}, ..., c_{i_n j_n}), c_{ij}) \to \tau(c_{i_1 j_1}, ..., c_{i_n j_n}) = \tau(c_{i_1 l_1}, ..., c_{i_n l_n})$, where $\tau(v_1, ..., v_n)$ is a term of $\mathscr{L}^{**}$ which contains only constants c_{kl} such that $k \leqslant i$, the two sequences of constants

$$\langle c_{i_1 j_1}, ..., c_{i_n j_n} \rangle, \qquad \langle c_{i_1 l_1}, ..., c_{i_n l_n} \rangle$$

are increasing, and $i < i_1, ..., i_n$.

The theory Σ resembles sets of formulas used by SILVER [1966] for other purposes, but here we have doubly indexed constants. The sentences (c) will insure that the constants c_{ij} are cofinal in the set of all terms applied to constants. The sentences (d) state that when the value of a term is less than c_{ij}, its value is independent of the second indices of the constants c_{kl} where $k > i$. These sentences will insure that no element has too many predecessors.

It is important to observe that the set Σ of sentences of $\mathscr{L}^{**}$ is "homogeneous" in the following sense. Let us call two increasing sequences

$$\langle c_{i_1 j_1}, ..., c_{i_n j_n} \rangle, \qquad \langle c_{k_1 l_1}, ..., c_{k_n l_n} \rangle$$

similar iff

$$i_p = i_q \quad \text{iff} \quad k_p = k_q, \qquad p, q = 1, ..., n.$$

Then whenever Σ contains a sentence σ, it also contains every sentence formed by replacing the sequence of all constants occurring in σ by a similar sequence of constants.

LEMMA 2.3. Suppose $\mathfrak{A}$ is a model whose theory is consistent with Σ, and λ is a singular cardinal. Then there exists a λ-like model $\mathfrak{B}$ which is elementarily equivalent to $\mathfrak{A}$.

PROOF: Let Γ be the theory of $\mathfrak{A}$. Then $\Gamma \cup \Sigma$ is consistent. It suffices to prove that Γ has a λ-like model. Let μ_α, $\alpha < \mathrm{cf}(\lambda)$, be a sequence of cardinals $\mu_\alpha < \lambda$ whose supremum is λ. We form an uncountable language $\mathscr{L}'$ by adding to $\mathscr{L}^*$ a doubly indexed sequence of constants

$$c_{\alpha\beta}, \quad \text{where} \quad \alpha < \mathrm{cf}(\lambda), \qquad \beta < \mu_\alpha.$$

We order the pairs $\langle \alpha, \beta \rangle$ lexicographically, and define an increasing sequence of constants of $\mathscr{L}'$ exactly as we did for $\mathscr{L}^{**}$. Let Σ' be the set of all sentences of $\mathscr{L}'$ of the forms (a)–(d), except that this time the constants c_{ij} stand for constants in the language $\mathscr{L}'$ instead of $\mathscr{L}^{**}$.

We claim that $\Gamma \cup \Sigma'$ is consistent. To prove this claim, let Σ'_0 be any finite subset of Σ'. Let $c_{\alpha_1 \beta_1}, ..., c_{\alpha_n \beta_n}$ be an increasing list of all the constants occurring in Σ_0'. Then there is a similar increasing sequence $c_{i_1 j_1}, \ldots, c_{i_n j_n}$ of constants of $\mathscr{L}^{**}$, where "similar" is as defined above. Let Σ_0 be the (finite) set of sentences of $\mathscr{L}^{**}$ formed from Σ_0' by replacing the constants $c_{\alpha_p \beta_p}$ by $c_{i_p j_p}$. Because of the "homogeneity" property which we have observed above for Σ, and from the definition of Σ', we see that $\Sigma_0 \subset \Sigma$. Since $\Gamma \cup \Sigma$ is consistent, $\Gamma \cup \Sigma_0$ is consistent. None of the constants occur in Γ, and Σ_0 is obtained from Σ_0' by a one to one substitution of constants. Therefore $\Gamma \cup \Sigma_0'$ is consistent, and hence $\Gamma \cup \Sigma'$ is consistent.

By the compactness theorem, $\Gamma \cup \Sigma'$ has a model

$$\mathfrak{B}' = \langle B, M, S_0, S_1, \ldots, \ldots, b_{\alpha\beta}, \ldots \rangle, \qquad \alpha < \mathrm{cf}(\lambda), \qquad \beta < \mu_\alpha.$$

By (a), the reduct $\mathfrak{B}^*$ of $\mathfrak{B}'$ to the language $\mathscr{L}^*$ is a model of T_{Skolem}. Hence the submodel of $\mathfrak{B}^*$ generated by the elements $b_{\alpha\beta}$ is an elementary submodel. It follows that the submodel of $\mathfrak{B}'$ generated by the elements $b_{\alpha\beta}$ is also an elementary submodel, and hence is also a model of Σ'. We may therefore choose the model $\mathfrak{B}'$ of Σ' such that it is generated by the elements $b_{\alpha\beta}$.

Now let $\mathfrak{B}$ be the reduct of $\mathfrak{B}'$ to the language $\mathscr{L}$. Then $\mathfrak{B}$ is still a model of Γ. By (a), M is a linear ordering of $\mathfrak{B}$, so $\mathfrak{B}$ is an ordered model. We show that $\mathfrak{B}$ is λ-like. By (b), the $b_{\alpha\beta}$ are all different. There are $\Sigma_{\alpha < \mathrm{cf}(\lambda)} \mu_\alpha = \lambda$ pairs $\langle \alpha, \beta \rangle$. Therefore $|B| \geqslant \lambda$. Since $\mathfrak{B}'$ is generated by the $b_{\alpha\beta}$, and there are only countably many terms in the language $\mathscr{L}^*$, thus only λ terms in $\mathscr{L}'$, we have $|B| \leqslant \lambda$, and hence $|B| = \lambda$.

Consider any element $b \in B$. Then we have

$$b = \tau(b_{\alpha_1 \beta_1}, \ldots, b_{\alpha_n \beta_n})$$

for some term of $\mathscr{L}^*$ and some increasing sequence of constants of $\mathscr{L}'$. By (c), we have $M(b, b_{\alpha\beta})$, where α is chosen so that $\alpha_1, \ldots, \alpha_n < \alpha$. Thus to show that b has fewer than λ predecessors in the structure $\langle B, M \rangle$, it suffices to show that $b_{\alpha\beta}$ has fewer than λ predecessors. Let us say that two increasing sequences

$$\langle b_{\alpha_1 \beta_1}, \ldots, b_{\alpha_m \beta_m} \rangle, \qquad \langle b_{\gamma_1 \delta_1}, \ldots, b_{\gamma_m \delta_m} \rangle$$

are *equivalent* iff for all $p \leqslant m$,

$$\alpha_p = \gamma_p, \quad \text{and if} \quad \alpha_p \leqslant \alpha \quad \text{then} \quad \beta_p = \delta_p.$$

(The property of being equivalent is stronger than the property of being similar.) The number of equivalence classes is at most $\omega \cdot (\sum_{\gamma \leqslant \alpha} \mu_\gamma) \cdot \mathrm{cf}(\lambda)$, and since $\alpha < \mathrm{cf}(\lambda) < \lambda$, $\omega < \lambda$, and each $\mu_\gamma < \lambda$, this number is less than λ. So there are fewer than λ equivalence classes. But by (d), if

$$M\left(\tau(b_{\alpha_1\beta_1}, \ldots, b_{\alpha_m\beta_m}), \beta_{\alpha\beta}\right) \quad \text{and} \quad M\left(\tau(b_{\gamma_1\delta_1}, \ldots, b_{\gamma_m\delta_m}), b_{\alpha\beta}\right),$$

then

$$\tau(b_{\alpha_1\beta_1}, \ldots, b_{\alpha_m\beta_m}) = \tau(b_{\gamma_1\delta_1}, \ldots, b_{\gamma_m\delta_m})$$

whenever the sequences are equivalent. Therefore, since $\mathscr{L}^*$ has only countably many terms, the element $b_{\alpha\beta}$ has fewer than λ predecessors in the ordering M, and so does the original element b. This shows that the model $\mathfrak{B}$ of Γ is λ-like, and completes our proof.

We now prove an elementary lemma which allows us to simplify the sentences (d).

LEMMA 2.4. Every sentence in Σ of the form (d) is a consequence of those sentences in Σ of the form (d) which have the additional property that $\sum_{m=1}^{n} |j_m - l_m| = 1$. (So the sequences $\langle j_1, \ldots, j_n \rangle$ and $\langle l_1, \ldots, l_n \rangle$ differ at only one position, and their difference at that position is 1.)

PROOF: Let σ be an arbitrary sentence in Σ of the form (d). If the sequences of constants

$$\langle c_{i_1 j_1}, \ldots, c_{i_n j_n} \rangle, \qquad \langle c_{i_1 l_1}, \ldots, c_{i_n l_n} \rangle$$

are identical, then σ is valid.

Suppose that these sequences of constants are different. It is easily seen that we can get from the first of these sequences to the second in a finite number of steps, where at each step we have an increasing n-tuple of constants which differs from the preceding step in exactly one position, and at this position the difference is exactly 1. By this process we obtain a finite sequence of sentences

$$\sigma_1, \ldots, \sigma_r \in \Sigma$$

all of the form (d) and all with the additional property given in the statement of the lemma. Moreover, σ is a consequence of $\sigma_1, \ldots, \sigma_r$.

LEMMA 2.5. Let κ be a strong limit cardinal and let $\mathfrak{A}$ be a κ-like model. Then the theory of $\mathfrak{A}$ is consistent with Σ.

PROOF: Expand $\mathfrak{A}$ to a model $\mathfrak{A}^*$ of T_{Skolem}. It suffices to prove that every finite subset $\Sigma_0 \subset \Sigma$ is satisfied in $\mathfrak{A}^*$ by some interpretation of the constants. By Lemma 2.4 we may assume that every $\sigma \in \Sigma_0$ of the form (d) has the extra property $\sum_{m=1}^{n} |j_m - l_m| = 1$.

Since κ is a limit cardinal, we may write

$$\kappa = \sup\{\mu_\alpha : \alpha < \mathrm{cf}(\kappa)\}, \quad \text{where each} \quad \mu_\alpha < \kappa.$$

The structure $\langle A, L \rangle$ is a κ-like ordering, so we may choose a strictly increasing cofinal sequence $d(\alpha)$, $\alpha < \mathrm{cf}(\kappa)$, in $\langle A, L \rangle$, such that for each α there are at least μ_α elements between $d(\alpha)$ and $d(\alpha+1)$. Define a function $F : A \rightarrow \mathrm{cf}(\kappa)$ by letting $F(b)$ be the least α such that $L(b, d(\alpha))$. Then for each α, $|F^{-1}(\alpha+1)| \geqslant \mu_\alpha$. This puts us in a position to use Lemmas 1.6 and 1.7.

Σ_0 is finite, so we may choose positive integers r, s large enough so that all the constants occurring in Σ_0 are among c_{ij}, $1 \leqslant i \leqslant s$ and $1 \leqslant j \leqslant r$. Each element

$$b = \langle b_1, ..., b_s \rangle = \langle \{b_{11}, ..., b_{1r}\}, ..., \{b_{s1}, ..., b_{sr}\}\rangle \in [F]^{r,s},$$

with the b_{ij} written in increasing order with respect to L, determines an interpretation of the constants c_{ij} in $\mathfrak{A}^*$. Denote the model $\mathfrak{A}^*$ with this interpretation of the constants by $(\mathfrak{A}^*, b)$. The notation $\sigma(b)$ will be used to mean that σ holds in the model $(\mathfrak{A}^*, b)$, and similarly for terms.

To prove the lemma it suffices to show that the set of all $b \in [F]^{r,s}$, such that $\sigma(b)$ for all $\sigma \in \Sigma_0$, is large (since Lemma 1.5 tells us that large sets are non-empty). It is easily seen that if σ is of the form (a) or (b), then $\sigma(b)$ holds for all $b \in [F]^{r,s}$.

We now consider sentences of the form (c). For each $\sigma \in \Sigma_0$ of the form (c), let f_σ be the function

$$f_\sigma : [F]^{r,s-1} \rightarrow \mathrm{cf}(\kappa)$$

defined by

$$f_\sigma(b_1, ..., b_{s-1}) = F(\tau(b_{i_1 j_1}, ..., b_{i_n j_n})), \tag{1}$$

where the term $\tau(c_{i_1 j_1}, ..., c_{i_n j_n})$ is described in (c). The definition is meaningful because $i_1, ..., i_n \leqslant i-1 \leqslant s-1$. Now let

$$f : [F]^{r,s-1} \rightarrow \mathrm{cf}(\kappa)$$

be the pointwise maximum of the (finitely many) functions f_σ, where $\sigma \in \Sigma_0$ and σ is of the form (c). By Lemma 1.6, the set

$$S_0 = \{b \in [F]^{r,s} : f(b_1, ..., b_{s-1}) < F(b_{s1})\}$$

is large.

Let us partition S_0 as follows. Two elements $a, b \in S_0$ are in the same partition class iff

$$\{\sigma \in \Sigma_0 : \sigma(a)\} = \{\sigma \in \Sigma_0 : \sigma(b)\}.$$

There are at most 2^t partition classes, where $t = |\Sigma_0|$. Therefore, by Lemma

1.7, at least one of the partition classes, call it S_1, is large. Then there is a set $\Sigma_1 \subset \Sigma_0$ such that for all $a \in S_1$,

$$\Sigma_1 = \{\sigma \in \Sigma_0 : \sigma(a)\}.$$

We claim that $\Sigma_1 = \Sigma_0$. Once this is established our proof will be complete. By a previous remark, all $\sigma \in \Sigma_0$ of the forms (a) or (b) belong to Σ_1.

Suppose $\sigma \in \Sigma_0$ has the form (c). Since S_1 is large there exist

$$\beta_1 < \cdots < \beta_s < \cdots < \beta_{2 \cdot s} < \mathrm{cf}(\kappa),$$

$$b_1 \in [F^{-1}(\beta_1)]^r, \ldots, b_{2 \cdot s} \in [F^{-1}(\beta_{2 \cdot s})]^r$$

such that

$$[F|(b_1 \cup \cdots \cup b_{2 \cdot s})]^{r, s} \subset S_1.$$

In particular,

$$\langle b_1, \ldots, b_s \rangle \in S_1, \qquad a = \langle b_1, \ldots, b_{i-1}, b_s, \ldots, b_{2 \cdot s - i} \rangle \in S_1.$$

Since $S_1 \subset S_0$, we have

$$f_\sigma(b_1, \ldots, b_{s-1}) \leqslant f(b_1, \ldots, b_{s-1}) < F(b_{s1}) = \beta_s.$$

Hence by (1),

$$F(\tau(b_{i_1 j_1}, \ldots, b_{i_n j_n})) < \beta_s.$$

It follows that

$$L(\tau(b_{i_1 j_1}, \ldots, b_{i_n j_n}), b_{sj}).$$

Therefore $\sigma(a)$ holds, and since $a \in S_1$, $\sigma \in \Sigma_1$.

Finally, let $\sigma \in \Sigma_0$ be of the form (d), and such that $\sum_{m=1}^{n} |j_m - l_m| = 1$. Suppose $\sigma \notin \Sigma_1$. Let q be the unique $m \leqslant n$ such that $j_m \neq l_m$, and let $j_q + 1 = l_q$. To avoid double subscripts we shall hereafter write $i' = i_q, j' = j_q, l' = l_q$. Consider the following strategy for the player I in the game $G(S_1, s)$:

$$\mu_m(\beta_1, \ldots, \beta_{m-1}) = r, \quad \text{if} \quad m \neq i',$$

$$\mu_{i'}(\beta_1, \ldots, \beta_{i'-1}) = 2 \cdot (r + 1) + \lambda(\beta_i)^{++},$$

where $\lambda(\beta)$ is the number of predecessors of the element $d(\beta)$ in the structure $\langle A, L \rangle$. To check that this is a strategy, we note that since $\langle A, L \rangle$ is κ-like and κ is a limit cardinal, $2 \cdot (r + 1) + \lambda(\beta_i)^{++}$ is less than κ; also, $i < i'$ by (d). Now S_1 is large, so I has no winning strategy for $G(S_1, s)$. Hence there is a sequence $\beta_1, \ldots, \beta_s$ of moves which wins the game for the player II against the above strategy. That is, there exist

$$Y_1 \in [F^{-1}(\beta_1)]^{\mu_1}, \ldots, Y_s \in [F^{-1}(\beta_s)]^{\mu_s}$$

such that

$$[Y_1]^r \times \cdots \times [Y_s]^r \subset S_1.$$

Since $|Y_{i'}| = 2 \cdot (r+1) + \lambda(\beta_i)^{++}$, there exist $x, y \in Y_{i'}$ such that in the ordered structure $\langle Y_{i'}, L \rangle$ there are at least r elements before x, at least r elements after y, and at least $\lambda(\beta_i)^+$ elements between x and y. There exists

$$b \in [Y_1]^r \times \cdots \times [Y_s]^r$$

such that $b_{i'j'} = x$ and $b_{i'l'} = y$. For any z between x and y, let

$$t(z) = \tau\big(b_{i_1 j_1}, \ldots, b_{i_{q-1} j_{q-1}}, z, b_{i_{q+1} j_{q+1}}, \ldots, b_{i_n j_n}\big).$$

Whenever

$$z_1, z_2 \in Y_{i'}, \, L(x, z_1), \, L(z_1, z_2), \, L(z_2, y), \tag{2}$$

there exists

$$a \in [Y_1]^r \times \cdots \times [Y_s]^r$$

such that

$$a_{i'j'} = z_1, \qquad a_{i'l'} = z_2, \quad \text{and} \quad a_{kl} = b_{kl} \quad \text{elsewhere.}$$

We have $a \in S_1$, and since $\sigma \notin \Sigma_1$, $\neg \sigma(a)$. We note that

$$\tau(a_{i_1 j_1}, \ldots, a_{i_n j_n}) = t(z_1), \qquad \tau(a_{i_1 l_1}, \ldots, a_{i_n l_n}) = t(z_2).$$

Therefore, $\neg \sigma(a)$ means

$$L(t(z_1), b_{ij}) \quad \text{and} \quad t(z_1) \neq t(z_2). \tag{3}$$

Since (3) holds for all z_1, z_2 which satisfy (2), and since there are at least $\lambda(\beta_i)^+$ elements of $Y_{i'}$ between x and y, the element b_{ij} of A has at least $\lambda(\beta_i)^+$ predecessors with respect to L. But $F(b_{ij}) = d(\beta_i)$, so $L(b_{ij}, d(\beta_i))$. Hence the element $d(\beta_i)$ has at least $\lambda(\beta_i)^+$ predecessors. This contradicts the definition of $\lambda(\beta_i)$ as the number of predecessors of $d(\beta_i)$. We conclude that $\sigma \in \Sigma_1$ after all, and our proof is complete.

Theorem 2.1 follows at once from Lemmas 2.3 and 2.5.

3. Some consequences and extensions of the main theorem

In this section we use Lemmas 2.3 and 2.5 and their proofs to get additional information about κ-like models. We begin with a series of corollaries.

COROLLARY 3.1. Let λ be a singular strong limit cardinal. Then a theory Γ in $\mathscr{L}$ has a λ-like model iff $\Gamma \cup \Sigma$ is consistent.

COROLLARY 3.2 (Compactness theorem). Let λ be a singular strong limit cardinal, and let Γ be a set of sentences of $\mathscr{L}$. If every finite subset of Γ has a λ-like model, then Γ has a λ-like model.

For the case $\mathrm{cf}(\lambda) > \omega$, the above compactness theorem was proved in another way by FUHRKEN [1965].

COROLLARY 3.3 (Completeness theorem). Let λ be a singular strong limit cardinal. Suppose the language $\mathscr{L}$ is recursive (that is, the sequence of numbers of places of the predicate symbols $P_0, P_1, \ldots$, is recursive). Then the set of all sentences of $\mathscr{L}$ which hold in all λ-like models is recursively enumerable (and hence has a recursive set of axioms).

PROOF: The set Σ is recursive. It follows from Corollary 3.1 that the set of all sentences of $\mathscr{L}$ which hold in all λ-like models is just the set of all consequences of Σ which belong to $\mathscr{L}$, and hence this set is recursively enumerable.

Let us now consider models

$$\mathfrak{A} = \langle A, U, L, R_0, R_1, \ldots \rangle$$

where U is a subset of A (i.e. a unary relation). We say that A is a *relatively ordered model* iff the restriction of L to U linearly orders U. We say that A is *relatively κ-like* iff $\mathfrak{A}$ is a relatively ordered model and $\langle U, L \rangle$ is κ-like. All of our above results can be generalized to relatively κ-like models. We indicate this generalization for Theorem 2.1.

COROLLARY 3.4. Let κ be a strong limit cardinal and let λ be a singular cardinal. Then every relatively κ-like model has an elementarily equivalent relatively λ-like model.

PROOF: Let $\mathfrak{A}$ be relatively κ-like. By a theorem of TARSKI and VAUGHT [1957], $\mathfrak{A}$ has an elementary submodel of power κ which contains U, and hence is also relatively κ-like. So we may assume that A has power κ. Let G be a one to one function of U onto A, and define the binary relation L' on A by

$$L'(G(u), G(v)) \quad \text{iff} \quad L(u, v).$$

Then the model

$$\mathfrak{A}' = \langle A, L', G, U, L, R_0, R_1, \ldots \rangle$$

is κ-like. Hence by Theorem 2.1 there is a λ-like model

$$\mathfrak{B}' = \langle B, M', H, V, M, S_0, S_1, \ldots \rangle$$

elementarily equivalent to $\mathfrak{A}'$. Since H maps $\langle V, M \rangle$ isomorphically onto $\langle B, M' \rangle$, the reduct

$$\mathfrak{B} = \langle B, V, M, S_0, S_1, \ldots \rangle$$

is a relatively λ-like model elementarily equivalent to $\mathfrak{A}$.

A general result of FUHRKEN [1964], [1965] shows that theorems about κ-like models can be reformulated as theorems about the quantifier "there exist at least κ" introduced by MOSTOWSKI [1957]. Given a language $\mathscr{L}$ and a cardinal κ, a new language Q_κ is formed by adding to $\mathscr{L}$ the new quantifier symbol Q and interpreting Q as "there exist at least κ". The set of all valid sentences of Q_κ is denoted by V_κ. (For details see FUHRKEN [1965].) A restatement of our results in terms of the languages Q_κ is given in the next corollary.

COROLLARY 3.5. (i) If κ is a strong limit cardinal and λ is a singular cardinal, then every set of sentences of Q_κ which has a Q_κ-model also has a Q_λ-model.

(ii) If κ is a strong limit cardinal and λ is a singular cardinal, then $V_\lambda \subset V_\kappa$.

(iii) If κ, λ are both singular strong limit cardinals, then $V_\kappa = V_\lambda$.

(iv) (Completeness theorem). If λ is a singular strong limit cardinal and the language $\mathscr{L}$ is recursive, then the set V_λ is recursively enumerable.

(v) (Compactness theorem). If λ is a singular strong limit cardinal, then any set of sentences of Q_λ which is finitely satisfiable is satisfiable.

VAUGHT [1964] showed that V_{ω_1} is recursively enumerable (and so is V_{λ^+}, if λ is regular and GCH). When $\mathrm{cf}(\lambda) > \omega$, the compactness theorem (v) above was proved by FUHRKEN [1965]. The analogue of Corollary 3.5 for the languages Q_κ without identity was proved by YASUHARA [1966].

Up to this point we have always assumed $\mathscr{L}$ to be countable. We shall now show that this assumption can be relaxed somewhat.

THEOREM 3.6. Theorem 2.1 and all its corollaries still hold if the language $\mathscr{L}$ is uncountable but has fewer than λ symbols.

PROOF: The proof of Lemma 2.3 still goes through as long as $\mathscr{L}$ has fewer than λ symbols. Lemmas 2.4 and 2.5 obviously remain true with no restriction at all on the number of symbols of $\mathscr{L}$. For Lemma 2.5, to show that the theory of $\mathfrak{A}$ is consistent with a finite subset $\Sigma_0 \subset \Sigma$, we can pretend that $\mathscr{L}$ has only those predicate and function symbols which occur in Σ_0.

The completeness theorems for λ-like models in the case of an uncountable language must, of course, be stated in terms of an appropriate notion of recursiveness for uncountable sets. Our compactness theorem in the uncountable case for the language Q_λ may be stated as follows in the terminology of FUHRKEN [1965]: If λ is a singular strong limit cardinal, then Q_λ is (μ, ω)-compact for all $\mu < \lambda$. FUHRKEN [1965] obtained (μ, ω)-compactness for all $\mu < \text{cf}(\lambda)$.

Another very natural quantifier, the "equicardinality" quantifier, was suggested by Chang. Let Q_{eq} be the language which has the same symbols as Q_κ, but where the formula $(Qx)\,\varphi(x)$ holds in a model $\mathfrak{A}$ if and only if the set of all $a \in A$ such that $\mathfrak{A} \vDash \varphi[a]$ has the same cardinality as the set A. To avoid trivial complications we admit only infinite models.

COROLLARY 3.7. (i) (Löwenheim-Skolem theorem). Suppose κ is a strong limit cardinal and λ is a singular cardinal. Then every theory in Q_{eq} which has a model of power κ has a model of power λ.

(ii) (Compactness). (GCH). Any set of sentences of Q_{eq} which is finitely satisfiable is satisfiable.

(iii) (Completeness). (GCH). If the language $\mathscr{L}$ is recursive, then the set of all valid sentences of Q_{eq} is recursively enumerable.

Part (i) holds if $\mathscr{L}$ has fewer than λ symbols, while parts (ii) and (iii) hold with no restriction on the cardinality of $\mathscr{L}$.

The arguments needed to derive Corollary 3.7 from known results and our Theorem 2.1 are developed in FUHRKEN [1964], [1965], and SLOMSON [1967]. Therefore we omit the proofs. To obtain the completeness of Q_{eq}, (iii) above, Craig proved that it is sufficient to show that the set $\bigcap_\kappa V_\kappa$ is recursively enumerable. Slomson pointed out that the recursive enumerability of $\bigcap_\kappa V_\kappa$ follows at once from the results of this paper and previous theorems (assuming the GCH).

For other Löwenheim-Skolem theorems for Q_{eq}, see SLOMSON [1967]. In two special cases, Corollary 3.7 was already known, even without the GCH: The case of Q_{eq} without an identity symbol was done by YASUHARA [1966], and the case of Q_{eq} with only monadic predicate symbols by SLOMSON [1967]. In each case, elegant complete axioms for the language are given.

Our next theorem sharpens the conclusion of Theorem 2.1 by giving more information about the order type of the λ-like model $\mathfrak{B}$, and also shows that $\mathfrak{B}$ can have large "homogeneous" sets. In an ordered model $\mathfrak{A}$, a subset $X \subset A$ is said to be *homogeneous* (or *indiscernible*) iff for any two finite sequences
$$\langle x_1, ..., x_n \rangle, \qquad \langle y_1, ..., y_n \rangle$$
of elements of X which are both strictly increasing with respect to L, the

expanded models

$$(\mathfrak{A}, x_1, \ldots, x_n) \quad \text{and} \quad (\mathfrak{A}, y_1, \ldots, y_n)$$

are elementarily equivalent. (This notion is due to EHRENFEUCHT and MOS-TOWSKI [1956].)

THEOREM 3.8. Suppose κ is a strong limit cardinal and λ is a singular cardinal. Let $\mathfrak{A}$ be a κ-like model. Then there is a model $\mathfrak{B}$ which is elementarily equivalent to $\mathfrak{A}$ such that ·

(i) $\mathfrak{B}$ is λ-like;

(ii) $\langle B, M \rangle$ has a cofinal subset of order type λ;

(iii) for each $\mu < \lambda$, there is a subset $X \subset B$ of power μ which is homogeneous in $\mathfrak{B}$;

(iv) there is a cofinal subset $Y \subset B$ which is homogeneous in $\mathfrak{B}$.

Let K be any set of cardinals less than λ such that $\inf(K) \geqslant |K|$ and $\sup(K) = \lambda$. Then the model $\mathfrak{B}$ above may be chosen so that, if b_M denotes the set of all predecessors of b in $\langle B, M \rangle$, then

(v) $K = \{|b_M| : b \in B \text{ and } \inf(K) \leqslant |b_M|\}$.

We shall give an outline of the proof. First we enlarge the set Σ. Define Δ to be the set Σ plus all sentences of $\mathscr{L}^{**}$ of the form

(e) $$\varphi(c_{i_1 j_1}, \ldots, c_{i_n j_n}) \leftrightarrow \varphi(c_{k_1 l_1}, \ldots, c_{k_n l_n}),$$

where $\varphi(v_1, \ldots, v_n)$ is a formula of $\mathscr{L}^*$ and the two sequences of constants are similar in the sense of the preceding section.

The proof of Lemma 2.5 may be improved to show that: If $\mathfrak{A}$ is κ-like then the theory of $\mathfrak{A}$ is consistent with Δ. This is done as follows. Consider a finite $\Delta_0 \subset \Delta$. We define S_1 as in the proof of 2.5. Using Lemma 1.7, we obtain a large set $S_2 \subset S_1$ such that whenever a formula $\varphi \leftrightarrow \varphi'$ of the form (e) is in Δ_0 and $a, b \in S_2$, we have $\varphi(a)$ iff $\varphi(b)$. It now can be shown that if $a \in S_2$, then $\sigma(a)$ holds for all $\sigma \in \Delta_0$.

The rest of the proof is like the proof of Lemma 2.3. Let δ be the order type of $\langle K, < \rangle$ and let $\mu_\alpha, \alpha < \delta$, be an increasing enumeration of the set K. Let Z be the set of all integers (including negative integers). Form the language $\mathscr{L}''$ by adding to $\mathscr{L}^*$ new constants

$$c_{\langle \alpha, m \rangle \beta}, \quad \alpha < \delta, \quad m \in Z, \quad \beta < \mu_\alpha.$$

We then order the subscripts lexicographically, and form the set Δ'' of all sentences of $\mathscr{L}''$ of the forms (a)–(e), with $\langle \alpha, m \rangle$'s for the first index and β's for the second index. As in the proof of 2.3, the union of Δ'' with the theory of $\mathfrak{A}$ is consistent, and thus has a model

$$\mathfrak{B}'' = \langle B, M, R_0, R_1, \ldots, \ldots, b_{\langle \alpha, m \rangle \beta}, \ldots \rangle$$

which is generated by the elements $b_{\langle \alpha, m \rangle \beta}$.

The proof that the reduct $\mathfrak{B}$ of $\mathfrak{B}''$ is λ-like is exactly as before. The elements $b_{\langle \alpha, 0 \rangle \beta}$ form a cofinal subset of order type λ, so (ii) holds. For each fixed α, the elements $b_{\langle \alpha, 0 \rangle \beta}$ form a set of power μ_α which is homogeneous in $\mathfrak{B}$. Since the supremum of the cardinals μ_α is λ and any subset of a homogeneous set is homogeneous, (iii) follows. The elements $b_{\langle \alpha, 0 \rangle 0}$ form a cofinal subset of $\mathfrak{B}$ which is homogeneous in $\mathfrak{B}$, so (iv) holds. To verify (v), first observe that by (c), each element $b_{\langle \alpha, m \rangle \beta}$ has at least the μ_α predecessors $b_{\langle \alpha, m-1 \rangle \gamma}$, $\gamma < \mu_\alpha$. By (d), the element $b_{\langle \alpha, m \rangle \beta}$ has at most $\omega \cdot (\sum_{\gamma \leqslant \alpha} \mu_\gamma) \cdot |K| = \mu_\alpha$ predecessors, so it has exactly μ_α predecessors. Finally, one shows that an arbitrary $b \in B$ is either caught between some pair $b_{\langle \alpha, m \rangle 0}$ and $b_{\langle \alpha, m+1 \rangle 0}$, whence it has exactly μ_α predecessors, or else it is less than all the elements $b_{\langle \alpha, m \rangle \beta}$, whence it has at most $|K|$ predecessors. Since K is exactly the set of all the cardinals μ_α, $\alpha < \delta$, (v) follows.

Part (v) of the above theorem improves a result in KEISLER [1967a]. Theorem 3.8 above also holds for an uncountable language $\mathscr{L}$, with, say μ symbols, provided that $\mu < \lambda$ and $\mu \leqslant \inf(K)$.

We conclude this paper with an application to models of set theory. We shall use Lemma 2.3 and the proof of Lemma 2.5 to show that, for each singular cardinal λ, every complete extension of a certain theory $ZC(\mathscr{L})$ has a λ-like model. The theory $ZC(\mathscr{L})$ is given by a set of axioms which may be described as Zermelo set theory with a choice function.

Let our language $\mathscr{L}$ have a binary predicate symbol $\in$, two unary function symbols R, C and possibly other predicate and function symbols (perhaps uncountably many of them). The theory $ZC(\mathscr{L})$ has the following axioms:

The axioms of extensionality, pairs, unions, infinity and power sets (our results below also hold if the axiom of infinity is left out);

The axiom scheme of subsets with respect of all formulas of $\mathscr{L}$;

The recursive definition of the set of all sets of rank less than v_1, that is (using standard abbreviations),

$$(\forall v_1)(\neg \operatorname{ord}(v_1) \to R(v_1) = 0);$$

$$(\forall v_1)[\operatorname{ord}(v_1) \to (\forall v_2)[v_2 \in R(v_1) \leftrightarrow (\exists v_3)(v_3 \in v_1 \wedge v_2 \subseteq R(v_3))]];$$

the axiom of regularity in the form

$$(\forall v_2)(\exists v_1)(v_2 \in R(v_1));$$

a strong form of the axiom of choice, namely

$$(\forall v_1)(v_1 = 0 \vee C(v_1) \in v_1).$$

The models of $ZC(\mathcal{L})$ are not ordered models. Nevertheless there is a natural way to define the notion of a κ-like model as follows. A model $\mathfrak{A}$ of $ZC(\mathcal{L})$ is said to be κ-*like* iff A has power κ but for all $a \in A$,

$$|\{x \in A : \mathfrak{A} \vDash x \in R(a)\}| < \kappa$$

(that is, the set $R(a)$ has power less than κ as seen from the outside).

THEOREM 3.9. Let λ be a singular cardinal, greater than the number of symbols of $\mathcal{L}$. Then every complete extension of $ZC(\mathcal{L})$ has a λ-like model.

PROOF: Let us first define an appropriate linear ordering on $ZC(\mathcal{L})$. Using the choice function, we can construct a formula $\varphi_<(v_1, v_2)$ of $\mathcal{L}$ such that from $ZC(\mathcal{L})$ one can prove the axioms of linear order with respect to $\varphi_<(v_1, v_2)$, and also the sentence

$$(\forall v_2)[\text{ord}(v_2) \to (\forall v_1)(\varphi_<(v_1, v_2) \leftrightarrow v_1 \in R(v_2))]. \tag{1}$$

The formula $\varphi_<(v_1, v_2)$ may be defined informally as follows. Either $r(v_1) < r(v_2)$, or else $r(v_1) = r(v_2)$ and $l(v_1, v_2)$, where $r(v_1)$ is the rank of v_1 (i.e. the least v_3 such that $v_1 \subset R(v_3)$), and l is the linear ordering of the set $\{v_4 : r(v_4) = r(v_1)\}$ with $r(v_1)$ as least element, which is chosen by C.

We may suppose without loss of generality that the language $\mathcal{L}$ has the extra predicate symbol $P_<$ and $ZC(\mathcal{L})$ has the extra axiom

$$(\forall v_1, v_2)(P_<(v_1, v_2) \leftrightarrow \varphi_<(v_1, v_2)). \tag{2}$$

It is well-known that there is an expansion $\mathcal{L}^*$ of the language $\mathcal{L}$ and a theory T_{Skolem} in $\mathcal{L}^*$ such that all the conditions (i)–(iv) for T_{Skolem} hold and also:

(i′) Every model $\mathfrak{A}$ of $ZC(\mathcal{L})$ has a *unique* expansion to a model of $T_{\text{Skolem}} \cup ZC(\mathcal{L}^*)$, and every formula of $\mathcal{L}^*$ is equivalent to a formula of $\mathcal{L}$ with respect to $T_{\text{Skolem}} \cup ZC(\mathcal{L}^*)$.

For example, the ι-theory described in MONTAGUE and VAUGHT [1959] will do for T_{Skolem}.

Now let Γ be any complete extension of $ZC(\mathcal{L})$, and let $\mathfrak{A}$ be a model of Γ. Then A is linearly ordered by the interpretation L of $P_<$. Let $\mathfrak{A}^*$ be the unique expansion of $\mathfrak{A}$ to a model of $T_{\text{Skolem}} \cup ZC(\mathcal{L}^*)$. We wish to show that the theory of $\mathfrak{A}^*$ is consistent with the set Σ of sentences in the language

$\mathscr{L}^{**}$. To do this we must imitate the proof of Lemma 2.5 but compute cardinals within the model $\mathfrak{A}^*$. We have made no assumption about the power of A, but within $\mathfrak{A}^*$ the sets $R(a)$ have power $2(0, a)$ when a is an ordinal of $\mathfrak{A}^*$. The notion of a cardinal number may be defined in $\mathfrak{A}^*$, using the definition due to Scott: define $|v_1|$ to be the set of all sets of minimal rank which are cardinally equivalent to v_1. Then $|v_1|$ is given by a term in $\mathscr{L}^*$, and the formula $(\exists v_2)(v_1 = |v_2|)$ says that v_1 is a cardinal number.

The natural approach is to have the whole model $\mathfrak{A}$ take the place of κ, and have the class of ordinals of $\mathfrak{A}$ take the place of $\mathrm{cf}(\kappa)$, in the proof of Lemma 2.5. The difficulty is that the order type of the ordinals of $\mathfrak{A}$ might not be "regular". When the axiom scheme of replacement holds in $\mathfrak{A}$, then it also holds in $\mathfrak{A}^*$ in view of (i'), and this difficulty does not arise. When replacement fails, we get around the difficulty in the following way. There is a term $\pi(v_1)$ of $\mathscr{L}^*$ which maps a set a of $\mathfrak{A}^*$ onto a proper class in the model $\mathfrak{A}^*$ (that is, there is no set in $\mathfrak{A}^*$ containing all $\pi(v_1), v_1 \in a$). Then the term $r(\pi(v_1))$ maps a onto a cofinal class of ordinals of $\mathfrak{A}^*$. It follows that there is a well ordered structure $\langle a, l \rangle$ in $\mathfrak{A}^*$ which the term $r(\pi(v_1))$ maps isomorphically onto a cofinal class of ordinals. The same holds for any cofinal substructure of $\langle a, l \rangle$. Hence, by taking a cofinal substructure of minimal order type, we may get $\langle a, l \rangle$ to be regular in the sense that any cofinal substructure of $\langle a, l \rangle$ is isomorphic to $\langle a, l \rangle$. Because of the choice function C, there is a term of $\mathscr{L}^*$ with no free variables which picks out such a structure $\langle a, l \rangle$ in the model $\mathfrak{A}^*$.

Now let $\mathrm{ord}'(v_1)$ mean "v_1 is an ordinal", if the axiom scheme of replacement holds in $\mathfrak{A}$, and let it mean "$v_1 = r(\pi(v_2))$ for some $v_2 \in a$" otherwise. Let $F(v_1)$ be the least v_2 such that $\mathrm{ord}'(v_2)$ and $r(v_1) \leqslant v_2$, and define $F^{-1}(v_1)$ in the obvious way. Then F and F^{-1} are given by terms of $\mathscr{L}^*$ in the model $\mathfrak{A}^*$.

We now define the notion of a large *sentence* $\varphi(c_{11}, \ldots, c_{st})$ of the language $\mathscr{L}^{**}$, corresponding to our previous notion of a large set. For each φ and each positive integer p, we consider the game $G(\varphi, p)$. Let

$$a_1, \ldots, a_p, b_1, \ldots, b_p \in A. \tag{3}$$

We say that player II *wins* the game $G(\varphi, p)$ iff the following formula is satisfied in the model $\mathfrak{A}^*$ by the elements (3):

$$(a_1, \ldots, a_p \text{ are cardinals}) \rightarrow [\mathrm{ord}'(b_1) \wedge \cdots \wedge \mathrm{ord}'(b_p) \wedge b_1 < \cdots < b_p$$
$$\wedge\, (\exists y_1 \in [F^{-1}(b_1)]^{a_1}, \ldots, y_p \in [F^{-1}(b_p)]^{a_p})(\forall x)(x \in [F|(y_1 \cup \cdots \cup y_p)]^{t.s}$$
$$\rightarrow \varphi(x))].$$

We say that the sentence φ is *large* iff for all positive integers p,

$$\mathfrak{A}^* \vDash \forall a_1 \exists b_1 \ldots \forall a_p \exists b_p \text{ "II wins } G(\varphi, p)".$$

In place of Lemma 1.6, one can prove: For each term

$$\tau(c_{11}, \ldots, c_{s-1,t})$$

of $\mathscr{L}^{**}$, the sentence

$$P_<(\tau(c_{11}, \ldots, c_{s-1,t}), c_{s1})$$

is large.

In place of Lemma 1.7, one can prove: If a sentence of $\mathscr{L}^{**}$ is large and if for all interpretations a of the constants of $\mathscr{L}^{**}$ in $\mathfrak{A}^*$ we have

$$(\mathfrak{A}^*, a) \vDash \varphi \leftrightarrow \varphi_1 \vee \cdots \vee \varphi_n,$$

then one of the sentences φ_m, $1 \leqslant m \leqslant n$, is large.

Using the above two lemmas one can then prove that the theory of $\mathfrak{A}^*$ is consistent with Σ. The three proofs are like the proofs of Lemmas 1.6, 1.7 and 2.5, with only straightforward changes. We omit the details. It follows from Lemma 2.3 that there is a λ-like ordered model $\mathfrak{B}^*$ elementarily equivalent to $\mathfrak{A}^*$. Then $\mathfrak{B}^*$ is a model of Γ and also satisfies the sentences (1), (2). It follows from (1), (2), and the fact that $\mathfrak{B}^*$ is λ-like that for each ordinal b of $\mathfrak{B}$, we have

$$\{x \in B : \mathfrak{B}^* \vDash x \in R(b)\} = \{x \in B : \mathfrak{B}^* \vDash P_<(x, b)\},$$

and the set on the right side of the equation has power less than λ. It follows that the reduct $\mathfrak{B}$ of $\mathfrak{B}^*$ to $\mathscr{L}$ is a λ-like model in the sense of models of $ZC(\mathscr{L})$, and is also a model of Γ. Our proof is complete.

The above theorem also holds for models of Zermelo-Fraenkel set theory with a choice function, and for Zermelo-Fraenkel set theory with the axiom of constructibility. In the former case, the function $R(v_1)$ is definable, while in the second case a choice function $C(v_1)$ is also definable. From Theorem 3.8 we see that every complete extension of $ZC(\mathscr{L})$ has a λ-like model $\mathfrak{B}$ which satisfies the stronger conclusions of that theorem. (First apply Theorem 3.9 above to show that every complete extension of $ZC(\mathscr{L})$ has a κ-like model for some singular strong limit cardinal κ, and then apply Theorem 3.8.) Theorems similar to Theorem 3.8 for models of Zermelo-Fraenkel set theory are proved by KEISLER and MORLEY [1967].

Using Theorem 3.9, we can reformulate Corollary 3.1 with a more natural set of sentences in place of Σ. Let $\mathscr{L}$ be a language which has among its predicate symbols the binary predicate symbol $P_<$. Let $\mathscr{L} + \{\in, R, C\}$ be the language formed by adding to $\mathscr{L}$ the binary predicate symbol $\in$ and the two unary function symbols R, C.

THEOREM 3.10. Let λ be a singular strong limit cardinal greater than the number of symbols of $\mathscr{L}$. Then a theory Γ in $\mathscr{L}$ has a λ-like model iff Γ is consistent with the set Θ of sentences of $\mathscr{L} + \{\in, R, C\}$ given below:
  (a') the axioms of $\mathrm{ZC}(\mathscr{L} + \{\in, R, C\})$;
  (b') the axioms of linear order in $P_<$;
  (c') $(\exists v_3)(\forall v_2)[\mathrm{ord}(v_2) \wedge v_3 \in v_2 \rightarrow (\forall v_1)(P_<(v_1, v_2) \leftrightarrow v_1 \in R(v_2))]$.

PROOF: If Γ is consistent with Θ, then the proof of Theorem 3.9 shows that Γ has a λ-like model. We need only observe that for the proof of Theorem 3.9 it is enough that the linear ordering denoted by $P_<$ satisfies the sentence (1) for all sufficiently large ordinals v_2.

Suppose, conversely, that Γ has a λ-like model. We show that Γ is consistent with Θ. Let κ be a singular strong limit cardinal of the form $\kappa = 2(0, \alpha + \omega)$, where $2(0, \alpha)$ is greater than the number of symbols of $\mathscr{L}$. Then by Theorem 3.8, with

$$K = \{2(0, \alpha + n) : n < \omega\},$$

Γ has a κ-like model $\mathfrak{A}$ such that for each $n < \omega$ there is an element $a_n \in A$ with exactly $2(0, \alpha + n)$ predecessors in the ordering L. Now consider the set $R(\alpha + \omega)$, which clearly has power $2(0, \alpha + \omega)$. Each of its subsets $R(\alpha + n)$ has power $2(0, \alpha + n)$, $n < \omega$. Therefore there is a one to one function f of $R(\alpha + \omega)$ onto $\mathfrak{A}$ such that for all $n < \omega$, f maps the set $R(\alpha + n)$ onto the set of all predecessors of the element a_n in the ordering L and $f(\alpha + n) = a_n$.

Let C be a choice function for the set of sets $R(\alpha + \omega)$, that is, a function of $R(\alpha + \omega)$ into itself such that if $x \neq 0$ then $C(x) \in x$. Expand the model $\mathfrak{A}$ by giving the symbols $\in, R, C$ the interpretations which they inherit from the $\in, R$ and C of $R(\alpha + \omega)$ under the mapping f. Then the expanded model is easily seen to be a model of $\Gamma \cup \Theta$, so $\Gamma \cup \Theta$ is consistent.

References

CHANG, C.C., A note on the two cardinal problem, Proc. Am. Math. Soc. **16** (1965) 1148–1155.

EHRENFEUCHT, A. and A. MOSTOWSKI, Models of axiomatic theories admitting automorphisms, Fund. Math. **43** (1956) 50–68.

ERDÖS, P., A. HAJNAL and R. RADO, Partition relations for cardinal numbers, Acta Math. **16** (1965) 93–196.

ERDÖS, P. and R. RADO, A partition calculus in set theory, Bull. Am. Math. Soc. **62** (1956) 427–489.

FUHRKEN, G., Skolem-type normal forms for first-order languages with a generalized quantifier, Fund. Math. **54** (1964) 291–302.

FUHRKEN, G., Languages with the added quantifier "there exist at least $\aleph_\alpha$", in: The Theory of Models, eds. J.W. Addison, L. Henkin and A. Tarski (Amsterdam, North-Holland Publ. Co., 1965) pp. 121–131.

HELLING, M., Model theoretic problems for some extensions of first order languages, Doctoral dissertation, Univ. of Calif., Berkeley, 1966.

KEISLER, H.J., Weakly well-ordered models, Notices Am. Math. Soc. **14** (1967) abstract 67T-286, p. 414.

KEISLER, H.J., Ultraproducts of finite sets, J. Symb. Logic 32 (1967)

KEISLER, H.J. and M. MORLEY, Elementary extensions of models of set theory, Israel J. Math., to appear.

MACDOWELL, R. and E. SPECKER, Modelle der Arithmetik, in: Infinitistic Methods, Proc. of the Symp. on Foundations of Math., Warsaw 1959 (New York, 1961) pp. 257–263.

MORLEY, M., Categoricity in power, Trans. Am. Math. Soc. **114** (1965) 514–538.

MORLEY, M., Omitting classes of elements, in: The Theory of Models, eds. J.W. Addison, L. Henkin and A. Tarski (Amsterdam, North-Holland Publ. Co., 1965) pp. 265–273.

MORLEY, M. and R. VAUGHT, Homogeneous universal models, Math. Scand. **11** (1962) 37–57.

MOSTOWSKI, A., On a generalization of quantifiers, Fund. Math. **44** (1957) 12–36.

ROBINSON, A., Introduction to model theory and to the metamathematics of algebra (Amsterdam, North-Holland Publ. Co., 1963; second ed. 1965).

ROWBOTTOM, F., Large cardinals and small constructible sets, Doctoral dissertation, Univ. of Wisconsin, Madison, Wis., 1964.

SILVER, J., Some applications of model theory in set theory, Doctoral dissertation, Univ. of California, Berkeley, Calif., 1966.

SLOMSON, A., Some problems in mathematical logic, D. Phil. thesis, Oxford, 1967.

TARSKI, A. and R. VAUGHT, Arithmetical extensions of relational systems, Compositio Math. **13** (1957) 81–102.

VAUGHT, R., The Löwenheim-Skolem theorem, in: Logic, Methodology and Philosophy of Science, ed. Y. Bar-Hillel (Amsterdam, North-Holland Publ. Co., 1965) pp. 81–89.

VAUGHT, R., The completeness of logic with the added quantifier "there are uncountably many", Fund. Math. **54** (1964) 303–304.

YASUHARA, M., Syntactical and semantical properties of generalized quantifiers, J. Symb. Logic **31** (1966) 617–632.

RECURSION THEORY AS A BRANCH OF MODEL THEORY[1]

R. MONTAGUE

University of California, Los Angeles, USA

1. Introductory and historical remarks

The desirability of generalizing the theory of recursive functions and relations has for some time been widely appreciated. The goal was to obtain notions of recursiveness, recursive enumerability, and the like which will have interest in connection not only with the natural numbers but also with structures of an arbitrary or almost arbitrary sort, nondenumerable as well as denumerable.

To some logicians it has also appeared desirable to unify two of the dominant subfields of contemporary logic, model theory and recursion theory. It is of course possible by routine methods to translate the notions of recursion theory into the language of model theory; but to do this in such a way that the translations will have a natural and simple model-theoretic content, and the methods of proof a common character with those of general model theory, has not heretofore been fully accomplished.

The present paper seeks to fulfill both objectives. It contains a theory of recursiveness applicable to any model (or structure) whatsoever, and forms a natural branch of the general theory of definability within a model. I should mention several attempts to fulfill the first objective, that of generalizing recursiveness, and to some extent also to fulfill the second (though they have perhaps been more successful in connection with the first than with the second). Three of the other attempts antedate mine, and one follows it. The chronological order appears to be the following: FRAÏSSÉ [1961]; LACOMBE [1964] and [1964a]; KREISEL [1965]; the present theory for the special case in which $\mathfrak{a} = \aleph_0$, which was obtained in the fall of 1965[2]; and Moschovakis'

---

[1] The research reported here was supported in part by U.S. National Science Foundation Grants GP-4594 and GP-7706. I wish also to express my gratitude, for valuable criticism, to Mr. Lung-Ock Chung, Dr. Charles Howard, Drs. J. A. W. Kamp, Dr. P. E. R. Martin-Löf, Mr. Peter Tripodes, and especially Mr. Perry Smith and Mr. Barry Kurtzman.

theory of search computability, which was obtained in the spring of 1966 and is reported in a forthcoming paper called 'Abstract first-order computability'. All the authors mentioned showed that their notions, when specialized to the natural numbers, reduce to the standard notions of recursion theory. But a generalization of concepts is empty unless it permits general theorems; and only Moschovakis and I (in the spring of 1966 and the late fall of 1965 respectively) showed that generalizations of the standard theorems of recursion theory could be obtained for our respective theories. It turns out, however, that the five general notions mentioned, with suitable minor specializations in each case, are all equivalent. This surprising fact was shown, at different times and for different pairs of notions, in LACOMBE [1964a] and in unpublished work of Moschovakis and his student Mr. Carl Gordon; Mr. Gordon is responsible for the equivalences involving the present theory.[3]

The present notions appear in one way to have a more natural intuitive content than those considered by other authors. In the case of the other notions there is at least on the face of things room for speculation as to whether the notions are sufficiently inclusive; one might wonder, for instance, whether a slight extension might lead to a more natural, or at least equally natural, notion of recursiveness. The present notions, however, have a very natural boundary – considered, it is true, in terms of definability rather than computability.

The present theory is in one direction more general than the five theories mentioned above. Technically speaking, the additional generality consists in considering an arbitrary, or almost arbitrary, cardinal $\mathfrak{a}$ in the development below, and not only the special case in which $\mathfrak{a} = \aleph_0$; the more general version was obtained in June, 1966, reported in a talk in Los Angeles on October 14, 1966, and partially summarized in the abstract MONTAGUE [1967].

The notions and theorems of the generalized arithmetical hierarchy are presented below. Proofs are omitted, as well as the statement of some of the less important lemmas. Some proofs are trivial; but others are not, and will be presented in a monograph now in preparation. The general notions can be extended in an obvious way so as to treat the analytic and higher-order hierarchies, as well as the theory of functionals and operators. The possibility of obtaining general theorems in these domains has not yet been much

---

[2] This theory (for $\mathfrak{a} = \aleph_0$) was presented in conversations during November and December, 1965, to Dr. Charles Howard, Professor Yiannis Moschovakis, and several students. The first public presentation occurred in Stockholm on March 11, 1966.

[3] Another general theory, of considerable interest but not fully meeting the requirements of the first paragraph of this paper, is to be found in KRIPKE [1964], [1964a] and [1964b]; in particular, Kripke's theory, though not restricted to particular cardinalities, applies naturally only to structures of which the members are ordinals.

explored; I therefore content myself with a mere sketch, in an Appendix, of general notions applicable to operators and functionals.

2. Preliminaries

We consider an object language with the following symbols:

(1) For each natural number n, a denumerable sequence $v_{0,n}, ..., v_{k,n}, ...$ of *variables of type n*. (By an *individual* or *set variable* is understood one of which the type is respectively 0 or a positive natural number.)

(2) For each finite sequence s of natural numbers, an unbounded sequence $P_{0,s}, ..., P_{\alpha,s}, ...$ of *predicates of type s*.

(3) The *logical constants* $\in, \neg, \wedge, \vee, [\,,\,], \vee$ ('is a member of', 'not', 'and', 'or', left bracket, right bracket, 'for some' respectively).

Speaking a little more formally, we make the following assumption: if n, n', k, k' are natural numbers, s, s' are finite sequences of natural numbers, α, α' are ordinals, the pair $\langle k, n \rangle \neq \langle k', n' \rangle$, and $\langle s, \alpha \rangle \neq \langle s', \alpha' \rangle$, then the set $\{\in, \neg, \wedge, \vee, [\,,\,], \vee, v_{k,n}, v_{k',n'}, P_{\alpha,s}, P_{\alpha',s'}\}$ contains exactly 11 members, each of which is a finite nonempty sequence, and none of which is a subsequence of another.

All of our development will be based on this assumption, together with the axioms of von Neumann-Bernays (or Morse-Kelley) set theory, including the Axiom of Choice. The *logical constants* are understood to be $\in, \neg, \wedge, \vee, [\,,\,]$, and $\vee$; a *variable of type n* is a sequence $v_{k,n}$, where k is a natural number; a *variable* is a sequence which, for some natural number n, is a variable of type n; a *predicate of type s* is a sequence $P_{\alpha,s}$, where α is an ordinal; a *predicate* is a sequence which, for some finite sequence s of natural numbers, is a predicate of type s; a *symbol* is either a logical constant, a variable, or a predicate; and an *expression* is a sequence formed by the concatenation of a finite nonzero number of symbols. It is clear that the predicates, and hence also the symbols and expressions, are too numerous to form a set. To say that one expression *occurs in* another, or that the second *contains* the first, is simply to say that the first is a subsequence of the second. Concatenation of sequences will be indicated by juxtaposition.

Atomic formulas have the form $Pu_0 ... u_{n-1}$, where P is a predicate constant of some type $\langle k_0, ..., k_{n-1} \rangle$ and $u_0, ..., u_{n-1}$ are variables of types $k_0, ..., k_{n-1}$ respectively, or the form $u \in v$, where, for some natural number k, u and v are variables of types k and $k+1$ respectively.

Formulas in general are built up from atomic formulas in the usual way, using $\neg, \wedge, \vee$, brackets, and the existential quantifier. Quantification is to occur in connection with both individual and set variables. The *free* and *bound* variables of a formula are to be characterized as usual.

If n is any natural number, $\mathfrak{a}$ any cardinal, and A any set, then the nth *power set of A* (relativized to $\mathfrak{a}$) is characterized by the following recursion:

$$U^{0,\mathfrak{a}}A = A,$$

$U^{n+1,\mathfrak{a}}A =$ the set of all subsets of $U^{n,\mathfrak{a}}A$ which have cardinality less than $\mathfrak{a}$.

If $s = \langle k_0, ..., k_{n-1} \rangle$ and s is a finite sequence of natural numbers, then the set of all *relations of type s over A* (relative to $\mathfrak{a}$) is characterized as follows:

$$R^{s,\mathfrak{a}}A = \text{the set of all subsets of the Cartesian product}$$
$$(U^{k_0,\mathfrak{a}}A) \times \cdots \times (U^{k_{n-1},\mathfrak{a}}A).$$

If $\mathfrak{a}$ is again a cardinal, then an $\mathfrak{a}$-*model* is an ordered pair $\langle A, F \rangle$ such that (1) A is a nonempty set, (2) F is a function of which the domain is a set of predicates, and (3) $F(P) \in R^{s,\mathfrak{a}}A$ whenever P is a predicate of type s in the domain of F. If $\mathfrak{A} = \langle A, F \rangle$, then by $\text{Lng}_{\mathfrak{A}}$, or the *language* of $\mathfrak{A}$, I understand the domain of F. If in addition P is a member of $\text{Lng}_{\mathfrak{A}}$, then $P_{\mathfrak{A}}$ is to be $F(P)$. If further $\mathfrak{a}$ is a cardinal and n a natural number, then $U_n^{\mathfrak{A},\mathfrak{a}}$, or the *universe* of $\mathfrak{A}$ of type n (relative to $\mathfrak{a}$), is $U^{n,\mathfrak{a}}A$. We set $U_0^{\mathfrak{A}} = A = U_0^{\mathfrak{A},\mathfrak{a}}$.

Suppose that $\mathfrak{A} = \langle A, F \rangle$ and G is a function of which the domain is a set of predicates not in $\text{Lng}_{\mathfrak{A}}$. Then $\mathfrak{A}^{\wedge}G$, or $\mathfrak{A}$ *augmented by G*, is $\langle A, F \cup G \rangle$. If $\mathfrak{A}$ is an $\mathfrak{a}$-model, and $G(P)$ is in $R^{s,\mathfrak{a}}A$ whenever P is a predicate of type s in the domain of G, then $\mathfrak{A}^{\wedge}G$ will also clearly be an $\mathfrak{a}$-model. An *assignment in* $\mathfrak{A}$ (of values to variables, relative to $\mathfrak{a}$) is a function of which the domain is a set of variables and of which the value for a variable in that set of any type n is a member of $U_n^{\mathfrak{A},\mathfrak{a}}$.

Suppose that ϕ is a formula, $\mathfrak{a}$ a cardinal, $\mathfrak{A}$ an $\mathfrak{a}$-model, and f an assignment in $\mathfrak{A}$ relative to $\mathfrak{a}$. Then f is said to *satisfy* ϕ in $\mathfrak{A}$ relative to $\mathfrak{a}$ if (roughly speaking; an exact recursive definition could be easily constructed on the pattern of TARSKI and VAUGHT [1957]) all predicates occurring in ϕ are in $\text{Lng}_{\mathfrak{A}}$, all free variables of ϕ are in the domain of f, and ϕ is true when (1) each free variable u of ϕ is taken as denoting $f(u)$, (2) for each natural number n, the bound variables of ϕ of type n are taken as ranging over the set $U_n^{\mathfrak{A},\mathfrak{a}}$, (3) each predicate P in ϕ is taken as denoting $P_{\mathfrak{A}}$, and (4) logical constants (including $\in$) are interpreted as usual.

Thus we have laid the basis of what might be called *general weak higher-order logic*; the name is suggested by the fact that if we set $\mathfrak{a} = \aleph_0$ and restrict attention to formulas whose variables all have type 0 or 1, we obtain what Tarski and others have called *weak second-order logic*. It should also be mentioned (though this will play no part in current considerations) that if $\mathfrak{a}$ is chosen sufficiently large relative to the cardinal of $U_0^{\mathfrak{A}}$, we obtain as another specialization the ordinary higher-order logic of $\mathfrak{A}$ with finite types.

The following notation will facilitate reference to finite assignments. If $x_0, \ldots, x_{n-1}$ are distinct objects, then $\begin{pmatrix} x_0 \cdots x_{n-1} \\ y_0 \quad y_{n-1} \end{pmatrix}$ is to be that function f of which the domain is $\{x_0, \ldots, x_{n-1}\}$ and which is such that $f(x_i) = y_i$ for all $i < n$.

If $\mathfrak{A} = \langle A, F \rangle$ then by $R^{\mathfrak{A}, \mathfrak{a}}$, or the set of *typed relations connected with* $\mathfrak{A}$ *and* $\mathfrak{a}$, is understood the set of pairs $\langle s, X \rangle$, where s is a finite sequence of natural numbers and $X \in R^{s, \mathfrak{a}} A$. If $R \in R^{\mathfrak{A}, \mathfrak{a}}$ and $R = \langle s, X \rangle$, then the *type* of R (also called τR) is s, and the *extension* of R (also called R^*) is X. By $\bar{R}^{\mathfrak{A}, \mathfrak{a}}$, or the *complement* of R relative to $\mathfrak{A}$ and $\mathfrak{a}$, we understand $\langle s, (U_{k_0}^{\mathfrak{A}, \mathfrak{a}} \times \cdots \times U_{k_{n-1}}^{\mathfrak{A}, \mathfrak{a}}) - R^* \rangle$, where s is the type of R and $s = \langle k_0, \ldots, k_{n-1} \rangle$. If K is a set of relations connected with $\mathfrak{A}$ and $\mathfrak{a}$, then $C^{\mathfrak{A}, \mathfrak{a}}(K)$ is to be the set of complements $\bar{R}^{\mathfrak{A}, \mathfrak{a}}$ of relations R in K. If R is a relation of type $\langle n, k \rangle$, then $\check{R}$, or the *converse* of R, is the relation of type $\langle k, n \rangle$ of which the extension is $\{\langle y, x \rangle : \langle x, y \rangle \in R^*\}$.

Now suppose that ϕ is a formula and R a relation connected with $\mathfrak{A}$ and $\mathfrak{a}$. Then ϕ is said to *define* R in $\mathfrak{A}$ (relative to $\mathfrak{a}$) if there exist natural numbers $k_0, \ldots, k_{n-1}$ such that (1) the type of R is $\langle k_0, \ldots, k_{n-1} \rangle$, (2) the free variables of ϕ are in $\{v_{0,k_0}, \ldots, v_{n-1, k_{n-1}}\}$, (3) the predicates occurring in ϕ are all in $\mathrm{Lng}_{\mathfrak{A}}$, and (4) R^* is the set of sequences $\langle x_0, \ldots, x_{n-1} \rangle$ such that $\begin{pmatrix} v_{0, k_0} \cdots v_{n-1, k_{n-1}} \\ x_0 \quad\quad x_{n-1} \end{pmatrix}$ is an assignment satisfying ϕ in $\mathfrak{A}$ relative to $\mathfrak{a}$. If in addition K is a set of relations connected with $\mathfrak{A}$ and $\mathfrak{a}$, then ϕ is said to *define* R *in* $\mathfrak{A}$ *in terms of members of* K (relative to $\mathfrak{a}$) if there is a function G such that (1) the domain of G is a set of predicates not in $\mathrm{Lng}_{\mathfrak{A}}$, (2) $\langle s, G(P) \rangle$ is in K, whenever P is a predicate of type s in the domain of G, and (3) ϕ defines R in $\mathfrak{A}^{\wedge} G$ (relative to $\mathfrak{a}$). We say that R is *definable in* $\mathfrak{A}$ (relative to $\mathfrak{a}$) if there is a formula defining R in $\mathfrak{A}$ (relative to $\mathfrak{a}$), and *definable in* $\mathfrak{A}$ *in terms of members of* K (relative to $\mathfrak{a}$) if there is a formula defining R in $\mathfrak{A}$ (relative to $\mathfrak{a}$) in terms of members of K.

An *existential quantification* of a relation R (relative to $\mathfrak{A}$ and $\mathfrak{a}$) is a relation S which is defined in terms of members of $\{R\}$ (in $\mathfrak{A}$, relative to $\mathfrak{a}$) by a formula of the form $\bigvee u\, Px_0 \ldots x_{n-1}$, where $u, x_0, \ldots, x_{n-1}$ are variables and P is a predicate constant not in $\mathrm{Lng}_{\mathfrak{A}}$; and $\Sigma^{\mathfrak{A}, \mathfrak{a}}(K)$ is to be the set of existential quantifications (relative to $\mathfrak{A}$ and $\mathfrak{a}$) of relations in the set K.

It is a bit unpleasant to speak of typed objects rather than their extensions; but in connection with definability it is necessary to do so, or else to substitute another corresponding complication, as the following example may tend to indicate. Let $\mathfrak{a}$ be a cardinal greater than 0, and $\mathfrak{A}$ be an $\mathfrak{a}$-model such that $U_0^{\mathfrak{A}}$ contains Λ (the empty set) together with at least one other element, and such that $\mathrm{Lng}_{\mathfrak{A}}$ is empty. According to the characterization above, $\langle\langle 0\rangle, \{\langle\Lambda\rangle\}\rangle$ is not definable in $\mathfrak{A}$ (relative to $\mathfrak{a}$); but $\langle\langle 1\rangle, \{\langle\Lambda\rangle\}\rangle$ is so definable, and indeed by the formula $\neg \bigvee v_{1,0} v_{1,0} \in v_{0,1}$. Loosely speaking, we could describe the situation thus. The unit set of Λ, if regarded as a 1-place relation of individuals, is (like all other unit sets of individuals) not definable in $\mathfrak{A}$; but it *is* definable in $\mathfrak{A}$ if it is regarded as a 1-place relation of *sets* of individuals.

3. The basic notions

Let us now construct a hierarchy of formulas. By Φ, or the class of *elementary formulas*, is understood the intersection of all classes Γ such that (1) $Pu_0 \ldots u_{n-1}$ is in Γ whenever P is a predicate constant of type $\langle k_0, \ldots, k_{n-1}\rangle$ and each u_i (for $i < n$) is a variable of type k_i, (2) $[\phi \wedge \psi]$ and $[\phi \vee \psi]$ are in Γ whenever ϕ and ψ are in Γ, and (3) $\bigvee u[u \in v \wedge \phi]$ and $\neg \bigvee u[u \in v \wedge \neg \phi]$ are in Γ whenever ϕ is in Γ, u is a variable of type k (for some natural number k), and v is a variable of type $k+1$. Thus in elementary formulas all quantifiers are bounded by membership in given sets, and predicates occur only positively. If n is any natural number, the class Σ_n of *n-quantifier existential formulas* is introduced by the following recursion; here we do not count bounded quantifiers. Σ_0 is the class of formulas $\neg \phi$ for ϕ in Φ; Σ_{n+1} is the class of formulas $\bigvee u \neg \phi$, where u is a variable and ϕ is in Σ_n.

This is the main classification of formulas (and derivatively of relations; see below) in which we shall be interested. For restricted purposes, however, a more refined classification is sometimes needed. By Φ_k or $\Sigma_{n,k}$ is understood the class of formulas in Φ or Σ_n respectively of which all the variables have types less than k.

Now given any model $\mathfrak{A}$, any cardinal $\mathfrak{a}$, and any set K of objects connected with $\mathfrak{A}$ and $\mathfrak{a}$, we may form a classification of relations corresponding to our classification of formulas. In particular, if Γ is any class of formulas, $\Gamma^{\mathfrak{A},\mathfrak{a}}(K)$ is the set of relations R such that, for some ϕ in Γ, ϕ defines R in $\mathfrak{A}$ in terms of members of K (relative to $\mathfrak{a}$).

Some additional categories of relations may also be introduced. For instance, $\Delta_n^{\mathfrak{A},\mathfrak{a}}(K)$ is to be the intersection of $\Sigma_n^{\mathfrak{A},\mathfrak{a}}(K)$ and $C^{\mathfrak{A},\mathfrak{a}}(\Sigma_n^{\mathfrak{A},\mathfrak{a}}(K))$, and $\Delta_{n,k}^{\mathfrak{A},\mathfrak{a}}(K)$ the intersection of $\Sigma_{n,k}^{\mathfrak{A},\mathfrak{a}}(K)$ and $C^{\mathfrak{A},\mathfrak{a}}(\Sigma_{n,k}^{\mathfrak{A},\mathfrak{a}}(K))$. Further, $\Omega_n^{\mathfrak{A},\mathfrak{a}}(K)$ is to be $\Delta_n^{\mathfrak{A},\mathfrak{a}}(K \cup C^{\mathfrak{A},\mathfrak{a}}(K))$.

Let us understand $\mathrm{F0}_n^{\mathfrak{A}}$ (or the set of *n-place first-order relations connected with* $\mathfrak{A}$) to be the set of all pairs $\langle s, B\rangle$, where s is the n-place sequence all constituents of which are 0 and B is a set of n-place sequences of members of $U_0^{\mathfrak{A}}$; and $\mathrm{F0}^{\mathfrak{A}}$ (or the set of *first-order relations connected with* $\mathfrak{A}$) to be the union of the sets $\mathrm{F0}_n^{\mathfrak{A}}$, where n is a natural number. Let Z, S be the predicates $P_{0,\langle 0\rangle}$, $P_{0,\langle 0,0\rangle}$ respectively; and let $\mathfrak{P}$ be the *standard Peano model*, that is, the model such that $\mathrm{Lng}_{\mathfrak{P}} = \{Z, S\}$, $U_0^{\mathfrak{P}} =$ the set of natural numbers, $Z_{\mathfrak{P}} = \{\langle 0\rangle\}$, and $S_{\mathfrak{P}} = \{\langle x, x+1\rangle : x \in U_0^{\mathfrak{P}}\}$. (Thus $Z_{\mathfrak{P}}$ is the property of being 0, and $S_{\mathfrak{P}}$ the successor relation between natural numbers.)

I suggest $\Omega_1^{\mathfrak{A},\mathfrak{a}}(\Lambda) \cap \mathrm{F0}^{\mathfrak{A}}$ $(= \Delta_1^{\mathfrak{A},\mathfrak{a}}(\Lambda) \cap \mathrm{F0}^{\mathfrak{A}})$ as the general model-theoretic counterpart of the set of recursive relations, $\Omega_1^{\mathfrak{A},\mathfrak{a}}(\{S\}) \cap \mathrm{F0}^{\mathfrak{A}}$ (where $S \in \mathrm{F0}^{\mathfrak{A}}$) as the counterpart of the set of relations recursive in the relation S, $\Sigma_1^{\mathfrak{A},\mathfrak{a}}(\Lambda) \cap \mathrm{F0}^{\mathfrak{A}}$ as the counterpart of the set of recursively enumerable relations, and more generally $\Sigma_n^{\mathfrak{A},\mathfrak{a}}(\Lambda) \cap \mathrm{F0}^{\mathfrak{A}}$ (if $n > 0$) as the counterpart of the set of existential n-quantifier relations in the Kleene arithmetical hierarchy. This suggestion becomes reasonable in the light of the fact (which will be stated below in Section 9, after other theorems that would simplify its proof) that in the special case in which $\mathfrak{A} = \mathfrak{P}$ and $\mathfrak{a} = \aleph_0$, $\Omega_1^{\mathfrak{A},\mathfrak{a}}(\Lambda) \cap \mathrm{F0}^{\mathfrak{A}}$ coincides exactly with the usual set of recursive relations among natural numbers, $\Omega_1^{\mathfrak{A},\mathfrak{a}}(\{S\}) \cap \mathrm{F0}^{\mathfrak{A}}$ coincides with the set of relations recursive in S (in the usual sense) whenever $S \in \mathrm{F0}^{\mathfrak{P}}$, and analogous identities apply to the other sets mentioned above.

4. Elementary lemmas; the generalization of Post's Theorem

We now make some assumptions which are to act as implicit hypotheses of lemmas, theorems, and remarks.

CONVENTION 1 (to be assumed through the remainder of this paper). (1) $\mathfrak{a}$ is a cardinal greater than 2; (2) $\mathfrak{A}$ is an $\mathfrak{a}$-model; (3) $k, \ldots, r$ are natural numbers.

Throughout this paper we shall keep in mind a fixed cardinal $\mathfrak{a}$ and a fixed $\mathfrak{a}$-model $\mathfrak{A}$; accordingly, we shall frequently omit the superscripts '$\mathfrak{a}$', '$\mathfrak{A}$' and the qualifications 'relative to $\mathfrak{a}$', 'relative to $\mathfrak{A}$' when it is these particular objects that are involved.

The following theorem is completely obvious.

THEOREM 1. Suppose that $K, L \subseteq R^{\mathfrak{A}, \mathfrak{a}}$. Then

(1) $K \subseteq \Sigma(K) \subseteq R^{\mathfrak{A}, \mathfrak{a}}$;
(2) $K \subseteq \Phi(K) \subseteq R^{\mathfrak{A}, \mathfrak{a}}$;
(3) if $K \subseteq L$, then $\Phi(K) \subseteq \Phi(L)$;
(4) $C(K) \subseteq R^{\mathfrak{A}, \mathfrak{a}}$;
(5) $C(C(K)) = K$;
(6) $C(K) = \bigcup \{C(\{R\}) : R \in K\}$;
(7) $\Sigma(K) = \bigcup \{\Sigma(\{R\}) : R \in K\}$.

The following theorem would require proof but is still simple.

THEOREM 2. Suppose that $K \subseteq R^{\mathfrak{A}, \mathfrak{a}}$. Then

(1) $\Phi(\Phi(K)) = \Phi(K)$,
(2) $\Sigma(\Sigma(K)) \subseteq \Sigma(\Phi(K))$,
(3) $\Phi(\Sigma(\Phi(K))) = \Sigma(\Phi(K))$.

To continue our development we must make an additional assumption.

CONVENTION 2 (to be assumed through the remainder of this paper). For each $P \in \text{Lng}_{\mathfrak{A}}$, $\langle \tau P, P_{\mathfrak{A}} \rangle \in C^{\mathfrak{A}}(\Sigma^{\mathfrak{A}, \mathfrak{a}}(\Phi^{\mathfrak{A}, \mathfrak{a}}(\Lambda)))$.

The import of this convention is that the complement of every primitive relation of $\mathfrak{A}$ (that is, every relation represented in $\mathfrak{A}$ by a predicate) is 'recursively enumerable' in the generalized sense, that is, definable in $\mathfrak{A}$ by an existential quantification of an elementary formula. It is easily seen that Convention 2 holds in the standard specialization:

Remark 1. If $\mathfrak{A} = \mathfrak{P}$ and $\mathfrak{a} = \aleph_0$, then Convention 2 holds.

It will follow from Theorem 24 below that the hypothesis '$\mathfrak{a} = \aleph_0$' can be weakened to '$\mathfrak{a} \geqslant \aleph_0$'.

THEOREM 3. If $K \subseteq R^{\mathfrak{A}, \mathfrak{a}}$, then $\Phi(C(\Sigma(\Phi(K)))) = C(\Sigma(\Phi(K)))$.

The following obvious theorem provides, so to speak, a recursive definition of the basic classes of relations in our hierarchy. Parts (3) and (4) repeat the explicit definitions of other classes of relations.

THEOREM 4. Suppose that $K \subseteq R^{\mathfrak{A}, \mathfrak{a}}$. Then

(1) $\Sigma_0(K) = C(\Phi(K))$,
(2) $\Sigma_{n+1}(K) = \Sigma(C(\Sigma_n(K)))$,
(3) $\Delta_n(K) = \Sigma_n(K) \cap C(\Sigma_n(K))$,
(4) $\Omega_n(K) = \Delta_n(K \cup C(K))$.

The remaining theorems of this section follow in a purely algebraic way from Theorems 1–4, without resort to the meanings of the notions '$R^{\mathfrak{A},a}$', '$\Sigma(K)$', '$\Phi(K)$', '$C(K)$', '$\Sigma_n(K)$'.

THEOREM 5. Suppose that $K, L \subseteq R^{\mathfrak{A},a}$. Then
(1) $C(K \cap L) = C(K) \cap C(L)$;
(2) if $K \subseteq L$, then $\Sigma_n(K) \subseteq \Sigma_n(L)$, $\Delta_n(K) \subseteq \Delta_n(L)$, and $\Omega_n(K) \subseteq \Omega_n(L)$;
(3) $C(\Delta_n(K)) = \Delta_n(K)$;
(4) $C(\Omega_n(K)) = \Omega_n(K)$;
(5) if $C(K) \subseteq K$, then $\Omega_n(K) = \Delta_n(K)$.

THEOREM 6. Suppose that $K \subseteq R^{\mathfrak{A},a}$. Then
(1) $\Phi(C(\Sigma_n(K))) = C(\Sigma_n(K))$;
(2) if $n \neq 0$, then $\Phi(\Sigma_n(K)) = \Sigma_n(K)$;
(3) $\Sigma_1(C(\Sigma_n(K))) = \Sigma_{n+1}(K)$;
(4) if $n \neq 0$, then $\Sigma_1(\Sigma_n(K)) = \Sigma_n(K)$;
(5) $\Delta_1(C(\Sigma_n(K))) = \Delta_{n+1}(K)$;
(6) if $n \neq 0$, then $\Delta_1(\Sigma_n(K)) = \Delta_n(K)$;
(7) if $n \neq 0$, then $\Delta_1(\Delta_n(K)) = \Delta_n(K)$;
(8) if $n \neq 0$, then $\Omega_1(\Omega_n(K)) = \Omega_n(K)$;
(9) if p is even, then $\Sigma_n(K) \subseteq \Sigma_{n+p}(K)$;
(10) if p is odd, then $\Sigma_n(K) \subseteq \Sigma_{n+p}(C(K))$;
(11) if n is even, then $K \subseteq C(\Sigma_n(K))$;
(12) if n is odd, then $K \subseteq \Sigma_n(K)$.

The following simple consequence is the general version of Post's Theorem, according to which the relations recursive in n-quantifier relations coincide with the relations expressible in both $(n+1)$-quantifier forms.

THEOREM 7. If $C(K) \subseteq K \subseteq R^{\mathfrak{A},a}$, then $\Omega_1(\Sigma_n(K) \cup C(\Sigma_n(K))) = \Delta_{n+1}(K)$.

THEOREM 8. Suppose that $K \subseteq R^{\mathfrak{A},a}$. Then
(1) $\Sigma_n(\Phi(K)) = \Sigma_n(K)$;
(2) if $n \neq 0$, then $\Sigma_n(\Sigma_1(K)) = \Sigma_n(K)$;
(3) $\Sigma_n(C(\Sigma_1(K))) = \Sigma_{n+1}(K)$;
(4) if $n \neq 0$, then $\Sigma_n(\Omega_1(K)) = \Sigma_n(K \cup C(K))$;
(5) $\Sigma_n(C(\Sigma_p(K))) = \Sigma_{n+p}(K)$;
(6) if $n \neq 0$, then $\Sigma_n(\Sigma_{p+1}(K)) = \Sigma_{n+p}(K)$;
(7) $\Sigma_n(K) = \bigcup \{\Sigma_n(\{R\}): R \in \Phi(K)\}$;
(8) if $n \neq 0$, then $\Phi(K) \subseteq \Omega_n(K)$.

The following theorem exhibits the connection between the present hierarchy – $\Sigma_0(K)$, $C(\Sigma_0(K))$, $\Sigma_1(K)$, $C(\Sigma_1(K))$, ... – and a hierarchy of a more customary sort, based on the universal as well as the existential quantifier. Such a hierarchy would be expressed in the style of Addison as

$$\Delta_1^o(K), \Sigma_1^o(K), \Pi_1^o(K), \Sigma_2^o(K), ...,$$

while in our symbolization the same hierarchy would become

$$\Omega_1(K), \Sigma(\Omega_1(K)), C(\Sigma(C(\Omega_1(K)))), \Sigma(C(\Sigma(C(\Omega_1(K))))), ...$$

THEOREM 9. Suppose that $K \subseteq R^{\mathfrak{A}, \mathfrak{a}}$. Then
(1) $\Sigma_1(K \cup C(K)) = \Sigma\Omega_1(K)$,
(2) $\Sigma_2(K \cup C(K)) = \Sigma(C(\Sigma(C(\Omega_1(K)))))$,
(3) $\Sigma_{n+2}(K) = \Sigma(C(\Sigma(C(\Sigma_n(K)))))$.

5. Some special relations

By $I_n^{\mathfrak{A}, \mathfrak{a}}$ is understood the *identity relation* on $U_n^{\mathfrak{A}, \mathfrak{a}}$, that is, the pair $\langle \langle n, n \rangle, \{\langle x, x \rangle : x \in U_n^{\mathfrak{A}, \mathfrak{a}}\} \rangle$; and by $E_n^{\mathfrak{A}, \mathfrak{a}}$ the *membership relation* of level n relative to $\mathfrak{A}$ and $\mathfrak{a}$, that is, the pair $\langle \langle n, n+1 \rangle, \{\langle x, y \rangle : y \in U_{n+1}^{\mathfrak{A}, \mathfrak{a}} \text{ and } x \in y\} \rangle$. As in the previous section, we shall frequently omit the superscripts '$\mathfrak{A}$' and '$\mathfrak{a}$'.

LEMMA 1. (1) $I_{n+p} \in \Phi(\{I_n\})$,
(2) $\overline{I_{n+p}} \in \Phi(\{\overline{I_n}\})$,
(3) $E_{n+p} \in \Phi(\{I_n\})$,
(4) $\overline{E_{n+p}} \in \Phi(\{\overline{I_n}\})$,
(5) $I_{n+p+1} \in \Phi(\{E_n\})$,
(6) $\overline{I_{n+p+1}} \in \Phi(\{\overline{E_n}\})$.

THEOREM 10. If $R \in R^{\mathfrak{A}, \mathfrak{a}}$, then R is definable in $\mathfrak{A}$ in terms of members of K (relative to $\mathfrak{a}$) if and only if there is a natural number n such that $R \in \Sigma_n(K \cup C(K) \cup \{\overline{I_0}, I_0\})$.

LEMMA 2. Suppose that $K \subseteq R^{\mathfrak{A}, \mathfrak{a}}$ and $\Delta_1(K) \neq \Lambda$. Then
(1) $\langle \langle k_0, ..., k_{n-1} \rangle, U_{k_0} \times \cdots \times U_{k_{n-1}} \rangle \in \Delta_1(K)$;
(2) $\langle \langle k_0, ..., k_{n-1} \rangle, \Lambda \rangle \in \Delta_1(K)$;
(3) if $n \geq 1$, then $\langle \langle n \rangle, \{\langle \Lambda \rangle\} \rangle \in \Delta_1(K)$;
(4) if $n \geq 2$, then $\langle \langle n \rangle, \{\langle \{\Lambda\} \rangle\} \rangle \in \Delta_1(K)$.

Remark 2. Suppose that $K \subseteq R^{\mathfrak{A}, \mathfrak{a}}$. If either $\mathrm{Lng}_{\mathfrak{A}} \neq \Lambda$ or there exists R such that $R, \bar{R} \in K$, then $\Delta_1(K) \neq \Lambda$.

By $\{x\}_n$ we understand the unit set formed from x and n levels higher than x; the notion is defined recursively as follows:

$$\{x\}_0 = x,$$
$$\{x\}_{n+1} = \{\{x\}_n\}.$$

By $\langle x, y \rangle_{n,k}$ is understood $\{\{x\}_{k+1}, \{\{x\}_k, \{y\}_n\}\}$, which is an ordered pair primarily of interest when x has type n and y has type k; in that case the members of $\langle x, y \rangle_{n,k}$ will have the same type and $\langle x, y \rangle_{n,k}$ will have type $n+k+2$. We say that u is an (n, k)-*pair* (connected with $\mathfrak{A}$ and $\mathfrak{a}$) if $u = \langle x, y \rangle_{n,k}$, for some $x \in U_n$ and $y \in U_k$. If u is such a pair, then $1_{n,k} u$ is the unique object x such that, for some y, $u = \langle x, y \rangle_{n,k}$; and $2_{n,k} u$ is the unique object y such that, for some x, $u = \langle x, y \rangle_{n,k}$.

LEMMA 3. (1) If F is the relation (connected with $\mathfrak{A}$ and $\mathfrak{a}$) of type $\langle n, n, n+1 \rangle$ of which the extension is $\{\langle x, y, \{x, y\} \rangle : x, y \in U_n\}$, then $F \in \Phi(\{I_n\})$.

(2) If F is the relation of type $\langle k, k+n \rangle$ of which the extension is $\{\langle x, \{x\}_n \rangle : x \in U_k\}$, then $F \in \Phi(\{I_k\})$.

(3) If F is the relation of type $\langle n, k, n+k+2 \rangle$ of which the extension is $\{\langle x, y, \langle x, y \rangle_{n,k} \rangle : x \in U_n \text{ and } y \in U_k\}$, then $F \in \Phi(\{I_n, I_k\})$.

(4) If P is the relation of type $\langle n+k+2 \rangle$ of which the extension is $\{\langle u \rangle : u \text{ is an } (n, k)\text{-pair}\}$, then $P \in \Phi(\{I_n, I_k\})$.

(5) If F is the relation of type $\langle n+k+2, n \rangle$ of which the extension is $\{\langle u, 1_{n,k} u \rangle : u \text{ is an } (n, k)\text{-pair}\}$, then $F \in \Phi(\{I_n, I_k\})$.

(6) If F is the relation of type $\langle n+k+2, k \rangle$ of which the extension is $\{\langle u, 2_{n,k} u \rangle : u \text{ is an } (n, k)\text{-pair}\}$, then $F \in \Phi(\{I_n, I_k\})$.

The following lemma establishes a connection between the hierarchies associated with the same model but two distinct cardinals.

LEMMA 4. Suppose that $\mathfrak{b}$ is a cardinal less than or equal to $\mathfrak{a}$, $K \subseteq R^{\mathfrak{A}, \mathfrak{b}}$, and L is the set of relations $\langle \langle p \rangle, \{\langle x \rangle : x \in U_p^{\mathfrak{A}, \mathfrak{b}}\} \rangle$, where p is a natural number greater than 0. Then $\Sigma_n^{\mathfrak{A}, \mathfrak{b}}(K) \subseteq \Sigma_n^{\mathfrak{A}, \mathfrak{a}}(K \cup L \cup C^{\mathfrak{A}, \mathfrak{a}}(L))$.

6. Functional relations

Suppose that R is a relation of type $\langle k_0, \ldots, k_n \rangle$ connected with $\mathfrak{A}$ and $\mathfrak{a}$. Then R is said to be a *functional relation* if $y = z$ whenever $\langle x_0, \ldots, x_{n-1}, y \rangle$, $\langle x_0, \ldots, x_{n-1}, z \rangle \in R^*$. D$R$, or the *typed domain of* R, is that relation of type

$\langle k_0, ..., k_{n-1} \rangle$ of which the extension is $\{\langle x_0, ..., x_{n-1} \rangle :$ for some y, $\langle x_0, ..., x_{n-1}, y \rangle \in R^*\}$; and $\Box R$, or the *typed range of* R, is that relation of type $\langle k_n \rangle$ of which the extension is $\{\langle y \rangle :$ for some $x_0, ..., x_{n-1}, \langle x_0, ..., x_{n-1}, y \rangle \in R^*\}$. R is *total* (relative to $\mathfrak{A}$ and $\mathfrak{a}$) if and only if $(\Box R)^* = U_{k_0} \times \cdots \times U_{k_{n-1}}$. If R is a functional relation and $\langle x_0, ..., x_{n-1} \rangle \in (\Box R)^*$, then $R(x_0, ..., x_{n-1})$ is that object y such that $\langle x_0, ..., x_{n-1}, y \rangle \in R^*$.

LEMMA 5. *If F is a functional relation of type $\langle k_0, ..., k_m \rangle$, then $F \in C(\Sigma_1(\{F, \overline{DF}, \overline{I_{k_m}}\}))$.*

THEOREM 11. *If F is a functional relation of type $\langle k_0, ..., k_m \rangle$, $K \subseteq R^{\mathfrak{A}, \mathfrak{a}}$, $n \neq 0$, and $DF, I_{k_m} \in C(\Sigma_n(K))$, then $F \in \Sigma_n(K)$ if and only if $F \in \Delta_n(K)$.*

THEOREM 12. *Suppose that R is a relation of type $\langle k_0, ..., k_r \rangle$, F is a functional relation of type $\langle p_0, ..., p_{n-1}, k_r \rangle$, and S is that relation of type $\langle k_0, ..., k_{r-1}, p_0, ..., p_{n-1} \rangle$ of which the extension is $\{\langle x_0, ..., x_{r-1}, y_0, ..., y_{n-1} \rangle : \langle y_0, ..., y_{n-1} \rangle \in (DF)^*$ and $\langle x_0, ..., x_{r-1}, F(y_0, ..., y_{n-1}) \rangle \in R^*\}$. Then $S \in \Sigma_1(\{F, R\}) \cap C(\Sigma_1(\{F, \overline{R}, \overline{DF}\}))$.*

THEOREM 13. *Suppose that $F_0, ..., F_{k-1}$ are total functional relations of the respective types $\langle p_0, ..., p_{n-1}, q_0 \rangle, ..., \langle p_0, ..., p_{n-1}, q_{k-1} \rangle$, G is a total functional relation of type $\langle q_0, ..., q_{k-1}, r \rangle$, and H is that total functional relation of type $\langle p_0, ..., p_{n-1}, r \rangle$ such that, for all $x_0, ..., x_{n-1}$ in $U_{p_0}, ..., U_{p_{n-1}}$ respectively,*

$$H(x_0, ..., x_{n-1}) = G(F_0(x_0, ..., x_{n-1}), ..., F_{k-1}(x_0, ..., x_{n-1})).$$

Then $H \in \Delta_1(\{F_0, ..., F_{k-1}, G, \bar{G}\})$.

7. Closure under inductive and recursive definition

By the *confinality* of a *cardinal* $\mathfrak{a}$ is understood the least cardinal $\mathfrak{b}$ such that there exists a set K of cardinality $\mathfrak{b}$ of which the members are sets of cardinality less than $\mathfrak{a}$ and of which the union has cardinality $\mathfrak{a}$. The cardinal $\mathfrak{a}$ is *regular* if and only if it is its own confinality.

CONVENTION 3 (to be assumed through the remainder of this paper). $\mathfrak{a}$ is an infinite regular cardinal.

We shall continue to deal with a fixed cardinal and a fixed model, and consequently for the most part omit reference to them. If R is a relation of which the type is a 2-place sequence, we shall understand the assertions that xRy and that $\langle x, y\rangle \in R^*$ as synonymous.

The following basic theorem, from which most of the other theorems of the present section can be derived, concerns inductive definitions based on a binary relation $\prec$ regarded as giving the intended ordering of the members of $U_n^{\mathfrak{A},\mathfrak{a}}$. We may justify such definitions without imposing any assumptions on $\prec$.

THEOREM 14. If $\prec$ is a relation (connected with $\mathfrak{A}$ and $\mathfrak{a}$) of type $\langle n, n\rangle$ and R a relation of type $\langle k_0, \ldots, k_{r-1}, n+1, n\rangle$, then there exists a relation P of type $\langle k_0, \ldots, k_{r-1}, n\rangle$ such that (1) $P \in \Sigma_1 (\{R, \prec, I_n\})$ and (2) for all $x_0, \ldots, x_{r-1}, y$ in $U_{k_0}, \ldots, U_{k_{r-1}}, U_n$ respectively, $\langle x_0, \ldots, x_{r-1}, y\rangle \in P^*$ if and only if there is $p \in U_{n+1}$ such that

(i) for all $k \in p$, $\langle x_0, \ldots, x_{r-1}, k\rangle \in P^*$ and $k \prec y$, and

(ii) $\langle x_0, \ldots, x_{r-1}, p, y\rangle \in R^*$.

If R is, for some n, a relation of type $\langle n, n\rangle$, then R is said to be *well-founded* if, for every nonempty set A, there exists $x \in A$ such that there is no $y \in A$ for which yRx. To obtain the uniqueness of the relation of which Theorem 14 asserts the existence, we must assume that the intended ordering is well-founded.

THEOREM 15. If the hypothesis of Theorem 14 holds, and in addition $\prec$ is well-founded, then there is exactly one relation P of type $\langle k_0, \ldots, k_{r-1}, n\rangle$ for which Theorem 14 (2) holds.

The next theorem generalizes the principle of *course-of-values recursion* for the introduction of functions. Rather than speaking in terms of a relation that orders the members of U_n, it is convenient here to associate with each $x \in U_n$ a subset $P(x)$ of U_n, regarded as the set of *predecessors* of x. We must assume, however, the well-foundedness of the predecessor relation thus induced.

THEOREM 16. Suppose that P is a total functional relation of type $\langle n, n+1\rangle$, that $\langle\langle n, n\rangle, \{\langle x, y\rangle : y \in U_n$ and $x \in P(y)\}\rangle$ is well-founded, and that G is a total functional relation of type $\langle k_0, \ldots, k_{r-1}, n, n+p+3, p\rangle$. Then

(1) there is exactly one total functional relation F of type $\langle k_0, \ldots, k_{r-1}, n, p\rangle$ such that, for all $x_0, \ldots, x_{r-1}, y$ in $U_{k_0}, \ldots, U_{k_{r-1}}, U_n$ respectively,

$$F(x_0, \ldots, x_{r-1}, y) = G(x_0, \ldots, x_{r-1}, y, \{\langle z, F(x_0, \ldots, x_{r-1}, z)\rangle_{n,p} : z \in P(y)\});$$

(2) if F satisfies (1), then $F \in \Delta_1 (\{P, G, \bar{I_n}, I_n, \bar{I_p}, I_p\})$.

The following theorem, like Theorem 14, concerns a form of inductive definition, but one with the advantage that the relations introduced are *recursive* (in the generalized sense) in given relations (including the functional relation P which assigns to each object of appropriate type the set of all its predecessors).

THEOREM 17. Suppose that P is a total functional relation of type $\langle n, n+1 \rangle$, that $\langle \langle n, n \rangle, \{\langle x, y \rangle : y \in U_n \text{ and } x \in P(y)\}\rangle$ is well-founded, and that S is a relation of type $\langle k_0, ..., k_{r-1}, n, n+1 \rangle$. Then

(1) there is exactly one relation R of type $\langle k_0, ..., k_{r-1}, n \rangle$ such that, for all $x_0, ..., x_{r-1}, y$ in $U_{k_0}, ..., U_{k_r}, U_n$ respectively,

$$\langle x_0, ..., x_{r-1}, y \rangle \in R^* \text{ if and only if } \langle x_0, ..., x_{r-1}, y, \{z : \langle x_0, ..., x_{r-1}, z \rangle \in R^*$$
$$\text{and } z \in P(y)\}\rangle \in S^*;$$

(2) if R satisfies (1), then $R \in \Delta_1 (\{P, S, \bar{S}, \overline{I_n}, I_n\})$.

8. Reductions in type

A superficial acquaintance with weak higher-order logic might lead one to suggest a hierarchy of relations based on two features of their defining formulas – quantificational structure of the sort we have indeed taken into account, and the types of the variables quantified. The second feature turns out, however, not to provide interesting distinctions. In certain senses, and under the broad assumptions enumerated in the convention below, our standard hierarchy, based on the full weak higher-order logic, can be reduced to the corresponding hierarchy within weak third-order logic (that part of weak higher-order logic which involves variables of types 0, 1, 2 exclusively). This fact, which is embodied in Theorems 18, 19 and 20 below, will play an important role in obtaining generalizations of the enumeration and hierarchy theorems of recursion theory.

CONVENTION 4 (to be assumed through the remainder of this paper). (1) F is a relation (connected with $\mathfrak{A}$ and $\mathfrak{a}$) having type $\langle 1, 0 \rangle$ and having as its extension a one-to-one correspondence between $U_1^{\mathfrak{A}, \mathfrak{a}}$ and a subset of $U_0^{\mathfrak{A}}$. (2) For each $P \in \text{Lng}_{\mathfrak{A}}$, $\langle \tau P, P_{\mathfrak{A}} \rangle \in \text{F0}^{\mathfrak{A}}$.

Convention 4(2) is of course satisfied by the standard model $\mathfrak{P}$; and if $\mathfrak{A} = \mathfrak{P}$ and $\mathfrak{a} = \aleph_0$, then there obviously exists F satisfying Convention 4(1). Convention 4(1) does, however, impose certain limitations on the relative size of a and the cardinal of $U_0^{\mathfrak{A}}$; general observations on this point are given in the Remark below.

The cardinals $\beth_\alpha$, for α an arbitrary ordinal, are introduced by the following recursion:

$\beth_0 = \aleph_0$;

if α is any ordinal, then $\beth_{\alpha+1} = 2^{\beth_\alpha}$;

if α is a nonzero limit ordinal, then $\beth_\alpha$ is the least upper bound of the cardinals $\beth_\gamma$, for $\gamma < \alpha$.

We say that b is a *limit beth* if $b = \beth_\alpha$, for some α that is either 0 or a nonzero limit ordinal. By b^+ is understood the *cardinal successor* of b, that is, the least cardinal greater than b. It is clear that no limit beth is a power of 2 (that is, of the form 2^c, for some cardinal c), and that if we were to assume the Generalized Continuum Hypothesis, it would follow that every infinite cardinal is either a limit beth or a power of 2.

Remark 3. Suppose that b is the cardinal of $U_0^{\mathfrak{A}}$. Then

(1) there exists F satisfying Convention 4(1) if and only if a is less than or equal to the least cardinal c such that $b < b^c$;

(2) if c is a cardinal, $b = 2^c$, and $a \leqslant c^+$, then there exists F satisfying convention 4(1);

(3) if b is a limit beth, then there exists F satisfying Convention 4(1) if and only if a is less than or equal to the confinality of b;

(4) if $a \leqslant \aleph_0 \leqslant b$, then there exists F satisfying Convention 4(1).

This remark can be strengthened: in the cases covered by parts (2) and (3) (and hence in that covered by (4)) we may assert the existence of a one-to-one correspondence which satisfies not only Convention 4(1) but also the condition (which will play a part below) that the image within $U_0^{\mathfrak{A}}$ of the membership relation is well-founded.

Remark 4. Suppose that b is the cardinal of $U_0^{\mathfrak{A}}$. If either (1) $b = 2^c$ and $a \leqslant c^+$, for some cardinal c, or (2) b is a limit beth and a is less than or equal to the confinality of b, then there exists F satisfying Convention 4(1) and such that $\langle\langle 0, 0\rangle, \{\langle x, y\rangle : \langle y\rangle \in (\mathsf{C}F)^* \text{ and } x \in \check{F}(y)\}\rangle$ is well-founded.

With the correspondence F and each natural number n we may associate a correspondence $F_{(n)}$ (or $F_{(n)}^{\mathfrak{A}, a}$ if we wish to render explicit the dependence on $\mathfrak{A}$ and a) characterized recursively as follows:

$F_{(0)} = I_0^{\mathfrak{A}}$;

if n is a natural number, then $F_{(n+1)}$ is a total functional relation of type $\langle n+1, 0\rangle$ such that, for each $a \in U_{n+1}$, $F_{(n+1)}(a) = F(\{F_{(n)}(b): b \in a\})$. If $a \in U_n$, we may think of $F_{(n)}(a)$ as that member of U_0 which 'represents' a; notice that $F_{(1)} = F$. If R is a relation of type $\langle k_0, \ldots, k_{r-1}\rangle$, then by R_F, or the *first-order reduction* of R according to F, is understood that relation in $F0_r$ of which the extension is $\{\langle F_{(k_0)}(a_0), \ldots, F_{(k_{r-1})}(a_{r-1})\rangle : \langle a_0, \ldots, a_{r-1}\rangle \in R^*\}$.

THEOREM 18. Suppose that $n \neq 0$ and $K \subseteq R^{\mathfrak{A}, a}$.
(1) If $R \in \Sigma_n(K)$, then $R_F \in \Sigma_{n,3}(\{S_F : S \in K\} \cup \{F, \bar{F}, \overline{\Omega F}\})$.
(2) If $R \in C(\Sigma_n(K))$, then $R_F \in C(\Sigma_{n,3}(\{S_F : S \in K\} \cup \{F, \bar{F}, \overline{\Omega F}\}))$.

THEOREM 19. Suppose that $n \neq 0$ and $K \subseteq R^{\mathfrak{A}, a}$. Then
(1) $\Sigma_n(K) \cap F0^{\mathfrak{A}} \subseteq \Sigma_{n,3}(\{S_F : S \in K\} \cup \{F, \bar{F}, \overline{\Omega F}\})$,
(2) $C(\Sigma_n(K)) \cap F0^{\mathfrak{A}} \subseteq C(\Sigma_{n,3}(\{S_F : S \in K\} \cup \{F, \bar{F}, \overline{\Omega F}\}))$.

THEOREM 20. Suppose that $n \neq 0$ and $K \subseteq F0^{\mathfrak{A}}$. Then
(1) $\Sigma_n(K \cup \{F, \bar{F}, \overline{\Omega F}\}) \cap F0^{\mathfrak{A}} \subseteq \Sigma_{n,3}(K \cup \{F, \bar{F}, \overline{\Omega F}\})$,
(2) $C(\Sigma_n(K \cup \{F, \bar{F}, \overline{\Omega F}\})) \cap F0^{\mathfrak{A}} \subseteq C(\Sigma_{n,3}(K \cup \{F, \bar{F}, \overline{\Omega F}\}))$.

9. Specialization to the standard model

It is the object of the present section to show that in the standard case in which $\mathfrak{A} = \mathfrak{B}$ and $a = \aleph_0$ the notions of our general hierarchy specialize to the expected notions of ordinary recursion theory.

By J, K, L are understood the *Cantor pairing functions*, defined as follows for arbitrary natural numbers x, y, z:

$J(x, y) = \frac{1}{2}((x+y)\cdot(x+y+1)) + x$,

$K(z)$ = the unique natural number x such that, for some natural number y, $z = J(x, y)$,

$L(z)$ = the unique natural number y such that, for some natural number x, $z = J(x, y)$.

Let us call x a *quasi-member* of y if x, y are natural numbers, $x < K(y)$, and $L(L(y))\cdot(x+1)+1$ divides $K(L(y))$. We say that a natural number y *represents a finite set* if (1) $K(y)$ is the least natural number such that every quasi-member of y is less than $K(y)$, (2) $L(L(y))$ is the least natural number which is different from 0 and is a multiple of all nonzero natural numbers less than $K(y)$, and (3) $K(L(y))$ is the least natural number which is different from 0 and is a multiple of all numbers $L(L(y))\cdot(x+1) + 1$ for which x is a quasi-member of y. Let s be the *natural enumeration of the numbers representing finite sets* (that is, the function enumerating them in increasing order). By Rep we understand that relation of type $\langle 1, 0\rangle$ connected with $\mathfrak{P}$ and $\aleph_0$ of which the extension is $\{\langle a, y\rangle : a \in U_1^{\mathfrak{P}, \aleph_0}, y \in U_0^{\mathfrak{P}}$, and $a = \{x : x$ is a quasi-member of $s(y)\}\}$.[4]

LEMMA 6. If $\mathfrak{A} = \mathfrak{P}$, $\mathfrak{a} = \aleph_0$, and $F = \text{Rep}$, then Convention 4 is satisfied.

If R is any relation connected with $\mathfrak{P}$ and $\aleph_0$, we may thus speak of the first-order reduction $R_{\text{Rep}}^{\mathfrak{P}, \aleph_0}$ of R according to Rep.

THEOREM 21. If $S \in R^{\mathfrak{P}, \aleph_0}$ and $R \in \Omega_1^{\mathfrak{P}, \aleph_0}(\{S\})$, then $R_{\text{Rep}}^{\mathfrak{P}, \aleph_0}$ is recursive in $S_{\text{Rep}}^{\mathfrak{P}, \aleph_0}$ (in the ordinary sense of 'recursive in'; see DAVIS [1958]).

LEMMA 7. $I_n^{\mathfrak{P}, \aleph_0}, E_n^{\mathfrak{P}, \aleph_0} \in \Delta_1^{\mathfrak{P}, \aleph_0}(\Lambda)$.

THEOREM 22. If $R, S \in \text{F0}^{\mathfrak{P}}$, then R is recursive in S if and only if $R \in \Omega_1^{\mathfrak{P}, \aleph_0}(\{S\})$.

LEMMA 8. $\text{Rep} \in \Delta_1^{\mathfrak{P}, \aleph_0}(\Lambda)$.

If $R \in \text{F0}^{\mathfrak{P}}$, then $\Sigma_n^0(R)$ or $\Pi_n^0(R)$ is to be understood as the set of first-order relations that are respectively Σ_n^0 in R or Π_n^0 in R, in the sense of the ordinary Kleene arithmetical hierarchy; for a characterization see DAVIS [1958], where, however, the less customary notations 'P_n^R' and 'Q_n^R' are used instead.

THEOREM 23. Suppose that $R \in \text{F0}^{\mathfrak{P}}$ and $n \neq 0$. Then $\Sigma_n^0(R) = \Sigma_n^{\mathfrak{P}, \aleph_0}(\{R, \bar{R}^{\mathfrak{P}, \aleph_0}\}) \cap \text{F0}^{\mathfrak{P}}$, and $\Pi_n^0(R) = C^{\mathfrak{P}, \aleph_0}(\Sigma_n^{\mathfrak{P}, \aleph_0}(\{R, \bar{R}^{\mathfrak{P}, \aleph_0}\})) \cap \text{F0}^{\mathfrak{P}}$.

The following useful theorem, together with its lemma, is due to Mr. Perry Smith.

LEMMA 9. If R is that relation of type $\langle 0, 0\rangle$ (connected with $\mathfrak{P}$ and $\aleph_0$) of which the extension is $\{\langle x, y\rangle : x, y$ are natural numbers and $x \leqslant y\}$ and $\mathfrak{b}$ is any infinite cardinal, then $R \in \Delta_1^{\mathfrak{P}, \mathfrak{b}}(\Lambda)$.

THEOREM 24. If $\mathfrak{b}$ is any infinite cardinal, $n \neq 0$, and $K \subseteq R^{\mathfrak{P}, \aleph_0}$ then $\Sigma_n^{\mathfrak{P}, \aleph_0}(K) \subseteq \Sigma_n^{\mathfrak{P}, \mathfrak{b}}(K)$.

At least one other kind of specialization holds some interest; and this

---

[4] We may read 'Rep(a)' as 'the representative of the set a'. This definition depends ultimately on ideas of Gödel, but more immediately on those of TRIPODES [1963]; the present form was developed by the author in connection with criticisms of Drs. J. A. W. Kamp and Messrs. Lung-Ock Chung and Perry Smith.

occurs when we consider, in place of $\mathfrak{P}$, various natural models of set theory (in the sense of MONTAGUE and VAUGHT [1959]). We can obtain, for example, all the general principles of set-theoretical recursion in MONTAGUE [1955] as special cases of theorems in Section 7; and the hierarchy theorems of Section 11 below have consequences that overlap with certain results in LÉVY [1965]. We shall not, however, go into any details here.

10. Recursive functions of expressions

A comprehensive treatment will not be attempted here; we present only as much material on these functions as will be needed in the next section.

If f is a function with domain A, n a natural number, and $\mathfrak{b}$ a cardinal, let us introduce $f^{n,\mathfrak{b}}$ by the following recursion:

$f^{0,\mathfrak{b}} = f$;

$f^{n+1,\mathfrak{b}}$ is that function with domain $U^{n+1,\mathfrak{b}} A$ such that, for each $x \in U^{n+1,\mathfrak{b}}A, f^{n+1,\mathfrak{b}}(x) = \{f^{n,\mathfrak{b}}(a): a \in x\}$.

Let us introduce $f^{s;\mathfrak{b}}$, for any finite sequence s of natural numbers, as follows:

if $s = \langle k_0, ..., k_{n-1} \rangle$, then $f^{s;\mathfrak{b}}$ is that function with domain $R^{s,\mathfrak{b}} A$ such that, for all $X \in R^{s,\mathfrak{b}} A, f^{s;\mathfrak{b}}(X) = \{\langle f^{k_0,\mathfrak{b}}(a_0), ..., f^{k_{n-1},\mathfrak{b}}(a_{n-1}) \rangle: \langle a_0, ..., a_{n-1} \rangle \in X\}$.

Thus $f^{n,\mathfrak{b}}$ and $f^{s;\mathfrak{b}}$ are the natural transformations induced by f of $U^{n,\mathfrak{b}}A$ and $R^{s,\mathfrak{b}}A$ respectively.

We say that f is an *isomorphism* from $\mathfrak{B}$ to $\mathfrak{C}$ if there is a cardinal $\mathfrak{b}$ such that $\mathfrak{B}$, $\mathfrak{C}$ are $\mathfrak{b}$-models, $\mathrm{Lng}_\mathfrak{B} = \mathrm{Lng}_\mathfrak{C}$, f is a biunique function, the domain of f is $U_0^\mathfrak{B}$, the range of f is $U_0^\mathfrak{C}$, and whenever P is a predicate of type s in $\mathrm{Lng}_\mathfrak{B}$, $P_\mathfrak{C} = f^{s;\mathfrak{b}}(P_\mathfrak{B})$. If $\mathfrak{b}$ is a cardinal and $\mathfrak{B}$, $\mathfrak{C}$ are $\mathfrak{b}$-models, we say that $\mathfrak{B}$ is *recursively embedded* in $\mathfrak{C}$ by f (relative to $\mathfrak{b}$) if there is a $\mathfrak{b}$-model $\mathfrak{D}$ such that f is an isomorphism from $\mathfrak{B}$ to $\mathfrak{D}$, $\langle \langle 0 \rangle, \{\langle x \rangle: x \in U_0^\mathfrak{D}\} \rangle \in \varDelta_1^{\mathfrak{C},\mathfrak{b}}(\varLambda)$, and for each $P \in \mathrm{Lng}_\mathfrak{D}$, $\langle \tau P, P_\mathfrak{D} \rangle \in \varDelta_1^{\mathfrak{C},\mathfrak{b}}(\varLambda)$. If $R \in R^{s,\mathfrak{b}}A$ and f is a function with domain A, then R^f, or the *image* of R under f, is understood to be $\langle s, f^{s;\mathfrak{b}}(R) \rangle$.

LEMMA 10. Suppose that $\mathfrak{b}$ is a cardinal, $n \neq 0$, $\mathfrak{B}$, $\mathfrak{C}$ are $\mathfrak{b}$-models, and $\mathfrak{B}$ is recursively embedded in $\mathfrak{C}$ by f (relative to $\mathfrak{b}$).

(1) If $R \in \varSigma_n^{\mathfrak{B},\mathfrak{b}}(\varLambda)$, then $R^f \in \varSigma_n^{\mathfrak{C},\mathfrak{b}}(\varLambda)$.

(2) If $R \in C^{\mathfrak{B},\mathfrak{b}}(\varSigma_n^{\mathfrak{B},\mathfrak{b}}(\varLambda))$, then $R^f \in C^{\mathfrak{C},\mathfrak{b}}(\varSigma_n^{\mathfrak{C},\mathfrak{b}}(\varLambda))$.

If P is the predicate $P_{\alpha,s}$, where α is an ordinal and s is the sequence $\langle k_0, ..., k_{n-1} \rangle$ of natural numbers, then the *index sequence* of P is to be

$\langle \alpha, k_0, ..., k_{n-1} \rangle$. We say that a predicate P *alphabetically precedes* a predicate Q if the index sequence of P precedes that of Q in the usual lexicographic ordering of sequences of ordinals.

Suppose that L is a finite set of predicates. By an *L-expression* is understood an expression such that all predicates occurring in it are in L, and the *alphabetic ordering* corresponding to L is that well-ordering relation of which the field is the set of L-expressions that are symbols and which is given by the list

$$Q_0, ..., Q_{n-1}, \in, \neg, \wedge, \vee, [,], \bigvee, v_{0,0}, v_{0,1}, v_{1,0}, v_{0,2}, v_{1,1}, ...,$$

where $L = \{Q_0, ..., Q_{n-1}\}$ and Q_i alphabetically precedes Q_j whenever $i < j < n$. By $\mathfrak{E}(L)$ is understood the *standard model formed by the L-expressions*, that is, that model such that, for some $S, R, C, (1) S = P_{1,\langle 0 \rangle}$, $R = P_{1,\langle 0,0 \rangle}$, $C = P_{1,\langle 0,0,0 \rangle}$, (2) $\mathrm{Lng}_{\mathfrak{E}(L)} = \{S, R, C\}$, (3) $U_0^{\mathfrak{E}(L)}$ is the set of L-expressions, (4) $S_{\mathfrak{E}(L)} = \{\langle \zeta \rangle : \zeta \in U_0^{\mathfrak{E}(L)}$ and ζ is a symbol$\}$, (5) $R_{\mathfrak{E}(L)}$ is the alphabetic ordering corresponding to L, and (6) $C_{\mathfrak{E}(L)}$ is the concatenation function for L-expressions, that is, $\{\langle \zeta, \eta, \zeta \eta \rangle : \zeta, \eta \in U_0^{\mathfrak{E}(L)}\}$.

At this point we must consider Gödel numberings of the L-expressions – that is, biunique correspondences, between the L-expressions and certain natural numbers, under which the images of certain syntactical relations are recursive. In particular, if L is again a finite set of predicates, we understand by an *L-numbering* a function which recursively embeds $\mathfrak{E}(L)$ in $\mathfrak{P}$ (relative to $\aleph_0$).

LEMMA 11. If L is a finite set of predicates, then there exists an L-numbering.

As far as the recursiveness of relations among expressions is concerned, the particular choice of a Gödel numbering is immaterial; it is easily shown by methods of MONTAGUE [1957], Chapter 4, that if g, g' are two L-numberings and R a first-order relation among L-expressions, then $R^g \in \Delta_1^{\mathfrak{P}, \aleph_0}(\Lambda)$ if and only if $R^{g'} \in \Delta_1^{\mathfrak{P}, \aleph_0}(\Lambda)$. The following lemma could be inferred from this fact (which would not otherwise be used in the present paper), but can also be proved directly.

LEMMA 12. Suppose that L is a finite set of predicates, g is an L-numbering, ζ is an L-expression, and R is either

$\langle \langle 0 \rangle, \{\langle \zeta \rangle\} \rangle$,

$\langle \langle 0 \rangle, \{\langle u \rangle : u$ is a variable of type $n\} \rangle$,

$\langle \langle 0 \rangle, \{\langle u \rangle : u$ is a variable$\} \rangle$,

$\langle \langle 0 \rangle, \{\langle \phi \rangle : \phi \in U_0^{\mathfrak{E}(L)}$ and ϕ is a formula$\} \rangle$,

$\langle \langle 0 \rangle, \{\langle \phi \rangle : \phi \in \Phi \cap U_0^{\mathfrak{E}(L)}\} \rangle$,

$\langle \langle 0 \rangle, \{\langle \phi \rangle : \phi \in \Sigma_n \cap U_0^{\mathfrak{E}(L)}\} \rangle$,

$\langle \langle 0, 0 \rangle, \{\langle \eta, \eta \rangle : \eta \in U_0^{\mathfrak{E}(L)}\} \rangle$,

$\langle\langle 0, 0\rangle, \{\langle u, \phi\rangle : \phi \in U_0^{\mathfrak{E}(L)}, \phi$ is a formula, and u is a free variable of $\phi\}\rangle$,
$\langle\langle 0, 0\rangle, \{\langle \eta, \theta\rangle : \eta, \theta \in U_0^{\mathfrak{E}(L)}$ and, for some symbol $\kappa, \eta = \theta\kappa\}\rangle$,
$\langle\langle 0, 0\rangle, \{\langle \eta, \kappa\rangle :$ there exists θ such that $\eta, \theta \in U_0^{\mathfrak{E}(L)}, \kappa$ is a symbol, and $\eta = \theta\kappa\}\rangle$.
Then $R^g \in \Delta_1^{\mathfrak{P}, \aleph_0}(\Lambda)$.

If ζ is any expression, then $\mathrm{Oc}(\zeta)$ is to be the set of expressions occurring in ζ.

LEMMA 13. Suppose that L is a finite set of predicates, g is an L-numbering, and R is the relation $\langle\langle 0, 1\rangle, \{\langle \zeta, \mathrm{Oc}(\zeta)\rangle : \zeta \in U_0^{\mathfrak{E}(L)}\}\rangle$. Then $R^g \in \Delta_1^{\mathfrak{P}, \aleph_0}(\Lambda)$.

11. Enumeration and hierarchy theorems

We assume the following in addition to Conventions 1–4.

CONVENTION 5 (to be assumed through the remainder of this paper). There exist distinct predicates P, Q, R of the respective types $\langle 1, 0\rangle$, $\langle 1, 0\rangle$, $\langle 0\rangle$ and not in $\mathrm{Lng}_{\mathfrak{A}}$ such that f recursively embeds (relative to $\mathfrak{a}$) the model $\mathfrak{P}$ in the model $\mathfrak{A}^\wedge \begin{pmatrix} P & Q & R \\ F & G & H \end{pmatrix}$, where $G = \bar{F}^{\mathfrak{A}, \mathfrak{a}}$ and $H = \overline{\mathsf{C}F}^{\mathfrak{A}, \mathfrak{a}}$.

THEOREM 25. If either (1) $\mathfrak{a} = \aleph_0$ or (2) $\langle\langle 0, 0\rangle, \{\langle x, y\rangle : \langle y\rangle \in (\mathsf{C}F)^*$ and $x \in \breve{F}(y)\}\rangle$ is well-founded, then there exists f satisfying Convention 5.

In connection with condition (2), compare Remark 4 above.

The following lemma is an immediate consequence of Convention 5, Theorem 24, and Lemma 10.

LEMMA 14. If $R \in \Delta_1^{\mathfrak{P}, \aleph_0}(\Lambda)$, then $R^f \in \Delta_1^{\mathfrak{A}, \mathfrak{a}}(\{F, \bar{F}^{\mathfrak{A}, \mathfrak{a}}, \overline{\mathsf{C}F}^{\mathfrak{A}, \mathfrak{a}}\})$.

CONVENTION 6 (also to be assumed through the remainder of this paper). (1) $\mathrm{Lng}_{\mathfrak{A}}$ is finite; (2) g is a $\mathrm{Lng}_{\mathfrak{A}}$-numbering.

By a *special assignment* (in $\mathfrak{A}$, relative to $\mathfrak{a}$) understand an assignment of values to variables (in $\mathfrak{A}$, relative to $\mathfrak{a}$) of which the domain is a finite set of variables of types less than 3. If h is such an assignment, we understand by $h^{(f, g)}$ the set $\{\langle f(g(u)), \{\{h(u)\}\}\rangle_{0,2} : u$ is a variable of type 0 in the domain of $h\} \cup \{\langle f(g(u)), \{h(u)\}\rangle_{0,2} : u$ is a variable of type 1 in the domain of $h\} \cup \{\langle f(g(u)), h(u)\rangle_{0,2} : u$ is a variable of type 2 in the domain of $h\}$.

LEMMA 15. (1) If h is a special assignment (in $\mathfrak{A}$, relative to $\mathfrak{a}$), then $h^{(f, g)} \in U_5^{\mathfrak{A}, \mathfrak{a}}$.
(2) If R is the relation of type $\langle 5, 0\rangle$ of which the extension is $\{\langle h^{(f, g)},$ $f(g(\phi))\rangle : \phi \in \Phi_3, h$ is a special assignment (in $\mathfrak{A}$, relative to $\mathfrak{a}$), and h satisfies ϕ in $\mathfrak{A}$ (relative to $\mathfrak{a}$)$\}$, then $R \in \Delta_1^{\mathfrak{A}, \mathfrak{a}}(\{F, \bar{F}, \overline{\mathsf{C}F}, \bar{I}_0, I_0\})$.

(3) If $n \neq 0$ and R is the relation of type $\langle 5, 0 \rangle$ of which the extension is $\{\langle h^{(f,g)}, f(g(\phi)) \rangle : \phi \in \Sigma_{n,3}, h$ is a special assignment, and h satisfies ϕ in $\mathfrak{A}$ (relative to $\mathfrak{a}$)$\}$, then $R \in \Sigma_n^{\mathfrak{A},\mathfrak{a}}(\{F, \bar{F}, \overline{\mathbb{Q}F}, \bar{I}_0, I_0\})$.

(4) If $n \neq 0$ and R is the relation of type $\langle 5, 0 \rangle$ of which the extension is $\{\langle h^{(f,g)}, f(g(\neg \phi)) \rangle : \phi \in \Sigma_{n,3}, h$ is a special assignment, and h satisfies $\neg \phi$ in $\mathfrak{A}$ (relative to $\mathfrak{a}$)$\}$, then $R \in C^{\mathfrak{A},\mathfrak{a}} (\Sigma_n^{\mathfrak{A},\mathfrak{a}}(\{F, \bar{F}, \overline{\mathbb{Q}F}, I_0, \bar{I}_0\}))$.

(5) If R is the relation of type $\langle 5, 0 \rangle$ of which the extension is $\{\langle h^{(f,g)} f(g(\phi)) \rangle :$ either $\phi \in \Sigma_{n,3}$ or $\phi = \neg \psi$ for some $\psi \in \Sigma_{n,3}, h$ is a special assignment, and h satisfies ϕ in $\mathfrak{A}$ (relative to $\mathfrak{a}$)$\}$, then $R \in \Delta_{n+1}^{\mathfrak{A},\mathfrak{a}} (\{F, \bar{F}, \overline{\mathbb{Q}F}, I_0, \bar{I}_0\})$.

The following three theorems generalize the ordinary enumeration theorems for the Kleene arithmetical hierarchy.

THEOREM 26. If $n \neq 0$, then there is $T \in \Sigma_n(\{F, \bar{F}, \overline{\mathbb{Q}F}, \bar{I}_0, I_0\}) \cap \mathrm{F0}_{k+1}$ such that for each $R \in \Sigma_n(\Lambda) \cap \mathrm{F0}_k$ there exists y in the range of f for which $R^* = \{\langle x_0, ..., x_{k-1} \rangle : \langle y, x_0, ..., x_{k-1} \rangle \in T^*\}$.

THEOREM 27. If $n \neq 0$, then there is $T \in C(\Sigma_n(\{F, \bar{F}, \overline{\mathbb{Q}F}, I_0, \bar{I}_0\})) \cap \mathrm{F0}_{k+1}$ such that for each $R \in C(\Sigma_n(\Lambda)) \cap \mathrm{F0}_k$ there exists y in the range of f for which $R^* = \{\langle x_0, ..., x_{k-1} \rangle : \langle y, x_0, ..., x_{k-1} \rangle \in T^*\}$.

THEOREM 28. If $n \neq 0$, then there is $T \in \Delta_{n+1}(\{F, \bar{F}, \overline{\mathbb{Q}F}, I_0, \bar{I}_0\}) \cap \mathrm{F0}_{k+1}$ such that for each $R \in [\Sigma_n(\Lambda) \cup C(\Sigma_n(\Lambda))] \cap \mathrm{F0}_k$ there exists y in the range of f such that $R^* = \{\langle x_0, ..., x_{k-1} \rangle : \langle y, x_0, ..., x_{k-1} \rangle \in T^*\}$.

By $\mathrm{Sing}^{\mathfrak{A}}$, or the set of *singletons* from $\mathfrak{A}$, is understood the set of all relations of the form $\langle \langle 0 \rangle, \{\langle y \rangle\} \rangle$, where $y \in U_0^{\mathfrak{A}}$. We cannot show that all singletons from $\mathfrak{A}$ are 'recursive' relative to $\mathfrak{A}$ and $\mathfrak{a}$ (that is, in $\Delta_1^{\mathfrak{A},\mathfrak{a}}(\Lambda)$); indeed, this assertion will certainly fail if $U_0^{\mathfrak{A}}$ is uncountable. It is not unnatural, however, to consider also recursiveness *in terms of* the set of singletons from $\mathfrak{A}$, and accordingly a hierarchy $\Sigma_0(\mathrm{Sing}^{\mathfrak{A}}), \Sigma_1(\mathrm{Sing}^{\mathfrak{A}}), ...$ which corresponds to definability in terms of elements. All finite first-order relations connected with $\mathfrak{A}$ and $\mathfrak{a}$ will obviously be in $\Delta_1(\mathrm{Sing}^{\mathfrak{A}})$; further, we have for this hierarchy the following analogues to Theorems 26–28.

THEOREM 29. If $n \neq 0$, then there is $T \in \Sigma_n(\{F, \bar{F}, \overline{\mathbb{Q}F}, I_0, \bar{I}_0\}) \cap \mathrm{F0}_{k+1}$ such that for each $R \in \Sigma_n(\mathrm{Sing}^{\mathfrak{A}}) \cap \mathrm{F0}_k$ there exists $y \in U_0^{\mathfrak{A}}$ for which $R^* = \{\langle x_0, ..., x_{k-1} \rangle : \langle y, x_0, ..., x_{k-1} \rangle \in T^*\}$.

THEOREM 30. If $n \neq 0$, then there is $T \in C(\Sigma_n(\{F, \bar{F}, \overline{\mathbb{Q}F}, I_0, \bar{I}_0\})) \cap \mathrm{F0}_{k+1}$ such that for each $R \in C(\Sigma_n(\mathrm{Sing}^{\mathfrak{A}})) \cap \mathrm{F0}_k$ there exists $y \in U_0^{\mathfrak{A}}$ for which $R^* = \{\langle x_0, ..., x_{k-1} \rangle : \langle y, x_0, ..., x_{k-1} \rangle \in T^*\}$.

THEOREM 31. If $n \neq 0$, then there exists $T \in \Delta_{n+1}(\{F, \bar{F}, \overline{\mathbb{C}F}, I_0, \bar{I}_0\}) \cap \mathrm{F0}_{k+1}$ such that for each $R \in [\Sigma_n(\mathrm{Sing}^{\mathfrak{A}}) \cup C(\Sigma_n(\mathrm{Sing}^{\mathfrak{A}}))] \cap \mathrm{F0}_k$ there exists $y \in U_0^{\mathfrak{A}}$ for which $R^* = \{\langle x_0, \ldots, x_{k-1}\rangle : \langle y, x_0, \ldots, x_{k-1}\rangle \in T^*\}$.

From the enumeration Theorems 29–31 we may infer several *hierarchy theorems* asserting that at each level of our hierarchy first-order relations appear that appear at no lower level; this will happen, according to Theorems 32–34, whether or not our hierarchy is based on the singletons from $\mathfrak{A}$.

THEOREM 32. If $n, k \neq 0$, then $[\Sigma_n(\{F, \bar{F}, \overline{\mathbb{C}F}, I_0, \bar{I}_0\}) - C(\Sigma_n(\mathrm{Sing}^{\mathfrak{A}} \cup \{F, \bar{F}, \overline{\mathbb{C}F}, \bar{I}_0, I_0\}))] \cap \mathrm{F0}_k \neq \Lambda$.

THEOREM 33. If $n, k \neq 0$, then $[C(\Sigma_n(\{F, \bar{F}, \overline{\mathbb{C}F}, \bar{I}_0, I_0\})) - \Sigma_n(\mathrm{Sing}^{\mathfrak{A}} \cup \{F, \bar{F}, \overline{\mathbb{C}F}, \bar{I}_0, I_0\})] \cap \mathrm{F0}_k \neq \Lambda$.

THEOREM 34. If $n, k \neq 0$, then $[\Delta_{n+1}(\{F, \bar{F}, \overline{\mathbb{C}F}, I_0, \bar{I}_0\}) - (\Sigma_n(\mathrm{Sing}^{\mathfrak{A}} \cup \{F, \bar{F}, \overline{\mathbb{C}F}, I_0, \bar{I}_0\}) \cup C(\Sigma_n(\mathrm{Sing}^{\mathfrak{A}} \cup \{F, \bar{F}, \overline{\mathbb{C}F}, I_0, \bar{I}_0\})))] \cap \mathrm{F0}_k \neq \Lambda$.

We can simplify these formulations if we are willing to assume that I_0 is 'recursive' with respect to $\mathfrak{A}$ and $\mathfrak{a}$, and that there exists a 'recursive' F satisfying our conventions.

THEOREM 35. If $n, k \neq 0$ and $F, \mathbb{C}F, I_0 \in \Delta_1(\Lambda)$, then the following sets are nonempty:

$[\Sigma_n(\Lambda) - C(\Sigma_n(\mathrm{Sing}^{\mathfrak{A}}))] \cap \mathrm{F0}_k,$
$[C(\Sigma_n(\Lambda)) - \Sigma_n(\mathrm{Sing}^{\mathfrak{A}})] \cap \mathrm{F0}_k,$
$[\Delta_{n+1}(\Lambda) - (\Sigma_n(\mathrm{Sing}^{\mathfrak{A}}) \cup C(\Sigma_n(\mathrm{Sing}^{\mathfrak{A}})))] \cap \mathrm{F0}_k.$

The hypothesis of Theorem 35 may be weakened: we need only assume that $F, \mathbb{C}F, I_0$ occur somewhere in our hierarchy. In that case, however, we are not permitted to infer the existence of *first-order* relations.

THEOREM 36. If $n \neq 0$ and $F, \mathbb{C}F, I_0 \in \Sigma_m(\Lambda)$ for some m, then the following sets are nonempty:

$\Sigma_n(\Lambda) - C(\Sigma_n(\mathrm{Sing}^{\mathfrak{A}})),$
$C(\Sigma_n(\Lambda)) - \Sigma_n(\mathrm{Sing}^{\mathfrak{A}}),$
$\Delta_{n+1}(\Lambda) - [\Sigma_n(\mathrm{Sing}^{\mathfrak{A}}) \cup C(\Sigma_n(\mathrm{Sing}^{\mathfrak{A}}))].$

Appendix: functionals and operators

By a *relational type* is understood a finite sequence $\langle s_0, \ldots, s_{n-1}\rangle$ such that, for each $i < n$, s_i is either a natural number or a finite nonempty sequence of natural numbers. By a *typed relation* connected with $\mathfrak{A}$ and $\mathfrak{a}$ is now understood a pair $\langle\langle s_0, ..., s_{n-1}\rangle, X\rangle$, where $\langle s_0, ..., s_{n-1}\rangle$ is a relational type and $X \subseteq V_0 \times \cdots \times V_{n-1}$, where, for each $i < n$, either s_i is a natural number and $V_i = U_{s_i}^{\mathfrak{A},\mathfrak{a}}$ or s_i is a finite sequence of natural numbers and $V_i = R_{s_i}^{\mathfrak{A},\mathfrak{a}}$.

If s is any nonempty finite sequence of natural numbers, we add to our symbolism *predicate variables* $Q_{0,s}, ..., Q_{n,s}, ...$ *of type* s. We correspondingly enlarge the class of formulas and the classes $\Sigma_0, \Sigma_1, ...,$ allowing predicate variables of a given type to occur in the same way as predicate constants of that type. (In particular, predicate variables will not be quantified.) We extend the notion 'ϕ defines R in $\mathfrak{A}$ relative to $\mathfrak{a}$' in the natural way so as to apply to all formulas of the larger class; the relations defined may now be of arbitrary relational type. We obtain, of course, a corresponding enlargement of the sets $\Sigma_0^{\mathfrak{A},\mathfrak{a}}(K)$, $\Sigma_1^{\mathfrak{A},\mathfrak{a}}(K), ...$; these sets I propose as giving an appropriate classification not only of relations among individuals but also of relations having relations as relata.

I shall confine myself here to showing how to express the usual notion of a recursive functional in these terms. The situation is complicated, however, by the fact that the literature contains several such notions, differing only in minor respects; it will therefore be necessary to state several equivalences. Here we understand PF to be the set of *partial functions*, that is, the set of functional relations in $F0^{\mathfrak{B}}$, and TF to be the set of *total functions*, that is, the set of relations R in PF for which $(\mathsf{D}R)^* = \{\langle x\rangle : x \in U_0^{\mathfrak{B}}\}$.

Suppose that $\mathscr{F}$ is a relation of type $\langle\langle 0, 0\rangle, 0, 0\rangle$ connected with $\mathfrak{B}$ and $\aleph_0$. Then $\mathscr{F}$ is a recursive partial functional in the sense of SHOENFIELD [1967] if and only if $\mathscr{F}$ is a functional relation and there exists $\mathscr{R} \in \Sigma_1^{\mathfrak{B}, \aleph_0}(\Lambda)$ $\cap R_{\langle\langle 0,0\rangle, 0, 0\rangle}^{\mathfrak{B}, \aleph_0}$ for which $\mathscr{F}^* = \mathscr{R}^* \cap (\mathrm{TF} \times U_0^{\mathfrak{B}} \times U_0^{\mathfrak{B}})$.

Suppose now that $\mathscr{F}$ is a relation of type $\langle\langle 0, 0\rangle, 0\rangle$ connected with $\mathfrak{B}$ and $\aleph_0$, and that $K \subseteq \mathrm{PF}$. Then $\mathscr{F}$ is a partial recursive functional on K, in the sense of POUR-EL [1960], if and only if $\mathscr{F}$ is a functional relation and there exists $\mathscr{R} \in \Sigma_1^{\mathfrak{B}, \aleph_0}(\Lambda) \cap R_{\langle\langle 0,0\rangle, 0\rangle}^{\mathfrak{B}, \aleph_0}$ for which $\mathscr{F}^* = \mathscr{R}^* \cap (K \times U_0^{\mathfrak{B}})$.

Suppose again that $K \subseteq \mathrm{PF}$, but that $\mathscr{F}$ is a relation of type $\langle\langle 0, 0\rangle, \langle 0, 0\rangle\rangle$ connected with $\mathfrak{B}$ and $\aleph_0$. Then $\mathscr{F}$ is a partial recursive operator on K, in the sense of POUR-EL [1960], if and only if $\mathscr{F}$ is a functional relation, $(\mathsf{D}\mathscr{F})^* = \{\langle G\rangle : G \in K\}$, $(\mathsf{G}\mathscr{F})^* \subseteq \{\langle G\rangle : G \in \mathrm{PF}\}$, and there exists $\mathscr{R} \in \Sigma_1^{\mathfrak{B}, \aleph_0}$ $(\Lambda) \cap R_{\langle\langle 0,0\rangle, 0, 0\rangle}^{\mathfrak{B}, \aleph_0}$ for which $\{\langle G, x, y\rangle : G \in K$ and $\langle x, y\rangle \in \mathscr{F}(G)\} = \mathscr{R}^* \cap (K \times U_0^{\mathfrak{B}} \times U_0^{\mathfrak{B}})$.

Suppose again that $\mathscr{F}$ is a relation of type $\langle\langle 0, 0\rangle, \langle 0, 0\rangle\rangle$ connected with $\mathfrak{B}$ and $\aleph_0$. Then $\mathscr{F}$ is a partial recursive functional in the sense of KLEENE [1952] if and only if $\mathscr{F}$ is a partial recursive operator, in the sense of POUR-EL

[1960], on some subset of PF; and $\mathscr{F}$ is a general recursive functional in the sense of KLEENE [1952] if and only if $\mathscr{F}$ is a partial recursive operator, in the sense of POUR-EL [1960], on the set TF, and in addition $(\mathsf{G}\mathscr{F})^* \subseteq \{\langle G\rangle : G\in\mathrm{TF}\}$.

Suppose, however, that $\mathscr{F}$ is a relation of type $\langle\langle 0\rangle, \langle 0\rangle\rangle$ connected with $\mathfrak{P}$. In this case $\mathscr{F}$ is a general recursive functional in the sense of KLEENE [1952] if and only if $\mathscr{F}$ is a functional relation, $(\mathsf{D}\mathscr{F})^* = R_{\langle 0\rangle}^{\mathfrak{P}, \aleph_0}$ and the relation of type $\langle\langle 0\rangle, \langle 0\rangle, 0\rangle$ of which the extension is $\{\langle A, \bar{A}^{\mathfrak{P}, \aleph_0}, x\rangle : A\in R_{\langle 0\rangle}^{\mathfrak{P}, \aleph_0}$ and $\langle x\rangle\in\mathscr{F}(A)\}$ is a member of $\Delta_1^{\mathfrak{P}, \aleph_0}(\Lambda)$.

It is possible also to treat recursive objects of higher types within a natural (though not quite automatic) extension of the present framework.

References

DAVIS, M. [1958], *Computability and unsolvability* (New York, Toronto, London, 1958).

FRAÏSSÉ, R. [1961], Une notion de récursivité relative, in: *Infinitistic methods, Proc. Symp. on Foundations of mathematics in Warsaw, September, 1959* (Oxford, 1961).

KLEENE, S. C. [1952], *Introduction to metamathematics* (New York, 1952).

KREISEL, G. [1965], Model-theoretic invariants: applications to recursive and hyperarithmetic operations, in: *The theory of models* (Amsterdam, 1965).

KRIPKE, S. [1964], Transfinite recursions on admissible ordinals, I, *The Journal of Symbolic Logic* 29 (1964) 161.

KRIPKE, S. [1964a], Transfinite recursions on admissible ordinals, II, ibid., pp. 161–162.

KRIPKE, S. [1964b], Admissible ordinals and the analytic hierarchy, ibid., p. 162.

LACOMBE, D. [1964], Deux généralisations de la notion de la récursivité, *Comptes rendus de l'Académie de Sciences de Paris* 255 (1964) 3141–3143.

LACOMBE, D. [1964a], Deux généralisations de la notion de récursivité relative, ibid., pp. 3410–3413.

LÉVY, A. [1965], A hierarchy of formulas in set theory, *Memoirs of the American Mathematical Society*, no. 57 (1965).

MONTAGUE, R. [1955], Well-founded relations; generalizations of principles of induction and recursion, *Bulletin of the American Mathematical Society* 61 (1955) 442.

MONTAGUE, R. [1957], *Contributions to the axiomatic foundations of set theory*, Dissertation, University of California, Berkeley, 1957.

MONTAGUE, R. [1967], A generalization of recursion theory, *The Journal of Symbolic Logic* 32 (1967) 443–444.

MONTAGUE, R. and VAUGHT, R. L. [1959], Natural models of set theories, *Fundamenta Mathematicae* 47 (1959) 219–242.

POUR-EL, M. Boykan. [1960], A comparison of five 'computable' operators, *Zeitschrift für mathematische Logik und Grundlagen der Mathematik* 325 (1960) 325–339.

SHOENFIELD, J. R. [1967], *Mathematical logic* (Reading (Mass.), Menlo Park, London, Don Mills (Ontario), 1967).

TARSKI, A. and VAUGHT, R. L. [1957], Arithmetical extensions of relational systems, *Compositio Mathematicae* 13 (1957) 81–102.

TRIPODES, P. G. [1963], *On the elimination of recursive definitions*, Master's thesis, University of California, Los Angeles, 1963.

CRAIG'S INTERPOLATION THEOREM
IN SOME EXTENDED SYSTEMS OF LOGIC

A. MOSTOWSKI

Polish Academy of Science, Warsaw, Poland

The aim of this paper is to discuss some extensions of the predicate calculus and the status of the well-known interpolation theorem of Craig in these logics. We shall use some results of the descriptive set theory in order to show that the interpolation theorem fails if certain not too narrow general conditions are satisfied. In the final section we make some observations on the status of Beth theorem in extensions of the predicate logic. Our results in this direction are very incomplete and the subject seems to deserve a further study.

1. General definitions

We consider a logic $\mathscr{L}$ which is an extension of the usual predicate logic $\mathscr{L}_0$ with identity. We use Roman capitals P, Q, R, ..., possibly with indices, as predicates of $\mathscr{L}_0$ and lower case Roman letters as variables of $\mathscr{L}_0$. For each predicate X of $\mathscr{L}_0$ we denote by $q(X)$ its rank i.e. the number of its arguments. Formulae of $\mathscr{L}$ may contain symbols which do not belong to $\mathscr{L}_0$ and the grammatical structure of some formulae of $\mathscr{L}$ may be completely different from that of the formulae of $\mathscr{L}_0$. We assume however that to each formula F of $\mathscr{L}$ corresponds a set $\mathrm{Fr}(F)$ called the set of free variables of F. If $\mathrm{Fr}(F) = 0$, then F is called a sentence. Moreover we assume that the usual logical operations $\neg$, &, (ζ) ($=$ generalization upon the variable ζ of $\mathscr{L}_0$) are performable on formulae of $\mathscr{L}$ and that $\mathrm{Fr}(\neg F) = \mathrm{Fr}(F)$, $\mathrm{Fr}(F \,\&\, G) = \mathrm{Fr}(F) \cup \mathrm{Fr}(G)$, $\mathrm{Fr}((\zeta)F) = \mathrm{Fr}(F) - \{\zeta\}$. Other logical connectives such as $\vee$, $\equiv$ and $(\mathrm{E}\zeta)$ are introduced in the normal way. Furthermore we assume that all formulae of $\mathscr{L}_0$ are formulae of $\mathscr{L}$ and that the operations $\neg$, &, (ζ), Fr have the usual meaning when applied to formulae of $\mathscr{L}_0$.

If all free variables of F are variables of $\mathscr{L}_0$ then F is called normal.

If $M = \langle A, \mathscr{Q} \rangle$ where A is a set and $\mathscr{Q}$ is a function whose domain consists of all predicates and is such that $\mathscr{Q}(X) \subseteq A^{q(X)}$ for each predicate X, then we call M a model. A valuation of a normal formula F in M is a function v which correlates with each free variable of F an element of A.

A ternary relation $\vDash$ is called an adequate satisfaction relation for $\mathscr{L}$ if the following conditions are satisfied for all normal formulae F and models M:

(1) $M \vDash F[v]$ is defined whenever M is a model and v is a valuation of F in M;

(2) If F is a formula of $\mathscr{L}_0$, then $M \vDash F[v]$ holds if and only if v satisfies F in M in the usual sense;

(3) If F is $\neg G$, then $M \vDash F[v]$ is equivalent to non $M \vDash G[v]$ and if F is $G_1 \& G_2$, then $M \vDash F[v]$ is equivalent to $M \vDash G_1[v_1]$ and $M \vDash G_2[v_2]$ where v_i is the restriction of v to the set $\mathrm{Fr}(G_i)$, $i = 1, 2$;

(4) If F is $(\zeta) G$ then $M \vDash F[v]$ is equivalent to the statement: $M \vDash G[v']$ for every valuation v' of G which coincides with v on the free variables of F;

(5) Let F be a normal formula, P a predicate with n arguments and G a normal formula with n free variables. Then there is a normal formula F_0 with the same free variables as F such that the following is satisfied: whenever $M_0 = \langle A, \mathscr{Q}_0 \rangle$ is a model and $M = \langle A, \mathscr{Q} \rangle$ differs from M_0 just by the fact that $\mathscr{Q}(P) = \{x \in A^{\mathrm{Fr}(G)} : M_0 \vDash G(x)\}$ then $M_0 \vDash F_0[y] \equiv M \vDash F[y]$ for every $y \in A^{\mathrm{Fr}(F)}$.

F_0 is said to arise from F by a (functional) substitution of G for P (see CHURCH [1956] p. 192 for the actual construction of F_0 in case of the logic $\mathscr{L}_0$).

Assumption 1. There is an adequate satisfaction relation for $\mathscr{L}$.

One of such relations $\vDash$ will be selected once for all and all subsequent definitions will be relativised to it.

Using the relation $\vDash$ we define two notions with which we shall constantly deal:

If F, G are normal formulae, then we say that G is a consequence of F and write $F \vdash G$ if for every model M and for every valuation v of $F \& G$ in M the condition $M \vDash F[v|\mathrm{Fr}(F)]$ implies $M \vDash G[v|\mathrm{Fr}(G)]$.

If F is a normal formula, then we say that a predicate X does not occur in F if for each pair of models $M = \langle A, \mathscr{Q} \rangle$, $M' = \langle A, \mathscr{Q}' \rangle$ such that $\mathscr{Q}$ coincides with $\mathscr{Q}'$ except possibly on X the equivalence

$$M \vDash F[v] \equiv M' \vDash F[v]$$

holds for every valuation of F in M.

It is obvious that the truth or falsity of $M \vDash F[v]$ depends only on values of

$\mathscr{2}(X)$ for such predicates X as occur in F. We shall henceforth assume that in each formula occur only finitely many predicates.

Writing a formula with displayed predicates e.g. $F(P, Q, ..., S)$ we assume tacitly that $P, Q, ..., S$ are the only predicates which occur in F. The function q whose domain is the set of these predicates and whose value $q(X)$ is the rank of X is called the type of F. A model M of type q is the pair $\langle A, \mathscr{2} \rangle$ where $\mathscr{2}$ has the same domain as q and satisfies $\mathscr{2}(X) \subseteq A^{q(X)}$ for each X in the domain of q. We extend in the obvious way the satisfaction relation $M \vDash F[v]$ so that M may be any model whose type is an extension of the type of F.

2. Examples

We enumerate some well-known examples in which the assumptions made in section 1 are satisfied.

2.1. The weak second order logic $\mathscr{L}_w$ (cf. MOSTOWSKI [1961]). In this logic there are two types of variables: individual variables as in $\mathscr{L}_0$ and set variables which range over finite subsets of the universe.

2.2. The strong second order logic $\mathscr{L}_s$. The syntax of $\mathscr{L}_s$ is the same as that of $\mathscr{L}_w$ but the set variables range over arbitrary subsets of the universe.

There are various intermediate second order logics which all have the same syntax but differ in the range of the set-variables. We quote as examples the following possibilities:

2.3. The range of the set variables is the family of sets of a power $< \alpha$ contained in the universe.

2.4. We can define an increasing sequence $\mathscr{L}_\xi$ of logics as follows: $\mathscr{L}_0$ is $\mathscr{L}_w$; $\mathscr{L}_{\xi+1}$ has the same syntax but the range of set variables consists of those subsets of the universe which are definable in $\mathscr{L}_\xi$; if λ is the limit number, then the range of the set variables is the union of all preceding ranges.

2.5. Logics Q_α. The syntax of the logics Q_α differs from that of $\mathscr{L}_0$ by the presence of a new quantifier Q to be interpreted as: "there are at most α..." (cf. MOSTOWSKI [1957]).

2.6. Infinitary logics $\mathscr{L}_{\alpha,\beta}$ (cf. KARP [1964]) with or without identity.

2.7. Sub-logics of $\mathscr{L}_{\omega_1,\omega}$ obtained by allowing not all denumerable strings of symbols but only some regular ones, e.g. hyper-arithmetic (cf. BARWISE [1967]).

2.8. The full strong second order logic $\mathscr{L}_s^*$ has not only the set variables but for each $n > 0$ has infinitely many variables ranging over n-ary relations. The syntax and semantics of this logic have been described by TARSKI [1956].

2.9. Full weak second order logic $\mathscr{L}_w^*$ has the same syntax as $\mathscr{L}_s^*$ but its second order variables range over finite relations only.

Various intermediate full second order logics can be defined similarly as in 2.3.

3. The interpolation property

We return to the general case of a logic $\mathscr{L}$ satisfying the assumptions set forth in section 1. We shall say that $\mathscr{L}$ has the interpolation property if for arbitrary normal formulae F, G satisfying $F \vdash G$ there is an interpolation formula H such that $F \vdash H \vdash G$, $\mathrm{Fr}(H) \subseteq \mathrm{Fr}(F) \cap \mathrm{Fr}(G)$ and each predicate which occurs in H occurs also in F and in G. Thus $\mathscr{L}$ has the interpolation property if Craig's theorem is valid for normal formulae of $\mathscr{L}$.

We shall show that no $\mathscr{L}$ satisfying suitable assumptions has the interpolation property. The assumptions will be satisfied in cases $\mathscr{L} = \mathscr{L}_w$, $\mathscr{L} = \mathscr{L}_w^*$ and $\mathscr{L} = Q_0$. On the other hand it is known from the literature that Craig's theorem is satisfied for the full strong second order logic, for $\mathscr{L}_{\omega_1, \omega}$ with or without equality (cf. LOPEZ-ESCOBAR [1965]) and for some sublogics of $\mathscr{L}_{\omega_1, \omega}$ which were mentioned in 2.7 (cf. BARWISE [1967]).

For $\mathscr{L} = \mathscr{L}_{\alpha, \beta}$ with equality and with $(\alpha, \beta) \neq (\omega, \omega)$ and $(\alpha, \beta) \neq (\omega_1, \omega)$ Craig's theorem is not satisfied (cf. MALITZ [1965]). To the author's knowledge the problem of its validity for logics 2.3, 2.4 and 2.5 with $\alpha > 0$ is not solved.

We shall now formulate two assumptions from which we shall derive that $\mathscr{L}$ does not have the interpolation property.

Let ω be the set of integers and P_0, Q_0 the relations $x + y = z$, $x = yz$. The standard model of arithmetic is defined as $M_0 = \langle A, \mathscr{A} \rangle$ where $\mathscr{A}$ is a function with domain consisting of one predicate N of rank 1 and two predicates P, Q of rank 3 such that $\mathscr{A}(\mathrm{N}) = \omega$, $\mathscr{A}(\mathrm{P}) = P_0$, $\mathscr{A}(\mathrm{Q}) = Q_0$.

Assumption 2. There is a normal sentence $A = A(\mathrm{N}, \mathrm{P}, \mathrm{Q})$ such that $M_0 \vDash A$ and each model M of the same type as M_0 satisfying $M \vDash A$ is isomorphic to M_0.

3.1. Assumption 2 is satisfied for $\mathscr{L} = \mathscr{L}_w$, $\mathscr{L} = \mathscr{L}_w^*$ and $\mathscr{L} = Q_0$.

PROOF. We take as A the conjunction of sentences which say that N is the whole universe, that it is ordered by the relation $(\mathrm{E}y) \mathrm{P}(x, y, z)$, that it has the first element, that each element has a successor and that each element with the exception of the first has a predecessor. Moreover we include to A the recursive equations for addition and multiplication and the sentence which says that for every x in N there are only finitely many y

which precede x. In case of logics $\mathscr{L}_w$ and $\mathscr{L}_w^*$ this last sentence is

$$(z)\,(EX)\,(x)\,[(x \in X) \equiv (Ey)\,P\,(x, y, z)]$$

and in case of logic Q_0 it is

$$(z)\,(Qx)\,(Ey)\,P\,(x, y, z).$$

We now formulate assumption 3. For $k \in \omega$ and $q \in \omega^k$ we denote by $\mathscr{S}_q$ the k-fold Cartesian product of the spaces $P(\omega^{q(i)})$ where $P(X)$ denotes the family of all subsets of X. We conceive $\mathscr{S}_q$ as a topological space with the usual product topology.

Let $R_0, \ldots, R_{k-1}$ be predicates of ranks $q(0), \ldots, q(k-1)$. For $p = (p_0, \ldots, p_{k-1}) \in \mathscr{S}_q$ we denote by $M_0(p)$ the model $\langle \omega, \mathscr{Q} \rangle$ where $\mathscr{Q}$ has domain $\{N, P, Q, R_0, \ldots, R_{k-1}\}$ and $\mathscr{Q}(N) = \omega$, $\mathscr{Q}(P) = P_0$, $\mathscr{Q}(Q) = Q_0$, $\mathscr{Q}(R_i) = p_i$ for $i < k$.

For every normal sentence F of the same type as $M_0(p)$ we call the set

$$\{p \in \mathscr{S}_q : M_0(p) \vDash F\}$$

the spectrum of F.

Assumption 3. There is a recursive ordinal $\rho < \omega_1^0$ such that for each normal F the spectrum of F is a Borel set of a class $< \rho$.

3.2. Assumption 3 is satisfied for $\mathscr{L} = \mathscr{L}_w$, $\mathscr{L} = \mathscr{L}_w^*$ and $\mathscr{L} = Q_0$.

PROOF. Let F be a (not necessarily normal) formula of $\mathscr{L}_w$ with the free individual variables $x_1, \ldots, x_n$ and set variables $X_1, \ldots, X_m$. Let v and V be functions which correlate with each x_i an integer and with each X_j a finite subset of ω. We prove by induction on the length of F that there is an integer n depending only on F such that for arbitrary v, V the set

$$D_F(v, V) = \{p \in \mathscr{S}_q : M_0(p) \vDash F\,[V, v]\}$$

is Borel of class $< n$. The only case which is not entirely trivial is that when F has the form $(X)G$. In this case $D_F(v, V)$ is an intersection of sets $D_G(v, V')$ where V' ranges over valuations satisfying $V'|\mathrm{Fr}(F) = V$. This intersection is denumerable and hence $D_F(v, V)$ is Borel of class at most $n+1$ if $D_G(v, V')$ was of class $\leqslant n$. The case of logic $\mathscr{L}_w^*$ can be treated similarly.

For $\mathscr{L} = Q_0$ the theorem follows by the remark that to each F of Q_0 there is an F' of $\mathscr{L}_w$ such that the conditions $M \vDash F$ and $M \vDash F'$ are equivalent.

If $X \subseteq \mathscr{S}_q$, then the set $\{y \in P(\omega^{q(0)}): (Ep)\,[(y, p) \in X]\}$ will be called the projection of X. In next sections we shall prove that for arbitrary $\mathscr{L}$ satisfying assumptions 1–3 the following lemma is true:

3.3. There is a q such that $q(0) = 1$ and spectra $X', X'' \subseteq \mathscr{S}_q$ such that their projections T', T'' satisfy $T' = P(\omega) - T''$, $T' \notin \mathbf{G}_\rho$, $T'' \notin \mathbf{F}_\rho$ (cf. section 4 for the definitions of $\mathbf{F}_\rho$ and $\mathbf{G}_\rho$).

Assuming 3.3 we prove

3.4. If $\mathscr{L}$ satisfies assumptions 1–3 then $\mathscr{L}$ does not have the interpolation property.

PROOF. Let X', X'' from 3.3 be spectra of formulae B', B''. We can assume that in $B' \& B''$ occur only the predicates N, P, Q, R, $U_1, ..., U_{k-1}$ where R has 1 argument. Consider the sentences

$$B: A \& B' \& (x) N(x),$$
$$C: A \& (x) N(x) \rightarrow \neg\, C''(N, P, Q, R, U_1', ..., U_{k-1}')$$

where $U_1', ..., U_{k-1}'$ are predicates not occuring in $A \& B' \& B''$ with the same ranks as $U_1, ..., U_{k-1}$ and C'' results from B'' by substituting $U_i'(x_1, ..., x_{q_i})$ for U_i, $i = 1, ..., k-1$. We easily see that for each model M of the same type as $B \& C$ the condition $M \models B$ implies $M \models C$. For assume that $M \models B$. Hence $M \models A$ and we can assume that $M = M_0(r, p, q)$ where $r \in P(\omega)$ is the interpretation of R in M and p, q are interpretations in M of $U_1, ..., U_{k-1}$ and of $U_1', ..., U_{k-1}'$. Since the U_i' do not occur in B we obtain $M_0(r, p) \models B'$ whence $(r, p) \in X'$ and $r \in T'$. Hence $r \notin T''$ and therefore $(r, q) \notin X''$ which proves $M_0(r, q) \models \neg\, C''$. Since the U_i' do not occur in C'' we see that $M_0(r, p, q) \models C$.

Now assume that there is an interpolating sentence $D = D(N, P, Q, R)$ and let Z be the spectrum of D. From $B \vdash D \vdash C$ we obtain similarly as above that $r \in T' \rightarrow r \in Z \rightarrow r \notin T'' \equiv r \in T'$. Hence $Z = T'$ and by assumption 3 T' would be Borel of a class $< \rho$. This contradicts 3.3 since Borel sets whose classes are $< \rho$ belong to $\mathbf{G}_\rho$.

4. Borel sets and universal functions

We assume the basic facts concerning these sets as known (see e.g. KURATOWSKI [1966] p. 345). We define Borel classes by induction as follows: $\mathbf{G}_0$ is the family of open sets, $\mathbf{F}_0$ is the family of closed sets; for any ordinal $\alpha > 0$ we define $\mathbf{F}_\alpha$ as the family of denumerable intersections of sets which belong to $\bigcup_{\beta < \alpha} \mathbf{G}_\beta$ and $\mathbf{G}_\alpha$ as the family of denumerable unions of sets which belong to $\bigcup_{\beta < \alpha} \mathbf{F}_\beta$. For even α our notation agrees with that of Kuratowski; for odd α our $\mathbf{F}_\alpha$ is Kuratowski's $\mathbf{G}_\alpha$ and vice versa. If $X \in \mathbf{F}_\alpha \cup \mathbf{G}_\alpha$ then we say that X is of class α. We shall deal only with Borel classes whose indices are $\leq \rho$ where ρ is a fixed infinite recursive ordinal. Let $\prec$ be a recursive relation which orders ω in type $\rho + 1$; we can assume that 0 is the first and 1 the last element of ω.

Putting

$$\kappa(x, n) = \min\{t : (t \prec n) \& (y)_x(\kappa(y, n) \neq t)\}$$

we obtain a recursive function which enumerates (possibly with repetition) all integers which precede n under the ordering $\prec$. In the above formula $(y)_x$ means "for every y satisfying $y < x$" and the symbol $\min\{\ldots\}$ means 0 if the set $\{\ldots\}$ is void.

We denote by $J(i, j)$ the pairing function $\frac{1}{2}(i+j)(i+j+1)+i$. If $J(i, j) = m$, then we put $Km = i$, $Lm = j$.

Using functions K, L we can establish a one-one correspondence between non-negative integers and finite sequences of such integers. We put

$$K^0 n = n, \qquad K^{i+1} n = KK^i n.$$

To the integer n we let correspond a sequence of length $Ln + 1$ whose terms are

$$[n]_i = LK^{i+1} n \quad \text{for} \quad i < Ln, \qquad [n]_{Ln} = K^{Ln+1} n.$$

Thus e.g. if $Ln = 3$, then the 4 terms of the sequence which corresponds to n are

$$LKn, \qquad LK^2 n, \qquad LK^3 n, \qquad K^4 n.$$

A set $\varphi \subseteq \omega$ will be called a functional set if for any x it contains exactly one integer y such that $Ky = x$. We put $\varphi x = Ly$ and identify φ with the mapping $x \to Ly$. The set of all functional sets will be denoted by $\mathscr{B}$, its elements will always be denoted by small Greek letters.

For any $p \subseteq \omega$ and $i \in \omega$ we put

$$p^{(i)} = \{J(x, Lz) : J(J(i, x), z) \in p\}.$$

If $p = \varphi$ is a functional set then $\varphi^{(i)}$ is the set of pairs $J(x, L\varphi J(i, x))$ and hence is itself a functional set satisfying $\varphi^{(i)} x = L\varphi J(i, x)$. It is easy to see that the formula $\varphi \to (\varphi^{(0)}, \varphi^{(1)}, \ldots)$ defines a mapping of $\mathscr{B}$ onto $\mathscr{B}^\omega$.

In one place in our construction we shall use an enumeration of all primitive recursive functions of two arguments

$$u_0(i, j), \qquad u_1(i, j), \ldots$$

where the function $u(e, i, j) = u_e(i, j)$ is recursive.

We define a sub-base in $P(\omega)$ as the family consisting of the sets

$$\mathscr{U}_j^0 = \{p \in P(\omega) : j \in p\}, \qquad \mathscr{U}_j^1 = \{p \in P(\omega) : j \notin p\}.$$

Each subset of $P(\omega)$ which is simultaneously open and closed can be represented as a finite union of finite intersections of sets belonging to the sub-base. Since every finite set can be represented in the form

$$D_e = \{i < Ke : u_{Le}(i, i) = 0\}$$

we easily see that each closed and open set has the form

$$\mathcal{U}_{f,g,h} = \bigcup_{i \in D_f} \bigcap_{j \in D_i} \mathcal{U}_{u(h,i,j)}^{1 \dotminus u(g,i,j)}$$

where f, g, h are integers. To simplify the notation we put

$$\mathcal{U}_e = \mathcal{U}_{Ke, LKe, LLe}$$

and obtain thus an enumeration of closed and open sets.

The complement of $\mathcal{U}_e$ is also closed and open and thus representable as $\mathcal{U}_{e'}$. We note that whether a point p is or is not an element of $\mathcal{U}_j^i$ depends solely on whether j is or is not an element of p. Hence whether p is or is not an element of $\mathcal{U}_e$ depends solely on whether the integers $u(LLe, i, j)$ with $i \in D_{Ke}, j \in D_i$ are or are not elements of p. Thus if we put

$$N_e = \max \{u(LLe, i, j) : (i < Ke) \& (j < Ki)\}$$

we obtain the result $p \in \mathcal{U}_e \equiv p \cap N_e \in \mathcal{U}_e$. Since all subsets of N_e can be enumerated and their sequence depends recursively on e we see that the relation $\mathcal{U}_{e'} = P(\omega) - \mathcal{U}_e$ is recursive and hence so is the function

$$\bar{e} = \min \{e' : \mathcal{U}_{e'} = P(\omega) - \mathcal{U}_e\}.$$

We thus have for every e

$$\mathcal{U}_{\bar{e}} = P(\omega) - \mathcal{U}_e.$$

We define now by transfinite induction two functions Φ_n, Ψ_n. We put for φ in $\mathcal{B}$

(1) $$\Phi_0(\varphi) = \bigcup_e \mathcal{U}_{\varphi e}, \qquad \Psi_0(\varphi) = \bigcap_e \mathcal{U}_{\overline{\varphi e}}$$

and for $n \neq 0$

(2) $$\Phi_n(\varphi) = \bigcup_k \Psi_{\kappa(K\varphi k, n)}(\varphi^{(k)}),$$

(3) $$\Psi_n(\varphi) = \bigcap_k \Phi_{\kappa(K\varphi k, n)}(\varphi^{(k)}).$$

4.1. For each n in ω and each φ in $\mathcal{B}$

$$\Phi_n(\varphi) = P(\omega) - \Psi_n(\varphi).$$

Proof by transfinite induction on n presents no difficulty.

4.2. The range of Φ_n is the Borel class $\mathbf{G}_\alpha$ where α is the order type of integers preceding n in the ordering $\prec$; similarly the range of Ψ_n is the Borel class $\mathbf{F}_\alpha$.

PROOF. For $n=0$ the theorem is true because $\mathbf{G}_0$ is the class of all open sets and each open set in $P(\omega)$ is a union of a sequence of closed and open sets. Similarly $\mathbf{F}_0$ is the class of closed sets and each such set is the intersection of a sequence of closed and open sets.

Let us assume that $n \neq 0$ and the theorem is valid for integers which precede n. It is obvious from (2) and (3) that $\Phi_n(\varphi)$ is the union and $\Psi_n(\varphi)$ the intersection of sets which belong to $\bigcup_{\beta<\alpha} \mathbf{F}_\beta$ or to $\bigcup_{\beta<\alpha} \mathbf{G}_\beta$. Hence each value of Φ_n belongs to $\mathbf{G}_\alpha$ and each value of Ψ_n belongs to $\mathbf{F}_\alpha$.

Every set $X \in \mathbf{G}_\alpha$ can be represented as $\bigcup_k X_k$ where $X_k \in \mathbf{F}_{\beta k}$ with $\beta k < \alpha$. Let rk be the least integer such that the order type of its predecessor under the ordering $\prec$ is βk. In view of the definition of κ there is an integer sk such that $\kappa(sk, n) = rk$. By assumption

$$X_k = \Psi_{rk}(\psi_k)$$

where $\psi_k \in \mathcal{B}$. Now we determine φ such that $\varphi^{(k)} = \psi_k$ and $K\varphi k = sk$ for each k and obtain $X = \Phi_n(\varphi)$. The proof for Ψ_n is similar.

4.3. There are functions A, B of four arguments $n, q \in \omega$ and $\varphi, \vartheta \in \mathcal{B}$ such that for each $p \in P(\omega)$

(4) $$p \in \Phi_n(\varphi) \equiv (E\vartheta)(q)\left[p \in \mathcal{U}_{A(n, q, \varphi, \vartheta)}\right],$$

(5) $$p \in \Psi_n(\varphi) \equiv (E\vartheta)(q)\left[p \in \mathcal{U}_{B(n, q, \varphi, \vartheta)}\right].$$

PROOF. We define A, B by transfinite induction:

$$A(0, q, \varphi, \vartheta) = \varphi\vartheta 0, \, B(0, q, \varphi, \vartheta) = \overline{\varphi q};$$
$$A(n, q, \varphi, \vartheta) = B(\kappa(K\varphi K\vartheta 0, n), q, \varphi^{(K\vartheta 0)}, L\vartheta),$$
$$B(n, q, \varphi, \vartheta) = A(\kappa(K\varphi Kq, n), Lq, \varphi^{(Kq)}, \vartheta^{(Kq)})$$

(in the last two formulae we assume $n \neq 0$).

Verification of (4) and (5) for $n=0$ is very easy and we omit it.

To verify the formulae (4), (5) for $n \neq 0$ we use the well known rules for quantifiers. Using (2) and the inductive assumption we see that the left hand side of (4) is equivalent to

$$(Ek)(E\vartheta)(q)\left[p \in \mathcal{U}_{B(\kappa(K\varphi k, n), q, \varphi^{(k)}, \vartheta)}\right].$$

We can replace the quantifiers $(Ek)(E\vartheta)$ by a single quantifier $(E\zeta)$ replacing k by $K\zeta 0$ and ϑ by $L\zeta$. Changing ζ into ϑ we obtain the desired formula.

Similarly the left hand side of (5) is equivalent to

$$(k)\,(E\vartheta)\,(q)\,\big[p \in \mathcal{U}_{A(\kappa(K\varphi k,\,n),\,q,\,\varphi^{(k)},\,\vartheta)}\big].$$

We can replace the quantifiers $(k)\,(E\vartheta)\,(q)$ by $(E\zeta)\,(r)$ replacing k by Kr, q by Lr and ϑ by $\zeta^{(Kr)}$. Changing ζ into ϑ and r into q we obtain the result.

The inductive equations for the functions A, B can be written simpler if we introduce some abbreviations:

Let $\mathcal{X} = \mathcal{B} \times \mathcal{B} \times \omega$; thus the elements of $\mathcal{X}$ are triples (φ, ϑ, q) and A, B are functions of an integer n and of a point p ranging over $\mathcal{X}$.

We define two mappings f_1, f_2 of $\mathcal{X}$ into $\mathcal{X}$:

$$f_1(p) = (\varphi^{(K\vartheta 0)}, L\vartheta, q), \qquad f_2(p) = (\varphi^{(Kq)}, \vartheta^{(Kq)}, Lq)$$

and two functions κ_1, κ_2:

$$\kappa_1(n, p) = \kappa(K\varphi K\vartheta 0, n), \qquad \kappa_2(n, p) = \kappa(K\varphi Kq, n).$$

The recursion equations for the functions A, B can now be written thus: if $n \neq 0$, then

(6)
$$\begin{aligned} A(n, p) &= B(\kappa_1(n, p), f_1(p)), \\ B(n, p) &= A(\kappa_2(n, p), f_2(p)); \end{aligned}$$

if $n = 0$, then

(7) $$A(0, p) = U_1 p = \varphi\vartheta 0, \qquad B(0, p) = U_2 p = \varphi q.$$

5. Properties of spectra

Our aim is to prove that the relations $r = A(n, q, \varphi, \vartheta)$, $r = B(n, q, \varphi, \vartheta)$ are spectra. To establish this fact we need some general theorems about spectra. For the most part they are almost obvious and we only sketch their proofs.

5.1. Boolean operations performed on spectra yield spectra. The same holds true for the operations of identifying or permuting coordinates and for the operation of adding a "dummy" coordinate.

5.2. If $S \subseteq \mathcal{X} \times \omega$ is a spectrum, then so is the set $\{p \in \mathcal{X} : (x)[(p, x) \in S]\}$.

In 5.2. $\mathcal{X}$ may be any Cartesian product of finitely many spaces $[P(\omega)]^k$ and any finite number of copies of ω.

5.3. Every arithmetical relation is a spectrum.

5.4. The set $\{(p, x) \in P(\omega) \times \omega : x \in p\}$ is a spectrum.

5.5. The set $\mathcal{B}$ of functional sets is a spectrum.

5.6. The set $\{(p, r) \in P(\omega) \times \omega : p \in \mathcal{U}_r\}$ is a spectrum.

To prove 5.3 we use 5.1 and 5.2 and the remark that the relations $x = y + z$, $x = y$. z are spectra. The set mentioned in 5.4 is the spectrum of the formula Ux. 5.5 is established by using 5.1–5.3 and remarking that a point p is a functional set if and only if it satisfies the condition $(x)(E!y)[(y \epsilon p) \& (Ky = x)]$. Finally to prove 5.6 we remark that the set

$$ W = \{\langle p, i, j \rangle \in P(\omega) \times \{0, 1\} \times \omega : p \in \mathcal{U}_j^i \} $$

is a spectrum and the condition $p \in \mathcal{U}_r$ is obtained from the condition $\langle p, i, j \rangle \in W$ and the arithmetical relation $i \in D_e$ by means of the operations 5.1, 5.2.

The question arises whether counter-images of spectra are spectra. A partial answer is given in the next theorem:

5.7. Let $f : P(\omega) \rightarrow P(\omega)$ be a function satisfying the following condition: There is a normal formula $G = G(N, P, Q, U, x)$ with one free variable such that for every $p \in P(\omega)$ and every n in ω the equivalence holds:

$$ M_0(p) \vDash G[n] \equiv [n \epsilon f(p)] . $$

Then the counter-image $f^{-1}(S)$ of any spectrum $S \subseteq P(\omega)$ is a spectrum.

PROOF. Let S be the spectrum of $F = F(N, P, Q, U)$. Let F_0 arise from F by a substitution of G for U (cf. (1.5)) and let S_0 be the spectrum of F_0. Using (1.5) we obtain

$$ M_0(f(p)) \vDash F \equiv M_0(p) \vDash F_0 $$

and hence $f(p) \in S \equiv p \in S_0$, i.e. $f^{-1}(S) = S_0$.

As a corollary from 5.7 we obtain

5.8. If $S \subseteq \mathcal{X} \times P(\omega) \times \omega$ is a spectrum, then so is the set

$$ \{(p, \varphi, q) \in \mathcal{X} \times \mathcal{B} \times \omega : (p, \varphi^{(q)}, q) \in S\} . $$

To see this we merely notice that the function

$$ f : (p, \varphi, q) \rightarrow (p, \varphi^{(q)}, q) $$

satisfies the assumptions of 5.7.

Let us call a mapping f representable if its graph $\{(p, p') : p' = f(p)\}$ is a spectrum.

5.9. Functions $U_1, U_2, f_1, f_2, \kappa_1, \kappa_2$ defined at the end of section 4 are representable.

PROOF. We let $\mathcal{X} = \mathcal{B} \times \mathcal{B} \times \omega$ and denote points of $\mathcal{X}$ by $p = (\varphi, \vartheta, q)$ adding indices whenever necessary.

(a) U_1 is a mapping of $\mathcal{X}$ into ω given by $U_1 p = \varphi \vartheta 0$. Hence (p, k) belongs to the graph of U_1 if and only if $(Em)\{[J(0, m)\in\vartheta]\&[J(m, k)\in\varphi]\}$. It follows by 5.3, 5.4 and 5.1 that this set is a spectrum.

(b) The proof for U_2 is similar.

(c) The graph of κ_1 consists of points $(p, k)\in\mathcal{X}\times\omega$ which satisfy the condition

$$(Em)\,[(m = K\varphi K\vartheta 0)\,\&\,(k = \kappa(m, n))]\,.$$

We show similarly as in (a) that the relation $m = K\varphi K\vartheta 0$ defines a spectrum and hence in view of 5.2 the graph of κ_1 is a spectrum.

(d) The proof for κ_2 is similar.

(e) The graph of f_1 consists of points $(\varphi, \vartheta, q, \varphi', \vartheta', q')$ for which the following conditions are satisfied

$$(x)\,(Ey)\,[(y = J(K\vartheta 0, x))\,\&\,(\varphi'x = L\varphi y)]\,,$$
$$(x)\,[\vartheta'x = L\vartheta x]\,,\qquad q' = q\,.$$

Using 5.1–5.4 we easily infer that the graph of f_1 is a spectrum.

(f) The proof for f_2 is similar.

6. Proof of 3.3

The essential step in this proof is the following result:

6.1. The sets

$$\{(r, n, p)\in\omega^2 \times \mathcal{X}: r = A(n, p)\}\,,$$
$$\{(r, n, p)\in\omega^2 \times \mathcal{X}: r = B(n, p)\}$$

are projections of spectra.

PROOF. We shall deal only with the function A. In order to obtain the result stated in the theorem we must describe the process of calculating the value of A for given arguments n, p. The inductive equations (4.6) show that $A(n, p)$ is equal to $B(n_1, p_1)$ where n_1, p_1 are explicitly determined by n, p. The value of $B(n_1, p_1)$ is equal to $A(n_2, p_2)$ and so on. The sequence of points (n_i, p_i) must terminate after a finite number of steps with a term $(0, p_{k-1})$ because $n_{i+1} \prec n_i$. Thus according to (4.7) $A(n, p) = A(0, p_{k-1}) = U_1 p_{k-1}$ if $k-1$ is even and $A(n, p) = B(0, p_{k-1}) = U_2 p_{k-1}$ if $k-1$ is odd. We write briefly $A(n, p) = U_{\pi(k-1)} p_{k-1}$ where generally $\pi(j)$ (the parity of j) is equal to 1 for even j and to 2 for odd j.

It follows from these remarks that $r = A(n, p)$ if and only if there is an integer $k \geqslant 1$ and two sequences

$$n_0, n_1, \ldots, n_{k-1}, p_0, p_1, \ldots, p_{k-1}$$

both of length k the first consisting of integers and the second of elements of $\mathscr{X} = \mathscr{B} \times \mathscr{B} \times \omega$ such that

$$n_0 = n, \qquad p_0 = p,$$
$$n_{k-1} = 0, \qquad n_j \neq 0 \quad \text{for} \quad j < k-1,$$
$$r = U_{\pi(k-1)} p_{k-1}$$
$$(j)_{k-1} \{[n_{j+1} = \kappa_{\pi j}(n_j, p_j)] \& [p_{j+1} = f_{\pi j}(n_j, p_j)]\}.$$

We can replace the sequence n_j by the number $\tilde{n}$ corresponding to this sequence. Thus $L\tilde{n} = k-1$ (cf. p. 93). The terms n_j are then to be replaced by $[n]_j$ (see p. 93). The sequence of points p_j, which is really the sequence of triples $(\varphi_j, \vartheta_j, q_j)$, can be replaced by two functions $\tilde{\varphi}, \tilde{\vartheta}$ and the number $\tilde{q}$ corresponding to the sequence $q_0, \ldots, q_{k-1}$. We must everywhere replace $p_j = (\varphi_j, \vartheta_j, q_j)$ by $\tilde{p}_j = (\tilde{\varphi}^{(j)}, \tilde{\vartheta}^{(j)}, [\tilde{q}]_j)$. In this way we see that $r = A(n, p) = A(n, \varphi, \vartheta, q)$ if and only if there are two functions $\tilde{\varphi}, \tilde{\vartheta} \in \mathscr{B}$, an integer $k \geq 1$ and two integers $\tilde{n}, \tilde{q}$ such that the following conditions are satisfied:

(1) $$L\tilde{n} = L\tilde{q} = k - 1;$$

(2) $$([\tilde{n}]_0 = n) \& (x) \{[\tilde{\varphi}^{(0)} x = \varphi x] \& [\tilde{\vartheta}^{(0)} x = \vartheta x] \& ([\tilde{q}]_0 = q)\};$$

(3) $$([\tilde{n}]_{k-1} = 0) \& (j)_{k-1} ([\tilde{n}]_j \neq 0);$$

(4) $$r = U_{\pi(k-1)} \tilde{p}_{k-1};$$

(5) $$(j)_{k-1} \{[[\tilde{n}]_{j+1} = \kappa_{\pi j}([\tilde{n}]_j, \tilde{p}_j)] \& [\tilde{p}_{j+1} = f_{\pi j}([\tilde{n}]_j, \tilde{p}_j)]\}.$$

We can write this equivalence as

$$[r = A(n, p)] \equiv (E\tilde{\varphi}, \tilde{\vartheta})(Ek, \tilde{n}, \tilde{q})_\omega [(\tilde{\varphi} \in \mathscr{B}) \& (\tilde{\vartheta} \in \mathscr{B}) \&$$
$$(k \geq 1) \& (1) \& \ldots \& (5)].$$

In order to prove the theorem we have now to examine the 8 components of the conjunction in square brackets of the above formula and to show that the sets of points

$$(\tilde{\varphi}, \tilde{\vartheta}, \varphi, \vartheta, k, \tilde{q}, \tilde{n}, q, n, r) \in [P(\omega)]^4 \times \omega^6$$

which satisfy these components are spectra. For the first two components this results from the fact that $\mathscr{B}$ is a spectrum. For the components $k \geq 1$, (1) and (3) we obtain the result from the fact that all arithmetical relations are spectra (see 5.3). For the component (2) the result follows from 5.3 and the remark that for $\varphi, \tilde{\varphi} \in \mathscr{B}$ the condition $\varphi x = \tilde{\varphi}^{(0)} x$ is equivalent to

$$(Ez)[(J(x, Lz) \in \varphi) \& (J(J(0, x), z) \in \tilde{\varphi})].$$

This remark shows that the condition

$$(\varphi \in \mathscr{B}) \,\&\, (\tilde{\varphi} \in \mathscr{B}) \,\&\, (\varphi x = \tilde{\varphi}^{(0)} x)$$

determines a spectrum (see 5.3, 5.4). The same is true of the condition obtained from the above by prefixing it with the quantifier (x), cf. 5.2. We deal in the same way with other conjuncts in (2).

Let us now consider the component (4). This component is equivalent to an alternation $[(k-1 \text{ is even}) \,\&\, (r = U_1 \tilde{p}_{k-1})] \vee [(k-1 \text{ is odd}) \,\&\, (r = U_2 \tilde{p}_{k-1})]$. It will be sufficient to consider only the formula $r = U_1 \tilde{p}_{k-1}$.

According to 5.9 the set of quintuples $\langle r, \alpha, \beta, s, k \rangle$ where $r, s, k \in \omega$ and $\alpha, \beta \in \mathscr{B}$ such that $r = U_1(\alpha, \beta, s)$ is a spectrum. Using 5.8 twice we obtain the result that the set of quintuples $\langle r, \tilde{\varphi}, \tilde{\mathfrak{J}}, s, k \rangle$ such that $r = U_1(\tilde{\varphi}^{(k-1)}, \tilde{\mathfrak{J}}^{(k-1)}, s)$ is a spectrum. Replacing s by any arithmetical function of $\tilde{q}$, k we still have a spectrum. Hence the set of quintuples $\langle r, \tilde{\varphi}, \tilde{\mathfrak{J}}, q, k \rangle$ such that $r = U_1(\tilde{\varphi}^{(k-1)}, \tilde{\mathfrak{J}}^{(k-1)}, [\tilde{q}]_{k-1}) = U_1 \tilde{p}_{k-1}$ is a spectrum. We can still add superfluous ("dummy") coordinates φ, $\mathfrak{J}$, q, n and obtain the required result.

Finally we consider the last component (5). Similarly as in the previous case it is sufficient to discuss only the formulae

$$[\tilde{n}]_{j+1} = \kappa_i([\tilde{n}]_j, \tilde{p}_j) \quad \text{and} \quad \tilde{p}_{j+1} = f_i([\tilde{n}]_j, \tilde{p}_j)$$

where $i = 1$ or 2. We discuss only the second formula. The set of points $\langle \alpha, \beta, \gamma, \delta, x, y, z \rangle \in \mathscr{B}^4 \times \omega^3$ for which

(6) $(\alpha, \beta, x) = f_i(z, (\gamma, \delta, y))$

is a spectrum (cf. 5.9 (e)). We put $\alpha = \tilde{\varphi}^{(j+1)}$, $\beta = \tilde{\mathfrak{J}}^{(j+1)}$, $x = [\tilde{q}]_{j+1}$, $z = [\tilde{n}]_j$, $\gamma = \psi^{(h)}$, $\delta = \zeta^{(h)}$, $y = [s]_h$ and infer, using 5.8, that the set of points $\langle \tilde{\varphi}, \tilde{\mathfrak{J}}, \psi, \zeta, \tilde{q}, \tilde{n}, j, h, s \rangle$ for which (6) with the above substitutions is satisfied is a spectrum. We identify ψ with $\tilde{\varphi}$, ζ with $\tilde{\mathfrak{J}}$, h with j and s with $\tilde{q}$ and infer that the set of points

$$\langle \tilde{\varphi}, \tilde{\mathfrak{J}}, \tilde{n}, \tilde{q}, j \rangle$$

satisfying the equation $\tilde{p}_{j+1} = f_i([\tilde{n}]_j, \tilde{p}_j)$ is a spectrum. Adding the dummy variables establishes the required result. We notice, although this remark is by no means essential, that the relations $r = A(n, p)$ and $r = B(n, p)$ have been defined by formulae starting with just two quantifiers ranging over $\mathscr{B}$ and that we could easily reduce their number to 1.

PROOF of 3.3. According to 4.2. the range of the function Φ_1 is the Borel class $\mathbf{G}_\rho$. Hence by the diagonal theorem (KURATOWSKI [1966] p. 372)

the set
$$T' = \{\varphi \in \mathscr{B} : \varphi \notin \Phi_1(\varphi)\}$$
is not an element of $\mathbf{G}_\rho$.

Similarly the set
$$T'' = \{\varphi \in \mathscr{B} : \varphi \notin \Psi_1(\varphi)\}$$
is not an element of $\mathbf{F}_\rho$. Since, by 4.1,

$$\varphi \notin \Phi_1(\varphi) \equiv \varphi \in \Psi_1(\varphi),$$

the sets T', T'' satisfy the equation $T' = P(\omega) - T''$. It remains to show that T', T'' are projections of spectra. It will do to prove this for T'.

By 4.1 and 4.3

$$(\varphi \in T') \equiv [(\varphi \in \mathscr{B}) \& (\varphi \in \Psi_1(\varphi))] \equiv$$
$$(E\vartheta)(q)(Er)[(\varphi \in \mathscr{B}) \& (r = B(1, q, \varphi, \vartheta)) \& (\varphi \in \mathscr{U}_r)].$$

By 6.1 the condition in square brackets determines a projection of a spectrum. Thus (see the remark at the end of 6.1)

$$\varphi \in T' \equiv (E\vartheta)(q)(Er)(E\tilde{\varphi}, \tilde{\vartheta})[\langle \varphi, \vartheta, \tilde{\varphi}, \tilde{\vartheta}, r, q \rangle \in S]$$

where S is a spectrum. By the usual formal transformations we replace the right-hand side of this equivalence by

$$(E\vartheta, \xi, \eta, \zeta)(q)[\langle \varphi, \vartheta, \xi^{(q)}, \eta^{(q)}, \zeta q, q \rangle \in S].$$

According to 5.7 and 5.8 the set of points $\langle \varphi, \vartheta, \xi, \eta, \zeta, q \rangle$ which satisfy the condition in square brackets in the last formula is a spectrum. Hence T' is a projection of a spectrum.

Theorem 3.3 in thus proved. This establishes also theorem 3.4 which we proved on the basis of 3.3.

7. The Beth property

In this section we treat briefly another property of extensions of logic $\mathscr{L}_0$. For obvious reasons we shall call it the Beth property.

Let $\mathscr{L}$ be a logic satisfying the assumptions set forth in section 1, let F be a sentence of $\mathscr{L}$, R and R' two predicates with the same rank, say n, such that R' does not occur in F. We denote by F' the sentence obtained from F by a substitution of the formula $R'(x_1, ..., x_n)$ for the predicate R (cf. 1.5).

We say that $\mathscr{L}$ has the Beth property if for arbitrary F, R, R' as specified above the condition

(1) $F \& F' \vdash [R(x_1, ..., x_n) \equiv R'(x_1, ..., x_n)]$

implies the existence of a formula G such that (i) all predicates occurring in G occur in F, (ii) the predicate R does not occur in G, (iii) the free variables of G are just $x_1, ..., x_n$ and

(2) $F \vdash [R(x_1, ..., x_n) \equiv G]$.

7.1. The full strong second order logic has the Beth property.

PROOF. If (1) is valid, then we define G as

$$(EX)\,[F_1 \& X(x_1, ..., x_n)]$$

where F_1 results from F by a substitution of $X(x_1, ..., x_n)$ for R.

7.2. The weak second order logic does not have the Beth property.

We shall give only a sketch of the proof. First of all we define arithmetically a numbering of finite sequences of finite sets of integers and a Gödel numbering of formulae in which only the predicates N, P, Q occur. We consider the ternary relation Stsf: The sequence number x of integers and the sequence number y of finite sets satisfy the formula number z in the model M_0. It is not difficult to construct a formula $F(N, P, Q, R)$ which defines implicitly the relation R in the sense that if $M \vDash F$ then the interpretations of N, P, Q form a model isomorphic to M_0 and the interpretation of R is isomorphic to Stsf. For this formula F the condition (1) is satisfied but (2) is not as we can easily show using Tarski's theorem on undefinability of truth (TARSKI [1956]).

In a similar way we can show that neither the logic Q_0 nor $\mathscr{L}_w^*$ have Beth property. However no general criteria seem to be known for deciding whether a logic has the Beth property.

To conclude we remark that Tarski suggested the following proof that $\mathscr{L}_w$ does not have the Beth property.

Let $A(N, S)$ be a formula of $\mathscr{L}_w$ whose all models are isomorphic to $\langle \omega, \mathscr{Q} \rangle$ where $\mathscr{Q}(N) = \omega$ and $\mathscr{Q}(S)$ is the "less than" relation. If $F(N, S, P)$ and $G(N, S, P, Q)$ are inductive definitions of addition and multiplication then obviously

$$A(N, S) \& F(N, S, P) \& F(N, S, P') \vdash [P(x, y, z) \equiv P'(x, y, z)]$$

and

$$A(N, S) \& F(N, S, P) \& G(N, S, P, Q) \& G(N, S, P, Q') \vdash$$
$$[Q(x, y, z) \equiv Q'(x, y, z)].$$

If $\mathscr{L}_w$ had the Beth property there would exist formulae $H(N, S, x, y, z)$ and $K(N, S, x, y, z)$ such that

$$A(N, S) \vdash F^*(N, S, H) \& G^*(N, S, H, K)$$

where F^*, G^* are obtained from F, G by substituting H, K for P, Q. But then the full arithmetic would be derivable from $A(N, S)$ and the set of those sentences $T(N, S)$ of $\mathscr{L}_w$ containing only the predicates N, S which are valid in $\langle \omega, \mathscr{2} \rangle$ would be undecidable. This contradicts the well-known result of BÜCHI [1960].

A similar proof using the undecidability of arithmetic and the decidability of the theory of successor relation based on $\mathscr{L}_s$ (Büchi) shows that $\mathscr{L}_s$ does not have the Beth property.

References

BÜCHI, J.R., Weak second order arithmetic and finite automata, Z. Math. Logik und Grundl. Math. **8** (1960) 66–92.

BARWISE, K.J., Infinitary logic and admissible sets, unpublished thesis, Berkeley, California, 1967.

CHURCH, A., Introduction to mathematical logic, Vol. I (Princeton, Princeton University Press, 1956).

KARP, C., Languages with expressions of infinite length (Amsterdam, North-Holland Publ. Co, 1964).

KURATOWSKI, K., Topology, Vol. I (New York, Academic Press, and Warszawa, PWN, 1966).

LOPEZ-ESCOBAR, E.G.K., An interpolation theorem for denumerably long formulas, Fund. Math. **57** (1965) 253–272.

MALITZ, J., Problems in the model theory of infinite languages, unpublished thesis, Berkeley, California, 1965.

MOSTOWSKI, A., On a generalization of quantifiers, Fund. Math. **44** (1957) 12–36.

MOSTOWSKI, A., Concerning the problem of axiomatizability of the field of real numbers in the weak second order logic. Essays on the foundations of mathematics (Jerusalem, 1961).

TARSKI, A., The concept of truth in formalized languages. Logic, semantics, meta-mathematics (Clarendon Press, Oxford, 1956).

FORMALIZATION PRINCIPLE

G. TAKEUTI*

Institute for Advanced Study, Princeton, N.J., USA

A set theory T (not necessarily first order) is said to be "sufficiently strong" if T is true and the theory consisting of all true first order set theoretic sentences can be interpreted in T. Similarly, a set theory T on the class L of all constructible sets is said to be "sufficiently strong" if T is true on L and the theory consisting of all true first order sentences on L can be interpreted in T.

First, let us consider giving principles which generate a sufficiently strong set theory. Now imagine the following situation. A basic theory which we start with and several definable (in set theory) principles by which we get a new stronger true theory from a true theory are given. Then the closure of these principles is easily proved to be not sufficiently strong for the following reason. We can formalize the closure in the set theory and truth theory implies that this closure is not sufficiently strong. Therefore we know that they must be highly undefinable if there exist principles to generate a sufficiently strong set theory. Then the question is this. Is there any meaningful principle among these highly undefinable principles? In order to consider this question, we shall examine the above undefinability proof of our possible principles. In this proof, we assume the following principle.

PRINCIPLE: We know practically how to formalize a given well-defined theory.

This is rather well-supported heuristically: It might be a most successful and most basic practical principle of modern logic. Let us consider the use of this principle as a device to create new systems.

In order to be precise, we now state formal terminology. $\ulcorner \psi \urcorner$ is understood to be a Gödel number of a formula ψ. If S is a system, then "S is formalizable"

---

* Work partially supported by National Science Foundation grant GP-6132.

means that the notion $\mathrm{Prov}_S(\ulcorner\psi\urcorner)$ "ψ is provable in S" is definable. Let us suppose that a method, say E, to expand a system S to a new system is defined by the term of Prov_S. Now start with a basic system S_0 and apply E to all systems which are obtained by E from S_0. We obtain $E(S_0)$, $E(E(S_0))$, ... and $S_\omega = \bigcup_{n<\omega} E^n(S_0)$, where $E^n(S_0)$ means a system obtained from S_0 by n times application of E. We can again repeat this method to S_ω instead of S_0 and so on.

Obviously we cannot formalize the system thus obtained just because we have no a priori definition of Prov_S, though we are confident that we can find an appropriate definition of Prov_S for each definite individual system S. I think that such a principle E is a meaningful but undefinable principle.

Now we shall check the notion Prov_S. Our experience shows that there are many adequate definitions of Prov_S. What is the criterion of Prov_S? One necessary condition for Prov_S is the following.

Condition for Prov_S: $\mathrm{Prov}_S(\ulcorner\psi\urcorner)\leftrightarrow S\vdash\psi$.

Is this criterion enough to characterize Prov_S? The answer is yes. However, in order to know that Prov_S satisfies this condition, we have to know for what formulas ψ $\mathrm{Prov}_S(\ulcorner\psi\urcorner)$ and/or $S\vdash\psi$ is true. In many cases, we cannot decide $\mathrm{Prov}_S(\ulcorner\psi\urcorner)$ in S. Therefore the adequacy of a certain definition of Prov_S seems to be judged mainly by our mathematical intuition on how S is constructed. The difficulty in considering Prov_S is, we do not know anything more than the condition. What we know is that there will be one definition of Prov_S which will be chosen by our mathematical intuition.

Our formalization principle roughly means the following principle.

Formalization principle: If we have created a theory S and $\{\ulcorner\psi\urcorner | S\vdash\psi\}$ is definable in our language, then we can gain a right formalization Prov_S for S.

The important thing to do is to find a good property of a right formalization. In this paper, we are however interested merely in the sequence of axiom systems S_β such that a) $S_{\beta+1}=E(S_\beta)$ and b) $S_\alpha=\bigcup_{\beta<\alpha} S_\beta$ if α is a limit ordinal. (This kind of sequence was considered in FEFERMAN [1962] for arithmetic and in SWARD [1967] for first order set theories.) Our S_0 has ω-rule and our language is a transfinite type theory. Our E is the following.

Reflection principle: Expand S by adding $\mathrm{Prov}_S(\ulcorner\psi\urcorner)$ if $S\vdash\psi$, or $\neg\,\mathrm{Prov}_S(\ulcorner\psi\urcorner)$ otherwise for all sentences ψ.

We shall prove the following.

1) For every definable well-ordering $\prec$ of ω, there exists a definable sequence of axiom systems $S_\beta (\beta < \alpha_0)$ satisfying a) and b), where α_0 is the order type of $\prec$.

2) For every definable sequence of axiom systems $S_\beta (\beta < \alpha_0)$ satisfying a) and b), there exists a provable well-ordering $\prec$ of ω in $S_{\beta+1}$ such that the order type of $\prec$ is β. (A precise definition of a provable well-ordering in a system S will be given later.)

3) There exists a definable sequence of axiom systems $S_\beta (\beta \leqslant \alpha_0)$ satisfying a) and b) such that S_{α_0} is sufficiently strong on L.

The author believes that our mysterious ability of right formalization of a system S has some kind of uniform constructive nature from our knowledge on how S is constructed. Therefore the above-mentioned results make him believe that if we apply only right formalization, we can keep constructing axiom systems S_β very far so that we can reach a sufficiently strong theory on L. However he cannot express this feeling mathematically at this moment. Thus he merely conjectures that we can formulate such a property of a right formalization. If this can be done, then we may say the following.

Suppose that there exists an infinite mind M such that he can do the following.

1) He knows the system S_0 which will be defined later.

2) If he once gains a system S, then he knows what is provable in S. Therefore he can apply the reflection principle.

3) If he reaches a system S and S is definable in our language, then he knows at least one right formalization of Prov_S.

Then M creates a sufficiently strong set theory on L.

Gödel has presented a problem in GÖDEL [1965] of how to collect together all axioms of infinity in some non-constructive way. We think that this will be done by investigation on the formalization principle.

1. The language

Our language is similar to the transfinite type theory in TAKEUTI [to appear] but the intended interpretation will be different from the transfinite type theory there.

We start with the first order language of set theory which consists of individual constants 0, 1, 2, ... for all natural numbers, numerical variables $i_1, i_2, i_3, \ldots$ which range over all natural numbers, set variables $x_1, x_2, x_3, \ldots,$ one predicate constant $\in$, and logical symbols. (As a usually abbreviated notation, we use $\alpha, \beta, \gamma, \ldots$ as variables for ordinal numbers.) We define typed variables and extend the notion of formula inductively by introducing the "degrees" of (typed) variables and formulas. We define the degree of a first order variable a (denoted $\deg(a)$) to be 0; and the degree of a first order formula ψ (denoted $\deg(\psi)$) to be 0. For every formula (of first order) $A(i_1, i_2)$ having only numerical variables as free variables, variables of type A are introduced and denoted $X_1^A, X_2^A, X_3^A, \ldots$. We define $\deg(X^A)$ to be 1 and extend the notion of formula by adjoining variables of degree 1 and quantifiers with respect to the typed variables to our starting language. The degree of any formula in this language is defined to be the maximum of the degrees of the variables in it. Assume that we have introduced variables of degree n and formulas of degree n in this way. Then for every formula $A(i_1, i_2)$ of degree n having only numerical variables as free variables, we introduce variables of type A. The degree of a variable of type A where $A(i_1, i_2)$ is of degree n is defined to be $n+1$. The notion of formulas is extended by adjoining variables of degree $n+1$ and quantifiers with respect to variables of degree $n+1$ to the language. The degree of a formula is defined to be the maximum of the degrees of variables in it.

The intended interpretation of X^A is this. If A is a well-ordering of ω and the order type of A is α, then X^A is a variable of type α and if A is not a well-ordering of ω, then X^A is a variable of type 0, i.e., a first order variable. In order to stress that A is a well-ordering of ω, we sometimes use $X^{\prec}$ in place of X^A. According to this interpretation, we define that i_1 and i_2 in X^A are bound. The formula "A is a well-ordering of ω" can be easily expressed by using first order variables and A and is denoted $W(A)$. "$W(A)$ and the order type of A is α" is denoted $|A| = \alpha$, which is also expressed by using first order variables and A.

2. Provable well-ordering

When we talk about a system S of axioms, we always assume that S is some extension of $ZF + V = L$ in our language. S also contains axioms which assert that $\forall i$ is equivalent to $\forall x \in \omega$. We also assume ω-rule. Therefore $\forall i \psi(i)$ is provable in S if and only if all $\psi(0), \psi(1), \psi(2), \ldots$ are provable in S.

DEFINITION. A binary predicate $\prec$ in our language is said to be a provable well-ordering of ω in S if and only if the following conditions are satisfied.
1) $S \vdash W(\prec)$.
2) If m and n are two numerals, then one and only one of $n = m$, $S \vdash n \prec m$, and $S \vdash m \prec n$ holds.

DEFINITION. Let $\prec$ be a well-ordering of ω, and n be a numeral. $|n|_{\prec}$ is defined to be the order type of n in the well-ordering $\lessdot$. $\alpha = |n|_\lessdot$ can be expressed by using first order variables and $\lessdot$.

THEOREM. Let S be a true theory and $\lessdot$ and $\lesseqgtr$ be two provable well-orderings of ω in S and m and n be two numerals. Then one and only one of $|n|_\lessdot < |m|_\lesseqgtr$, $|m|_\lesseqgtr < |n|_\lessdot$, or $|n|_\lessdot = |m|_\lesseqgtr$ is provable is S.

PROOF: In this section, $A(n, m)$, $B(n, m)$ and $C(n, m)$ are defined to be $|n|_\lessdot < |m|_\lesseqgtr$, $|m|_\lesseqgtr < |n|_\lessdot$ and $|n|_\lessdot = |m|_\lesseqgtr$ respectively. We prove by transfinite induction on $|m|_\lesseqgtr$ that if $A(n, m)$, then $S \vdash A(n, m)$. As an inductive hypothesis, we assume that this is true for every $m' \lesseqgtr m$. Since $A(n, m)$, there exists a numeral k such that $C(n, k) \wedge k \lesseqgtr m$. By the inductive hypothesis, $S \vdash A(k', k)$ for every numeral $k' \lessdot n$. Since $k' \lessdot n$ is decidable in S, $S \vdash \forall k'(k' \lessdot n \to A(k', k))$ by using ω-rule.

Since $S \vdash k \lesseqgtr m$, $S \vdash A(n, m)$.

In the same way, $S \vdash B(n, m)$, if $B(n, m)$.

Since $C(n, m)$ is equivalent to $\forall k \lessdot nA(k, m) \wedge \forall k \lesseqgtr mB(n, k)$ and $k \lessdot n$ and $k \lesseqgtr m$ are decidable in S, $S \vdash C(n, m)$ if $C(n, m)$. Therefore one of $A(n, m)$, $B(n, m)$, and $C(n, m)$ is provable in S, and so $A(n, m)$, $B(n, m)$ and $C(n, m)$ are decidable in S.

THEOREM. Under the same hypothesis as the previous theorem, one and only one of $|\lessdot| < |\lesseqgtr|$, $|\lesseqgtr| < |\lessdot|$ and $|\lessdot| = |\lesseqgtr|$ is provable in S and so they are decidable in S.

PROOF: $|\lessdot| < |\lesseqgtr|$ is equivalent to $\exists m \forall nA(n, m)$. Therefore the theorem follows from the previous theorem.

DEFINITION. Let $\lessdot$ be a well-ordering of ω. The following well-ordering $\lesseqgtr$ is denoted $\lessdot + 1$.

$$i_1 \lesseqgtr i_2 \underset{df}{\leftrightarrow} \exists i(i \lessdot i_1 \wedge i \lessdot i_2 \wedge i_1 \lessdot i_2) \vee (i_1 \neq i_2 \wedge \forall i \neg (i \lessdot i_2)).$$

Clearly, if $W(\lessdot)$, then $W(\lessdot + 1)$ and $|\lessdot + 1| = |\lessdot| + 1$.

PROPOSITION. If $\lessdot$ is a provable well-ordering of ω in S, then so is $\lessdot + 1$.

$\lessdot + 2$, $\lessdot + 3, \ldots$ are defined to be $(\lessdot + 1) + 1$, $(\lessdot + 2) + 1, \ldots$ respectively.

3. The system S_0

Our intended interpretation of $X^\lessdot$ is a variable of type $|\lessdot|$. Therefore

$X^{\prec}$ corresponds to X^A in TAKEUTI [to appear], where $A(\alpha, \beta)$ is $\beta = \alpha + |\prec|$. Since S_0 is a subsystem of the system in 6.1 in Chapter I in TAKEUTI [to appear] in this sense, we shall simply present many provable formulas as axioms of S_0. For simplicity, we shall sometimes omit the universal quantifiers in front of the formulas and also omit the type sign if no confusion is to be feared, e.g. $\forall X^{\prec}(X \in X)$ means $\forall X^{\prec}(X^{\prec} \in X^{\prec})$.

DEFINITION. $X^A \equiv Y^B$ is defined to be

$$\forall Z^A(Z^A \in X \leftrightarrow Z^A \in Y) \wedge \forall Z^B(Z^B \in X \leftrightarrow Z^B \in Y).$$

S_0 consists of pure logic of type theory (of our language), $ZF + V = L$, where the axiom of replacement is generalized by introducing arbitrary type variables of our language, ω-rule and the following axiom-schemata. (All numbered formulas in this section are axiom-schemata in S_0.)

1. $X \equiv Y \rightarrow (F(X) \leftrightarrow F(Y))$,

where F is an arbitrary formula and X and Y should be precisely written by X^A and Y^B respectively. We always assume that a set variable is a special case of a typed variable and a numerical variable is a special case of a set variable.

2. $W(\prec) \rightarrow \exists Y^{\prec+1} \forall Z^{\prec}(Z \in Y \leftrightarrow F(Z))$.

3. $W(\prec), X^A \in Y^{\prec+1} \rightarrow \exists Z^{\prec}(Z \equiv X)$.

In general, $A_1, \ldots, A_n \rightarrow B$ is an abbreviation of $A_1 \wedge \cdots \wedge A_n \rightarrow B$.

4. $\neg W(\prec) \rightarrow \exists x(x \equiv X^{\prec})$.

5. $\exists X^A(x \equiv X^A)$.

6. $W(\prec), W(\ll), |\prec| \leqslant |\ll| \rightarrow \exists Y^{\prec}(X^{\prec} \equiv Y^{\prec})$.

DEFINITION. As an application of 2, we know that there exists a unique $Y^{\prec+1}$ such that

$$\forall Z^{\prec}(Z \in Y \leftrightarrow Z \equiv x \vee Z \equiv X^{\prec}).$$

This formula is sometimes abbreviated as $Y^{\prec+1} \equiv \{x, X^{\prec}\}$ or $Y \equiv \{x, X\}$. $\{\{x\}, \{x, X\}\}$ is abbreviated as $\langle x, X \rangle$. $\exists! Y^{\prec+2}(Y^{\prec+2} \equiv \langle x, X^{\prec} \rangle)$ is provable in S_0. ($\exists!$ is read "there exists a unique".)

DEFINITION. $Ty(\alpha, X^{\prec})$ is defined to be

$W(\prec) \rightarrow \exists Y^{\prec+3}(\forall Z^{\prec}(\langle 0, Z \rangle \in Y \leftrightarrow \exists x(x \equiv Z))$
$\quad \wedge \forall \beta(0 < \beta \leqslant \alpha \rightarrow \forall Z^{\prec}(\langle \beta, Z \rangle \in Y \leftrightarrow \forall Z_1^{\prec}(Z_1 \in Y \rightarrow \exists \gamma < \beta(\langle \gamma, Z_1 \rangle \in Y))))$
$\quad \wedge \langle \alpha, X^{\prec} \rangle \in Y).$

$Ty(\alpha, X^{\preccurlyeq})$ is also written $Ty(X^{\preccurlyeq})\leqslant\alpha$. As usual, we define $Ty(X^{\preccurlyeq})<\alpha$ and $Ty(X^{\preccurlyeq})=\alpha$ by using $Ty(X^{\preccurlyeq})\leqslant\alpha$. $Ty(X^{\preccurlyeq})$ satisfies the following properties.

a) $Ty(X^{\preccurlyeq})=0\leftrightarrow\exists x(x\equiv X)$.

b) $\alpha>0\rightarrow(Ty(X^{\preccurlyeq})\leqslant\alpha\leftrightarrow\forall Y^{\preccurlyeq}\in X^{\preccurlyeq}(Ty(Y)<\alpha))$.

We shall continue presenting axiom-schemata of S_0.

7. $W(\preccurlyeq)\rightarrow Ty(X^{\preccurlyeq})\leqslant|\preccurlyeq|$.

8. $W(\preccurlyeq), Ty(X^A)\leqslant|\preccurlyeq|\rightarrow\exists Y^{\preccurlyeq}(X\equiv Y)$.

9. $\alpha\leqslant|\preccurlyeq|\rightarrow\exists X^{\preccurlyeq}(Ty(X)=\alpha\wedge\forall Y^{\preccurlyeq}(Ty(Y)<\alpha\rightarrow(Y\in X\leftrightarrow F(Y))))$.

4. Truth definition

We fix a Gödel numbering of our language. The Gödel number of ψ is denoted $\ulcorner\psi\urcorner$ which is a natural number. Such notions as "i is a Gödel number of a formula", "i is a Gödel number of a formula of the form $\psi_1\wedge\psi_2$, i.e. a formula whose outermost logical symbol is $\wedge$", etc. are expressed by first order language. Therefore we use $\forall\ulcorner\psi\urcorner A(\ulcorner\psi\urcorner)$, $\forall\ulcorner\psi_1\wedge\psi_2\urcorner A(\ulcorner\psi_1\wedge\psi_2\urcorner)$, etc. to express "$\forall i$ ("i is a Gödel number of a formula" $\rightarrow A(i)$)", "$\forall i$ ("i is a Gödel number of a formula of the form $\psi_1\wedge\psi_2$" $\rightarrow A(i)$)", etc. respectively. Since $\ulcorner\psi_1\urcorner$ and $\ulcorner\psi_2\urcorner$ are easily expressed by using $\ulcorner\psi_1\wedge\psi_2\urcorner$, we use a notation like $\forall\ulcorner\psi_1\wedge\psi_2\urcorner B(\ulcorner\psi_1\urcorner,\ulcorner\psi_2\urcorner)$ as a special form of $\forall\ulcorner\psi_1\wedge\psi_2\urcorner A(\ulcorner\psi_1\wedge\psi_2\urcorner)$. The number of logical symbols in ψ and the degree of ψ (defined in Section 1) are primitive recursive functions of $\ulcorner\psi\urcorner$ and so easily expressed by first order language and we denote them as $Nl(\ulcorner\psi\urcorner)$ and $\deg(\ulcorner\psi\urcorner)$ respectively. $\mathrm{grad}(\ulcorner\psi\urcorner)$ is defined to be $\omega\cdot\deg(\ulcorner\psi\urcorner)+Nl(\ulcorner\psi\urcorner)$. $\mathrm{grad}(\ulcorner\psi\urcorner)$ is also said to be the grade of ψ. The Gödel numbers of the k-th numerical variable, k-th set variable and k-th variable of type A are denoted as $\ulcorner i_k\urcorner$, $\ulcorner x_k\urcorner$ and $\ulcorner X_k^A\urcorner$ respectively. The k-th numeral is denoted as $n(k)$.

DEFINITION. $Y^A\equiv X^{\preccurlyeq\prime}x$ is defined to be

$$(\exists!Z^{\preccurlyeq}(\langle x, Z\rangle\in X)\wedge\langle x, Y\rangle\in X)\vee(\neg\exists!Z^{\preccurlyeq}(\langle x, Z\rangle\in X)\wedge Y\equiv 0).$$

DEFINITION. $Y^{\preccurlyeq}\equiv S(x, \ulcorner x_k\urcorner, X^{\preccurlyeq})$ is defined to be

$$\forall Z_1^{\preccurlyeq}(\forall Z_2^{\preccurlyeq}\neg(Z_1\equiv\langle\ulcorner x_k\urcorner, Z_2\rangle)\rightarrow(Z_1\in X\leftrightarrow Z_1\in Y))$$
$$\wedge\forall Z^{\preccurlyeq}(\langle\ulcorner x_k\urcorner, Z\rangle\in Y\leftrightarrow Z\equiv x).$$

$Y^{\preccurlyeq}\equiv S(Z^B, \ulcorner X_k^A\urcorner, X^{\preccurlyeq})$ is defined to be

$$\forall Z_1^{\preccurlyeq}(\forall Z_2^{\preccurlyeq}\neg(Z_1\equiv\langle\ulcorner X_k^A\urcorner, Z_2\rangle)\rightarrow(Z_1\in X\leftrightarrow Z_1\in Y))$$
$$\wedge\forall Z_1^{\preccurlyeq}(\langle\ulcorner X_k^A\urcorner, Z_1\rangle\in Y\leftrightarrow Z_1\equiv Z).$$

DEFINITION. $T_{\prec}(\alpha, X^{\prec+3})$ is defined to be the conjunction of the following formulas.

1) $\forall \ulcorner X_k^A \in X_j^B \urcorner \forall Y^{\prec}(\langle \ulcorner X_k^A \in X_j^B \urcorner, Y \rangle \in X \leftrightarrow Y' \ulcorner X_k^A \urcorner \in Y' \ulcorner X_j^B \urcorner)$.

2) $\forall \ulcorner \neg \psi \urcorner (\mathrm{grad}(\ulcorner \neg \psi \urcorner) \leqslant \alpha \to \forall Y^{\prec}(\langle \ulcorner \neg \psi \urcorner, Y \rangle \in X \leftrightarrow \neg \langle \ulcorner \psi \urcorner, Y \rangle \in X))$.

3) $\forall \ulcorner \psi_1 \wedge \psi_2 \urcorner (\mathrm{grad}(\ulcorner \psi_1 \wedge \psi_2 \urcorner) \leqslant \alpha \to \forall Y^{\prec}(\langle \ulcorner \psi_1 \wedge \psi_2 \urcorner, Y \rangle \in X$
$\leftrightarrow \langle \ulcorner \psi_1 \urcorner, Y \rangle \in X \wedge \langle \ulcorner \psi_2 \urcorner, Y \rangle \in X))$.

4) $\forall \ulcorner \forall x_k \psi \urcorner (\mathrm{grad}(\ulcorner \forall x_k \psi \urcorner) \leqslant \alpha \to \forall Y^{\prec}(\langle \ulcorner \forall x_k \psi \urcorner, Y \rangle \in X$
$\leftrightarrow \forall x \forall Z^{\prec}(Z \equiv S(x, \ulcorner x_k \urcorner, Y) \to \langle \ulcorner \psi \urcorner, Z \rangle \in X))$.

5) $\forall \ulcorner \forall X_k^A \psi \urcorner (\mathrm{grad}(\ulcorner \forall X_k^A \psi \urcorner) \leqslant \alpha \to \forall Y^{\prec}(\langle \ulcorner \forall X_k^A \psi \urcorner, Y \rangle \in X$
$\leftrightarrow \forall Z^{\prec} \forall Y_1^{\prec}(Ty(Z^{\prec}) \leqslant |\prec| \wedge Y_1 \equiv S(Z, \ulcorner X_k^A \urcorner, Y) \to \langle \ulcorner \psi \urcorner, Y_1 \rangle \in X)))$,

where $i_1 \prec i_2$ is $\langle \ulcorner A(n(i_1), n(i_2)) \urcorner, Y \rangle \in X$.

By transfinite induction on α, we have

PROPOSITION. The following are provable in S_0.

1) $\forall \alpha \exists X^{\prec+3} T_{\prec}(\alpha, X)$.

2) $\mathrm{grad}(\ulcorner \psi \urcorner) \leqslant \alpha, \mathrm{grad}(\ulcorner \psi \urcorner) \leqslant \beta,$

$$T_{\prec}(\alpha, X_1^{\prec+3}), T_{\prec}(\beta, X_2^{\prec+3}) \to (\langle \ulcorner \psi \urcorner, Y \rangle \in X_1 \leftrightarrow \langle \ulcorner \psi \urcorner, Y \rangle \in X_2).$$

DEFINITION. $T_{\prec}(\ulcorner \psi \urcorner, Y^{\prec})$ is defined to be

$$\exists \alpha \exists X^{\prec+3}(\mathrm{grad}(\ulcorner \psi \urcorner) \leqslant \alpha \wedge T_{\prec}(\alpha, X) \wedge \langle \ulcorner \psi \urcorner, Y \rangle \in X).$$

By transfinite induction on $\mathrm{grad}(\ulcorner \psi \urcorner)$, we have

PROPOSITION. The following are provable in S_0.

1) $T_{\prec}(\ulcorner X_k^A \in X_j^B \urcorner, Y^{\prec}) \leftrightarrow Y' \ulcorner X_k^A \urcorner \in Y' \ulcorner X_j^B \urcorner$.

2) $T_{\prec}(\ulcorner \neg \psi \urcorner, Y^{\prec}) \leftrightarrow \neg T_{\prec}(\ulcorner \psi \urcorner, Y)$.

3) $T_{\prec}(\ulcorner \psi_1 \wedge \psi_2 \urcorner, Y^{\prec}) \leftrightarrow T_{\prec}(\ulcorner \psi_1 \urcorner, Y) \wedge T_{\prec}(\ulcorner \psi_2 \urcorner, Y)$.

4) $T_{\prec}(\ulcorner \forall x_k \psi \urcorner, Y^{\prec}) \leftrightarrow \forall x T_{\prec}(\ulcorner \psi \urcorner, Z^{\prec})$, where $Z \equiv S(x, \ulcorner x_k \urcorner, Y)$.

5) $T_{\prec}(\ulcorner \forall X_k^A \psi \urcorner, Y^{\prec}) \leftrightarrow \forall Z^{\prec}(Ty(Z) \leqslant |\prec| \to T_{\prec}(\ulcorner \psi \urcorner, Y_1^{\prec}))$,
where $i_1 \prec i_2$ is $T_{\prec}(\ulcorner A(n(i_1), n(i_2)) \urcorner, Y^{\prec})$ and $Y_1^{\prec} \equiv S(Z, \ulcorner X_k^A \urcorner, Y)$.

6) $\forall \ulcorner X_k^A \urcorner (\text{``} \ulcorner X_k^A \urcorner$ is free in $\ulcorner \psi \urcorner \text{''} \to Y_1^{\prec\prime} \ulcorner X_k^A \urcorner \equiv Y_2^{\prec\prime} \ulcorner X_k^A \urcorner)$
$\to (T_{\prec}(\ulcorner \psi \urcorner, Y_1^{\prec}) \leftrightarrow T_{\prec}(\ulcorner \psi \urcorner, Y_2^{\prec}))$.

DEFINITION. Let ψ be a formula and $X_{k_1}^{A_1}, \ldots, X_{k_n}^{A_n}$ be all free variables in ψ. $\psi((Y^{\prec}))$ is obtained from ψ by replacing $X_{k_1}^{A_1}, \ldots, X_{k_n}^{A_n}$ by $Y' \ulcorner X_{k_1}^{A_1} \urcorner, \ldots, Y' \ulcorner X_{k_n}^{A_n} \urcorner$ respectively.

By transfinite induction on the grade of ψ, we have

THEOREM. Let ψ be a formula and $\prec_1, \ldots, \prec_n$ be all types in ψ. Then the following is provable in S_0.

$$(W(\lessdot_1) \to |\lessdot_1| + 3 \leqslant |\lessdot|), \ldots, (W(\lessdot_n) \to |\lessdot_n| + 3 \leqslant |\lessdot|),$$
$$W(\lessdot) \to (T_\lessdot(\ulcorner\psi\urcorner, Y^\lessdot) \leftrightarrow \psi((Y^\lessdot))).$$

DEFINITION. $T_\lessdot(\ulcorner\psi\urcorner, 0)$ is denoted $T_\lessdot(\ulcorner\psi\urcorner)$.

As a corollary of the previous theorem we have

THEOREM. Let ψ be a closed formula and $\lessdot_1, \ldots, \lessdot_n$ be all the types in ψ. Then the following is provable in S_0.

$$(W(\lessdot_1) \to |\lessdot_1| + 3 \leqslant |\lessdot|), \ldots, (W(\lessdot_n) \to |\lessdot_n| + 3 \leqslant |\lessdot|),$$
$$W(\lessdot) \to (T_\lessdot(\ulcorner\psi\urcorner) \leftrightarrow \psi).$$

5. Transfinite applications of reflection principle

In this section, the system of axioms S is always an extension of S_0 and "a formula is provable in S" means that it is provable from S by using logical inferences and ω-rule. Let $S(\ulcorner\psi\urcorner)$ express that ψ is an axiom of S. Then $\mathrm{Prov}_S(\ulcorner\psi\urcorner)$, which means "$\psi$ is provable in S", can be expressed by using first order language and $S(i_1)$. We fix one such uniform way to define $\mathrm{Prov}_S(i_1)$ from $S(i_1)$.

Now we shall consider S_0. $S_0(i_1)$ can be easily expressed by the first order language. Therefore there exists a first order formula T_0 such that

$$S_0 \vdash T_0(\ulcorner S_0(i_1)\urcorner, \ulcorner\psi\urcorner) \leftrightarrow S_0(\ulcorner\psi\urcorner).$$

Moreover the following is provable for every $\lessdot$ in S_0.

$$|\lessdot| > 0 \to (T_\lessdot(\ulcorner S_0(\ulcorner\psi\urcorner)\urcorner) \leftrightarrow S_0(\ulcorner\psi\urcorner)).$$

Now consider an arbitrary system S. Let $\tilde{S}$ be the system $E(S)$, where E is the reflection principle in the introduction. Then $\tilde{S}(i_1)$ is expressed by

$$S(i_1) \lor \exists\ulcorner\psi\urcorner(\text{``}\ulcorner\psi\urcorner\text{ is closed''} \land ((\mathrm{Prov}_S(\ulcorner\psi\urcorner) \land i_1 = \ulcorner\mathrm{Prov}_S(\ulcorner\psi\urcorner)\urcorner)$$
$$\lor (\neg\,\mathrm{Prov}_S(\ulcorner\psi\urcorner) \land i_1 = \ulcorner\neg\,\mathrm{Prov}_S(\ulcorner\psi\urcorner)\urcorner))).$$

Therefore, there exists a primitive recursive function f such that

$$\ulcorner\tilde{S}(i_1)\urcorner = f(\ulcorner S(i_1)\urcorner).$$

We fix one of such functions f. Using a theorem in the previous section, we have

THEOREM. Let $\lessdot_1, \ldots, \lessdot_n$ be all the types in $S(i_1)$. Then the following is provable in S_0.

$$(W(\lessdot_1) \to |\lessdot_1| + 3 \leqslant |\lessdot|), \ldots, (W(\lessdot_n) \to |\lessdot_n| + 3 \leqslant |\lessdot|),$$
$$W(\lessdot), \text{``}\ulcorner \psi \urcorner \text{ is closed''} \to (T_\lessdot (\ulcorner \tilde{S}(\ulcorner \psi \urcorner) \urcorner) \leftrightarrow \tilde{S}(\ulcorner \psi \urcorner)).$$

Now let $\lessdot$ and $\eqslantless$ be two well-orderings of ω and the order type of any type in $\lessdot$ be less than $|\eqslantless|$ and $|\lessdot|$ and $|\eqslantless|$ be limit ordinals. We can easily construct a new well-ordering $\eqslantless\cdot$ of ω such that $\eqslantless\cdot$ is expressed by using first order language, $\lessdot$, and $\eqslantless$ and $|\eqslantless\cdot| = |\eqslantless| + |\lessdot|$. We fix a method to construct such a well-ordering $\eqslantless\cdot$ and denote it $\eqslantless + \lessdot$. In the same way, for every j, we fix a method to define j_0 and a well-ordering $\eqslantless\cdot$ such that j_0 and $\eqslantless\cdot$ are expressed by using first order language, $\lessdot$, and $\eqslantless$ and $|j_0|_\lessdot$ is zero or a limit ordinal and $|j|_\lessdot - |j_0|_\lessdot$ is a natural number and $|\eqslantless\cdot| = |\eqslantless| + |j_0|_\lessdot + 6 \cdot |j|_\lessdot - |j_0|_\lessdot$. In this section we denote this well-ordering $\eqslantless\cdot$ by $\lessdot_j$. Let $\psi(i_1)$ be a formula and m be a numeral. $\ulcorner \psi(m) \urcorner$ is expressed by the first order language and $\ulcorner \psi(i_1) \urcorner$. $\ulcorner \psi(m) \urcorner$ is denoted by $\mathrm{Sub}_{i_1}^m \ulcorner \psi(i_1) \urcorner$. The operation Sub can be defined independently from $\ulcorner \psi(i_1) \urcorner$ and m.

Now we shall explicitly define a system obtained from S_0 by applying the operation $E |\lessdot|$ times. The explicit definition of $\lessdot$ is necessary to do so.

DEFINITION. $R^\lessdot(h, i_2, i_3)$ is defined to be the conjunction of the following formulas.

1) $\forall j_1 (\forall j_2 (j_1 \leqq j_2) \to h'j_1 = \ulcorner S_0(i_1) \urcorner)$,

where $j_1 \leqq j_2$ is an abbreviation of $j_1 \lessdot j_2 \vee j_1 = j_2$. In this section, we assume that j_0 is the first element in $\lessdot$. So we use $h'j_0 = \ulcorner S_0(i_1) \urcorner$ instead of 1).

2) $\forall j_1 \lessdot i_2 \forall j_2$ ("j_2 is the successor of j_1 in $\lessdot$") $\to h'j_2 = f(h'j_1))$. In this section we denote "the successor of j_1 in $\lessdot$" $(j_1 + 1)_\lessdot$. So we use $\forall j \lessdot i_2 (h'(j+1)_\lessdot = f(h'j))$ instead of 2).

3) $\forall j \lessdot i_2 (|j|_\lessdot \in K_{\mathrm{II}} \to h'j = \mathrm{Sub}_{i_2}^{n(j)} \mathrm{Sub}_{i_3}^{n(i_3)} i_3)$ where K_{II} is the class of all limit ordinal numbers. $S^\lessdot(i_1, i_2, i_3)$ is defined to be

$$\exists h (R^\lessdot(h, i_1, i_2, i_3) \wedge (|i_2|_\lessdot \in K_{\mathrm{II}} \to \exists j \lessdot i_2 T_{\lessdot_{i_2}}(\mathrm{Sub}_{i_1}^{n(i_1)} h'j))$$
$$\wedge \forall j (|i_2|_\lessdot \notin K_{\mathrm{II}} \to T_{\lessdot_{i_2}}(\mathrm{Sub}_{i_1}^{n(i_1)} h'j))).$$

Let m be $\ulcorner S^\lessdot(i_1, i_2, i_3) \urcorner$ and $S^\lessdot(i_1, i_2)$ be $S^\lessdot(i_1, i_2, m)$. Then 3) becomes the following in $S^\lessdot(i_1, i_2)$.

$$\forall j \lessdot i_2 (|j|_\lessdot \in K_{\mathrm{II}} \to h'j = \mathrm{Sub}_{i_2}^{n(j)} \mathrm{Sub}_{i_3}^{n(m)} \ulcorner S^\lessdot(i_1, i_2, i_3) \urcorner)$$

i.e.

$$\forall j \lessdot i_2 (|j|_\lessdot \in K_{\mathrm{II}} \to h'j = \ulcorner S^\lessdot(i_1, n(j)) \urcorner).$$

Therefore we have the following.

PROPOSITION. Under the assumption in this section, the following is provable in S_0.

$$S^{\prec}(i_1, i_2) \leftrightarrow \exists h \, (h'j_0 = \ulcorner S_0(i_1) \urcorner \wedge \forall j \prec i_2 (h'(j+1)_{\prec} = f(h'j))$$
$$\wedge \, \forall j \prec i_2 (|j|_{\prec} \in K_{\mathrm{II}} \to h'j = \ulcorner S^{\prec}(i_1, n(j)) \urcorner)$$
$$\wedge \, (|i_2|_{\prec} \in K_{\mathrm{II}} \to \exists j \prec i_2 T_{<i_2}(\mathrm{Sub}_{i_1}^{n(i_1)} h'j))$$
$$\wedge \, (|i_2|_{\prec} \notin K_{\mathrm{II}} \to T_{<i_2}(\mathrm{Sub}_{i_1}^{n(i_1)} h'i_2))).$$

DEFINITION. $R^{\prec}(h, i)$ is defined to be

$$h'j_0 = \ulcorner S_0(i_1) \urcorner \wedge \forall j \prec i (h'(j+1)_{\prec} = f(h'j))$$
$$\wedge \, \forall j \prec i (|j|_{\prec} \in K_{\mathrm{II}} \to h'j = \ulcorner S^{\prec}(i_1, n(j)) \urcorner).$$

PROPOSITION. Under the assumption in this section, the following are provable in S_0.
1) $\exists h R^{\prec}(h, i)$.
2) $R^{\prec}(h_1, i_1), R^{\prec}(h_2, i_2), j \prec i_1, j \prec i_2 \to h'_1 j = h'_2 j$.
3) $R^{\prec}(h, i), j \prec i, j_1 \leq j, |j_1|_{\prec} \in K_{\mathrm{II}} \vee |j_1|_{\prec} = 0,$
   $\forall j_2 (j_1 \prec j_2 \leq j \to \neg |j_2|_{\prec} \in K_{\mathrm{II}}) \to$
"$h'j$ is a Gödel number of a formula ψ and every typed variable in ψ is in $S^{\prec}(i_1, i_2)$, i.e. in $\prec$ and $T_{\prec j_1}$".
PROOF: 1) is proved by transfinite induction on i. 2) is proved by transfinite induction on j. The first part of 3) is proved by transfinite induction on j. The second part of 3) follows from the definition of $R^{\prec}(h, i), f$ and $S^{\prec}(i_1, i_2)$.

PROPOSITION. Under the assumption in this section, the following is provable in S_0. $R^{\prec}(h_1, i), j \prec i \to (S^{\prec}(i_1, j) \leftrightarrow T_{<i}(\mathrm{Sub}_{i_1}^{n(i_1)} h'j))$.
PROOF: This is proved by transfinite induction on j. If $|j|_{\prec} \notin K_{\mathrm{II}}$, then it suffices to show $T_{<i}(\mathrm{Sub}_{i_1}^{n(i_1)} h'j) \leftrightarrow T_{<j}(\mathrm{Sub}_{i_1}^{n(i_1)} h'j)$. This follows from 3) in the previous proposition. If $|j|_{\prec} \in K_{\mathrm{II}}$, then it suffices to show $S^{\prec}(i_1, j) \leftrightarrow T_{<i}(\ulcorner S^{\prec}(n(i_1), n(j)) \urcorner)$, which also follows from 3) in the previous proposition and

$$\forall j \prec i (|j|_{\prec} \in K_{\mathrm{II}} \to h'j = \ulcorner S^{\prec}(i_1, n(j)) \urcorner) \quad \text{in} \quad R^{\prec}(h, i).$$

DEFINITION. $S_1^{\prec}(i_1)$ is defined to be $S^{\prec}(i_1, i)$. The system of axioms consisting of closed formulas ψ satisfying $S_1^{\prec}(\ulcorner \psi \urcorner)$ is denoted as $S_1^{\prec}$.

THEOREM. Under the assumption in this section, the following are provable in S_0.
1) $S_{j_0}^{\prec}(i_1) \leftrightarrow S_0(i_1)$.

2) $j_1 = (j+1)_\prec \to (S^\prec_{j_0}(i_1) \leftrightarrow E(S^\prec_j)(i_1))$, where $E(S)(i_1)$ is $S(i_1) \vee \exists \ulcorner \psi \urcorner (``\ulcorner \psi \urcorner$ is closed" $\wedge$

$((\mathrm{Prov}_S(\ulcorner \psi \urcorner) \wedge i_1 = \ulcorner \mathrm{Prov}_S(\ulcorner \psi \urcorner) \urcorner)$
$$\vee (\neg \mathrm{Prov}_S(\ulcorner \psi \urcorner) \wedge i_1 = \ulcorner \neg \mathrm{Prov}_S(\ulcorner \psi \urcorner) \urcorner))).$$

3) $|i|_\prec \in K_{\mathrm{II}} \to (S^\prec_i(i_1) \leftrightarrow \exists j \prec i S^\prec_j(i_1))$.

PROOF: Proof is by transfinite induction on j_1 and i. 1) is obvious. Proof of 2): By the previous propositions, we may assume $R^\prec(h, j_1)$ and so

$$S^\prec_{j_1}(i_1) \leftrightarrow T_{<_{j_1}}(\mathrm{Sub}^{n(i_1)}_{i_1} h' j_1) \leftrightarrow T_{<_{j_1}}(\mathrm{Sub}^{n(i_1)}_{i_1} f(h'j))$$
$$\leftrightarrow E(T_{<_{j_1}}(\mathrm{Sub}^{n(i_1)}_{i_1} h'j))(i_1) \leftrightarrow E(S^\prec_j)(i_1).$$

Proof of 3): By the previous propositions, we may assume $R^\prec(h, i)$ and so

$$S^\prec_i(i_1) \leftrightarrow \exists j \prec i T_{<_i}(\mathrm{Sub}^{n(i_1)}_{i_1} h'j) \leftrightarrow \exists j \prec i S^\prec_j(i_1).$$

Let $<$ be the usual ordering of ω. Let i be the integer satisfying $|i|_{\prec + <} = = |\prec| + 1$. $S_\prec$ is defined to be $S^{\prec + <}_i$. The theorem means that if $<$ be a well-ordering of ω, then there exists a sequence Q of systems S_α such that Q starts with S_0 and the successor of S in Q is $E(S)$ and the α-th member of Q is $\bigcup_{\beta < \alpha} S_\beta$ if α is a limit ordinal and the length of Q is $|<|$.

Now, we shall prove an additional property of $S^\prec$.

PROPOSITION. There exists a provable well-ordering $\prec$ of ω in $E(S)$, whose order type is greater than the order type of any provable well-ordering of ω in S.

PROOF: We shall prove this by enumerating all provable well-orderings of ω in S. Let j be Gödel's pairing function of ω. (j is a 1-1 map from $\omega \times \omega$ onto ω.) Then define $\prec$ as follows.

1. If $e_1 < e_2$, then $j(e_1, n) \prec j(e_2, m)$ for any n and m.

2. If e is not a Gödel number of a provable well-ordering in S, then $j(e, n) \prec j(e, m)$ if and only if $n < m$.

3. If ψ is a provable well-ordering of ω is S, then $j(\ulcorner \psi \urcorner, n) \prec j(\ulcorner \psi \urcorner, m)$ if and only if $n \overset{\psi}{<} m$.

Such an ordering $\prec$ is easily expressed by using Prov_S and shown to be a provable well-ordering of ω in $E(S)$. It is obvious that $\prec$ satisfies the condition in the proposition.

THEOREM. In $S^\prec_{(i+1)\prec}$, there exists a provable well-ordering of ω whose order type is greater than $|i|_\prec$.

PROOF: This is proved by transfinite induction on $|i|_{\ll}$ and the previous proposition.

6. The theory on L and remarks

Since the truth definition of the first order sentences can be expressed by using second order language and the second order language is a part of our language, we can define the following notion P in our system. $P(n)$ is defined to be "n is a Gödel number of a first order formula $\psi(x_1)$ in which x_1 is only free variable and $\exists!\alpha\psi(\alpha)$". Now $\ll$ is defined as follows.

1) If $\neg P(n)$ and $\neg P(m)$, then $n \ll m$ is defined to be $n < m$.
2) $n \ll m$ if $\neg P(n)$ and $P(m)$.
3) $\ulcorner\psi_1(x_1)\urcorner \ll \ulcorner\psi_2(x_1)\urcorner$ if $\ulcorner\psi_1(x_1)\urcorner < \ulcorner\psi_2(x_1)\urcorner \wedge P(\ulcorner\psi_1(x_1)\urcorner)$
$$\wedge P(\ulcorner\psi_2(x_1)\urcorner) \wedge \exists\alpha(\psi_1(\alpha) \wedge \psi_2(\alpha)).$$
4) $\ulcorner\psi_1(x_1)\urcorner \ll \ulcorner\psi_2(x_1)\urcorner$ if $P(\ulcorner\psi_1(x_1)\urcorner) \wedge P(\ulcorner\psi_2(x_1)\urcorner)$
$$\wedge \exists\alpha\exists\beta(\alpha < \beta \wedge \psi_1(\alpha) \wedge \psi_2(\beta)).$$

$\ll$ is easily expressed in our language and is a well-ordering of ω. It is known that $F''|\ll|$ is elementarily equivalent with L, where F is Gödel's function constructing L. From the results in Section 5 follows that there exists a provable well-ordering $\ll$ of ω in $S^{\ll}$ such that $|\ll| = |\ll|$. Then $F'|\ll|$ is definable in $S^{\ll}$ and we claim that every first order sentence relativized to $F'|\ll|$ is decidable in $S^{\ll}$. Since $S^{\ll}$ has ω-rule, it suffices to show that $F'|i_1|_{\ll} \in F'|i_2|_{\ll}$ is decidable in $S^{\ll}$. This can be easily proved by transfinite induction on $j(|i_2|_{\ll}, |i_1|_{\ll})$, where j is Gödel's pairing function of ordinals, since $S^{\ll}$ has ω-rule and $|i_1|_{\ll} < |i_2|_{\ll}$ i.e. $i_1 \ll i_2$ is decidable in $S^{\ll}$. This means that $S^{\ll}$ is sufficiently strong on L.

Remark. Every notion like Prov in this paper is considered in L. Therefore we have to show that transfinite type theory is compatible with $V = L$. However something similar has been done for very strong transfinite type theory in TAKEUTI [to appear].

Open problems.

1. Let α be the supremum of all definable well-orderings of ω in our language. Is $F''\alpha$ elementarily equivalent to L?

2. Is it possible to introduce new axiom-schemata on width (cf. TAKEUTI [to appear]) and to establish our result on V assuming that V is very wide?

References

1. FEFERMAN, S., Transfinite recursive progressions of axiomatic theories, J. Symb. Logic **27** (1962) 259–316.
2. GÖDEL, K., Remarks before the Princeton Bicentennial Conf. on Problems in mathematics, in: The undecidable, ed. M. Davis (Raven Press, New York, 1965) pp. 84–88.
3. SWARD, G., Transfinite sequences of axiom systems for set theory, Thesis, University of Illionois, 1967.
4. TAKEUTI, G., The universe of set theory, to appear.

Section 2

Foundations of Mathematical Theories

AUTONOMOUS TRANSFINITE PROGRESSIONS AND THE EXTENT OF PREDICATIVE MATHEMATICS

S. FEFERMAN[1]

Stanford University, Stanford, California, USA

1. General introduction

This is a report on formal proof-theoretic results relevant to the program of characterizing the informal notions of *predicative definition* and *predicative proof*[2], here treated throughout under the assumption that *the set of natural numbers is given.*

An immediate consequence of this assumption is that the meanings of arithmetical definitions of properties of natural numbers are (taken to be) completely determined. These can be represented by formulas from a formal system of elementary number theory (Z) where the quantifiers are intended to range over the set of natural numbers. Then the proofs represented by derivations of the classical system (Z) are immediately acceptable.

The basic predicative step at any stage consists in enlarging the (collection of) collections of definitions previously obtained by allowing definitions containing quantifiers ranging over these earlier collections. Formally, this is the principal step in the formation of the *ramified* systems, with the rules

---

[1] Research supported in part by Grant DA-ARO(D)-31-124-G655.

[2] The explicit introduction of these notions is due to Poincaré; cf. POINCARÉ [1963] Ch. 4 for his discussion of their significance. While his informal remarks make clear certain of the basic notions they are not unambiguous and in some cases are in actual conflict with each other; in other words, his own views would seem to be a mixture. For example, he rejects the assumption of any completed infinite totality, but accepts proof by induction on the natural numbers applied to statements containing numerical quantifiers, without any explicit restriction of the laws of logic. We are here concerned to give one coherent conception in the original mixture, namely that of predicativity given the totality of natural numbers. (It is not clear at present what other coherent conceptions can be extracted from the mixture.) The reader is referred to KREISEL [1960] and FEFERMAN [1964] for surveys of the technical developments which led from the conceptions introduced by Poincaré to the formal axiomatizations considered here.

of classical logic and induction on the natural numbers applied to the extended language.

Finally, the basic step can be iterated transfinitely often relative to any ordering relation provided one already has a predicative proof which shows this iteration to be a well-determined process. We study below the effect of various formal conditions, related to this requirement; we call them conditions of *autonomy*. The principal autonomous condition considered is that one already has a formal proof of the statement which expresses, under an impredicative interpretation, that the ordering is a well-ordering. The orderings satisfying this condition will be called 'predicative well-orderings', though strictly speaking we have given no independent meaning to 'well-ordering' in predicative terms.

The predicative definitions and proofs considered here are supposed to be all those which are generated by the foregoing processes. Put differently, the predicative definitions are all those whose meaning can be ultimately reduced to numerical quantification. The formal results bearing on these notions are summarized in 1.1 and 1.2.

1.1. *Background and earlier work*

KREISEL [1958] proposed that an appropriate technical tool for characterizing various informal notions of proof was Turing's notion of ordinal logic provided the ordinals used are properly restricted; or, as one calls it now, an *autonomous transfinite progression of formal systems* $\{T_a\}$. He sketched there two such progressions $\{P_a\}$ and $\{R_a\}$ intended to correspond to the notions of *finitist* and *predicative* proof, respectively; a formally improved version of $\{P_a\}$ was presented in KREISEL [1965] pp. 169–173. The main conclusions drawn in these papers for the case of the $\{P_a\}$ are that (Z) is a conservative extension of $\bigcup P_a$ (a autonomous) and that ε_0 is the least upper bound of the ordinals $o(a)$ for autonomous a.

In a subsequent paper, KREISEL [1962] discussed the well-known defects of ramified systems for the development of classical analysis. He suggested as an alternative the use of subsystems of classical (unramified) analysis which can be predicatively justified, i.e., seen to have models at predicatively justified levels of the ramified hierarchy. In particular, he introduced the *hyperarithmetic comprehension rule* (HCR) as a means of proof which would lead from predicatively justifiable statements of classical analysis to new such statements.

I introduced (FEFERMAN [1964]) a progression $\{H_a\}$ of unramified systems with (HCR) as the main rule of inference, and with a certain *reflection prin-*

ciple (to be described below) as the basic means of passing from one system to the next. In Part II of that paper I sketched intertranslations between the autonomous progressions $\{R_a\}$ and $\{H_a\}$. A certain classical ordinal Γ_0 was identified there as the least upper bound of the autonomous $o(a)$. This result for ramified progressions was obtained independently by SCHÜTTE [1963], [1965].

One of the most useful methods for dealing with the proof theory of various progressions has been the extension of Gentzen's cut-elimination results to 'semi-formal' systems permitting *infinitely long derivations*, initiated by Novikov and Lorenzen and developed extensively by SCHÜTTE [1960]. Infinitary systems of this sort corresponding to the progressions $\{R_a\}$ and $\{H_a\}$ are denoted here by (R^+) and (H^+). FEFERMAN [1964] also gives intertranslations between (R^+) and (H^+); further, Γ_0 remains the least upper bound of the autonomously provable well-orderings in these wider classes of derivations (by cut-elimination arguments for systems with transfinite ramification having their source in SCHÜTTE [1960]).[3]

1.2. *New results*

These various notions and results will be explained in more detail in Sections 2–4 below, and improved by eliminating certain features of the earlier systems which may have seemed to be ad hoc. For example, the work of FEFERMAN and KREISEL [1968] allows one to show that no new theorems are obtained when the rule (HCR) is replaced by a formally more general rule for introducing sets determined by *provably definite formulas* (Section 2.3).

Infinitary unramified systems are developed further in Section 5. TAIT [1968] has shown how to use a cut-elimination result for systems with *infinitely long formulas* (as well as derivations) to get a direct proof that Γ_0 is an upper bound for the (H^+)-autonomous well-orderings. A smoother variant of this argument is sketched in Section 5.2; the improvement rests on an interpolation theorem for infinitary formulas due to BARWISE [1967].

In both these progressions, the autonomy condition restricts only the ordinal lengths of the trees of derivations and formulas. The next step is to consider sharper restrictions requiring that the trees themselves (and not only their ordinals) be already defined; and, even more stringently, that the trees be previously proved to represent derivations or formulas, resp. (Sec-

---

[3] The forthcoming FEFERMAN [1968a] is the first of some papers which will contain a detailed exposition of the proofs of the various results outlined in the second half of FEFERMAN [1964].

tion 5.3). In the most restricted case, the autonomous infinitary system turns out to be a conservative extension of $\bigcup H_a$ (a autonomous).

The results obtained thus establish *stability properties* of the various autonomous progressions of systems considered. The ordinal Γ_0 appears as the limit of the autonomous ordinals in all cases, whether the systems are finitary or infinitary. If the languages of two progressions are comparable one gets in many cases conservative extension and otherwise natural inter-translation results.

The significance of these results for the problem of determining a complete axiomatization of predicative mathematics is discussed in the conclusion.

2. Preliminaries for systems with finite formulas

2.1. *Basic syntax and logic*

A language which provides for quantification over the natural numbers as well as over certain definitions of properties of natural numbers must in effect be at least of 2nd-order. For simplicity, we restrict attention throughout to just 2nd-order theories (cf. FEFERMAN [1966] for some stability results involving higher type extensions in the language of set theory).

The syntax is specified as follows. We have 1st-order variables x, y, z, ... and 2nd-order variables X, Y, Z, ... In the case of ramified systems each 2nd-order variable is, in addition, of a specified rank, given by an element of the field of an ordering in the natural numbers; it is assumed that each element has a unique successor in the ordering. There is a constant symbol $\bar{0}$ and a list $'$, f_0, f_1, ... of function symbols for specific primitive recursive functions.[4] The atomic formulas are those of the form $t_1 = t_2$, $t \in X$, $X = Y$ (t, t_1, t_2 1st-order terms). Arbitrary formulas are built up by the usual operations of propositional calculus and the quantifiers in both types; the letters $\mathfrak{F}$, $\mathfrak{G}$ range over these. A formula without bound 2nd-order variables is said to be *arithmetical*; letters $\mathfrak{A}$, $\mathfrak{B}$ range over these formulas. In the ramified case, the rank of any formula $\mathfrak{F}$ is taken to be the maximum of $(0, \text{rank}(Y_i), \text{rank}(Z_j)+1)$ where Y_i, Z_j range over the free, resp. bound variables of $\mathfrak{F}$.

The intended range of the 1st order ('numerical') variables is the set of natural numbers. When ranges are specified for the 2nd order variables each formula $\mathfrak{F}(x)$ with one free variable is regarded as a definition of a property of natural numbers. Ranges for the 2nd-order variables may be specified as

---

[4] With suitable axiomatic basis, it is sufficient to take a pairing function f_0 and its inverses f_1, f_2.

certain collections of definitions. Then a formula $x \in X$ is satisfied by an assignment of a natural number n to x and a formula $\mathfrak{F}$ to X ($\mathfrak{F}$ from such a collection) if $\mathfrak{F}$ holds at n, i.e., if $\mathfrak{F}(\bar{n})$ is true. A formula $X = Y$ is taken to hold under an assignment of $\mathfrak{F}$, $\mathfrak{G}$ to X, Y resp. when $\mathfrak{F}$, $\mathfrak{G}$ hold of exactly the same natural numbers. Unless otherwise specified, $\mathfrak{F}(x)$ will stand for a formula which may contain free variables ('parameters') other than x; such formulas can be regarded as relative definitions under suitable conditions.

The basic logical apparatus of all systems considered consists of the axioms and rules for classical many-sorted predicate calculus with equality. The basic non-logical axioms throughout are, first, extensionality $\wedge X, Y [\wedge x (x \in X \leftrightarrow x \in Y) \rightarrow X = Y]$ and all instances of induction on the natural numbers, $\mathfrak{F}(\bar{0}) \wedge \wedge x [\mathfrak{F}(x) \rightarrow \mathfrak{F}(x')] \rightarrow \wedge x \mathfrak{F}(x)$. This is called the system of 2nd-order number theory or *elementary* analysis. In certain cases, it will also be permitted to apply instances of the comprehension axiom scheme:

$$\vee X \wedge x [x \in X \leftrightarrow \mathfrak{F}(x)]. \tag{2.1}$$

In the ramified case this is allowed whenever the rank of X is at least as large as the rank of $\mathfrak{F}$.

2.2. *Ramified systems*

The predicative interpretation of a ramified system with finite ranks is now evident. The range of the variables of rank 0 consists of all arithmetical formulas $\mathfrak{A}$, and of rank $n+1$ of all formulas $\mathfrak{F}$ of rank $\leqslant n$ (in all cases with just one free variable). The extension of this interpretation to formulas with variables of rank taken from a predicatively recognized transfinite well-ordering is also clear, since a formula $\mathfrak{F}$ with just a free numerical variable is of limit rank α if and only if it is of rank β for some $\beta < \alpha$.

It is more troublesome to give an adequate axiomatic account of the situation at limit ranks. For example, at stage ω one needs something like the following reflection principle, for each formula $\mathfrak{G}(X)$: given that for each n, $\wedge X^n \mathfrak{G}(X^n)$ is predicatively provable, we may infer $\wedge X^\omega \mathfrak{G}(X^\omega)$. For technical purposes this can be simplified by introduction of 'variable ranks' into the symbolism; cf. SCHÜTTE [1963].

Because of the foregoing, transfinite progressions of unramified systems are easier to describe syntactically than the corresponding progressions of ramified systems. Thus while the latter are basic for a direct axiomatization of predicativity, the present exposition will concentrate on the former for the sake of simplicity. The reader is referred to FEFERMAN [1964] pp. 21–22 for more details concerning progressions of ramified systems.

2.3. *Unramified systems; provably definite formulas*

The formulas of the unramified language do not have a direct predicative interpretation. Nevertheless, there is a large class of non-trivial instances of the comprehension schema (2.1) with predicative character, i.e., which lead only to theorems permitting some predicative interpretation. An informal idea which lies behind this is due to Poincaré: predicative classifications "cannot be disordered by the introduction of new elements" (POINCARÉ [1963] p. 47)[5].

Adjoin a new sort of 2nd-order variable $X^*, Y^*, Z^*,\ldots$ to the given language. Associate with each formula $\mathfrak{F}$ the formula $\mathfrak{F}^*$ obtained by replacing each bound 2nd-order variable Z_i of $\mathfrak{F}$ by the corresponding variable Z_i^*. Let S be a set of sentences in the original language, S^* the set of $\mathfrak{G}^*$ for $\mathfrak{G}$ in S. A formula $\mathfrak{F}$ of the original language is said to be *provably definite relative to S* if $(\mathfrak{F}\leftrightarrow\mathfrak{F}^*)$ can be inferred from $S \cup S^* \cup \{\wedge X \vee X^*(X=X^*)\}$; intuitively speaking, the meaning of $\mathfrak{F}$ (assuming S) at any given elements is undisturbed by the introduction of new sets satisfying S.[6]

Throughout the following we use the letters $\mathfrak{P}$ and $\mathfrak{Q}$ to denote *essentially* $\prod_1$, resp. $\sum_1$ formulas, i.e. those in prenex form with all type 1 quantifiers universal, resp. existential. We write $[\mathfrak{F}\leftrightarrow\mathfrak{P},\mathfrak{Q}]$ as an abbreviation for $[\mathfrak{F}\leftrightarrow\mathfrak{P}] \wedge [\mathfrak{P}\leftrightarrow\mathfrak{Q}]$. It is easily seen that for any S,

$$\text{if } S \vdash [\mathfrak{F}\leftrightarrow\mathfrak{P},\mathfrak{Q}] \text{ then } \mathfrak{F} \text{ is provably definite relative to } S. \qquad (2.2)$$

Conversely, following FEFERMAN and KREISEL [1968], it is shown in FEFERMAN [1968b] that:

THEOREM

If $\mathfrak{F}$ is provably definite relative to S then we can find $\mathfrak{P}, \mathfrak{Q}$ such that $S \vdash [\mathfrak{F}\leftrightarrow\mathfrak{P},\mathfrak{Q}]$.[7] $\qquad (2.3)$

---

[5] Poincaré had the natural numbers as a 'potential totality' in mind in this passage; but the idea is equally applicable to definitions in which the property of being a natural number is fixed and the predicative definitions of properties of natural numbers constitute the potential totality considered.

[6] Model-theoretically speaking, using completeness, this is equivalent to saying that $\mathfrak{F}$ is invariant under extensions $M \subseteq M^*$ in models of S when the domains of objects of 1st order are the same in M and M^*.

[7] This is very closely related to the results of FEFERMAN and KREISEL [1968], though not explicitly stated there; the proof is along the lines of the arguments described l.c. Sections 4 and 5. In FEFERMAN [1968b] and [1968c], I shall give new uniform proofs of all these results covering various infinitary languages as well. As stated, (2.3) applies only to finitary

Kreisel's rule (HCR) is the following:

If $\wedge x[\mathfrak{F}(x)\leftrightarrow\mathfrak{P}(x),\mathfrak{Q}(x)]$ *has been proved, infer* $\vee X \wedge x[x\in X\leftrightarrow\mathfrak{F}(x)]$.
(2.4)

By (2.2) and (2.3), systems of finite formulas based on (HCR) will give the same theorems as systems which permit the application of the comprehension axiom (2.1) whenever $\mathfrak{F}$ has been shown to be provably definite relative to the theorems previously obtained. Because it is simpler to describe syntactically, the unramified systems in the following are formulated using (HCR).

3. Autonomous infinite derivations of finite formulas

First consider formal systems described in impredicative terms, using ordinals. The autonomy condition considered here requires proof of the formal statements $WF(\leqslant)$ expressing under the standard impredicative interpretation, that certain ordering relations are well-founded. In the systems studied, all statements which are formally proved are true under this interpretation.

Consider any formula $(x\leqslant y)$ with two free variables and any formula $\mathfrak{F}(x)$; write $TI_x(\mathfrak{F}(x); \leqslant)$ for the conjunction of $\wedge x, y, z(x\leqslant y\wedge y\leqslant z\rightarrow$ $\rightarrow x\leqslant z)\wedge \wedge x, y(x\leqslant y\wedge y\leqslant x\rightarrow x=y)$ (partial ordering) with $\wedge x[x\leqslant x\wedge$ $\wedge \wedge y(y\prec x\rightarrow\mathfrak{F}(y))\rightarrow\mathfrak{F}(x)]\rightarrow \wedge x(x\leqslant x\rightarrow\mathfrak{F}(x))$ (transfinite induction). Then take $I(\leqslant)$ to be $\wedge XTI_x(x\in X; \leqslant)$; this is equivalent to the statement $WF(\leqslant)$ of well-foundedness of $\leqslant$, under the relative arithmetic comprehension axiom. We write $WO(\leqslant)$ for the conjunction of $I(\leqslant)$ with $\wedge x, y(x\leqslant x\wedge$ $\wedge y\leqslant y\rightarrow x\leqslant y\vee y\leqslant x)$ (simple ordering).

When $I(\leqslant)$ is true we can assign ordinals $o(x)$ to elements x of the field of $\leqslant$ by the recursion $o(x)=\sup_{y\prec x}o(y)$. We then take $o(\leqslant)=$ $\sup_{x\leqslant x}o(x)$; this is called the length of the relation $\leqslant$. This notation is extended to well-founded trees T in the natural numbers.

The unramified system (H^+) with infinite derivation trees of finite formulas consists of the axioms and rules of 2nd order number theory mentioned in Section 2.1 together with the rule (HCR) and the ω-rule:

$$from\ \mathfrak{F}(\bar{0}), ..., \mathfrak{F}(\bar{n}), ... infer\ \wedge x\mathfrak{F}(x).$$
(3.1)

Then the class of (H^+)-*autonomous derivations, theorems and ordinals* is defined inductively by: (i) each finite ordinal belongs to the class; (ii) if $\mathcal{D}$

---

languages; an extension of it to systems with infinitely long derivations, even of only finite formulas seems to require the introduction of infinite formulas (cf. Section 5 below).

is a derivation and $o(\mathscr{D})$ belongs then $\mathscr{D}$ itself belongs: (iii) if a derivation $\mathscr{D}$ belongs and $\mathscr{D}$ proves $\mathfrak{F}$ then the theorem $\mathfrak{F}$ belongs; and (iv) if $\bigwedge x,y$ $[x \leqslant y \leftrightarrow \mathfrak{P}(x, y), \mathfrak{Q}(x, y)] \wedge I(\leqslant)$ belongs then $o(\leqslant)$ and all smaller ordinals belong. $\overline{\mathrm{Aut}}(\mathrm{H}^+)$ denotes the least ordinal which is not (H^+)-autonomous.

$\overline{\mathrm{Aut}}(\mathrm{R}^+)$ is defined in a similar way for the infinitary ramified system (R^+). Note that the variable X in a formula $I(\leqslant)$ is in this case ranked. However, if $I(\leqslant)$ can be proved it can also be proved for any other rank introduced, simply by raising all ranks in the derivation of $I(\leqslant)$ by a fixed amount; also $I(\leqslant)$ will be true when ranks are dropped.

The main result (FEFERMAN [1964]) for the ordinals obtained here is formulated in terms of the hierarchy of critical functions $\kappa^{(\nu)}$ of ordinals, defined inductively as follows: $\kappa^{(0)}(\alpha) = \omega^\alpha$, and for $\nu > 0$, $\kappa^{(\nu)}$ is the normal function which enumerates $\{\xi: \text{for all } \mu < \nu, \kappa^{(\mu)}(\xi) = \xi\}$.[8] Then Γ_0 is defined as the least fixed point of the function $\lambda \nu \kappa^{(\nu)}(0)$. Thus $\Gamma_0 = \lim_n \gamma_n$ where $\gamma_0 = 0$, $\gamma_{n+1} = \kappa^{(\gamma_n)}(0)$.

THEOREM

$$\overline{\mathrm{Aut}}(\mathrm{R}^+) = \overline{\mathrm{Aut}}(\mathrm{H}^+) = \Gamma_0. \tag{3.2}$$

As we remarked in Section 1, the result $\overline{\mathrm{Aut}}(\mathrm{R}^+) = \Gamma_0$ was obtained independently by SCHÜTTE [1963], [1965]. My proof of $\overline{\mathrm{Aut}}(\mathrm{R}^+) \leqslant \Gamma_0$ was very similar to his (cut-elimination arguments going back to SCHÜTTE [1960]). I proved $\overline{\mathrm{Aut}}(\mathrm{H}^+) \leqslant \overline{\mathrm{Aut}}(\mathrm{R}^+)$ by showing how to associate with each (H^+)-derivation $\mathscr{D}$ of a formula $\mathfrak{F}$ with $o(\mathscr{D}) = \alpha$ an (R^+)-derivation $\mathscr{D}'$ of a ramified formula $\mathrm{F}^{(\omega^\alpha)}$ with $o(\mathscr{D}') \leqslant \omega^2 \cdot \alpha$. Section 5 below now provides a simple direct proof of $\overline{\mathrm{Aut}}(\mathrm{H}^+) \leqslant \Gamma_0$. It is also not difficult to get a direct proof of $\Gamma_0 \leqslant \overline{\mathrm{Aut}}(\mathrm{H}^+)$ by translating (R^+) into (H^+), cf. FEFERMAN [1964] 6.19. Thus natural intertranslation results are the basis of the first equality in (3.2).

4. Autonomous progressions of formal systems

The general idea of a transfinite progression $\{T_\alpha\}$ of formal systems (in the usual sense) is this: One specifies T_0 and the extension principle for passing from T_α to $T_{\alpha+1}$; at limit ordinals one takes $T_\alpha = \bigcup_{\beta < \alpha} T_\beta$. We call these the *progression conditions*.

For the case of immediate interest, suppose $\mathrm{Pr}_{H_\alpha}(\ulcorner \mathfrak{F} \urcorner)$ expresses that the

---

[8] In the notation of FEFERMAN [1964], $\kappa^{(\nu)}(\alpha) = \chi_\alpha^{(\nu)}$.

formula $\mathfrak{F}$ is derivable from H_α by means of the usual logical rules together with the rule (HCR). The *reflection principle* for H_α is the formalized ω-rule consisting of all instances (with $\wedge\, x\mathfrak{F}(x)$ a sentence) of

$$\wedge\, xPr_{H_\alpha}(\ulcorner\mathfrak{F}(\bar{x})\urcorner) \rightarrow \wedge\, x\mathfrak{F}(x). \qquad (4.1)$$

Then a progression $\{H_\alpha\}$ of unramified theories is determined as follows: H_0 consists of the axioms of elementary analysis, and $H_{\alpha+1}$ is to be H_α together with all instances of (4.1).

This idea is made precise by giving a canonical means of forming the Pr_{H_α} from the *formal description*[9] of the sets H_α; this in turn depends on the notations for the ordinals used, i.e., by which ordering and by which definition of the ordering the ordinals are given. Following Turing's original work on ordinal logics, FEFERMAN [1962] gave a general treatment of progressions $\{T_a\}$ with a in the set O of recursive ordinal notations. In view of the problematic use of well ordering in predicative mathematics, two points of this treatment are important. For a wide class of extension principles, including (4.1), the recursion theorem associates with an arbitrary natural number a, a definition τ_a of a set T_a of axioms in such a way that (i) the progression conditions hold for an arithmetical class of 'pseudo-notations' including O and (ii) elementary proofs of (i) can be given ('verifiable progression formulas', l.c. p. 284).

The restriction to recursive notations was continued in the treatment of the progression $\{H_a\}$ in FEFERMAN [1964]. However, in this case the restriction is ad hoc since not only recursive definitions are predicative. Instead, a more appropriate notion here is as follows. The class of (H)-*autonomous theorems and ordinals* is defined inductively by: (i) each theorem of H_0 belongs to the class; (ii) if $\wedge\, x, y[x\leqslant y\leftrightarrow\mathfrak{P}(x, y), \mathfrak{Q}(x, y)] \wedge I(\leqslant)$ belongs then $o(\leqslant)$ and all smaller ordinals belong; (iii) if $\wedge\, x, y[x\leqslant y\leftrightarrow\mathfrak{P}(x, y), \mathfrak{Q}(x, y)] \wedge \wedge WO(\leqslant)$ belongs and we have *any* formula $Pr_{H_a}(x)$ for which the formalizations of the progression conditions, with a ranging over the field of $\leqslant$, belong to the class – then for each $a\leqslant a$ and theorem $\mathfrak{F}$ of H_a, $\mathfrak{F}$ belongs. We now take $\overline{Aut}(H)$ to be the least non-(H)-autonomous ordinal.

By the corresponding modification in the case of ramified theories in FEFERMAN [1964] one obtains the notions of (R)-*autonomous theorems and ordinals* and $\overline{Aut}(R)$. Then

---

[9] In FEFERMAN [1962] and earlier publications, I spoke of giving a collection of axioms *intensionally* as opposed to giving it *extensionally*, i.e., merely as a set. To avoid confusion with the philosophical problem of *intensions* it seems now preferable to use other terminology such as (for a formula which defines a set), *formal presentation of a set*.

THEOREM

$$\overline{\mathrm{Aut}}(R) = \overline{\mathrm{Aut}}(H) = \Gamma_0. \tag{4.2}$$

Obviously Γ_0 is an upper bound by the result (3.2). The proofs of the reverse inequalities are somewhat more delicate, cf. FEFERMAN [1964] pp. 24–25. Once again natural intertranslations are involved in the first equality stated.

It is not immediate that the set of (H)-autonomous theorems is a subsystem of classical analysis. However, in my 1964 paper I described a single axiomatization (IR) of this set of theorems which is obviously contained in classical analysis. With slight modification, the axioms of (IR) are those of 2nd order number theory and the rules are (HCR) together with rules which permit us to infer $\mathrm{TI}_x(\mathfrak{F}(x); \leqslant)$ and transfinite recursion on $\leqslant$ whenever we have proved

$$\bigwedge x, y [x \leqslant y \leftrightarrow \mathfrak{P}(x, y), \mathfrak{Q}(x, y)] \wedge I(\leqslant).$$

5. Autonomous infinite derivations of infinite formulas

5.1. Background and preliminaries

Some of the sources for the consideration of infinitely long formulas here are as follows. First, Kreisel suggested in his 1962 paper (p. 317) that the stability results should remain unaffected when such formulas are introduced autonomously. Second, TAIT [1968] showed how a cut-elimination theorem for derivations in a form of infinitary *arithmetical analysis* (ramified analysis of rank 0) could be used to get a more direct proof of $\overline{\mathrm{Aut}}(H^+) \leqslant \Gamma_0$. Finally, a result of FEFERMAN [1968b] corresponding to (2.3) for provably definite formulas under infinitely long derivations seems to require in general the use of infinitely long $\mathfrak{P}, \mathfrak{Q}$.[10] Detailed proofs of the new results here will appear elsewhere.

We consider infinitely long formulas (with finitely many free variables) of the unramified 2nd order language, built up from the standard atomic formulas by means of the usual (finite) logical operations and quantifiers and countably long conjunctions $\prod$ and disjunctions $\sum$. Each such formula $\mathfrak{F}$ is regarded as a well-founded tree. We continue to use the letters $\mathfrak{A}, \mathfrak{B}$ for arithmetical formulas, which as before contain no bound 2nd-order variables. The letters $\mathfrak{P}, \mathfrak{Q}$ are now used for *universal*, resp. *existential* formulas i.e., those built up from atomic formulas and their negations using only $\prod, \sum$

---

[10] The technical reason for this is that while cut-elimination results hold for infinitely long derivations of finite formulas, the interpolation results needed for the arguments of FEFERMAN and KREISEL [1968], and FEFERMAN [1968b] require infinitely long formulas.

and universal, resp. existential, quantifiers of either type. Every essentially $\prod_1 (\sum_1)$ finite formula is provably equivalent to a universal (existential) formula under the hypothesis of

$$\bigwedge x \sum_{n < \omega} (x = \bar{n}), \tag{5.1}$$

which permits elimination of 1st order quantifiers in favor of infinite conjunctions and disjunctions entirely. Thus, also extensionality can be put in the form

$$\bigwedge X, Y \left[\prod_{n < \omega} (\bar{n} \in X \leftrightarrow \bar{n} \in Y) \to X = Y \right] \tag{5.2}$$

when (5.1) is assumed; we abbreviate (5.2) as Ext. To get a system including elementary analysis we need only adjoin Z_0, the usual initial axioms of (Z) for $'$, f_0, f_1, ...

The infinitary system (A^+) of arithmetical analysis is specified here as follows. For each arithmetical formula $\mathfrak{A}$ with free variables $x, y_1, ..., y_n$, $Y_1, ..., Y_m$ we have an instance of the comprehension axiom:

$$(CA_{\mathfrak{A}}) \bigwedge y_1, ..., y_n, Y_1, ..., Y_m \bigvee X \bigwedge x [x \in X \leftrightarrow$$
$$\mathfrak{A}(x, y_1, ..., y_n, Y_1, ..., Y_m)]. \tag{5.3}$$

An (A^+)-derivation $\mathscr{D}$ is one which permits (5.1), (5.2), Z_0, and instances of (5.3) as initial non-logical hypotheses. For convenience it is assumed that the logical rules are presented in Gentzen sequent-form including the cut-rule and rules for $=$ (e.g., the rules given by LOPEZ-ESCOBAR [1965]). We shall say that $\mathscr{D}$ proves $\mathfrak{F}$ if it proves the sequent $\to \mathfrak{F}$.

By an (L^+)-derivation $\mathscr{D}$ we mean one which is purely logical, i.e. none of (5.1)–(5.3) are assumed in $\mathscr{D}$. Given an (A^+)-derivation $\mathscr{D}$ let $CA(\mathscr{D})$ be the collection of formulas A such that $(CA_{\mathfrak{A}})$ appears as an hypothesis in $\mathscr{D}$. Suppose such a $\mathscr{D}$ proves $\Gamma \to \Delta$; then we can associate directly with $\mathscr{D}$ an (L^+)-derivation $\mathscr{D}'$ of

$$\bigwedge x \sum_{n < \omega} x = \bar{n}, \text{Ext}, Z_0, \prod_{\mathfrak{A} \in CA(\mathscr{D})} (CA_{\mathfrak{A}}), \Gamma \to \Delta.$$

Infinitary derivations $\mathscr{D}$ can be coded by trees in such a way that the trees of formulas $\mathfrak{F}$ appearing in $\mathscr{D}$ can be derived from $\mathscr{D}$ (so that in particular, $o(\mathfrak{F}) \leqslant o(\mathscr{D})$). Thus when introducing notions of autonomy here it is only necessary to specify under what conditions a derivation $\mathscr{D}$ will be accepted. This is given three successively stronger senses.

5.2. Autonomy in the first sense

The class of (A^+)-*autonomous*(1) *derivations, theorems and ordinals* is defined inductively by: (i) each finite ordinal belongs to the class; (ii) if $\mathscr{D}$ is

an (A^+)-derivation and $o(\mathscr{D})$ belongs then $\mathscr{D}$ itself belongs; (iii) if a derivation $\mathscr{D}$ belongs and $\mathscr{D}$ proves $\mathfrak{F}$ then $\mathfrak{F}$ belongs; and (iv) if $\bigwedge x, y [x \leqslant y \leftrightarrow \leftrightarrow \mathfrak{P}(x, y), \mathfrak{Q}(x, y)] \wedge I(\leqslant)$ belongs then $o(\leqslant)$ and all smaller ordinals belong. $\overline{\mathrm{Aut}}_1(A^+)$ is the least ordinal which is not (A^+)-autonomous(1).
The principal result here is the following.

THEOREM

(i) $\overline{\mathrm{Aut}}_1(A^+) = \Gamma_0$.   (ii)   *The set of (A^+)-autonomous(1) theorems is closed under the rule* (HCR) *and hence is an extension of*   (5.4)
the set of (H^+)-*autonomous theorems.*

We shall only indicate the main steps of the proof. $\Gamma_0 \leqslant \overline{\mathrm{Aut}}_1(A^+)$ follows from the fact that the set of (A^+)-autonomous (1) theorems is closed under the second and third rules of (IR) with recursive $\leqslant$. The reverse inequality and (ii) can be obtained from the following:

with each (A^+)-derivation $\mathscr{D}$ of $(\mathfrak{P} \leftrightarrow \mathfrak{Q})$ such that $o(\mathscr{D}) < \Gamma_0$ can be associated an arithmetical $\mathfrak{B}$ and (A^+)-derivation $\mathscr{D}'$ of $(\mathfrak{B} \leftrightarrow \mathfrak{P})$ (5.5)
with $o(\mathscr{D}') < \Gamma_0$.

To see this, assume the hypothesis of (5.5). Consider the definitional extension got by introducing a function symbol $F_{\mathfrak{A}}$ for each $\mathfrak{A} \in \mathrm{CA}(\mathscr{D})$ with corresponding axiom

$$(\mathrm{CA}_{\mathfrak{A}}^*) \ \bigwedge x, y_1, \ldots, y_n, Y_1, \ldots, Y_m [x \in F_{\mathfrak{A}}(y_1, \ldots, y_n, Y_1, \ldots, Y_m) \leftrightarrow$$
$$\mathfrak{A}(x, y_1, \ldots, y_n, Y_1, \ldots, Y_m)].   (5.6)$$

Then we can get an (L^+)-derivation $\mathscr{D}^*$ with $o(\mathscr{D}^*) < \Gamma_0$ of

$$\bigwedge x \sum_{n < \omega} x = \bar{n}, \ \mathrm{Ext}, \ Z_0, \ \prod_{\mathfrak{A} \in \mathrm{CA}(\mathscr{D})} (\mathrm{CA}_{\mathfrak{A}}^*), \ \mathfrak{P} \to \mathfrak{Q}.   (5.7)$$

The hypothesis Δ here consists of universal formulas, the conclusion is existential. It follows from an interpolation theorem of BARWISE [1967] that there is a quantifier-free (interpolant) $\mathfrak{B}_1$ and (L^+)-derivations $\mathscr{D}_1, \mathscr{D}_2$ of $\Delta \to \mathfrak{B}_1$ and $\mathfrak{B}_1 \to \mathfrak{Q}$ resp., such that $o(\mathscr{D}_1) < \Gamma_0$, $o(\mathscr{D}_2) < \Gamma_0$.[11] $\mathfrak{B}_1$ may contain the function symbols $F_{\mathfrak{A}}$ for $\mathfrak{A} \in \mathrm{CA}(\mathscr{D})$, but these can now be eliminated by substitution to give the required $\mathfrak{B}$.

---

[11] The bounds $< \Gamma_0$ are not given explicitly in BARWISE [1967], but the additional information is not hard to obtain from the following refinement of the cut-elimination theorem for (L^+)-derivations (cf., e.g., FEFERMAN [1968b]): if $\mathscr{D}$ is an (L^+)-derivation, $o(\mathscr{D}) = \alpha$ and $v = \sup[o(\mathfrak{F}) + 1, \mathfrak{F}$ a cut-formula in $\mathscr{D}]$ then we can find a cut-free derivation $\mathscr{D}'$ of the same conclusion as $\mathscr{D}$ with $o(\mathscr{D}) \leqslant' \kappa^{(v)}(\alpha)$.

5.3. *Autonomy in stronger senses*

The tree of a derivation $\mathscr{D}$ is given by the set $Tr_{\mathscr{D}}$ of sequence numbers $x = \langle x_0, \ldots, x_k \rangle$ of initial segments of the branches. Then for (A^+)-autonomy (2) we require that the *set of x in $Tr_{\mathscr{D}}$ be already defined by a provably definite formula.* The preceding theorem (5.4) continues to hold if '1' is replaced throughout by '2'.

Finally, for (A^+)-autonomy (3) we require in addition that *there be already a proof that the formula which in fact defines $Tr_{\mathscr{D}}$ satisfies the defining conditions (including well-foundedness) for an (A^+)-derivation.* While every true arithmetical sentence is (A^+)-autonomous (2), the stronger requirement in this last notion allows us to obtain:

THEOREM

The set of (A^+)-autonomous(3) theorems is a conservative extension of (IR). $\qquad$ (5.8)

6. Conclusion

The work described here leads us to the following two theses: (1) Γ_0 is the least upper bound of the *predicative ordinals* in the sense that: (1)* whenever iteration of the basic predicative step relative to any ordering relation $\leqslant$ can be predicatively justified we have $o(\leqslant) < \Gamma_0$, and (1)** such iteration can be predicatively justified for each initial segment of the natural well-ordering $\leqslant_{\Gamma_0}$ of order-type Γ_0(in ω). (2) The set of (R)-autonomous theorems coincides with the set of predicatively provable statements of analysis.

I believe both these to be correct and that the stability results described here provide some evidence for (1) (though, of course, they do not exclude systematic error). In particular, the evidence for (1)* is rather convincing and can be put as follows: nothing like the ramified progressions will go beyond Γ_0, given that predicative justification of iteration relative to $\leqslant$ must yield well-ordering of $\leqslant$ under the impredicative interpretation. I expect that convincing evidence for (1)** will be provided by an explanation of the autonomy conditions in predicative terms and a re-examination of the proof that $\Gamma_0 \leqslant \overline{\text{Aut}}(R)$. The same kind of analysis will of course be required in order to support (2).

It may not be possible to obtain as definitive results for predicativity as Gödel's completeness theorem for predicate logic with respect to intuitive logical validity. Nevertheless, it is certainly possible to subject (1) and (2) to a greater variety of tests, using the most evident properties of predicativity such as (a) every arithmetic definition is predicative and (b) every predicatively defined set is hyperarithmetic (by Spector's work, cf. FEFERMAN [1964] pp. 9–10 and also by the argument there p. 11).

The most obvious objection to (1)* was discussed and answered by KREISEL [1965] p. 178 (3.631). He also raised the possibility of a more interesting objection: for a predicative proof of $I(\leqslant_{\Gamma_0})$ it would be sufficient to give a predicative proof that for all linear orderings $\leqslant$, $I(\leqslant) \rightarrow I(K(\leqslant))$; here K is a natural extension to linear orderings of the function on well-orderings with $o(K(\leqslant)) = \kappa^{(o(\leqslant))}(0)$. However, this possibility is excluded by an example, recently communicated to us by H. Friedman, of a recursive ordering $\leqslant$ which contains no hyperarithmetic descending sequences but for which $K(\leqslant)$ contains an arithmetic (in fact, primitive recursive) descending sequence. For this conflicts with (a) and (b) since $I(\leqslant) \rightarrow I(K(\leqslant))$ is false when relativized to any subclass C of the hyperarithmetic sets which contains all arithmetic sets.[12] Both this test question and its solution provide very nice examples of what we have in mind.

A correction to FEFERMAN [1964] Section 4, where I used the term 'predicative definability' as if it could be treated independently of considerations of predicative justification. I discussed the commonly stated thesis that the predicatively definable sets are just the hyperarithmetic sets, but defended only the part (b) of it above.[13] In any case, the terminology there was suspect,

---

[12] This is analogous to the result of PARIKH [1966] which produces an ordering $\leqslant$ well-ordered with respect to recursive descending sequences but for which $2^{\leqslant}$ has a primitive recursive descending sequence. This can be used (cf. KREISEL [1968], 6(b)) to refute an 'argument' against ε_0 as the upper bound for finitist well-orderings on the assumptions: all primitive recursive descending sequences are finitist and all finitist functions are recursive.
[13] The limitations of the theory of hyperarithmetic sets for an analysis of predicative definitions are pointed out in KREISEL [1962] pp. 318–319, particularly the remark on p. 318 and (b) on p. 319; the impredicative element in going beyond Γ_0 is located explicitly. Perhaps it is useful to supplement this discussion as follows. Definitions given in, say, the languages considered here presuppose an interpretation of the logical operations; if this interpretation is to be classical, the *range* of the quantifiers must be given, and to be predicative the *whole range* must be previously comprehended. Consider KLEENE's [1959] *basis theorems* from this point of view (which are, formally, similar to Poincaré's idea cited in Section 2.3 above), and coinsider the definition of H_{Γ_0} by a formula $\vee X \mathfrak{A}(n, X)$ with the properties: $H_{\Gamma_0} = \{n : \vee X \mathfrak{A}(n, X)\}$ and $\wedge n, X[\mathfrak{A}(n, X) \rightarrow X$ is recursive in H_a for some $a \prec \Gamma_0]$. Though each X 'needed' in this definition occurs in the hyperarithmetic hierarchy before Γ_0, even granting that each such set is predicatively definable is not sufficient for a conclusion that this definition is predicative. It would also be necessary to first recognize predicatively the iteration of the jump operation relative to $\leqslant_{\Gamma_0}$ in order to comprehend the entire range of X needed here.

since predicativity is primarily connected with definability and the main claim of that paper was that only the ramified hierarchy up to Γ_0 was predicatively justified. It should be added that the only essential place where 'provability' intervenes in our work is in the autonomy condition concerning the number of iterations of predicative definition processes, in other words, where a precise substitute for the, as yet incompletely analyzed, idea of predicative ordinal is treated.

References

BARWISE, K.J., Infinitary logic and admissible sets, Dissertation, Stanford University, 1967.

FEFERMAN, S., Transfinite recursive progressions of axiomatic theories, J. Symb. Logic 27 (1962) 259–316.

FEFERMAN, S., Systems of predicative analysis, J. Symb. Logic 29 (1964) 1–30.

FEFERMAN, S., Predicative provability in set theory, (Research Announcement) Bull. Am. Math. Soc. 72 (1966) 486–489.

FEFERMAN, S., Systems of predicative analysis II: Representations of ordinals, J. Symb. Logic (1968a) to appear.

FEFERMAN, S., Lectures on proof theory, Proc. Leeds 1967 Summer Institute in Logic (1968b) to appear.

FEFERMAN, S., Persistent and invariant formulas for outer extensions (1968c) to appear.

FEFERMAN, S. and G. KREISEL, Persistent and invariant formulas relative to theories of higher order, (Research Announcement) Bull. Am. Math. Soc. 72 (1968) 480–485.

KLEENE, S.C., Quantification of number-theoretic functions, Compositio Math. 14 (1959) 23–40.

KREISEL, G., Ordinal logics and the characterization of informal concepts of proof, Proc. Intern. Congress of Mathematicians, 14–21 August 1958, pp. 289–299.

KREISEL, G., La prédicativité, Bull. Soc. Math. de France 88 (1960) 371–391.

KREISEL, G., The axiom of choice and the class of hyperarithmetic functions, Indag. Math. 24 (1962) 307–319.

KREISEL, G., Mathematical logic, in: Lectures on Modern Mathematics Vol. III, ed. T.L. Saaty (New York, Wiley, 1965) pp. 95–195.

KREISEL, G., A survey of proof theory, J. Symb. Logic (1968) to appear.

LOPEZ-ESCOBAR, E.G.K., An interpolation theorem for denumerably long formulas, Fund. Math. 57 (1965) 253–272.

PARIKH, R.J., Some generalizations of the notion of well-ordering, Z. math. Logik und Grundl. Math. 12 (1966) 333–340.

POINCARÉ, H., Mathematics and Science: Last Essays (Transl. of: Dernières Pensées) (New York, Dover, 1963).

SCHÜTTE, K., Beweistheorie (Berlin, Springer, 1960).

SCHÜTTE, K., Predicative well-orderings, in: Formal Systems and Recursive Functions, eds. J.N. Crossley and M. Dummett (Amsterdam, North-Holland, Publ. Co., 1963) pp. 279–302.

SCHÜTTE, K., Eine Grenze für die Beweisbarkeit der Transfiniten Induktion in der verzweigten Typenlogik, Arch. math. Logik und Grundlagenforschung 7 (1965) 45–60.

TAIT, W.W., Normal derivability in classical logic (1968) to appear.

CONSTRUCTIVE FUNCTIONS IN
"THE FOUNDATIONS OF INTUITIONISTIC MATHEMATICS"

S. C. KLEENE

The University of Wisconsin, Madison, Wis., USA

This paper has a modest aim: to say what we can about constructive functions in the formal system of intuitionistic analysis in our recent monograph with Vesley (KLEENE and VESLEY [1965], hereafter cited as "FIM"). Meanwhile, bold new initiatives have been taken in the formalization of intuitionistic analysis by Kreisel, Kripke and Myhill.

The formal system of FIM has been criticized on the ground that its symbolism lacks a distinction between constructive functions and free choice sequences. Unquestionably, this distinction is vital for intuitionism. The fact that we did not make it in the symbolism is not an oversight. Indeed, we personally were led into the study of intuitionism (since 1939) by asking the question whether the constructive operations, functions, etc. of intuitionism can be identified with general (or partial) recursive functions. So it was a natural step for us to propose to identify the "laws" in Brouwer's definition of 'set' or 'spread' with general recursive functions, as we did in 1941 (unpublished then, published in [1950a]) and BETH did in [1947]. Yet in FIM (1965) we left out this identification.

In FIM we aimed to set up as simple a system as we could in which the standard intuitionistic analysis (or theory of the continuum) can be developed.[1] To us it seemed more interesting to confirm that this analysis can be developed with only what we used, than to set up at once a more powerful system. The field was thereby left open to anyone (including ourselves) to add more for further purposes.

The reason we didn't supply separate variables for constructive functions is that we took the constructiveness of the function α to be implicit in the

---

[1] We stopped short of the theory of species of higher order. Species of first order are present in one sense (they are expressed by formulas), though not in another (there are no variables for them).

intuitionistic meaning of the existential quantifier $\exists\alpha$, when the existence is affirmed outright or absolutely, as in any closed provable formula $\exists\alpha A(\alpha)$.

Of course, there are also existence statements which are relative. For example, intuitionism certainly accepts $\exists\beta\ \forall x\ \beta(x)=\alpha(2x)$ or $\forall\alpha\ \exists\beta\ \forall x\ \beta(x)=\alpha(2x)$. Here the $\forall\alpha$ expresses that the successive values of α are chosen completely freely (from the universal spread); then the $\exists\beta$ expresses that the β can be constructed from the α (indeed, by omitting the 2nd, 4th, 6th, ... values of α). The same proposition can be expressed in an idiom of absolute existence, by using (instead of the function variable β) a functional variable F, thus: $\exists F\ \forall\alpha\ \forall x\ F(\alpha)(x)=\alpha(2x)$.

It seemed to us, when we finally came to write FIM Chapter I, that there is a certain elegance in letting the constructiveness be expressed contextually, when altogether intuitionism deals not only with absolute constructions and free choices, but also with a rich variety of relative constructions, at least under one interpretation.

Now, maybe this is a matter of taste; or maybe we made a definite mistake, not by accident but by misjudgement, in leaving out separate constructive-function variables in FIM.[2]

Let us at any rate get the facts straight about the situation in FIM.[3] For I think I can say fairly that FIM was written very slowly and carefully; and e.g. the careful development of the intuitionistic theory of the continuum in Vesley's Chapter III deserves not to be disparaged or discarded on the ground of alleged deficiencies in Kleene's formalization in Chapter I, without a careful hearing.

True: FIM does not have a separate sort of variables specifically for con-

---

[2] Another point in the formalization in FIM criticized by MYHILL [1967] is that the free choice sequences are extensional. Certainly, extensional free choice sequences are intuitionistically acceptable; for these, one restricts the freedom of the choices only by the choice law adopted in advance. Since in fact the intuitionistic theory of the continuum can be developed using only extensional choice sequences, it seems more interesting to do so. The complication of nonextensional free choice sequences (where at each choice one picks both a function value and a new choice law within the preceding one) can be left until a need arises, as perhaps for the formalization of Brouwer's "historical" arguments.

[3] In [1967a] MYHILL also criticizes the formalization in FIM pp. 64–69 of Brouwer's longer proof of the bar theorem, as "circular from the point of view of one who does not accept the theorem and superfluous from the point of view of one who does". — It was exactly our purpose in FIM pp. 64–69 to lead the reader to recognize the circularity or superfluity of the longer proof. Kreisel's inductive definition of the species K of continuous functionals (in the unpublished notes of the Stanford seminar on the foundations of analysis in 1963) now provides an alternative postulate to the bar theorem itself that some may find more fundamental and intuitive (cf. FIM p. 51). It constitutes another way of introducing the reversal of direction (cf. pp. 50, 65).

structive functions. Nor does it have a prime formula $C(\alpha)$, for which more or less in the way of properties might be postulated, to express that α is a constructive function. However, FIM does certainly have a composite formula $GR(\alpha)$ expressing that α is a general recursive function, and thus, if Church's thesis is used, a constructive function. Using our normal form theorem (e.g. p. 288 of KLEENE [1952b], hereafter cited as "IM"), we can take for $GR(\alpha)$ the following formula.

$$GR(\alpha): \qquad \exists e \, \forall x \, \exists y \, [T_1(e, x, y) \, \& \, U(y) = \alpha(x)],$$

where T_1 and U express a suitable primitive recursive predicate and function respectively. All primitive recursive predicates are numeralwise expressible, and expressible under the interpretation, even in just the number-theoretic part of the intuitionistic system of FIM, and indeed in the intuitionistic system of IM (cf. p. 244). And if, for the version of the normal form theorem selected, $U(y)$ is not expressible by a term, we can simply replace $U(y) = \alpha(x)$ above by $U(y, \alpha(x))$ where $U(y, z)$ expresses the representing predicate $U(y) = z$ of $U(y)$. (We won't bother to do so in the present paper.) Alternatively, we can now construe Postulate Group D of FIM, as we left open the possibility of doing on p. 19, to include the recursion equations for further primitive recursive functions sufficient to give us $T_1(e, x, y)$ as a standard formula (FIM p. 27) and $U(y)$ as a term.

Thus it is not true, if we avail ourselves of Church's thesis, that one cannot in FIM express the notion of a Brouwer (i.e. constructive) spread. To say that σ is the choice law for such a spread, we can simply write $GR(\sigma) \& Spr(\sigma)$ (FIM p. 56).

The notion of a spread would obviously make no sense if the values of the choice "law" — so-to-speak, the fencing within which one must stay along any path of successive free choices — were not predetermined. So, I believe, Brouwer envisaged his choice laws as being what we are now calling constructive or computable functions (or by Church's thesis, general recursive functions).

However, it was our intention in FIM to represent Brouwer's and Heyting's thinking in its essentials as we understood it, but without following them slavishly. It appears to us that what is essential to the spread concept is not that the choice law be constructive (as ordinarily), but merely that it be fixed and knowable, potentially ad infinitum, in advance of making the choices for any member of the spread.

We illustrate this by defending FIM *R14.9 p. 167, which is of the form $\alpha, \beta \in R' \supset \exists \sigma \{Spr(\sigma) \& A(\alpha, \beta, \sigma)\}$. This has been criticized as attributing to spreads a property Brouwer would never have claimed for them; for, on taking α and β to be the same, it says that every choice sequence α chosen from R' constitutes a one-element spread!

What *R14.9 means is as follows. Suppose there are two persons who are choosing, say Myhill and I. Let us picture Myhill as sitting in a booth, choosing successive values of α and of β, each from the spread R', and passing them out through a window. Myhill is industrious and untiring, but I am in no hurry. Now is there any reason why I cannot in a leisurely manner choose the successive values of γ from a spread whose choice "law" σ is a certain function constructively determined from α and β? (The actual definition of σ from α and β is shown on p. 167.) For, as we conduct this exercise, σ is just as much determined and available to me, for the purpose of fencing to confine my choices for γ, as if its values were computed. Indeed, we can imagine Myhill crouched down inside the booth where I cannot see him. So I need not know that the booth contains Myhill making free choices rather than a Turing machine computing values. The output as it comes to me outside the booth is indistinguishable at every finite stage. And what I do with the output is the same in either case. I have only to test the admissibility under the choice law σ of values of γ I would like to choose. Each time I want to make a test, if enough of an initial segment of the values of α and β hasn't appeared yet to determine the value of σ I need, I simply wait for Myhill or the machine to produce sufficient further ones, as he or it eventually will. I don't see why this isn't a perfectly good intuitionistic conception, even if Brouwer didn't think of it (maybe he did).[4] For each way Myhill may choose the sequences α and β, I get my spread σ. Altogether, we have a family of spreads σ, correlated to the pairs of free choice sequences α and β chosen from the spread R'. So I believe *R14.9 is a useful theorem (for its intended purpose), which I see no reason to forego, though its specialization to $\alpha = \beta$ is hardly of much interest in its correct interpretation.

Of course, the use of the symbolism $\text{Spr}(\sigma)$ in *R14.9 may be misleading to one who has in mind only the absolutely constructive spreads of Brouwer.

In the starred results of FIM, $\text{Spr}(\sigma)$ appears in three situations.

One is illustrated by *R14.9 (just discussed), which would be false if we substituted for $\text{Spr}(\sigma)$ the symbols $\text{GR}(\sigma)\,\&\,\text{Spr}(\sigma)$ to claim an absolutely

---

[4] I am understanding that Brouwer in his notion of 'free choice sequence' does really mean that values are successively chosen, as he seems to say; and not that he is just using a picturesque circumlocution for talking about the choice law. But even in the latter reading, one choice law depending on the choices under another seems to me a perfectly good intuitionistic conception — another, more complicated, circumlocution is then involved.

constructive spread (Brouwer); the spread σ in *R14.9 is only constructive relative to α and β.

The second situation is illustrated by *26.4 p. 57, *26.7 p. 62 and *27.4 p. 74, which have the form $\mathrm{Spr}(\sigma)\,\&\,A(\sigma)\supset B$ or $\mathrm{Spr}(\sigma)\,\&\,A(\sigma)\supset B(\sigma)$. So, trivially, the results would also hold if $\mathrm{Spr}(\sigma)$ had been replaced by $\mathrm{GR}(\sigma)\,\&\,\mathrm{Spr}(\sigma)$. But (as it seemed to us), why should we do that, since the results hold in the stronger forms given? (Early in our enterprise, the $\mathrm{GR}(\sigma)$ would have been built into the definition of $\mathrm{Spr}(\sigma)$; but later we came to regard this as superfluous.)

The third situation is illustrated by *R0.8 p. 136, which has the form of a closed formula $\exists\sigma[\mathrm{Spr}(\sigma)\,\&\,A(\sigma)]$. Here, in view of the above remark that a provable closed $\exists\alpha$-formula asserts the existence of a constructive function, the meaning is that the σ is a Brouwer (constructive) spread. (Indeed, this is shown by the formula for σ in the proof of *R0.8.)

The reader who has become familiar with the difference between formal contexts in FIM where a construction is asserted as performable absolutely and where it is only asserted as performable relatively will not, we believe, be disturbed by the use of $\mathrm{Spr}(\sigma)$ for "σ is a spread" in both absolute and relative senses.

Should a person wish to use constructive spreads in the formalism of FIM in contexts where the constructivity is not implicit, e.g. in the antecedent of an implication, like the second situation but with the constructiveness essential to the implication, he need only write $\mathrm{GR}(\sigma)\,\&\,\mathrm{Spr}(\sigma)$, if he is willing to work under Church's thesis.

Returning to the third situation, where we have taken the constructiveness to be given implicitly, it is a fair question now whether the results can also be established with the constructiveness explicit. Thus, could we have proved *R0.8 in the form $\exists\sigma[\mathrm{GR}(\sigma)\,\&\,\mathrm{Spr}(\sigma)\,\&\,A(\sigma)]$? This question is not quite fully formulated, as we haven't said just how $\mathrm{GR}(\sigma)$ is to be chosen. (Different proofs of our normal form theorem give different choices of T_1 and U.) In the particular case of *R0.8, the formula introducing σ is simply a formalized course-of-values recursion, so σ is primitive recursive. In any decent formalized theory of general recursive functions, we should certainly be able to prove $\mathrm{GR}(\sigma)$ for the σ in the proof of *R0.8.

To answer the question in general, we propose to prove the following metamathematical theorem, for a suitable proof of the normal form theorem.

In the intuitionistic formal system of analysis of FIM *(or in the basic system there), if* $\vdash \exists\alpha\,A(\alpha)$ *where* $\exists\alpha\,A(\alpha)$ *is closed, then* $\vdash \exists\alpha[\mathrm{GR}(\alpha)\,\&\,A(\alpha)]$.

Indeed, if $\vdash \exists \alpha A(\alpha)$ *where* $\exists \alpha A(\alpha)$ *is closed, then, for a suitable natural number* e,

$$\vdash \forall x \exists y\, T_1(e, x, y)\, \&\, \forall \alpha \{\forall x \exists y\, [T_1(e, x, y)\, \&\, U(y) = \alpha(x)] \supset A(\alpha)\}.$$

The latter formula expresses that e is the Gödel number or index of a general recursive function α such that $A(\alpha)$.[5]

I say that I propose to prove this theorem (so officially, I am formulating a problem), because the moment of this Congress has arrived before I have had time for final editing and checking of a probable proof of which I have completed a first draft.[6]

The key to this probable proof is a formalized realizability notion, differing from the formalizations of the realizability notions in FIM. To state this new notion $\varepsilon\, q\, E$ concisely, we shall use the abbreviation "$!!\{\tau\}[\alpha]\, \&\, [A(\{\tau\}[\alpha])]$" (read "$\{\tau\}[\alpha]$ is properly defined, and $A(\{\tau\}[\alpha])$") for

$$\forall t \exists! y\, \tau(2^{t+1} * \bar{\alpha}(y)) > 0\, \&\, \forall \beta\, [\forall t \exists y\, \tau(2^{t+1} * \bar{\alpha}(y)) = \beta(t) + 1 \supset A(\beta)],$$

with the obvious stipulations on the variables. Cf. FIM p. 91 for the informal notion thus formalized (and for the stipulations on the variables, p. 9). For example, using this abbreviation, Clauses 4 and 8 of KLEENE [1964a] p. 33 can be written thus:

r4. $\varepsilon r (A \supset B)$ is $\forall \alpha \{\alpha r A \supset\, !!\{\varepsilon\}[\alpha]\, \&\, [\{\varepsilon\}[\alpha] r B]\}$.

r8. $\varepsilon r \forall \alpha\, A(\alpha)$ is $\forall \alpha \{!!\{\varepsilon\}[\alpha]\, \&\, [\{\varepsilon\}[\alpha] r A(\alpha)]\}$.

We use similar abbreviations corresponding to the informal notations "$\{\tau\}[a]$", "$\{\tau\}$" and "$\{\tau\}[a_1, ..., a_k, \alpha_1, ..., \alpha_l]$" of FIM p. 92 as the above does to "$\{\tau\}[\alpha]$" of FIM p. 91.

Now we define a formula $\varepsilon\, q\, E$ for each formula E of FIM, by recursion on the number of (occurrences of) logical symbols in E, as follows.

q1. $\varepsilon\, q\, P$ is P, for P a prime formula.

q2. $\varepsilon\, q\, (A\, \&\, B)$ is $(\varepsilon)_0\, q\, A\, \&\, (\varepsilon)_1\, q\, B$.

q3. $\varepsilon\, q\, (A \vee B)$ is

$$[(\varepsilon(0))_0 = 0 \supset (\varepsilon)_1\, q\, A\, \&\, A]\, \&\, [(\varepsilon(0))_0 \neq 0 \supset (\varepsilon)_1\, q\, B\, \&\, B].$$

---

[5] A Turing machine can compute the e from a given proof of the formula supposed to be provable.

[6] My work in formalizing recursion theory and realizability theory is considerably further along than when I referred to it in FIM (bottom p. 110 and top p. 111) and in Kleene [1964a] (p. 34 footnote 5, and top p. 42). Then some parts of the path to be traversed were uncharted; but now I have mapped the whole journey in considerable detail, subject to final verifications.

q4. $\varepsilon\,q\,(A \supset B)$ is $\forall a\,\{a\,q\,A\,\&\,A \supset\,!!\,\{\varepsilon\}[a]\,\&\,[\{\varepsilon\}[a]\,q\,B]\}$.

q5. $\varepsilon\,q\,\neg\,A$ is $\forall a\,\neg\,(a\,q\,A\,\&\,A)$.

q6. $\varepsilon\,q\,\forall x\,A(x)$ is $\forall x\,\{!!\,\{\varepsilon\}[x]\,\&\,[\{\varepsilon\}[x]\,q\,A(x)]\}$.

q7. $\varepsilon\,q\,\exists x\,A(x)$ is $(\varepsilon)_1\,q\,A((\varepsilon(0))_0)\,\&\,A((\varepsilon(0))_0)$.

q8. $\varepsilon\,q\,\forall a\,A(a)$ is $\forall a\,\{!!\,\{\varepsilon\}[a]\,\&\,[\{\varepsilon\}[a]\,q\,A(a)]\}$.

q9. $\varepsilon\,q\,\exists a\,A(a)$ is $!!\,\{(\varepsilon)_0\}\,\&\,[(\varepsilon)_1\,q\,A(\{(\varepsilon)_0\})\,\&\,A(\{(\varepsilon)_0\})]$.

The formula $\varepsilon\,q\,E$ is related to $\varepsilon\,r\,E$ in somewhat the same way as in IM p. 503 'e realizes-($\vdash$) E' (i.e. 'e realizes-($\Gamma\,\vdash$) E' for Γ empty) is related to 'e realizes E'. But, e.g. in Clause q4 here the modification of Clause r4 consists in inserting "$\&\,A$", while in IM (for Γ empty) the corresponding insertion is of "and $\vdash A$", which of course does not formalize as "$\&\,A$" simply.

We plan to show that, where "$\vdash_I$" expresses provability in the intuitionistic system I of FIM:

(***) $\mathit{If}\,\vdash_I E,$ then $\vdash_I \exists\varepsilon\,[GR(\varepsilon)\,\&\,\varepsilon\,q\,\forall E]$,

or more briefly $\vdash_I E \rightarrow \vdash_I \exists\varepsilon_{GR(\varepsilon)}\,\varepsilon\,q\,\forall E$. The proof of this should differ only slightly from a proof of the following, where "B" refers to the basic system:

(**) $\mathit{If}\,\vdash_I E,$ then $\vdash_B \exists\varepsilon\,[GR(\varepsilon)\,\&\,\varepsilon\,r\,\forall E]$.

Thus the work to be done to fill in the gaps here and in KLEENE [1964a] p. 42 footnote 9 should be performable in parallel.

Suppose now that (***) has been established. Then, if $\vdash \exists a A(a)$ where $\exists a A(a)$ is closed, we would have

$$\vdash \exists\varepsilon\,[GR(\varepsilon)\,\&\,!!\,\{(\varepsilon)_0\}\,\&\,[(\varepsilon)_1\,q\,A(\{(\varepsilon)_0\})\,\&\,A(\{(\varepsilon)_0\})]],$$

whence easily

$$\vdash \exists\varepsilon\,[GR(\varepsilon)\,\&\,!!\,\{(\varepsilon)_0\}\,\&\,[A(\{(\varepsilon)_0\})]].$$

Thence our desired result in the first form will follow, if the formal theory of general and partial recursive functions allows (as it should) the inference that, when ε is general recursive, and $\{(\varepsilon)_0\}$ is properly defined, $\{(\varepsilon)_0\}$ is a general recursive function. To get the second form, we use the consideration that in the proof of (***), as in that of (**), we would actually do the work, not with $\exists\varepsilon_{GR(\varepsilon)}$ prefixed to the statement that ε realizes the closure $\forall E$ of E, but instead using (a formal representation of) a realization function for E itself, paralleling the informal proof of Theorem 9.3(a) in FIM pp. 105–109.

This treatment should also give results like the following, for the full intuitionistic system I of FIM. (Previously, only the first two were established, by a different method, by JOAN RAND MOSCHOVAKIS [1965], for the basic system B and various subsystems of that.)

If ⊢ A ∨ B *where* A ∨ B *is closed, then* ⊢ A *or* ⊢ B.

If ⊢ ∃xA(x) *where* ∃xA(x) *is closed, then, for some number* x, ⊢ A(x).

If ⊢ ∀x∃yA(x, y) *where* ∀x∃yA(x, y) *is closed, then* ⊢ ∃α[GR(α) & ∀x A(x, α(x))]*, and, for some number* e, ⊢∀x∃y[T₁(e, x, y) & A(x, U(y))] *and, when* α *is the general recursive function having the Gödel number (or index)* e, (x) {⊢ A(x, y) *for* y=α(x)}.[5]

In contrast to the last result e.g., at least by use of classical informal reasoning with the realizability notion of FIM (cf. pp. 97–99):

There is a closed formula ∀x∃yA(x, y) *such that*

$$\forall x\, \exists y\, A(x, y) \supset \exists\alpha\, [GR(\alpha)\, \&\, \forall x\, A(x, \alpha(x))]$$

and equivalently

$$\forall x\, \exists y\, A(x, y) \supset \exists e\, \forall x\, \exists y\, [T_1(e, x, y)\, \&\, A(x, U(y))]$$

are unprovable in I.

References

BETH, E. W.
  1947. *Semantical considerations on intuitionistic mathematics*, Kon. Ned. Akad. Wet., Proc. Sect. Sci., vol. 50, pp. 1246–1251 (— Indag. Math., vol. 9, pp. 572–577).
KLEENE, S. C.
  1950a. *Recursive functions and intuitionistic mathematics*, Proc. Intern. Congress Math. (Cambridge, Mass., USA, Aug. 30–Sept. 6, 1950), 1952, vol. 1, pp. 679–685.
  1952b. *Introduction to metamathematics* (Amsterdam, North-Holland Publ. Co.; Groningen, Noordhoff; New York and Toronto, Van Nostrand).
  1964a. *Classical extensions of intuitionistic mathematics*, in: Logic, methodology and philosophy of science, ed. Y. Bar-Hillel (Amsterdam, North-Holland Publ. Co., 1965 pp. 31–44.
KLEENE, S. C. and VESLEY, R. E.
  1965. *The foundations of intuitionistic mathematics, especially in relation to recursive functions* (Amsterdam, North-Holland Publ. Co.).
MOSCHOVAKIS, JOAN RAND
  1965. *Disjunction, existence and λ-eliminability in formalized intuitionistic analysis*, Ph. D. thesis, Univ. of Wisconsin.
MYHILL, J.
  1967. *Notes towards an axiomatization of intuitionistic analysis*, Logique et analyse 35, pp. 280–297.
  1967a. *Formal systems of intuitionistic analysis I*, these proceedings, pp. 161–178.

FUNCTIONS, ORDINALS, SPECIES *

G. KREISEL

Department of Philosophy, Stanford University, Stanford, Calif., USA

Introduction

At a symposium on constructivity ten years ago, also held at Amsterdam, I considered in KREISEL [1959] ('K' for short) an obvious extension of Gödel's functional interpretation of Heyting's arithmetic (GÖDEL [1958], 'G' for short). The objective was to study the proof theory of formal classical analysis, formulated as a two-sorted axiomatic theory with variables for natural numbers and number theoretic functions, and basic relations of equality and function evaluation. (For details on alternative formulations, e.g. using sets of natural numbers instead of number theoretic functions with the basic relations of membership and successor; see e.g. KREISEL [1968b].) As in (G), with each formula A of analysis is associated an "interpretation" A' of the form $\exists s \forall t \, A_0(s,t)$ where s and t are sequences of variables for functions of finite type and A_0 is an elementary quantifier-free relation.

My specific proposal was to let s and t range over the so-called *continuous* functionals or, more simply, 'functions' of (K) pp. 114–117, defined in terms of suitable 'neighborhood' or 'representing' functions. The conjecture was that, for *negative* A (i.e., formulae A built up from negated atomic formulae by means of $\neg$, $\wedge$ and $\forall$), if A is formally derivable in classical analysis then A' is intuitionistically valid, when s and t range over functions defined by freely chosen neighborhood functions. Note that, for this interpretation, A' is expressed in the language of intuitionistic analysis as given, e.g., in KLEENE and VESLEY [1965], KREISEL [1965] or TROELSTRA (this volume).

Behind the conjecture was, first, the so-called *principal result* of (K) p. 120 which may be stated as follows.

Let (QF–AC) denote the schema

$$\forall x^\sigma \exists y^\tau A(x, y) \to \exists z^\rho \forall x^\sigma A(x, zx)$$

where A is quantifier-free (hence 'QF'); x and y are variables of type σ and

---

* The preparation of this paper was supported in part by NSF Grant #GP-6726.

τ, and z is a variable for functions with arguments of type σ and values of type τ, or type $(\sigma \rightarrow \tau)$ for short. Then

For any class of functions (of finite type) *containing the functions listed in the system* T *of* (G) *and satisfying* (QF–AC) *and for all negative A, we have the* **classical** *equivalence* $A \leftrightarrow A'$.

Further it was shown in (K) p. 116, 4.141, that the continuous functions of finite type satisfy (QF–AC), and z can even be chosen to be *recursively* continuous.[1]

Second I expected the use of classical predicate logic to be eliminable as long as only *formally* derivable A are considered; cf. GöDEL [1932] for first order arithmetic in place of analysis.

In the specific sense in which I intended it this proposal has failed. For analyses of the notion of free choice sequence [for a summary of *one* analysis see KREISEL [1965], of another see TROELSTRA (this volume), and for a comparison see the last section of KREISEL [1968a]], in terms of which the continuous functions are defined, have shown that *the evident axioms for free choice sequences are unexpectedly weak*; in particular, for some formal theorems A, A' cannot be derived from known axioms.

What remains is to apply the proposal to *subsystems* of classical analysis. The purpose of the present lecture is to summarize work in the last ten years on the proposal, and to put the results in perspective by comparing them with other work on subsystems. As a byproduct of independent interest, we get distinctions between different *kinds* of constructive functions of finite (and transfinite) type, e.g., in connection with the axiom of choice; cf. footnote 2.

1. Main proof theoretic result (SPECTOR [1962])

If A is provable in classical analysis, then $A_0(s_A, t)$ can be derived, for variable t and a suitable constant s_A, in the quantifier-free system $T \cup BR$ where BR is Spector's schema of *bar recursion*.

To describe BR we need a few definitions. For each pair of types (τ, σ), let $a^\tau(c^\tau)$ be a variable for (finite sequences of) type τ objects; let $[c]$ denote the type $(0 \rightarrow \tau)$ object such that $[c](n)$ is the n-th element of c for $n \leqslant l(c)$, the length of c, and $[c](n) = $ some constant for $n > l(c)$; finally let Y be a variable of type $(0 \rightarrow \tau) \rightarrow 0$ and let G and H be variables for functionals

---

[1] The two results were not formulated separately in (K). Note that the principal result as formulated here, answers question 6.11 on p. 123 l.c. since the effective operations (4.2 on p. 117) satisfy $T \cup$ (QF–AC).

whose value is of type σ, and whose arguments have types that make sense below. Let BR_τ^σ assert the existence of a function $\varphi_{(\tau,\sigma)}$ (or simply φ) such that

$$\varphi(Y; c; G, H) = G(Y, c) \quad \text{if} \quad Y([c]) < l(c)$$
$$= H[Y; c; \lambda a \varphi(Y; c*a; G, H)] \quad \text{otherwise.}$$

Denote $\bigcup_\sigma BR_\tau^\sigma$ by BR_τ and $\bigcup_\tau BR_\tau$ by BR when σ and τ range over finite types.

Spector's proof has since been simplified and refined in HOWARD [1968] where also a useful variant of BR, namely the *rule* of bar recursion, is treated.

To get a full *converse* to Spector's result, one considers classical analysis with the *principle of dependent choices* $[\mathbf{Z}_1 \cup \mathbf{DC}_1$ in the notation of HOWARD and KREISEL [1966], and not $\mathbf{Z}_1 \cup \mathbf{AC}_{01}$ treated by Spector].

A is formally derivable in $\mathbf{Z}_1 \cup \mathbf{DC}_1$ *if and only if there is a constant* s_0 *such that* $A_0(s_0, t)$ *is formally derivable in* $\mathbf{T} \cup \mathbf{BR}$. (To prove this one verifies by use of $\mathbf{Z}_1 \cup \mathbf{DC}_1$ that the continuous functions of finite type are a model of $\mathbf{T} \cup \mathbf{BR}$.)

While these results are, perhaps, proof theoretically satisfactory, the main foundational problem is wide open: *For what kinds of constructive functions and for what pairs (τ, σ) do there exist $\varphi_{(\tau,\sigma)}$ satisfying the defining equations* BR_τ^σ?

The reader should distinguish here between *primitive* notions of (constructive) functions of higher type as in (G), and *defined* ones, as in Section 3 below or in (K). It is not unreasonable to expect [cf. footnote 2 of SPECTOR [1962]] that, if some BR_τ^σ is really evident for a *primitive* notion, then BR will be valid generally. But for defined notions one must expect the validity of BR_τ^σ to depend on (τ, σ).

2. Primitive notion of function (G)

Let us note first that the existence of $\varphi_{(0,0)}$, i.e., the validity of the simplest instance of BR, is not at all plausible for the notion of function described in (G)[2], since here Y is supposed to be defined for constructive arguments

---

[2] *Correction.* My account in (K) of Gödel's notion in (G) was written before I saw (G). I failed to emphasize decidable definitional equality between terms of all types in (G) and hence the absence of extensionality. To mention a more specific difference: The full axiom of choice $A_{\sigma\tau}$ for all pairs of finite types σ and τ, holds for the notion in (G), but not for the (extensional) notions of effective operation and continuous function described in (K); for example see 2.43, p. 133 of KREISEL [1965]. However, these matters do not arise below in the discussion of $\varphi_{(0,0)}$. Note also that the particular functions asserted to exist in (G) (the schemata of T) *are* extensional; this is so because, without *ad hoc* assumptions, we know so little about all possible constructive rules that an operation which we *know* to be defined for all of them, is also defined for free choice sequences.

only, not for arbitrary functions. Indeed if we specialize the notion (G), and consider only *recursive* number theoretic functions and (hereditarily) extensional operations, we get the effective operations of 4.2 on p. 117 of (K), and the following

Negative result. There are specific effective operations Y, G, H such that the equation for $\varphi_{(0,0)}$ cannot be satisfied for all c.

Sketch of proof. We use an effective operation Y_1, defined for all recursive binary, i.e., $(0, 1)$, sequences, which violates Brouwer's fan theorem; specifically there is a non-recursive binary function α such that no $\bar{\alpha}n$ is Y_1-secured and $Y_1([\bar{\alpha}n])$ is unbounded (in the notation of Section 1). Let Y be an effective operation such that

$Y([c]) = lc^*$ if c is Y_1-secured and c^* is the shortest initial segment of c which is Y_1-secured,

$Y([c]) \geqslant lc$ if c is not Y_1-secured.

Choose G and H so that, for sequences c containing an element > 1, $G(Y, c) = 0 = H(Y, c, \psi)$ for all ψ of appropriate type; and for binary sequences c,

$$G(Y, c) = 1$$

and

$$H[Y, c, \lambda y \varphi(Y; c*y, G, H)] = 1 + \max[\varphi(Y; c*0; G, H), \varphi(Y; c*1; G, H)].$$

Then $\varphi(Y; c; G, H)$ is not defined for $c = \bar{\alpha}n$.

Positive result. We now use BR_0, more precisely BR_0^2 [where 1 stands for $(0 \rightarrow 0)$, and 2 for $(1 \rightarrow 0)$], as a *technical auxiliary* to reduce a certain subsystem of classical analysis to axioms for the notion implicit in (G). Of course we do not prove the *validity* of BR_0^2 for this notion, but we prove the *consistency* of $T \cup \mathrm{BR}_0^2$ by use of (evident properties of) this notion. The subsystem in question is $\mathbf{Z}_1 \cup (\Sigma_1^1 - \mathbf{DC}_1)$ which includes so-called hyperarithmetic analysis $\mathbf{Z}_1 \cup (\Delta_1^1 - \mathrm{CA})$. Since the minimum ω-model of the latter consists of all the hyperarithmetic sets, the system *seemed* to be impredicative (see last section of SPECTOR [1962]).

First we apply the appendix of HOWARD [1968] to interpret $\mathbf{Z}_1 \cup (\Sigma_1^1 - \mathbf{DC}_1)$ in $T \cup \mathrm{BR}_1^1$; this is reduced to $T \cup \mathrm{BR}_0^2$, imitating the reduction of bar induction of type one to type zero in HOWARD and KREISEL [1966].

Next, appealing to an unpublished analysis of computations of $T \cup \mathrm{BR}_0^2$ by Howard, we find that computability follows by definition by recursion on $\chi_{\varepsilon_0}(1)$, where, as in FEFERMAN [1964], $\chi_0\alpha = \omega^\alpha$, and for $\beta > 0$, χ_β enumerates the set of ordinals

$$\{\alpha : (\forall\gamma < \beta)(\chi_\gamma\alpha = \alpha)\}.$$

Recall that $\chi_{\varepsilon_0}(1)$ is the proof theoretic ordinal (least upper bound for provable Σ_1^1-well orderings) of ramified analysis of level ε_0.[3]

Finally we wish to interpret ramified analysis of level ε_0, using evident axioms about Gödel's notion (G). Strictly speaking, (G) treats only functions of *finite* type, and the proof theoretic ordinal of the axioms T listed by Gödel, is ε_0, very much smaller than $\chi_{\varepsilon_0}(1)$. However, once the iteration through finite types is accepted at all, there is certainly no reason to stop at ω. Whatever doubts there may be about further iteration we certainly know enough about ε_0 to iterate to type ε_0.

General formal result. Ramified analysis of level α can be interpreted in the quantifier free system $T^{\omega\cdot\alpha}$ obtained by natural extension of Gödel's T to type $\omega\cdot\alpha$.

Since $\omega\cdot\varepsilon_0 = \varepsilon_0$, we have the interpretation required.

Discussion. The detailed description of T^α for $\alpha \geqslant \omega$ has not been published. The reader can get a general idea by thinking of T^α as a (finite) codification of the corresponding infinite terms in TAIT [1965]. There remains the delicate question: up to what α are we 'entitled' to iterate Gödel's type structure in (G) once we have accepted the basic notion? More generally: what exactly must we know about an ordering to iterate some given process along this ordering? In the current theory of autonomous progressions [see FEFERMAN (this volume)], one iterates through $\underset{\alpha}{\leqslant}$ if, for a given functional Y of type 2,

$$(*) \qquad\qquad \neg\, a(1 + Ya) \underset{\alpha}{\leqslant} a(Ya)$$

be proved for free variable a of type 1, i.e., the sequence $a0, a1, \ldots$ does not descend beyond Ya. This condition is weak because (*) *expresses* only that constructive descending sequences terminate. [It is, for instance, not plausible that this justifies iteration even of a process as elementary as doubling! See the discussion in KREISEL [1968b], Section 6d; but see Section 6 below for applications where this weakness is harmless.] Now the axioms T^α are such that if (*) is *proved* from them, (*) holds also for free choice sequences a, and so $\underset{\alpha}{\leqslant}$ is truly well founded. So further analysis may show that the

---

[3] The relation between $Z_1 \cup (\Sigma_1^1 - DC_1)$ and formal ramified analysis of level ε_0 was first established by FRIEDMAN [1967] by a quite different method.

autonomy condition is exact after all! Note that *if* the autonomy condition is granted, the proof theoretic strength of the axioms 'inherent' in Gödel's notion (G) is measured by Feferman-Schütte's Γ, where Γ is the least solution of $\chi_\Gamma(1) = \Gamma$. In other words, Gödel's notion of function is an alternative way of formulating the idea of *reduction to the notion of natural numbers*.

3. Ordinals (in the sense of BROUWER [1927]):

well-founded *decidable* relations. We now come to the principal *foundational*[4] application of Section 1, where BR is restricted to BR_0 or BR_1.[5] As in Section 2, the application depends on two things: the discovery of an interesting subsystem of classical analysis which can be interpreted in $T \cup BR_0$ and second the discovery of a kind of function for which $T \cup BR_0$ is valid; or, à la rigueur, the discovery of properties (of these functions) from which the consistency of $T \cup BR_0$ or, better still, the computability of all terms of $T \cup BR_0$, is easier to establish than the consistency of the subsystem.

The subsystem in question is the so-called elementary theory of well founded relations, i.e., Z_1 together with the schema $WF(R) \to TI(R, A)$ for arithmetic R (in the notation of HOWARD and KREISEL [1966]); in full,

$$\forall f \{\forall g \, \exists x \, \neg \, R[f, g(x+1), g(x)]$$
$$\to [\forall x (\forall y [R(f, y, x) \to Ay] \to Ax) \to \forall x \, Ax]\}$$

or even, if now g is thought of as enumerating a sequence of functions, $g_0, g_1, \dots$

$$\forall f \{\forall g \, \exists x \, \neg \, R(f, g_{x+1}, g_x)$$
$$\to [\forall h (\forall k [R(f, k, h) \to Ak] \to Ah) \to \forall h \, Ah]\} \, .$$

For proof theoretic properties of these systems see Sections 9 and 10 and Note V of KREISEL [1968b].

---

[4] The formal differences between the interpretations in $T \cup BR$ and $T \cup BR_0$ are minor; but there are some, e.g. the form of extensionality needed; see HOWARD [1968]. However, minor formal differences are quite consistent with essential differences in the meaning of two theories! think of the *geometric* interest of a result for n-dimensional Euclidean space, where $n \leq 3$ and $n > 3$.

[5] As already mentioned BR_1, i.e., $BR_{0 \to 0}$, is reducible to BR_0, but not, in general, $BR_{\tau \to 0}$ to BR_τ. Observe that the type of the variable Y in BR_1 is $(0 \to (0 \to 0)) \to 0$ which is an instance both of $(0 \to (0 \to \sigma)) \to 0$ and of $(0 \to (\sigma \to 0)) \to 0$ for $\sigma = 0$. Quite generally, $(0 \to (0 \to \sigma)) \to 0$ can be mapped, in T, onto $(0 \to \sigma) \to 0$, but $(0 \to (\sigma \to 0)) \to 0$ in general cannot.

Another good system that can be interpreted in $T \cup BR_0$ is elementary *intuitionistic* analysis H of Howard and Kreisel [1966] together with the schema above for *arbitrary* formulae R in the language of H (Howard [1968]).

Let us turn to the second question: what functions satisfy $T \cup BR_0$?

Positive result. The continuous functions of (K) can be proved to satisfy $T \cup BR_0$ in intuitionistic analysis above. (Recall from Section 1 that on their classical interpretation, in fact by methods of $Z_1 \cup DC_1$, they satisfy all of $T \cup BR$!)

Various straightforward proofs can be given. For reference below it is perhaps best to use an 'inductive' procedure, going back to Brouwer [1927], to generate the class K of neighborhood functions of type 2 functionals. Let e, f denote number theoretic functions considered as defined on finite sequences (coded by the numbers) n, m with 0 coding the empty sequence:

$$\forall e \, \forall x \, [\forall n \, (en = x + 1) \to Ke]$$
$$\forall e \, \{[e0 = 0 \land \forall y \, \exists f \, (Kf \land \forall n \, [e(\hat{y}*n) = fn])] \to Ke\}.$$

We consider the smallest class K satisfying the conditions above. K is *picked out* from the primitive class of number theoretic functions, say, in the sense of (G). As our model of $T \cup BR_0$ we start with K, apply the operations of T and the operations $\varphi_{(0,\sigma)}$ for each σ. What has to be proved is that $\varphi_{(0,\sigma)}$ is well defined on the objects in this model. This is obvious for $Y \in K$ and so we have to show that K is closed under the operations above. To verify this, we use a fundamental property of K, namely the *axiom of choice* in the form

$$\forall y \, \exists f \, [Ke \land A(y, f)] \to \exists e \, \forall y \, (Ke \land \forall f \, \{\forall n \, [e(\hat{y}*n) = fn] \to A(y, f)\}).$$

Negative Result. We can of course *formulate* in the language of intuitionistic analysis that there is a neighborhood function $\varphi_{(2,\sigma)}$ of appropriate type that satisfies BR_2^σ: but we cannot *prove* this from current axioms such as Kleene and Vesley [1965], Kreisel [1965], or Troelstra (this volume).

Proof. Specializing (Howard [1968]), the subsystem $Z_1 \cup (\Sigma_1^1 - CA)$ can be interpreted in $T \cup BR_0 \cup BR_2$, but the consistency of the systems of intuitionistic analysis above can be proved in $Z_1 \cup (\Sigma_1^1 - CA)$ by Note V of Kreisel [1968b].

Discussion. Both the positive and the negative results can be sharpened. First, as in Section 2, it is unreasonable to restrict oneself to *finite* σ; having accepted K, one would consider BR_0^σ for transfinite σ; see Problem 1.

Correspondingly, in the language of analysis, having accepted K, one should permit the definition of species by recursion on K; see Problem 4. Further, even if BR_2 is not satisfied by the continuous functions of finite type, its consistency may be provable from axioms for BR_0^σ for suitable σ (see Problems 2 and 3), analogous to the justification of BR_0^2 in Section 2 from T^{ε_0}. Second, since (of course) the formal systems mentioned are incomplete the negative result is inconclusive. Not only, as we have just said, might the *consistency* of BR_2 be provable from BR_0^σ, but the negative result leaves open whether BR_2 is valid for the specific class of continuous functions. See Problem 5 concerning hypotheses to decide this question.

4. A critical step:

well founded (undecidable) sub-species of a given species. Let us see what happens if we try to generalize Section 3 to get a model for BR_2 say.[6] So let us consider, in analogy to K, the following species K' of type 2 functions, where such functions are denoted by E, F and finite sequences of elements of K by $\vec{e}, \vec{f}$:

$$\forall x \, \forall E \, [\forall \vec{f} \, (E\vec{f} = x + 1) \to K'(E)]$$
$$\forall E \, \{(\forall e \in K) \, (\exists F \in K') \, \forall \vec{f} \, [E(\hat{e} * \vec{f}) = F(\vec{f})] \to K'(E)\}.$$

Granted the inductive *definition* of K', what about its properties? To repeat the work of Section 3 we need some such *axiom of choice* for K' as

$$(\forall e \in K) \, (\exists ! F \in K') \, A(e, F) \to (\exists E \in K') \, (\forall e \in K) \, (\exists F \in K') \cdot$$
$$\cdot \{\forall \vec{f} \, [E(\hat{e} * \vec{f}) = F(\vec{f})] \wedge A(e, F)\}.$$

But this does not seem to be valid since K is an undecidable species! Note that the *uniqueness* condition on F cannot be expected to help (in extending a *partial* 'function' defined on K to a function E); recall the following example of footnote 17, p. 130 of KREISEL [1965], writing K_0 for $\{x : \exists y \, T(x, x, y)\}$. We certainly have

$$(\forall x \in K_0) \, \exists ! u \, [T(x, x, y) \wedge (\forall z < u) \neg T(x, x, z)].$$

But we do not expect a total function f satisfying

$$(\forall x \in K_0) \, [T(x, x, fx) \wedge (\forall z < fx) \neg T(x, x, z)].$$

---

[6] We do *not* wish to claim that $T \cup BR$ is, constructively, unjustifiable; on the contrary, see the next section. The purpose is to analyze a specific, *prima facie* plausible, extension of Section 3.

There is another way of looking at the matter. We can think of K as describing a method of generating all well founded trees with natural numbers at their nodes; specifically, trees with a constructive characteristic function (determining what sequences are initial segments of a branch of the tree). In contrast, K' has to be regarded as a method of generating trees at whose nodes we have elements of the undecidable species K. So we are concerned with well founded *species*, and K' corresponds to a species of species (of natural numbers). The next section will show that, once the notion of species of natural numbers is used, we get an instantaneous interpretation of classical analysis, and hence, by the theory of constructible sets of natural numbers, an interpretation of $Z_1 \cup DC_1$, and, by Section 1, of $T \cup BR$. Consequently, the proposed 'generalization' of Section 3 is foundationally sensible only if we can pin-point a clear difference between the use of species-variables involved here, and the general use of Section 5 below.

5. Species of natural numbers

Recall first that, by use of GÖDEL [1932], classical analysis formulated in terms of sets of numbers (and not of number theoretic functions) with the *comprehension axiom* (CA) in the notation of KREISEL [1968b] can be interpreted in the intuitionistic theory of (impredicative) species of natural numbers, that is, formally, (CA) with intuitionistic instead of classical logic, cf. Section 9 of KREISEL [1968b]. This result depends on the easy observation that the negative 'translation' of the instance $\exists X \forall y (y \in X \leftrightarrow Ay)$ of (CA), which is

$$\neg \forall X \neg \forall y (\neg\neg y \in X \leftrightarrow A^- y)$$

where A^- is the negative translation of A, is intuitionistically derivable from the instance $\exists X \forall y (y \in X \leftrightarrow A^- y)$ of (CA).[7]

Is (CA) *valid for the notion of species* (of natural numbers)? Clearly, if quantification over species is *meaningful* at all, (CA) holds: for Ay to be intuitionistically meaningful, we must have a notion of: *proof of Ay* (KREISEL [1965], p. 128, 2.31) and this knowledge determines *per se* a species X such that $\forall y (y \in X \leftrightarrow Ay)$.

What could go wrong? Of course there is the common place objection to

---

[7] In contrast to (CA), AC or DC do *not* imply their negative translations. For proof theoretic properties of these various systems see KREISEL [1968b], Section 9 (i) and 11c; also Problem 6 below. *Historical note* concerning GÖDEL [1932]: *tertium non datur* is 'harmless' in the context of the (impredicative) theory of species, but not in the context of constructive functions; observe that (CA) follows from the axiom of choice by *t.n.d.*, and apply KREISEL [1968b], §9b (i) and (iii).

impredicative notions allegedly connected with the paradoxes; more precisely we consider here species of arbitrary species instead of sets of arbitrary sets, and take care to derive the paradoxes intuitionistically. Evidently *this* objection is as weak here as in the case of set theory since we are considering species *of* natural numbers, and not of arbitrary species.[8]

Subspecies of a given species. I believe there are close parallels between the usual theory (in Zermelo's hierarchy) of the power set operation applied to a *given* set and the impredicative theory of species. But since the comparison has not been treated in the literature let us spell it out.

Given a set, or, in Cantor's words, a manifold conceived as a unity, then we apply operations to it, in particular, we conceive as a unity the totality of all its subsets. If one really needed a proof to show that the manifold of all such conceptions cannot itself be conceived as a unity, one might well appeal to the paradoxes.

In intuitionistic mathematics the situation is quite similar. Of course when we think of, say, the species of natural numbers, we do not regard it as a 'completed' *extension*; but we do think of it as a notion we have *grasped completely*, and for this reason, we have also grasped the notion of *proof* 'about' it, e.g. the meaning of the universal numerical quantifier, cf. the reducibility hypothesis of KREISEL [1965] (p. 126, 2.215). I propose to express this by postulating that a notion which defines a species of natural numbers is (reducible to) a *construction*, i.e., something that can in turn be the subject of our mathematical thought. Formally, for any such notion $\rho(a, y)$ (a is a proof that y belongs to the species considered) there is a construction c_ρ and a functor F_ρ such that

$$\rho(a, y) = c_\rho(F_\rho a, y) \quad \text{and} \quad c_\rho(a, y) = 1 \supset \rho(a, y) = 1;$$

(where the implication $\supset$ is interpreted truth functionally since it is applied to decidable relations); thus c_ρ defines the *same* species as ρ.

Of course it is not claimed that the impredicative species above are our constructions in the sense of our having, so to speak, 'listed' them all before speaking about them, 'listed' in the idealized sense of having given a rule of construction indexed by natural numbers or even ordinals. But note that Heyting's own interpretation of the logical operations, e.g., of implication, certainly does not refer to any 'list' of possible proofs of the antecedent. It simply assumes that we know what a proof is.

---

[8] See Problem 6 concerning a possible objection on grounds of nonconstructivity.

So, if the analysis above of the constructive character of subspecies of a given, i.e., completely grasped, species is accepted, quantification over species of natural numbers does not involve ideas that are radically different from those implicit in Heyting's interpretation of the propositional operations.

The moral is not that Heyting's interpretation is non-constructive! nor that a more elementary interpretation such as Gödel's (G), is foundationally uninteresting. The moral is that its foundational interest depends on something subtler than mere constructive validity.

6. General comment

The work reported here illustrates the typical problems and methods of *proof theory*, in particular the interplay between formal reductions, as in Section 1, and analyses of significant informal notions such as those mentioned in the title (Sections 2, 3, 5). For each such notion we found *some* valid principles, say, S^-, so to speak an approximation from *below* (such as T^{ε_0} in Section 2 or the axioms for K in Section 3); and an approximation from *above*, say S^+, of autonomous progressions with a weak autonomy condition (as in Section 2 or Problem 1). To *reduce* given formal principles to the informal notion considered, it is sufficient to interpret them in S^- (for instance $T \cup BR_0^2$ in T^{ε_0} in Section 2); for irreducibility it is sufficient to show that their consistency, i.e., the minimal adequacy condition that has to be satisfied, cannot be proved in S^+ (for instance $T \cup BR_0$ cannot be reduced to T^Γ and hence not to the notion of function (G)).

The need for paying attention not only to the axioms, but to the interpretation of the logical operations, particularly in constructive foundations, is clear from the discussion in Section 5 above, and hence the particular role of quantifier-, so to speak, logic-free principles in constructive foundations.

7. Problems

implicit in Sections 3 and 5. We need a few definitions.

For any term t of type $(0 \to (0 \to 0))$, say $t(x, y)$, such that $t(x, y) = 1$ can be proved in the system T of (G) to define a discrete ordering, let $T^t \cup BR_0^t$ be the formal extension of $T \cup BR_0$ to types indexed by elements in the field of t. (The restriction on t will not involve any loss of generality because, below, we shall only consider recursive well orderings, and any such ordering is primitive recursively homomorphic to a primitive recursive well ordering.)

Next, let $\mathcal{O}$ be the least class of terms t such that $t \in \mathcal{O}$ whenever, for variable

a of type 1 and some constant Y of type 2,

$$t[a(1 + Ya), Ya] \neq 1$$

can be proved in $T \cup BR_0$ or in $T^{t'} \cup BR_0^{t'}$ for some $t' \in \mathcal{O}$. Let λ define the direct sum of the orderings $t \in \mathcal{O}$ in some natural way. (Since we *describe* formal systems, we deal with *definitions* t and not the *abstract orderings* defined by t.)

Problem 1. Describe the ordinal of λ by extending Bachmann's notation, cf. GERBER [1967].

Problem 2. For $t \in \mathcal{O}$, does $T^t \cup BR_0^t$ have a model in $\Delta_2^1 - CA$ or, equivalently, in $\Sigma_2^1 - DC_1$? Conversely

Problem 3. Can $\Delta_2^1 - CA$ be interpreted in $T^\lambda \cup BR_0^\lambda$?
We now describe an extension of the theory of K given e.g. in Section 1 of KREISEL [1968a] or TROELSTRA (this volume), by adding new constants P_i for species of functions, and the following definition principle by 're-cursion on K'.

Let $A_i x$ be any formula not containing P_j for $j \geqslant i$ (nor the variables n and e); let B_i be obtained from a formula B, built up without use of P_j ($j \geqslant i$), n or f, from the dummy symbol Q for a predicate of natural numbers, by replacing

$$Qy \quad \text{by} \quad \exists f \, \forall n [P_i f \wedge e(\hat{y}*n) = fn].$$

Then

$$\forall e (P_i e \to Ke),$$
$$\forall x \, \forall e [\forall n (en = x + 1) \to (P_i e \leftrightarrow A_i x)],$$
$$\forall e [e0 = 0 \to (P_i e \leftrightarrow B_i)].$$

Problem 4. Is the system above of the same proof theoretic strength as $T^\lambda \cup BR_0^\lambda$?
To improve the negative result of Section 3, recall that the existence of $\varphi_{(2,\sigma)}$ can be *expressed* by a statement A^σ in the language of free choice sequences. Let A_1^σ, A_2^σ be the statements in the language of constructive functions equivalent to A^σ on the two analyses of free choice sequences in TROELSTRA (this volume), resp. KREISEL [1965] (or perhaps (a, α) and (a_σ, α) in the notation of the last section of KREISEL [1968a]). We cannot refute A_1^σ nor A_2^σ since our axioms for constructive functions are satisfied if arbitrary functions are allowed and then BR_2^σ is valid.

Problem 5. Can either A_1^q or A_2^q be refuted if all constructive functions are recursive?[9]

Finally, coming to Section 5 and the constructive character of the theory of species, we know that if $\forall x \exists y\, A(x, y)$ is proved then there is a numeral e such that also $\forall x \exists z[T(e, x, z) \wedge A(x, Uz)]$ is provable (in the system).

Problem 6. Is it consistent to add to the theory of species the schema

$$\forall x \exists y\, A(x, y) \to \exists e\, \forall x \exists z\,[T(e, x, z) \wedge A(x, Uz)],$$

for all closed formulae $\forall x \exists y\, A(x, y)$?

Appendix

The reader may welcome some additional information on Gödel's functional interpretation (G), which is scattered in the literature.

Concerning the *notions* used in (G), a comparison with the notions used in Heyting's interpretation of the logical particles is in KREISEL [1965] (2.3, pp. 128–130, particularly the bottom of p. 128); a comparison with the notion of function of type 2 needed for the no-counterexample-interpretation is in KREISEL [1968b] (Note VIIb). The notion of function in (G) is essentially more elementary. It is less elementary than the notion of combinatorial operation in KREISEL [1965] (pp. 169–173).

Concerning the interpretation of the logical operations in (G), it combines the best of two worlds. It is more elementary than Heyting's since it is expressed in terms of the primitive notion of function in (G), but it allows one to use Heyting's elegant formal machinery. Heyting's rules are not complete (for the functional interpretation) for predicate calculus by footnote 1 on p. 113 of (K), and not known to be complete for propositional calculus. They *are* complete for the negative fragment by Theorem 4 of KREISEL [1958] (p. 322) since, on the interpretation (G),

$$\neg\, \forall x \neg\, \mathrm{Prov}\,(x, \ulcorner A \urcorner) \to \exists x\, \mathrm{Prov}\,(x, \ulcorner A \urcorner),$$

and so Theorem 2, p. 321 l.c. applies.

Finally it may be remarked (cf. footnote 38 of KREISEL [1968b]) that the interpretation (G) allows one to formulate the *general principle* used, but not

---

[9] *Correction.* This problem is open despite the assertion of KREISEL [1965] (p. 182, 4.322) since the latter was based on assumptions about free choice sequences which *themselves* imply that not all constructive functions are recursive; cf. the end of TROELSTRA (this volume).

stated, in BISHOP [1967]. A typical theorem about, say continuous functions of a real variable, takes the form: $\forall f\{C(f)\to\exists g[C(g)\wedge R(f,g)]\}$, where $C(f)$ expresses that f is continuous. The theorem may be non-constructive in the strong sense that there is *no* constructive Γ such that $\forall f\{C(f)\to$ $\to[C(\Gamma f)\wedge R(f,\Gamma f)\}$. The classical proof generally applies the law of the excluded middle, say $T(f)\vee\neg T(f)$, to get an intuitionistic derivation of

$$\forall f\{(C(f)\wedge[T(f)\vee\neg T(f)])\to\exists g[C(g)\wedge R(f,g)]\}.$$

The interpretation in (G) of $C(f)\wedge[T(f)\vee\neg T(f)]$ has the form $\exists s\,\forall t\,C_0(f,s,t)$, and g is now obtained *not* as a function of f only, but of f **together** with s. In any case s will include the modulus of continuity since this is provided by the interpretation of $C(f)$ itself. It is precisely this device of replacing traditional notions such as that of continuous function by the notion **together** with additional information, which leads to Bishop's constructive versions. The remarks above show that the possibility of *some* constructive version of any particular theorem is automatic; the remarkable discovery is that a little additional information goes a long way. One may compare this with axiomatization: the possibility of formalizing any particular proof about the rationals say, is automatic; the remarkable discovery of axiomatic algebra was how many proofs about the rationals hold for all formally real fields say.

References

BISHOP, E., Foundations of constructive analysis (N.Y., Mc. Graw-Hill, 1967).
BROUWER, L.E.J., Über Definitionsbereiche von Funktionen, Math. Ann. **97** (1927) 60–76.
FEFERMAN, S., Systems of predicative analysis, J. Symb. Logic **29** (1964) 1–30.
FEFERMAN, S., this volume, pp.121–135.
FRIEDMAN, H., Thesis, Massachusetts Institute for Technology, 1967.
GERBER, H., An extension of Schütte's Klammersymbols, Math. Ann. **174** (1967) 202–216.
GÖDEL, K., Zur intuitionistischen Arithmetik und Zahlentheorie, Ergebnisse eines mathematischen Kolloquiums (Vienna, 1932).
GÖDEL, K., Über eine bisher noch nicht benützte Erweiterung des finiten Standpunktes, Dialectica **12** (1958) 280–287.
HOWARD, W.A., Functional interpretation of bar induction by bar recursion, Compositio Mathematica **20** (1968).
HOWARD, W.A. and G. KREISEL, Transfinite induction and bar induction of types zero and one and the role of continuity in intuitionistic analysis, J. Symb. Logic **31** (1966) 325–358.
KLEENE, S.C. and R.E. VESLEY, Foundations of intuitionistic mathematics (Amsterdam, North-Holland Publ. Co., 1965).
KREISEL, G., Elementary completeness properties of intuitionistic logic with a note on negations of prenex formulae, J. Symb. Logic **23** (1958) 317–330.
KREISEL, G., Interpretation of classical analysis by means of constructive functionals of finite type, in: Constructivity in mathematics, ed. A. Heyting (Amsterdam, North-Holland Publ. Co., 1959) pp. 101–128.

KREISEL, G., Mathematical logic, in: Lectures on modern mathematics, vol. 3, ed. T.L. Saaty (N.Y., Wiley, 1965) pp. 95–195.

KREISEL, G., Lawless sequences of natural numbers, Compositio Mathematica (1968a).

KREISEL, G., A survey of proof theory, J. Symb. Logic 33 (1968b).

SPECTOR, C., Provably recursive functionals of analysis; a consistency proof of analysis by an extension of principles formulated in current intuitionistic mathematics, in: Recursive function theory, Proc. Symp. Pure Mathematics 5 (1962) pp. 1–27.

TAIT, W.W., Infinitely long terms of transfinite types, in: Formal systems and recursive functions, eds. J.N. Crossley and M.A.E. Dummett (Amsterdam, North-Holland Publ. Co., 1965) pp. 176–185.

TROELSTRA, A.S., this volume, pp. 201–223.

FORMAL SYSTEMS OF INTUITIONISTIC ANALYSIS I*

J. MYHILL

State University of New York, Buffalo, New York, USA

0. Brouwer is dead

And we at this congress have a peculiar responsibility to see that his thought does not die with him. Commonly, and not exclusively amongst non-intuitionists, he is thought to have been a hamstringer of classical mathematics by his criticism of the 'principle of ommiscience'. Even those who have accepted this criticism (Bishop in particular) not infrequently find some of his arguments (including all those which essentially involve the notion of a free choice sequence) mystical and of no mathematical value except heuristically. (But Bishop has shown that even this tiny fragment of Brouwer's thought equals classical mathematics in range and exceeds it in subtlety.) On the second level of sympathy with Brouwer's ideas are those who with Kleene and in a different way the earlier Kreisel accept the notion of free-choice sequence as long as it is either totally free or only *mathematically* restricted (not subject to the hazards of the 'creating subject's' adventures) but would this time relegate Brouwer's *historical* arguments to the realm of the mystical. (Aberth and the Russians lie somewhere between Bishop and Kleene in this series of levels.) At this second stage intuitionistic mathematics begins to diverge from classical (and not be a mere subsystem and subtilization of it like Bishop's system), but in ways which still are comprehensible without going too far afield from the classical conception. Only Kripke, the later Kreisel and myself outside of Holland seem to have gone all the way with Brouwer in taking seriously his introduction of the creating subject into mathematical arguments. I believe the amount added to mathematics by this bold stroke will in a few years be realized to exceed

---

* The research reported in Sections 1–5 was supported by the Office of Scientific Research, Contract # AF49 (638)-1643 through Hughes Aircraft Company, Fullerton, California. Sections 0 and 6 are additions specifically for this version.

by far whatever was putatively excised from it by the initial criticism – if indeed anything was.

If we can critize Brouwer at all (and none of this encomium is meant to suggest that his conception of mathematics is the *only* tenable one – which I do not believe for an instant – but simply that it is *wholly* intelligible and self-coherent) it is on the grounds of his rejection of formalization. To me the failure of existing formalisms to capture all the subtleties of his thought is no proof of the inadequancy of formalisms (to crystallize a *particular moment* in the flow of that thought, not to define it once and for all, which we would never ask in classical mathematics either) but a challenge to find more flexible and refined formalisms than have hitherto been found. This paper is the first (after my "Overture" [1967]) in a series devoted to this task.

1. Introduction

There are three axiomatizations of intuitionistic analysis in the literature; HEYTING [1930b], KLEENE and VESLEY [1965], KREISEL et al. [1963] and KREISEL [1963]. None of these are entirely adequate for the formalization of existing intuitionistic mathematics: Heyting's is seriously defective from the point of view of rigor (so much so that at times (cf. especially Section 12) there is room for serious doubt as to what the author had in mind); and in addition the system is not strong enough to prove even the bar theorem. Kleene's system does not maintain a needed distribution between effectively computable functions and free-choice sequences, so that in particular his notion of a spread (BAR-HILLEL et al. [1967] p. 56) does not coincide with Brouwer's, and has certain properties (e.g., Theorem 14.9, p. 167) which Brouwer would certainly never claim for it. Kreisel's system is not subject to any of these defects, but it is not adequate for the formalization of those arguments of Brouwer (references and discussion in HEYTING [1956] ch. VIII and KLEENE and VESLEY [1965] ch. IV) which involve the construction of free-choice sequences depending on the solution of problems. In addition neither Kreisel's system nor Kleene's contains a theory of species, and Heyting's theory of species is trivially inconsistent (the axiom $S \equiv T \rightarrow S \equiv T$ of HEYTING [1930b] gives an immediate contradiction with the axiom $x \equiv y \lor \neg (x \equiv y)$ of HEYTING [1930a]).

By "intuitionistic mathematics" we mean roughly the practice of Brouwer and Heyting, including the above-mentioned "empirical" arguments of Brouwer. We do not mean to include the extensions of current intuitionistic methods contemplated by KREISEL ([1963] p. 147), any more than we would wish to include reflection-principles in a system meant to codify the normal practices of set-theory. On the other hand we will not follow Brouwer or Heyting slavishly; for example we will use Kreisel's proof of the bar-theorem rather than BROUWER's [1927] which we find obscure [or KLEENE and VESLEY's ([1965] p. 64) which we find clear enough formally, but scarcely convincing to anyone who has any doubts about the bar-theorem]; and we venture to correct an argument of HEYTING ([1956] p. 118) which appears to us after formalization to contain a fallacy. In this series of papers we shall compare various possible formalizations, offering detailed arguments for and against each one. The purpose of the present (first) part is to present the one which seems to us most natural and adequate, together with some justification for certain of the choices we have made. Detailed justification will be forthcoming in later papers in the series (but cf. also MYHILL [1967]).

Very roughly speaking, the system is obtained from Kreisel's by dropping the $(\forall \alpha) (\exists \beta)$-continuity axiom and adding Kripke's schema (D1 below); but there are several other innovations amongst which the most important is the introduction of a new primitive idea, the idea of *lawfulness* symbolized by a boldface **D**. Roughly speaking **D**t, where t is any kind of term, says that t is determined by a law rather than a free choice or choices. This extends to arbitrary (finite) types Kreisel's distinction between free-choice sequences and (computable) functions at the lowest type.

2. The "underlying logic" and arithmetic

The underlying logic is an (infinitely) many-sorted intuitionistic functional calculus with identity. *Terms* are divided into types N, 0, 1, 2, ... A term of type N denotes a nonnegative integer; a term of type 0 denotes a free-choice sequence; a term of type $i > 0$ denotes a species of order i (a species is of order i if all its elements are of order $i - 1$). Terms of type N have one of the following 4 forms: 0; $t_1(t_2)$ where t_1 is of type 0 and t_2 is of type N; $\phi(t_1, ..., t_n)$ $(n \geqslant 1)$ where each of $t_1, ..., t_n$ are of types N or 0 and ϕ is a defined number-valued operation of the appropriate kind; or a numerical variable $a, b, c, ..., z$. Terms of type 0 have one of the following 4 forms: s; $(\lambda x)t$ where x is a variable of type N and t a term of type N; a defined number-valued operation with one number-valued argument; or a free-choice sequence variable $\alpha, ..., \omega$. Terms of type $i \geqslant 1$ have one of the following 3 forms: a defined species of type i; $\phi(t_1, ..., t_n)$ $(n \geqslant 1)$ where each of $t_1, ..., t_n$ are terms and ϕ is a defined species-valued operation with arguments of appropriate type and values of type i; or a species-variable $A^{(i)}, ..., Z^{(i)}$. In addition K has type 1.

Atomic formulas have one of the following 3 forms: $t_1 = t_2$ where t_1 and t_2 have the same type; $t_1 \in t_2$ where for some $i \geqslant 0$ t_1 has type i and t_2 has type $i+1$; Dt where t has any type except N. Other formulas are built up from these by connectives and quantifiers of all types.

The logical *axioms* are the standard ones for the intuitionistic predicate calculus: a suitable set can be obtained from KLEENE [1952] p. 82, KLEENE and VESLEY [1965] p. 13 by adding axioms for the new sorts of variables; also the standard axiom and schema for identity

$$\mathfrak{x} = \mathfrak{x}$$
$$\mathfrak{x} = \mathfrak{y} \,\&\, \mathfrak{A}(\mathfrak{x}) \to \mathfrak{A}(\mathfrak{y})$$

in all types and the (dispensable) scheme of *lambda-conversion*

$$((\lambda x) t\,(x))\,(t_1) = t(t_1)$$

(see KLEENE and VESLEY [1965] p. 14 for a precise statement) with t_1 and $t(x)$ of type N only. The logical *rules* are the usual ones. For *arithmetic* we have Peano's axioms for 0 and s with induction in the form

$$[0 \in S^{(1)} \,\&\, (\forall x)\,(x \in S^{(1)} \to s\,(x) \in S^{(1)})] \to (\forall y)\,(y \in S^{(1)})$$

where $t \in S^{(1)}$ with t of type N is short for $(\lambda x) t \in S^{(1)}$, where x is a numerical variable not occurring in t.

3. Axioms for analysis

GROUP A. Axioms of choice.

These we postulate as two schemata:

A1. $(\forall x)\,(\exists \alpha)\,\mathfrak{A}(x, \alpha) \to (\exists \beta)\,(\forall x)\,\mathfrak{A}(x, \beta(x))$

corresponding to KLEENE and VESLEY's 0.1 ([1965] p. 14) or **F2** of KREISEL et al. [1963], and

A2. $(D\mathfrak{x}_1 \,\&\, ... \,\&\, D\mathfrak{x}_n) \,\&\, (\forall x)\,(\exists \alpha)\,(D\alpha \,\&\, \mathfrak{A}(x, \alpha)) \to$
$$(\exists \beta)\,(D\beta \,\&\, (\forall x)\,\mathfrak{A}(x, \beta_x))$$

corresponding to Kreisel's **C2**.

Here the following symbolism is used: β_x is short for $(\lambda y)\,\beta(2^x \cdot 3^y)$, where multiplication and exponentiation receive their definition under the axioms **G** below; and $\mathfrak{x}_1, ..., \mathfrak{x}_n$ are all the variables occurring free in $\mathfrak{A}(x, \alpha)$, with the exception of numerical variables and α itself. The motivation of **A2** is that only if α depends solely on x (and not on any free-choice parameters occurring in $\mathfrak{A}$) can its value for each argument y be *computed* from x and y by a uniform effective procedure, so that the free choice parameters appearing in $\mathfrak{A}$ must be restricted to taking (computable) functions as values. It is not enough for us simply to do this however (as it is for Kreisel loc. cit.), because we have variables of higher type in whose values free-choice sequences might be indirectly involved if they were not restricted by the first hypothesis of **A2**. We presume that the schemata

$$(\forall x)\,(\exists y)\,\mathfrak{A}(x, y) \to (\exists \beta)\,(\forall x)\,\mathfrak{A}(x, \beta(x))$$

corresponding to Kleene's 2.2 and Kreisel's **F1**, and

$$(\mathbf{D}x_1 \,\&\, \ldots \,\&\, \mathbf{D}x_n) \,\&\, (\forall x)\,(\exists y)\,\mathfrak{A}(x, y) \to (\exists \beta)\,(\mathbf{D}\beta \,\&\, (\forall x)\,\mathfrak{A}(x, \beta(x)))$$

corresponding to Kreisel's **C1** are deducible from **A1** and **A2** respectively; if not they must be added as additional schemata.

Kleene's axioms 2.1–2 are thus our **A1** and **A2** respectively; but if we followed him in not distinguishing functions from other free-choice sequences we would not be able to make certain of the distinctions which Brouwer had in mind. We have already mentioned the apparent impossibility of defining (Brouwerian) *spread* in Kleene's system (our definition of spread is obtained from KLEENE and VESLEY [1965] p. 56 by adding the clause **D**σ): another example is the definition of (cardinal) equivalence of species which must be given by a *law*. (For example, of the set S_2 on p. 256 of BROUWER [1924] it is asserted that no one has established its 'zahlbarkeit'; this is true if the kind of correspondences used are to be lawlike, false if they are merely arbitrary $S^{(1)}$'s.)

GROUP B. Axioms of continuity.

In conformity with the analysis of free-choice sequences given informally in MYHILL [1967] and BAR-HILLEL et al. [1967] and developed formally in later papers of this series, we drop the $(\forall \alpha)\,(\exists \beta)$-continuity axiom (**F6** of KREISEL [1963], 27.1 of KLEENE and VESLEY [1965]) and replace it by the weaker

B1. $(\forall \alpha)\,(\exists x)\,\mathfrak{A}(\alpha, x) \to (\exists \beta)\,(\beta \in \mathbf{K} \,\&\, (\forall \alpha)\,(\exists x)\,(\exists z)$
$[\mathfrak{A}(\alpha, x) \,\&\, \beta \bar{\alpha}(z) = \mathrm{s}(x) \,\&\, (\forall w)\,(\beta \bar{\alpha}(w) \neq 0 \to w = z)])$

where $\bar{\alpha}(z)$ is defined in **G** below. Notice that we do not require that no free-choice (or unrestricted species-) parameters be present in $\mathfrak{A}$; thus x may depend upon values of such parameters and not only upon α. Hence β is not necessarily lawlike and **B1** does not correspond exactly to Kreisel's **F4**; the analogue of the latter is rather

B2. $(\mathbf{D}\mathfrak{x}_1 \& \ldots \& \mathbf{D}\mathfrak{x}_n) \& (\forall \alpha)(\exists x)\,\mathfrak{A}(\alpha, x) \to$
$(\exists \beta)\,(\mathbf{D}\beta \& \beta \in \mathrm{K} \& (\forall \alpha)(\exists x)(\exists z)\,[\mathfrak{A}(\alpha, x) \&$
$\beta\bar{\alpha}(z) = \mathrm{s}(x) \& (\forall w)\,(\beta\bar{\alpha}(w) \neq 0 \to w = z)])$

where $\mathfrak{x}_1, \ldots, \mathfrak{x}_n$ is a list of the free variables, other than α itself and number-variables, which occur in $\mathfrak{A}(\alpha, x)$.

Corresponding to Kreisel's **F5** (the $(\forall \alpha)(\exists f)$-continuity schema) we have

B3. $(\forall \alpha)(\exists \beta)\,(\mathbf{D}\beta \& \mathfrak{A}(\alpha, \beta)) \to (\exists \gamma)(\exists \phi)$
$[\gamma \in \mathrm{K} \& \mathbf{D}\phi \& (\forall \alpha)(\exists x)(\exists z)\,[\mathfrak{A}(\alpha, \phi_x) \& \gamma\bar{\alpha}(z) = \mathrm{s}(x)$
$\& (\forall w)\,(\gamma\bar{\alpha}(w) \neq 0 \to w = z)]]$

and

B4. $(\mathbf{D}\mathfrak{x}_1 \& \ldots \& \mathbf{D}\mathfrak{x}_n) \& (\forall \alpha)(\exists \beta)\,(\mathbf{D}\beta \& \mathfrak{A}(\alpha, \beta)) \to (\exists \gamma)(\exists \phi)\,(\gamma \in \mathrm{K} \& \mathbf{D}\gamma \&$
$\mathbf{D}\phi \& (\forall \alpha)(\exists x)(\exists z)\,[\mathfrak{A}(\alpha, \phi_x) \& \gamma\bar{\alpha}(z) = \mathrm{s}(x) \& (\forall w)\,(\gamma\alpha(w) \neq 0 \to w = z)])$.

Here $\mathfrak{x}_1, \ldots, \mathfrak{x}_n$ are as in **B2** and ϕ_x is short for $(\lambda y)\,\phi(2^x \cdot 3^y)$.

Kreisel introduced **B4** (with the $\mathfrak{x}_i$ all of type 0) with the remark that functionals from free-choice sequences to free-choice sequences are continuous with the product topology on both domain and range, while functionals from free-choice sequences to functions are continuous with the product topology on the domain and the discrete topology on the range. (We must, of course, drop the first part of this remark.) His immediate motivation was the elimination of bound free-choice sequence variables, which of course because of the absence of the $(\forall \alpha)(\exists \beta)$-continuity schema (and Kreisel's schema, cf. Section 4 below) we are unable to do. But **B3–4** (or at any rate one or the other of them) are necessary also in order to formalize some of Brouwer's arguments; cf. in particular BROUWER [1924] p. 253, line 3 from bottom.

GROUP C. The inductive definition of continuity.

C1. $\alpha \in \mathrm{Const} \to \alpha \in \mathrm{K}$

C2. $(\forall n)\,(\alpha_n \in \mathrm{K}) \to \alpha \in \mathrm{K}$

C3. $\mathrm{Const} \subset S^{(1)} \& (\forall \alpha)\,[(\forall n)\,(\alpha \in S^{(1)}) \to \alpha \in S^{(1)}] \to \mathrm{K} \subset S^{(1)}$.

Here Const is defined (under **G** below) by

$$\alpha \in \mathrm{Const} \leftrightarrow (\exists x)\,(\alpha(1) = \mathrm{s}(x)) \& (\forall z)\,(z \neq 1 \to \alpha(z) = 0),$$

$\alpha_n = (\lambda x)\alpha(\{n\}*x)$ where $\{n\} = 2^{n+1}$, and * is defined under **G** (1 is the number of the empty sequence); and $\subset$ receives its usual definition.

There are several comments on this definition (which we take from KREI-SEL et al. [1963] p. IV–20, though in essence it was certainly known to BROUWER ([1923] p. 4)). Firstly, practically its only use is in proving the bar theorem (or such results as the fan theorem, or the equivalence of well-ordering and transfinite induction, which can also be obtained from the bar theorem), or else in proving continuity in such forms as Kleene's (corresponding to our **B1**) and parallel K-free versions of **B2–4**. It can certainly be urged that there is an inelegance in introducing a new primitive for the sake of half-a-dozen theorems. (But cf. Section 4(2) below.) So far as ordinary bread-and-butter intuitionism is concerned we could certainly have replaced **B1–4** by their K-free versions and **C1–3** by the bar theorem. However, we believe that axioms should have a certain transparency which we did not personally find in the bar-theorem when we first encountered it, and which we did find in **C1–3** plus Kreisel's deduction of the bar-theorem from these and **B1** (or rather **B2**; see below for the distinction). We do not find BROU-WER's ([1927] p. 7) or KLEENE and VESLEY's ([1965] p. 50) dogmatic assertion of the bar-theorem quite convincing and as we said before we find Brouwer's longer proof of it in BROUWER [1927] obscure and Kleene's formalization of that proof (KLEENE and VESLEY [1965] pp. 64–68) circular from the point of view of one who does not accept the theorem and superfluous from the point of view of one who does.

Secondly, it should be repeated that our K is not the same as KREISEL et al.'s ([1963] p. IV–20). Our K is the species of all (representing free-choice sequences of) continuous functionals, while Kreisel's K is the species of all lawlike ones. This in turn affects the details of the derivation of the bar-theorem and of Kleene's 27.2 in the following manner: Kreisel, possessing only *lawlike* continuous functionals, first proves the special case of the bar-theorem in which no free-choice parameters occur and then proves the general case by appealing to his own schema (Sec. 4 below). (His starting-point is **B2** and **C3** with the added hypothesis $(\forall\alpha)(\alpha \in S^{(1)} \to D\alpha)$.) We cannot do this because we lack Kreisel's schema; however, we can get the bar-theorem directly, with non-lawlike parameters, if we use **B1** (which Kreisel lacks) instead of **B2**. Precisely similar modifications must be made in Kreisel's proof of Kleene's 27.2 (KREISEL et al. [1963] p. 22).

Thirdly, the axioms **C1–C3** can if desired be dispensed with (in the present (impredicative) system) in favor of a direct definition of K (see Sec. 4 below): we do not do this because someone might want to study the first-order part of our system alone, without species-variables (or else to develop a predicative system; Section 5 below).

GROUP D. Kripke's schema.

D1.
$$(\exists\alpha)\left[\begin{array}{l}(\forall x)\,(\alpha(x)=0)\leftrightarrow\neg\,\mathfrak{A}\,\&\\[2pt](\forall x)\,(\alpha(x)=0\vee\alpha(x)=1)\,\&\\[2pt](\exists x)\,(\alpha(x)=1)\rightarrow\mathfrak{A}\end{array}\right].$$

For the justification of this cf. MYHILL [1967], BAR-HILLEL et al. [1967] and KREISEL [1967]. To our best knowledge it is sufficient for the formalization of *all* Brouwer's empirical arguments except one – namely the proof that the virtual order of the continuum is not a pseudo-order (HEYTING [1956] p. 117). In this proof he uses something like

$$(\exists\alpha)\left[\begin{array}{l}J(\alpha,\mathfrak{A})\,\&\,(\forall S^{(1)})\,(DS^{(1)}\,\&\,\alpha\in S^{(1)}\rightarrow(\exists n))\\[4pt](\forall\beta)\,(J(\beta,\mathfrak{A})\,\&\,\beta\equiv_{n}\alpha\rightarrow\beta\in S^{(1)}))\end{array}\right] \qquad (*)$$

where $J(\alpha,\mathfrak{A})$ abbreviates the formula within the square brackets of D1 and where $\beta\equiv_{n}\alpha$ means $(\forall x<n)\,(\beta(x)=\alpha(x))$. But since this is a ἅπαξ λεγόμενον which introduces a wholly new dimension into empirical free-choice sequences (this dimension will be explored in a subsequent paper of this series), and since it is not hard to give another proof of the same result using **D1** instead, we do not feel justified in adding (*) as an axiom. (We believe however, that it is rather clearly valid on the interpretation given in MYHILL [1967].)

Incidentally we can get from **D1** the mentioned result as a negation of a quantified formula rather than a mere "nobody has the right to assert" statement. A similar remark applies to several other results which Brouwer states in the weaker form; in particular the *negation* (not merely the unassertability) of the Bolzano-Weierstrass theorem (BROUWER [1952]) follows from **D1**. (These two results are due to my student Richard Hull, whom we hope can be prevailed upon to publish them.)

GROUP E. Axioms of extensionality.

E1. $(\forall x)\,(\alpha(x)=\beta(x))\rightarrow\alpha=\beta$

E2. $(\forall\alpha)\,(\alpha\in S^{(1)}\leftrightarrow\alpha\in T^{(1)})\rightarrow S^{(1)}=T^{(1)}$

E3. $(\forall S^{(i)})\,(S^{(i)}\in T^{(i+1)}\leftrightarrow S^{(i)}\in U^{(i+1)})\rightarrow T^{(i+1)}=U^{(i+1)}$

$$(i=1,2,3,\ldots).$$

The ground of these axioms is simply that we only *use* species that are defined extensionally. We share HEYTING's feeling [1930b] that this is all that is needed for formalizing e.g. BROUWER's arguments [1924] and [1918–19], even though there are places (cf. in particular [1924] p. 246, line 19) where intensionally defined ones make a momentary appearance. The axiom schema of substitutivity in the form

$$\mathfrak{A}(\mathfrak{x}) \, \& \, \mathfrak{x} = \mathfrak{y} \to \mathfrak{A}(\mathfrak{y}),$$

it will be recalled, is assumed in our underlying logic; consequently also $\mathfrak{A}(\mathfrak{x}) \, \& \, \mathfrak{x} \equiv \mathfrak{y} \to \mathfrak{A}(\mathfrak{y})$, where $\equiv$ denotes extensional identity. Thus all contexts are extensional; this yields a considerable technical facility in the making of proofs while at the same time (because of the absence of variables for functionals) it enables us to make statements like **D1** which are non-extensional in the sence that the β does not depend extensionally on the free-choice parameters of $\mathfrak{A}$. (To digress: functional variables tend to be misleading anyway in some situations; for example if we define equivalence of species in terms of functionals we do not even get symmetry of this relation, while the definition in terms of correlating species of higher order leads to no such annoyance.)

Note. To make e.g. E2 true, we must strictly speaking interpret $\mathbf{D}\alpha$ as meaning 'α is *extensionally equivalent* to a lawlike sequence' rather than 'α is lawlike' (i.e. *given* by a law). For the latter notion extensionality (i.e. $\mathbf{D}\alpha \, \& \, \alpha \equiv \beta \to \mathbf{D}\beta$) would fail, while $\mathbf{D}\alpha \vee \neg (\mathbf{D}\alpha)$ would hold. We shall explore this alternative in later papers of this series.

GROUP F. **D**-axioms.

F1. $\mathbf{D}\mathfrak{x}_1 \, \& \, ... \, \& \, \mathbf{D}\mathfrak{x}_n \to \mathbf{D}\mathfrak{t}$

where $\mathfrak{t}$ is a term of any type except N, and where $\mathfrak{x}_1, ..., \mathfrak{x}_n$ are all the free variables of $\mathfrak{t}$ which are not of type N.

The motivation is as follows: KREISEL et al. [1963] observed that certain formulas (e.g. **B3–4** above) hold for constructive functions which do not hold for free-choice sequences generally; cf. in this connection the remarks immediately preceding Group B of axioms in this paper. (In Kreisel's system, constructive functions are not merely regarded as a *kind* of free-choice sequence: but this is a matter of notation since they are extensionally equal to certain free choice sequences, and the relevant form of extensionality holds, i.e.,

$$(\forall x) \, (f(x) = \alpha(x)) \to (\mathfrak{A}(\alpha) \leftrightarrow \mathfrak{A}(f)).)$$

The distinction having been made, it became apparent to Kreisel that certain existential axioms had double forms, one asserting the existence of a free-choice sequence and one the existence of a constructive function. For example while Kleene has only

$$(\forall x)\,(\exists y)\,\mathfrak{A}(x,\,y) \to (\exists \alpha)\,(\forall x)\,\mathfrak{A}(x,\,\alpha(x)) \tag{1}$$

(which is true if *all* Kleene's Greek letters are taken as ranging over constructive functions, or *all* of them as ranging over free-choice sequences), Kreisel breaks this up into

$$(\forall x)\,(\exists y)\,\mathfrak{A}(x,\,y) \to (\exists \alpha)\,(\forall x)\,\mathfrak{A}(x,\,\alpha(x)) \tag{2}$$

with α a free-choice variable, and

$$(\forall x)\,(\exists y)\,\mathfrak{A}_0(x,\,y) \to (\exists f)\,(\forall x)\,\mathfrak{A}_0(x,\,f(x)) \tag{3}$$

with f a variable for constructive functions, and with no free-choice variables occurring free in $\mathfrak{A}_0$. The idea is simple: if a y can be found for each x (in e.g., the case of (3) where $\mathfrak{A}_0$ has no parameters) there must be a rule to find it; otherwise we could never assert the antecedent of (3) at all. Likewise for each fixed value of the parameters in $\mathfrak{A}_0$, provided these are number or function-variables. If however there are free-choice parameters in $\mathfrak{A}$ we may need to know (finitely many values of) them to compute the y of (2). (The paradigm case is with $\mathfrak{A}(x,\,y)$ as $\beta(x)=y$.)

Similar remarks apply to Kleene's **D1**, which splits up into Kreisel's **F2** and **C2** (our **A1** and **A2**). There are also two other places where the presence or absence of free-choice parameters in a formula make a difference; in *Kreisel's schema* (discussed below, Section 4) and in his continuity axiom **F4**. This reads like our **B1** (with minor notational changes) except that $\mathfrak{A}$ is required to contain no free-choice parameters and that the free-choice variable β is replaced by a function-variable f (a β such that $\mathbf{D}\beta$ in our notation). However there is an asymmetry in Kreisel's treatment here; for there is a valid intuitionistic principle related to **F4** as Kreisel's **F1** and **F2** (our **A1**) are related to his **C1** and **C2** (our **A2**) respectively (in each of the three cases the first-named principle asserts the existence of a free-choice sequence β having a certain property, while the second one says that if there are no free-choice parameters present the β can be replaced by a constructive function f). This principle however (namely our **B1**) is not stated by Kreisel, and in fact he would need a new inductive definition (corresponding to our **C1–C3**) in order to state it. Similar remarks apply to various other axioms of KREISEL [1963]; we do not analyze all these cases in detail but simply tabulate the situation as follows:

Axiom			Kleene	Kreisel	This system
Choice	$\forall x \exists y$	Ordinary form	2.2	F1	Provable (cf. discussion after A2)
		D-form		C1	
	$\forall x \exists \alpha$	Ordinary form	0.1	F2	A1
		D-form		C2	A2
Continuity	$\forall \alpha \exists x$	Ordinary form	27.2	(See above)	B1
		D-Form		F4	B2
	$\forall \alpha \exists \beta$	Ordinary form	27.1	(See above)	(inconsistent with D1)
		D-form		F6	
	$\forall \alpha \exists f$	Ordinary form		(See above)	B3
		D-form		F5	B4
Kreisel's axiom		Ordinary form	Provable (cf. R14.9)	Provable (Kreisel contains Kleene)	Provable
		D-form		F3	(See Section 4 below)

However it is not merely out of a love of symmetry that we include the axioms **B1** and **B3**: we need e.g. **B1** to prove something as simple and fundamental as:

$$(\forall \alpha) (\exists x) \mathfrak{A} (\alpha, x) \to (\forall \alpha) (\exists x) (\exists y) (\forall \beta) (\beta \equiv \alpha \to \mathfrak{A} (\beta, y))$$

because we do not know how to deduce this from **B2** except by Kreisel's method in KLEENE and VESLEY [1965] or KREISEL et al. [1963] which employs **F3** which is not available to us.

So much for the motivation of distinguishing ordinary forms and **D**-forms of existential axioms. The remarks at the end of the section on the axioms of Group A give another motivation, namely that the distinction of lawlike and unlawlike is made much of by Brouwer himself, and many of his results (e.g. [1924] p. 253, line 3 from bottom) cannot even be stated in systems like Kleene's which does not make such a distinction. Kreisel needed to introduce the division at the lowest type only, because he had no species-variables. Once we have such variables however extension of the distinction to them is mandatory. Otherwise reference to free-choice sequences could be smuggled into instances of **D**-forms of our schemata indirectly for example by speaking, instead of a free-choice sequence itself, of its unit-species.

Example. We cannot write:

$$(\forall x)(\exists y)(\alpha(x) = y) \rightarrow (\exists f)(\forall x)(\alpha(x) = f(x)) \qquad (4)$$

because $\alpha(x) = y$ contains α free. But by the same token we cannot write:

$$(\forall x)(\exists y)[2^x \cdot 3^y \in S^{(1)}] \rightarrow (\exists f)(\forall x)[2^x \cdot 3^{f(x)} \in S^{(1)}]$$

because $S^{(1)}$ might be the set of all $2^x \cdot 3^{\alpha(x)}$, and then we could deduce (4) anyway.

GROUP G. Rules of definition.

G1. Definition of number-valued operations (functions and functionals (KLEENE and VESLEY [1965] p. 19)).

Such a definition consists of two formulas:

$$\phi(\mathfrak{x}_1 \ldots, \mathfrak{x}_n, 0) = \mathfrak{t}_1$$

$$\phi(\mathfrak{x}_1 \ldots, \mathfrak{x}_n, s(y)) = \mathfrak{t}_2$$

where ϕ is the symbol being defined; $n \geqslant 0$: $\mathfrak{x}_1, \ldots, \mathfrak{x}_n$ are different variables each having type N or 0: $\mathfrak{y}$ is not one of $\mathfrak{x}_1, \ldots, \mathfrak{x}_n$: $\mathfrak{t}_1$ is a term of type N not containing ϕ nor any symbol which is not primitive and has not yet been defined, and which contains ϕ only in subterms of the form $\phi(\mathfrak{t}_1^*, \ldots, \mathfrak{t}_n^*, y)$: and $\mathfrak{t}_2$ contains no free variables beyond $\mathfrak{x}_1, \ldots, \mathfrak{x}_n, y$.

These definitions, apart from those for $+$ and $\times$, are eliminable (Kleene op. cit. p. 19).

G2. Definition of species-valued operations and species.

Such a definition consists of a formula:

$$\alpha \in \phi(\mathfrak{x}_1, \ldots, \mathfrak{x}_n) \leftrightarrow \mathfrak{A} \qquad (5)$$

or

$$S^{(i)} \in \phi(\mathfrak{x}_1, \ldots, \mathfrak{x}_n) \leftrightarrow \mathfrak{A} \qquad (6)$$

where ϕ is the symbol being defined: $n \geqslant 0$: $\mathfrak{x}_1, \ldots, \mathfrak{x}_n$ are variables of any type distinct from each other and from α (from $S^{(i)}$): $i \geqslant 1$: and $\mathfrak{A}$ is a formula containing no variables free except α ($S^{(i)}$) and the $\mathfrak{x}_j$.

4. Reasons not to extend the system further

There are three (at least) ways in which we might consider extending the system: (1) by adjoining Kreisel's schema (**F3** of KREISEL et al. [1963]) in the form

$$\mathbf{D}\mathfrak{x}_1 \& \ldots \& \mathbf{D}\mathfrak{x}_n \& \mathfrak{A}(\alpha) \to (\exists \beta)\,(\beta \text{ is a spread} \& \alpha \in \beta \& (\forall \gamma)\,(\gamma \in \beta \to \mathfrak{A}(\gamma))) \quad (7)$$

where 'β is a spread' is defined as in KLEENE and VESLEY [1965] but with the addition $\mathbf{D}\beta$; where $\alpha \in \beta$ is also defined as in KLEENE and VESLEY [1965] p. 57; where γ is not one of $\mathfrak{x}_1, \ldots, \mathfrak{x}_n$, and where $\mathfrak{x}_1 \ldots \mathfrak{x}_n$ exhaust the free non-numerical variables of $\mathfrak{A}(\alpha)$ other than α itself: (2) by adjoining inductive definitions in either of the forms contemplated by Kreisel in KREISEL et al. [1963] and KREISEL [1963]: or (3) by adjoining Kreisel's axioms (KREISEL [1967]) for the *thinking subject*, namely

$$\vdash_n \mathfrak{A} \vee \neg \vdash_n \mathfrak{A}$$
$$(\vdash_n \mathfrak{A}) \to \mathfrak{A}$$
$$((\forall n)\, \neg \vdash_n \mathfrak{A}) \to \neg \mathfrak{A}$$

and possibly others such as

$$(\forall \mathfrak{x}_1 \ldots \mathfrak{x}_n)\,(\exists y) \vdash_y \mathfrak{A} \to (\exists y) \vdash_y (\forall \mathfrak{x}_1 \ldots \mathfrak{x}_n)\, \mathfrak{A}$$

$(\mathfrak{x}_1, \ldots, \mathfrak{x}_n$ of any types)

$$\tilde{\alpha}(x) = y \to \vdash_x \tilde{\alpha}(x) = y$$

(Kreisel); or

$$\mathbf{D}\alpha \& (\forall x)\,(\alpha(x+1) > \alpha(x)) \& (\forall x) \neg \vdash_{\alpha(x)} \mathfrak{A} \to \neg \mathfrak{A} \vee (\exists x) \vdash_x \mathfrak{A}$$

(Myhill: this will be discussed in a later paper of this series). We shall discuss these three possible extensions in turn.

Re (1). Kreisel's schema and Kripke's schema **D1** together imply the 'negation of Church's thesis' in the form

$$(\exists \alpha)\,(\mathbf{D}\alpha \& \neg\,(\exists n)\,(\forall x)\,(\forall y)\,(\alpha(x) = y \to \mathfrak{A}(n, x, y))) \quad (8)$$

where $\mathfrak{A}(n, x, y)$ is any formula in which only the indicated variables occur free. Outline of proof (details will appear in a later installment): Kripke's schema gives (8) without the $\mathbf{D}\alpha$, i.e., a *free choice sequence* not occurring among the functions enumerated by $\mathfrak{A}$ (by a diagonal argument); and then Kreisel's schema provides the $\mathbf{D}\alpha$ because it implies (KREISEL et al. [1963] p. IV–23) the schema

$$\mathbf{D}\mathfrak{x}_1 \& \ldots \& \mathbf{D}\mathfrak{x}_n \& (\exists \alpha)\, \mathfrak{A}(\alpha) \to (\exists \alpha)\,(\mathbf{D}\alpha \& \mathfrak{A}(\alpha))$$

where $\mathfrak{x}_1, \ldots, \mathfrak{x}_n$ are all the non-numerical free variables of $\mathfrak{A}(\alpha)$ other than α itself.

What are we to make of this? I do not quite share Kreisel's scepticism about all constructive functions being recursive: none the less I admit that there is room for some doubt, and we would presumably want Church's thesis to be independent in our system at least until some substantial further insight is gained.

To my mind the trouble with the above deduction lies in the shifting meaning of **D**. As soon as we admit empirically defined sequences (8), and therewith (7), loses its plausibility if we read **D** as 'mathematically defined'. If we read it as 'independent of acts of free choice' (hence including both 'mathematically defined' and 'empirically defined' or any combination of the two) it is perfectly true; but then the **D** in the definition of 'β is a spread' in Kreisel's schema has to be construed the same way. Hence: if we divide free-choice sequences into those which are mathematically defined and the rest, we have no reason to assert Kreisel's schema. If we divide them into those that are mathematically-or-empirically-defined and the rest, all the axioms require reexamination (we shall do this in later installments) and we cease to be able to define the notion of a (Brouwer) spread (and come up with one intermediate between the Brouwer-Kreisel one and the Kleene one). In that case we can prove (8) but it is certainly not the 'negation of Church's thesis' in any reasonable sense: it is an assertion of the existence of an empirically defined sequence not occurring in the sequence of sequences enumerated by $\mathfrak{A}$. For a complete analysis we need another predicate besides **D**, namely a predicate **E**α meaning α is empirically defined: then we can have both Kreisel's schema (with **E** replacing **D**) and Kripke's in the same system. But as long as we have only the twofold distinction of lawful and nonlawful sequences, the only form of Kreisel's schema that we can validly assert is the trivial one obtained by dropping **D**β altogether from the definition of 'spread' in (7) (i.e. by replacing 'spread' by 'Kleene spread' as per KLEENE and VESLEY [1965] p. 56).

Added in proof. Troelstra's paper in this symposium makes the above argument against Kreisel's schema entirely superfluous, and makes the above suggestion about **E** quite dubious.

Re (2). We do not need inductive definitions because (having higher-type variables) we can use the Frege-Dedekind device. (Kreisel's so-called 'counterexample to the definition [of an inductively defined species] as an intersection' in KREISEL et al. [1963] we find misleading stated: it shows only that (granted Church's thesis) there exists an inductively defined species whose extension differs from that of the species obtained by the Frege-Dedekind device using quantified species-variables over decidable species only, which we hardly consider surprising.) Thus in particular we can eliminate the inductive definitions **C1–C3** of K (and the primitive symbol K itself) if we use the direct definition

$$\alpha \in K \to (\forall S^{(1)}) \left[\text{Const} \subset S^{(1)} \& (\forall \beta) \left[(\forall n) (\beta_n \in S^{(1)}) \to \beta \in S^{(1)} \right] \to \alpha \in S^{(1)} \right]$$

however we do not do this in case someone wants to study the first-order fragment (or a predicative version) of our system. In view of Howard's proof of the equivalence of well-foundedness and transfinite induction (KREISEL et al. [1963]) and Vesley's forthcoming applications of this to the formulation of Brouwer's theory of ordinals (cf. KLEENE and VESLEY [1965] p. 65) we see no reason to adjoin to this first-order fragment any other inductive definitions beyond **C1–C3**; for it seems that only in the theory of ordinals does Brouwer employ such definitions (but cf. BROUWER [1927] and Section 5 below).

Re (3). Despite the illumination which Kreisel's axioms for the thinking subject shed upon Kripke's schema **D1**, we think the loss of extensionality too high a price to pay in technical facility. Various modifications and caveats of extensionality would have to be added in several other axioms (notably in **B1–B2**: HEYTING [1956] p. 118, slips up by using the fan theorem on an intensional context in his proof of $\neg (\forall \alpha) (\alpha \neq 0 \to \alpha \neq 0)$ which (essentially) proceeds from the axioms for the thinking subject). Had he used Kripke's schema instead he would not have made this mistake and would have gotten just the same result (of Kreisel's reply to Myhill in BAR-HILLEL et al. [1967]): and the same remark (that Kripke's schema can replace the $\vdash_n$ axioms with a consequent gain in technical facility and elegance) seems to apply to all of Brouwer's historical arguments so far as we have examined them.

5. Postscript on impredicative definitions

The above represents a formalization of *impredicative* intuitionism, following e.g. KREISEL [1963] p. 147 rather than e.g. GÖDEL [1932]. (It is to a conversation with Gödel that we owe this distinction, as well as a belief in the legitimacy of both forms: we here record sincere thanks to him.) For a formalization of predicative intuitionism (not the only one, but the closest we can find to Brouwer's own intentions) we make the following modifications.

In the formation-rules we reconstrue species-variables $S^{(i)}$ as ranging over species of type *i and order i* (i.e. defined without quantification over species of type $\geq i$) and we add for a technical reason (see G3 below) also *free* unramified variables for species of type *i*. These are used in atomic formulas $\mathscr{F}^{(i+1)}(t)$ with t of type $i \geq 0$, but never quantified.

In the underlying logic we adjoin a rule of (schematic) substitution for the new variables corresponding to the ordinary rule of substitution for predicate letters in the functional calculus. In the *axiom of induction* replace $0 \in S^{(1)}$ by $\mathscr{F}^{(1)}(\lambda x)\,0$ etc.; or else use a schema.

In the axioms of analysis make the following changes: in **C3** replace the ramified species-variable $S^{(1)}$ by an unramified $\mathscr{F}^{(1)}$; add to the extentionality axioms **E1–E3** also

E4. $$(\forall \alpha)\,(\mathscr{F}^{(1)}\alpha \to \mathscr{G}^{(1)}\alpha)\,\&\,\mathfrak{A}(\mathscr{F}^{(1)}) \to \mathfrak{A}(\mathscr{G}^{(1)})$$

E5. $$(\forall S^{(i)})\,(\mathscr{F}^{(i+1)}S^{(i)} \leftrightarrow \mathscr{G}^{(i+1)}S^{(i)})\,\&\,\mathfrak{A}(\mathscr{F}^{(i+1)}) \to \mathfrak{A}(\mathscr{G}^{(i+1)})$$

in G2, require in (5) that amongst $\mathfrak{x}_1, \ldots, \mathfrak{x}_n$ occur no script variables and no ordinary species-variables of any type except i, and that in $\mathfrak{A}$ occur no bound species-variables at all: in (6) that amongst $\mathfrak{x}_1, \ldots, \mathfrak{x}_n$ occur no script variables and no ordinary species-variables of any type $> i+1$, and that in $\mathfrak{A}$ occur no bound species-variables of any type $\geq i+1$. Finally adjoin the following *rule* **G3** *of inductive definition* (now necessary since we cannot use the Frege-Dedekind device; cf. (2) of Section 4 above). If

G3. $$\mathfrak{A}(\mathscr{F}^{(i+1)}, S^{(i)})\,\&\,\mathscr{F}^{(i+1)} \subset \mathscr{G}^{(i+1)} \to \mathfrak{A}(\mathscr{G}^{(i+1)}, S^{(i)})$$

is a theorem, where $\mathfrak{A}$ has no free variables beyond those indicated, we may introduce a new species-constant ϕ of type $i+1$ by the axioms

G3₁ϕ. $$\mathfrak{A}(\phi, S^{(i)}) \to S^{(i)} \in \phi$$

($\mathfrak{A}(\phi, S^{(i)})$ is obtained from $\mathfrak{A}(\mathscr{F}^{(i+1)}, S^{(i)})$ by replacing all subformulae $\mathscr{F}^{(i+1)}(\mathfrak{t})$ by $\mathfrak{t} \in \phi$); and

G3₂ϕ. $$(\forall S^{(i)})\,(\mathfrak{A}(\mathscr{F}^{(i+1)}, S^{(i)}) \to \mathscr{F}^{(i+1)}(S^{(i)}))$$
$$\to (\forall S^{(i)})\,(S^{(i)} \in \phi \to \mathscr{F}^{(i+1)}(S^{(i)}));$$

likewise reading '1' for '$i+1$' and 'α' for '$S^{(i)}$' throughout. It is thought that a rule of definition for inductively defined species with parameters (e.g. functions of ordinals) is derivable from **G3** with **G2**; otherwise it will have to be added as a new axiom.

Note (a) that in view of Vesley's work mentioned under (2) of Section 4 we could probably get by without such a rule, except perhaps for the definition of the species Σ defined in HEYTING [1956] p. 108; but Vesley's work seems intended as an extremely illuminating technical contribution rather than as a historically accurate rendering of Brouwer's intentions; (b) that we have only one order at each type (e.g. we have no species of say points in space that are defined by quantification over all first-order species of such points), thus only a fragment of the ramified hierarchy; but that this seems to be all that Brouwer uses; there is for example no splitting of cardinals or point-sets into a hierarchy as there would be on Weyl's treatment; (c) that occasional apparently impredicative definitions in Brouwer always seem to be eliminable, either (as in the case of the species just mentioned) by reducing them to inductive ones or else (as in the case of certain species defined in Brouwer [1948]) by replacing them by predicative special cases.

6. Addendum

Vesley recently observed that the (evidently valid) schema

A3. $[\mathfrak{A}(\Diamond) \,\&\, (\forall x)(\mathrm{Seq}\,(x) \,\&\, \mathfrak{A}(x) \to (\exists y)\,\mathfrak{A}(x^* \{y\}))] \to (\exists \alpha)\,(\forall n)\,\mathfrak{A}(\tilde{\alpha}(n))$

is probably independent of (the first-order fragment of) our system (Kleene's proof in Kleene and Vesley [1965] uses 27.1); if this is true we should certainly adjoin it as a new axiom, and also its mate (related to it as **A2** to **A1**).

A4. $[\mathbf{D}\mathfrak{x}_1 \,...,\mathbf{D}\mathfrak{x}_n \,\&\, \mathfrak{A}(\Diamond) \,\&\, (\forall x)\,(\mathrm{Seq}\,(x) \,\&\, \mathfrak{A}(x)$
$$\to (\exists y)\,\mathfrak{A}(x^* \{y\}))] \to (\exists \alpha)\,(\mathbf{D}\alpha \,\&\, (\forall n)\,\mathfrak{A}(\tilde{\alpha}(n)))$$

where $\mathfrak{x}_1,..., \mathfrak{x}_n$ are all the free non-numerical variables of $\mathfrak{A}$. The same is true of

A5. $(\forall x)\,(\mathfrak{A}(x) \to (\exists y)\,(\mathfrak{A}(y) \,\&\, \mathfrak{B}(x, y))) \to (\forall z)\,(\mathfrak{A}(z)$
$$\to (\exists \alpha)\,[(\forall x)\,(\mathfrak{B}(\alpha(x), \alpha(x+1)) \,\&\, \alpha(0)=z]) \quad \text{(Kreisel)}$$

and there are even stronger things on the same lines.

References

Bar-Hillel, Y., A. Heyting, G. Kreisel and J. Myhill, Discussion of Kreisel [1967], in: Problems in the philosophy of mathematics, ed. I. Lakatos (Amsterdam, North-Holland Publ. Co., 1967) pp. 172–186.

Brouwer, L. E. J., Begründung der Mengenlehre unabhangig vom logischen Sate vom ausgeschlossenen Dritten, Verhandel. Koninkl. Ned. Akad. Wetenschap, Amsterdam **12** (1918) no. 5, pp. 3–43 and **12** (1919) no. 7, pp. 3–33.

Brouwer, L. E. J., Virtuelle Ordnung und unerweiterbare Ordnung, Crelle's J. **157** (1927) 255–258.

Brouwer, L. E. J., Begründung der Funktionenlehre unabhangig vom logischen Satz vom ausgeschlossenen Dritten I, Verhandel. Koninkl. Ned. Akad. Wetenschap, Amsterdam **13** (1923) no. 2, pp. 3–24.

BROUWER, L. E. J., Zur Begründung der intuitionistischen Mathematik I, Math. Ann. 93 (1924) 244–256 (erratum 95, p. 472).

BROUWER, L. E. J., Uber Definitionsbereiche von Funktionen, Math. Ann. 97 (1927) 60–75.

BROUWER, L. E. J., Consciousness, philosophy and mathematics, Proc. Xth Intern. Congress of Philosophy, Amsterdam 1948 (Amsterdam, North-Holland Publ. Co., 1949) pp. 1235–1299.

BROUWER, L. E. J., Over accumulatiekernen van oneindige kernsoorten, Koninkl. Ned. Akad. Wetenschap, Amsterdam, Proc. 55 (1952) 439–442.

GÖDEL, K., Zur intuitionistischen Arithmetik und Zahlentheorie, Ergebnisse eines math. Koll. Heft 4 (1932) 34–38.

HEYTING, A., Die formalen Regeln der intuitionistischen Logik, Sitz.ber. Preuss. Akad. Wiss. Berlin 1930a, pp. 42–56.

HEYTING, A., Die formalen Regeln der intuitionistischen Mathematik III, Sitz.ber. Preuss. Akad. Wiss. Berlin 1930b, pp. 158–169.

HEYTING, A., Intuitionism (Amsterdam, North-Holland Publ. Co., 1956).

KLEENE, S. C., Introduction to metamathematics (Amsterdam, North-Holland Publ. Co., 1952).

KLEENE, S. C. and R. E. VESLEY, The foundations of intuitionistic mathematics (Amsterdam, North-Holland Publ. Co., 1965).

KREISEL, G., Mathematical logic, in: Lectures in modern mathematics, ed. Saaty (London, 1963) pp. 95–195.

KREISEL, G., Informal rigor and completeness proofs, in: Problems in the philosophy of mathematics, ed. I. Lakatos (Amsterdam, North-Holland Publ. Co., 1967) pp. 138–171.

KREISEL, G. et al., Report of the Seminar on the Foundations of Analysis, Mimeographed (Stanford, 1963).

MYHILL, J., Notes towards an axiomatization of intuitionistic analysis, Logique et Analyse 35 (1967) 280–297.

ON SIMPLE TYPE THEORY WITH EXTENSIONALITY

K. SCHÜTTE

University of Munich, Germany

TAKEUTI [1953] developed a formal system GLC of simple type theory in a Gentzen-like way. From his fundamental conjecture for GLC that every derivable formula is derivable without using the cut rule, he proved the consistency of classical analysis. In SCHÜTTE [1960], I formulated a similar formal system of simple type theory and gave a semantical equivalent to Takeuti's fundamental conjecture, using partial valuations. By means of this semantical equivalent, the fundamental conjecture has recently been proved in a nonconstructive way independently by M. Takahashi and D. Prawitz, whose papers are not yet published.

The system GLC does not require extensionality, and it is not possible to add an axiom or an inference rule for extensionality without violating the fundamental conjecture. In this paper, I describe a formal system STE of simple type theory with extensionality which has proof-theoretical properties similar to the system in SCHÜTTE [1960]. The completeness of simple type theory proved by HENKIN [1950] is provable for STE in a more syntactical way.

The strict derivability in STE which corresponds to cutfree derivability is characterized by partial valuations as in SCHÜTTE [1960]. The analogue to Takeuti's fundamental conjecture would be the statement that any derivable formula is strictly derivable, but this statement does not hold in STE in general. Of course, it holds for suitable subsystems of STE, and its proof can be useful to establish consistency of subsystems of analysis like Takeuti's constructive proofs of his fundamental conjecture for subsystems of GLC.

The system STE uses combinators with types so that bound variables are not needed. It contains equality symbols for all types as basic symbols which permits the definition of quantifiers as in HENKIN [1963].

1. The formal system STE

1.1. Definition of *types*. We assume that a set of *basic types* is given containing the type 0 for formulas. The inductive definition of types is the following one:

1.1.1. Any basic type is a type.

1.1.2. If α and β are types then $(\alpha\beta)$ is a type. ($(\alpha\beta)$ is to be understood as the type of mappings from the class of objects of type α into the class of objects of type β.)

We use small Greek letters as syntactical variables for types. For abbreviation we write $\alpha_1 \alpha_2 \ldots \alpha_n$ instead of $(\alpha_1(\alpha_2 \ldots (\alpha_{n-1} \alpha_n) \ldots))$ associating to the right.

1.2. *Basic terms*.

1.2.1. Denumerably many *variables* of type α for any type α.

1.2.2. An arbitrary number of *constants* of some types.

1.2.3. The *connectives* N of type 00 (for negation) and A of type 000 (for disjunction).

1.2.4. For every type α an *equality symbol* E_α of type $\alpha\alpha 0$.

1.2.5. For all types α, β, γ the *combinators* $K_{\alpha\beta}$ of type $\alpha\beta\alpha$ and $S_{\alpha\beta\gamma}$ of type $(\alpha\beta\gamma)(\alpha\beta)\alpha\gamma$.

1.3. Inductive definition of *terms*.

1.3.1. Any basic term of type α is a term of type α.

1.3.2. If $a^{\alpha\beta}$ and b^α are terms of types $\alpha\beta$ and α respectively, then $(a^{\alpha\beta} b^\alpha)$ is a term of type β.

The terms of type 0 are called *formulas*.

Syntactical variables:

$$a^\alpha, b^\alpha, c^\alpha \quad \text{for terms of type } \alpha,$$
$$x^\alpha, y^\alpha, z^\alpha \quad \text{for variables of type } \alpha,$$
$$p, q, r \quad \text{for formulas.}$$

For abbreviation we write $a_1^{\alpha_1} a_2^{\alpha_2} \ldots a_n^{\alpha_n}$ instead of $(\ldots(a_1^{\alpha_1} a_2^{\alpha_2}) \ldots a_n^{\alpha_n})$, associating to the left. We write $\neg p$, $p \vee q$, $p \rightarrow q$ instead of Np, Apq, $A(Np)q$ respectively.

1.4. *Combinations* are the terms of the following forms:

1.4.1. $K_{\alpha\beta} a^\alpha b^\beta$, converting to a^α,

1.4.2. $S_{\alpha\beta\gamma} a^{\alpha\beta\gamma} b^{\alpha\beta} c^\alpha$, converting to $a^{\alpha\beta\gamma} c^\alpha (b^{\alpha\beta} c^\alpha)$.

A term is called *irreducible* if it does not contain a combination.

1.5. *Prime formulas* are:

1.5.1. The irreducible formulas whose first symbol is a variable or a constant.

1.5.2. The irreducible formulas of the form $E_\tau a^\tau b^\tau$ where τ is a basic type different from 0.

1.6. Inductive definition of *positive parts* and *negative parts* of a formula r.

1.6.1. r is a positive part of r.

1.6.2. If Np is a positive (negative) part of r, then p is a negative (positive) part of r.

1.6.3. If Apq is a positive part of r, then p and q are positive parts of r.

Notations:

$F[p_+]$ (or $F[p_-]$) denotes a formula containing p as a positive (negative) part in a fixed place.

$F[p_+, q_-]$ denotes a formula containing a positive part p and a negative part q (each in a fixed place) such that there is no intersection between p and q in the formula.

1.7. Definition of some special terms.

1.7.1. $Y = E_\tau c^\tau c^\tau$ where c^τ is a distinguished constant of a basic type τ. (Y has the meaning of the "true formula".)

1.7.2. $\Pi_\alpha = E_{\alpha 0}(K_{0\alpha} Y)$ which is a term of type $(\alpha 0)0$. (Π_α is the universal quantifier for objects of type α.)

1.7.3. $\Lambda = N(\Pi_0(S_{000}AN))$. ($\Lambda$ has the meaning of the "false formula" expressing the negation of the law of the excluded middle.)

1.8. Definition. Let $G(x^\alpha)$ be a formula containing the variable x^α in some places. $G(x^\alpha)$ is called *primitive* with respect to x^α if it has one of the following forms:

1.8.1. The first symbol of $G(x^\alpha)$ is
either a variable different from x^α
or a constant
or a symbol E_τ where τ is a basic type different from 0.

1.8.2. $G(x^\alpha)$ is a formula $N(H(x^\alpha))$ where the first symbol of $H(x^\alpha)$ is
either a variable different from x^α
or a constant
or a symbol E_β where β is an arbitrary type.

1.9. *Axioms* and *basic inference rules*.

1.9.1. Axioms:

Every formula $F[p_+, p_-]$ where p is a prime formula.

1.9.2. Inference rules A introducing logical symbols.

A1. $F[p_-], F[q_-] \vdash F[(p \lor q)_-],$

A2. $F[(p \to q)_+], F[(q \to p)_+] \vdash F[E_0 pq_+],$

A3. $F[E_\beta (a^{\alpha\beta} x^\alpha) (b^{\alpha\beta} x^\alpha)_+] \vdash F[E_{\alpha\beta} a^{\alpha\beta} b^{\alpha\beta}{}_+]$

if the variable x^α does not occur in the conclusion,

A4. $F(a^\alpha) \vdash F(c^\alpha)$

where c^α is a combination converting to a^α
and $F(a^\alpha)$ is a formula containing a^α in some places.

1.9.3. Inference rules B for cancellation.

B1. $F[E_0 pq_-] \lor (p \lor q), F[E_0 pq_-] \lor (\neg p \lor \neg q) \vdash F[E_0 pq_-],$

B2. $F[E_{\alpha\beta} a^{\alpha\beta} b^{\alpha\beta}{}_-] \lor \neg E_\beta (a^{\alpha\beta} c^\alpha)(b^{\alpha\beta} c^\alpha) \vdash F[E_{\alpha\beta} a^{\alpha\beta} b^{\alpha\beta}{}_-],$

B3. $p \lor \neg E_\tau a^\tau a^\tau \vdash p$

where τ is a basic type different from 0
and a^τ is an irreducible term,

B4. $F[E_\alpha a^\alpha b^\alpha{}_-, G(a^\alpha)_+] \lor G(b^\alpha) \vdash F[E_\alpha a^\alpha b^\alpha{}_-, G(a^\alpha)_+]$

where $G(a^\alpha)$ is a formula such that $G(x^\alpha)$ is primitive with respect to x^α,

B5. $p \lor \curlywedge \vdash p.$

Remark. The inference rule B5 is (together with our axioms and other inference rules) equivalent to the *cut rule*

$$p \lor r, q \lor \neg r \vdash p \lor q.$$

1.10. Inductive definition of *derivability*.

1.10.1. Every axiom is derivable.

1.10.2. If the premises of a basic inference are derivable, then the conclusion is derivable.

We say that a formula is *strictly derivable* if it is derivable without using the rule B5.

2. Partial valuations of the system STE

2.1. Definition. A *partial valuation* is an assignment V of *at most one* of the two values t (truth) and f (falsehood) to any formula such that the following conditions are satisfied:

2.1.1. If p or $\neg p$ has a value, then both formulas have different values.

2.1.2. $V(p \vee q) = t$ iff $V(p) = t$ or $V(q) = t$. $V(p \vee q) = f$ iff $V(p) = f$ and $V(q) = f$.

2.1.3. If $V(E_0 pq) = t$, then both formulas p and q have the same value. $V(E_0 pq) = f$ iff both formulas p and q have different values.

2.1.4. If $V(E_{\alpha\beta} a^{\alpha\beta} b^{\alpha\beta}) = t$, then $V(E_\beta(a^{\alpha\beta} c^\alpha)(b^{\alpha\beta} c^\alpha)) = t$ for all terms c^α of type α. $V(E_{\alpha\beta} a^{\alpha\beta} b^{\alpha\beta}) = f$ iff $V(E_\beta(a^{\alpha\beta} x^\alpha)(b^{\alpha\beta} x^\alpha)) = f$ for some variable x^α.

2.1.5. $V(E_\tau a^\tau a^\tau) = t$ for all basic types τ different from 0.

2.1.6. If $V(E_\alpha a^\alpha b^\alpha) = t$ and $G(a^\alpha)$ has a value, then $G(b^\alpha)$ has the same value.

2.2. LEMMA 1. If a formula p is strictly derivable, then there is no partial valuation V such that $V(p) = f$.

Proof by induction on the length of the strict derivation of p.

2.3. LEMMA 2. If a formula p is not strictly derivable, then there is a partial valuation V such that $V(p) = f$.

To prove this lemma we use some auxiliary concepts.

2.3.1. We can define the *degree* of a formula such that the premises of a basic inference A have lower degrees than its conclusion. This degree is used to prove statement b) below.

2.3.2. We define *deduction strings* of a formula p inverse to the inference rules A and B1–B4 in such a way that the following properties are fulfilled:

a) If every deduction string of a formula p contains an axiom, then these deduction strings can be combined to a strict derivation of p.

b) If there is a deduction string S of p which does not contain an axiom, then a partial valuation can be defined in which every negative part in S has the value t and every positive part in S (in particular p) has the value f.

This gives a proof of Lemma 2.

2.4. From the Lemmata 1 and 2 we have:

THEOREM I. A formula p is strictly derivable if and only if there is no partial valuation in which p has the value f.

2.5. Definition. A *total valuation* is an assignment of *exactly one* of the two values t and f to any formula such that the conditions 2.1.1–2.1.6 for partial valuations are satisfied.

A total valuation defines a general model in the sense of HENKIN [1950] in a straightforward manner, and vice versa every general model determines a total valuation. These general models satisfy the requirements of full extensionality.

2.6. LEMMA 3. A formula p is derivable if and only if the formula $p \vee \curlywedge$ is strictly derivable.
Proof by induction on the length of derivations.

2.7. LEMMA 4. If the formula $\curlywedge$ has a value in a partial valuation V, then V is a total valuation and $V(\curlywedge) = f$.
Proof by the definition of partial valuations.

2.8. THEOREM II. A formula is derivable if and only if it has the value t in every total valuation.
This follows from Theorem I and Lemmata 3 and 4.

2.9. *Example of a derivable formula which is not strictly derivable.* Let p be the formula

$$E_0\left(x^{(00)0}\left(S_{000}K_{00}y_1^{00}\right)\right)\left(x^{(00)0}\left(S_{000}K_{00}y_2^{00}\right)\right)$$

where y_1^{00} and y_2^{00} are different variables and $x^{(00)0}$ is a variable. p is not strictly derivable because there is a partial valuation in which the formulas

$$x^{(00)0}\left(S_{000}K_{00}y_i^{00}\right) \qquad (i = 1, 2)$$

have different values. But one can derive the formula p using the fact that both combinations

$$S_{000}K_{00}y_i^{00}z^0 \qquad (i = 1, 2)$$

convert to the same term z^0.

References

CURRY, H.B. and R. FEYS, Combinatory logic (Amsterdam, North-Holland Publ. Co., 1958; second printing 1967).
HENKIN, L., Completeness in the theory of types, J. Symb. Logic **15** (1950) 81–91.
HENKIN, L., A theory of propositional types, Fund. Math. **52** (1963) 323–344.
SCHÜTTE, K., Syntactical and semantical properties of simple type theory, J. Symb. Logic **25** (1960) 305–326.
TAKEUTI, G., On a generalized logic calculus, Jap. J. Math. **23** (1953) 39–96.

CONSTRUCTIVE REASONING

W. W. TAIT

University of Illinois, Chicago, USA

TURING'S [1936–7] analysis of mechanical computation provides a precise model for the basic constructive concept of operating on finite configurations of atoms according to rules. I will formulate the model in terms of CURRY'S [1930] combinators. The *terms* are built up from the constants κ, π, ι and 0 by taking (st) to be a term whenever s and t are terms. $s_1 s_2 \dots s_n$ will be an abbreviation for $(\dots (s_1 s_2) \dots s_n)$. The *rules of conversion* are

$$\pi st \Rightarrow s, \quad \kappa rst \Rightarrow rt(st),$$

$$\iota rr \Rightarrow 0,$$

and when s and t are distinct,

$$\iota st \Rightarrow \pi 0.$$

It is required in each instance of these rules that the terms r, s and t which are involved be *normal*, i.e., contain no parts which are convertible by means of the rules. A sequence $s_0, \dots, s_n$ is called a *reduction*, and s_n a *reduct* of s_0, if each s_{i+1} $(i < n)$ is obtained by replacing some part r of s_i by t, where $r \Rightarrow t$. $s \dashv t$ will mean that t is a reduct of s. If s reduces to a normal term (nt), we say that it is *defined*. It is easy to show that s reduces to at most one nt. Two defined terms are *definitionally equal* (cf. GÖDEL [1958]) if they reduce to the same nt. I.e., s and t are definitionally equal, written $s \equiv t$, if $\iota st \dashv 0$. This relation is decidable, of course, only for defined terms (which do not form a decidable class).[1] A nt s has a natural interpretation as a partial operator on the class of nt: the value of s for the argument t is the nt to which st reduces, when it is defined. As has been customary in discussions of constructive mathematics, I will use the word *function* in the intensional sense of referring to the nt which defines the operation, so that identity of

---

[1] I am using the term *decidable* in the usual idealized sense, which ignores both our limited capacity to comprehend sufficiently long terms and the positive probability that we will misread symbols.

two functions means definitional equality, not extensional equality. For example, if we identify the natural numbers with the nt

$$0, \quad 1 = \pi 0, \quad 2 = \pi 1, \ldots,$$

then a numerical function of n variables is a nt s such that $s k_0 \ldots k_n$ reduces to a number for all numbers $k_0, \ldots, k_n$. It is well-known how to represent recursive functions by nt. The essential point is that *explicit definitions* can be represented: If $t(x_1, \ldots, x_n)$ is a term built up from the constants and the variables $x_1, \ldots, x_n$, then there is a term $\lambda x_1 \ldots x_n t(x_1, \ldots, x_n)$ built up from the constants in $t(x_1, \ldots, x_n)$, π and κ, such that for all nt $s_1, \ldots, s_n$, if $t(s_1, \ldots, s_n)$ is defined,

$$\left(\lambda x_1 \ldots x_n \cdot t(x_1, \ldots, x_n) \right) s_1 \ldots s_n \equiv t(s_1, \ldots, s_n).$$

Now, given a term $t(x)$ in the variable x, let $r = \lambda x . t(xx) \; \lambda x . t(xx)$. Then if $t(r)$ is defined,

$$r \equiv t(r).$$

This is the so-called *fixed point*, or *first recursion theorem*.

If u is a nt, let b^u range over the nt t such that $ut \exists 0$ – which we express by Ut. *Finitism* (HILBERT, e.g. [1925]) can be represented in terms of our model as being concerned with proving free variable propositions $A(b_1^{u_1}, \ldots, b_n^{u_n})$ of the form $s(b_1^{u_1}, \ldots, b_n^{u_n}) = 0$, where $s(b_1, \ldots, b_n)$ is a term built up from the constants and the variables $b_1, \ldots, b_n$. The "finite" element of finitism consists in this: Although the concept of an *arbitrary* element of U_i – or more precisely, an arbitrary reduction of a term $u_i t$ to 0 – is admitted, the concept of *all* elements of a U_i is not. A finitist proof of $A(b_1^{u_1}, \ldots, b_n^{u_n})$ is a description of how to transform arbitrary reductions $u_i t_i \exists 0 (i = 1, \ldots, n)$ into a reduction of $s(t_1, \ldots, t_n)$ to 0.[2] For example, the *principle of substitution*

$$\frac{A(b^u) \quad Us}{A(s)}$$

---

[2] This is not a precise definition of what is to be meant by a finitist proof, of course. But this imprecision does not affect the validity of the principles of inference which are actually introduced below. I do not intend here to give a mathematical theory of constructive proofs. KREISEL [1965] attempts to give such a theory of proofs, which is based on the assumption that it should be decidable whether or not an (intensional) object is a proof of a free variable formula (of a certain kind – in general, containing variables over proofs, themselves). But this is a highly idealized notion of proof; and for this reason, it is not clear what relevance this theory would have to the question of what methods of proof may be accepted as constructive. In any case, by introducing as mathematical objects such intensional objects as proofs, it goes beyond the conception of constructive mathematics which I want to discuss here, as being concerned with mechanical computations.

(where s may contain variables) is immediately justified on this conception. The way in which the structure of a reduction of ut to 0 can be used in constructing a reduction of $s(t)$ to 0 is illustrated in the case of numbers. By the fixed point theorem, there is a nt v such that $v0 \dashv 0$, $v(\pi s) \dashv vs$ when the right hand term is defined, and vs is undefined when s is a nt which is not of the form 0 or πt. Ns means $vs \equiv 0$ (s is a number), and variables without superscripts will range over N. The concept of an arbitrary element of N is simply the concept of an arbitrary finite sequence 0, 1, ..., k. Suppose that $U0$ and $U(\pi b^u)$ are proved. Then by substitution, $U1$, so $U2$, so $U3$, and so on up to any given number. I.e., given an arbitrary number c, Uc: The reduction of uc to 0 is obtained by replacing each step from t to πt in the sequence 0, 1, ..., c by the construction of a reduction of $u(\pi t)$ to 0 from the reduction of ut to 0. This justifies the *principle of mathematical induction*

$$\frac{U0 \quad U(\pi b^u)}{Uc}.$$

Again, suppose that Us and $U(tab^u)$ are proved. Then by substitution, $U(t0s)$, $U(t1(t0s))$, and so on up to any arbitrary given number c. Thus, if we introduce the nt ρ in the usual way with $\rho st0 \equiv s$ and $\rho st(\pi r) \equiv tr(\rho str)$ (when the right hand terms are defined), the *principle of primitive recursion*

$$\frac{Us \quad U(tab^u)}{U(\rho stc)}$$

is valid. In this way, we see that all the theorems of primitive recursive arithmetic (when suitably coded) are finitistically valid. In particular, the principle of definition by recursion up to ω^k (i.e., simple k-fold recursion) is valid for each k, since this can always be obtained by a sequence of primitive recursions. What about recursion up to ω^ω, i.e., two-fold nested recursion?[3] A simple example is ACKERMANN's [1928] function ξ with

$$\xi 0ba \equiv a + b,$$
$$\xi(\pi c)\, 0a \equiv \eta ca,$$
$$\xi(\pi c)(\pi b)\, a \equiv \xi c(\xi(\pi c)\, ba)\, a,$$

---

[3] See TAIT [1961] for the reduction of recursion up to ω^ω to two-fold nested recursion.

where $\eta ca \equiv 0$, 1 or a depending on whether $c \equiv 0$, 1 or $c > 1$. ξ is defined by a two-fold nested recursion from primitive recursive functions. Set $\xi_n ba \equiv \xi nba$. Then for each particular n, ξ_n is finitistically defined, i.e., $N(\xi_n ba)$ is valid; since ξ_0 is primitive recursive, and $\xi_{k+1} = \Phi \xi_R$, where Φ is a primitive recursive operation. The argument that ξ is a numerical function, i.e., $N(\xi cba)$, then proceeds by iteration on the sequence $0, 1, \ldots, c$ of the inference: If f is a numerical function, then so is Φf. But this is not a finitist proof, since the concept of a numerical function is not a finitist concept: $N(fa)$ does not have the form $s(f) \equiv 0$, but is a universal proposition. Of course, this does not prove that ξ is not a finitist function, only that the above argument is not finitistic. But, if iteration of the substitution principle is the only method available for defining finitist functions – and I do not see what else there can be – then it is easy to prove that each finitist function is primitive recursive.

It should be noted that the present analysis differs in its conception from KREISEL's [1965]. Kreisel regards the essential feature of a finitist proof to be its "visualizability", and that Hilbert was simply mistaken in thinking that this involves a restriction to finite structures (since we want to prove general propositions, e.g., $a + b = b + a$). In terms of his analysis of the concept of visualizability, he shows that recursion up to any ordinal $< \varepsilon_0$ can be justified. It is difficult perhaps to determine what Hilbert really had in mind, but the above discussion shows that non-trivial mathematics is possible under the restriction to finite structures (providing that we admit the concept of an *arbitrary* such structure). In particular, the kind of reasoning involved in proving $a + b = b + a$, for example, need not go beyond this conception.

The argument cited above that Ackermann's function ξ is well-defined requires that species V of nt be introduced whose defining conditions are not of the form $vt \equiv 0$, but are universal generalizations of such conditions. More generally, given species U and V, $W = V^U$ consists of the V-valued functions defined on U, i.e., the nt s such that $V(sb^u)$. A proof of $A(b^w)$ is a description of how a proof of $A(t)$ can be constructed from an arbitrary proof of Wt.[4] This is a generalization of the finitist concept of a universal proposition. But, in the finitist case, the proofs of $A(t)$ and Wt would be decidable syntactical objects (reductions); whereas in the present case (for

---

[4] Cf. footnote 2. Again, the imprecision of this notion does not affect the validity of the kinds of inference which are actually introduced below. I do not see that the question of whether a kind of inference is constructively valid always has an answer. But, *sometimes* we can answer it.

Wt, at least), they will involve logic themselves. The principles of substitution, mathematical induction and primitive recursion remain valid; and besides, we have

$$\frac{V(sb^u)}{Ws} \qquad \frac{A(a^v)}{A(b^w c^u)}.$$

Let $N_0 = N$, and having defined N_σ and N_τ, let $N_{(\sigma,\tau)} = N_\tau^{N_\sigma}$.[5] Then in terms of our model of computability, N_σ represents. GÖDEL'S [1958] reckonable functions of finite type σ. Moreover, all of the axioms and rules of inference of Gödel's theory $\mathcal{T}$ of functions of finite type follow immediately from the principles we have introduced. The propositional connectives in Gödel's system should be interpreted as truth functions, which are coded by nt; and his notion of definitional equality should be interpreted as $s \equiv t$, as we already noted. Thus, his axioms $b^\sigma \equiv c^\sigma v \; b^\sigma \equiv c^\sigma$ are immediate from the fact that the elements of N_σ are nt.

We have already seen that one function defined by recursion up to ω^ω, namely Ackermann's ξ, can be obtained by primitive recursion once variables are introduced over numerical functions (i.e., of types $(0, (0, ..., (0,))...))$. GÖDEL'S [1958] consistency proof for arithmetic shows much more: $\mathcal{T}$ is closed under recursion up to any ordinal $< \varepsilon_0$; i.e., definition of a function of any finite type by recursion up to an ordinal $< \varepsilon_0$ can be reduced to primitive recursion (generally involving functions of higher type). Namely, every such function is the unique solution Φ of a formula $\bigwedge x^\sigma R(x^\sigma, \Phi x^\sigma)$, where R is primitive recursive and $\bigwedge x^\sigma \bigvee y^\gamma R(x^\sigma, y^\gamma)$ is a theorem of the system $\mathcal{T}_0$ of arithmetic with quantification over finite types and the axioms of $\mathcal{T}$ added (where the schema of mathematical induction is extended to include all formulas of the system). This follows because induction up to any ordinal $< \varepsilon_0$ is provable in the system (cf. GENTZEN [1943]). But, as KREISEL [1959] noted, Gödel's consistency proof extends to this system; and so there is a ψ in $\mathcal{T}$ with $R(b^\sigma, \psi b^\sigma)$ a theorem of $\mathcal{T}$. An analysis of Gödel's proof yields the following direct method for reducing recursion up to ordinals $< \varepsilon_0$ to primitive recursion:

Let $\prec$ be a primitive recursive ordering of type α with least element 0; and let

$$a \leftrightarrow \langle a_0, ..., a_{|a|-1} \rangle$$

be some standard primitive recursive one-to-one correspondence between

---

[5] This definition of N_σ allows a nt to have many types. E.g., $\lambda x \cdot x$ is in each N_σ. We could take the elements of N_σ to be the pairs $\langle \sigma, s \rangle$ instead of simply the nt s.

numbers and finite sequences of numbers with

$$a_0 > a_1 > ... > a_{|a|-1}.$$

We assume that $|a| = 0$ just in case $a = 0$. $a \subset b$ will mean that either $|a| < |b|$ and $a_i = b_i$ for all $i < |a|$, or else there is a k less than $|a|$ and $|b|$ with $a_k \prec b_k$ and $a_i = b_i$ for all $i < k$. $\subset$ is a primitive recursive ordering of type 2^α with least element 0: If a_i represents α_i in the ordering $\prec$, then a represents $2^{\alpha_0} + 2^{\alpha_1} + \cdots + 2^{\alpha_n} (n = |a| - 1)$ in the ordering $\subset$. Let the function ϕ be defined by the (course-of-values) recursion

$$\phi b \equiv Fb(\bar{\phi} b)$$

up to 2^α, where ϕ is of type $(0, \sigma)$, F is of type $(0, ((0, \sigma), \sigma))$ and $\bar{\phi}$ is the course-of-values function for ϕ, i.e., $\bar{\phi} b \equiv \lambda x_{\subset b} \phi x$. (For $x \supseteq b$, we will assume that this takes some standard value 0_σ of type σ. E.g., $0_0 = 0$, $0_{(\sigma,\gamma)} = \lambda x . 0_\sigma$.) $\bar{\phi}$ is defined by

$$\bar{\phi} b \equiv \lambda x_{\subset b} Fx(\bar{\phi} x),$$

and ϕ is explicitly defined from $\bar{\phi}$; so it suffices to consider the special case

$$\phi b \equiv \lambda x_{\subset b} Fx(\phi x)$$

of recursions up to 2^α, where ϕ is of type $(0, (0, \sigma))$. We will show that ϕ can be defined using only recursion up to α and primitive recursion. For $n \leq |a|$, let $a^n = \langle a_0, ..., a_{n-1} \rangle$. Then if $n < |b|$,

$$a \subset b^{n+1} \leftrightarrow a \subseteq b^n \vee (n < |a| \wedge a^n \equiv b^n \wedge a_n \prec b_n).$$

We will define a function ψ with $\psi uvb \equiv \phi b^u$ if $u \leq |b|$ and $v \equiv b_{u-1} \vee u \equiv 0$. Then we can set $\phi b \equiv \psi |b| b_{|b|-1} b$, or if $b \equiv 0$, $\phi b \equiv 0_{(0,\sigma)}$. Now,

$$\psi uvb \equiv \lambda x_{\subset b} uFx(\phi x)$$

if $u \leq |b|$ and $u > 0 \rightarrow v \equiv b_u$, and it is $0_{(0,\sigma)}$ otherwise. Thus, $\psi 0vb \equiv 0_{(0,\sigma)}$, since $b^0 \equiv 0$. $\psi u + 1vb$ is defined primitive recursively from F and the ϕx with $x \subset b^{u+1}$. If $x \subseteq b^u$, then $\phi x \equiv \psi u b_{u-1} bx$(or 0_σ if $u \equiv 0$). If $x^u \equiv b^u$ and $x_u \prec b_u$, then $\phi x \equiv \overline{((\psi u + 1)v)} x_u x$, where $\overline{(\psi u + 1)} v \equiv \lambda z_{\prec v} \psi u + 1z$. Thus, we can write

$$\psi u + 1v \equiv Gu + 1v(\psi u)(\overline{(\psi u + 1)} v),$$

where G is primitive recursive in F. Define

$$\chi fuv \equiv Guvf\,(\overline{\overline{(\chi fu)}}\,v),$$

where f is of type $(0, (0, (0, \sigma)))$. This is a recursive up to α, i.e., on $\prec$. Then we can define ψ by the primitive recursion

$$\psi 0v \equiv \lambda x . \lambda y . 0_\sigma,$$
$$\psi u + 1v \equiv \chi(\psi u)\, u + 1v.\ ^6$$

This shows that recursion up to the ordinals $2^{\omega+1}$, $2^{2\omega+1}$, etc. can be reduced to primitive recursion and recursion up to $\omega+1$. If we represent $\omega+1$ by the ordering $1, 2, 3, \ldots, 0$, then recursion up to $\omega+1$ has the form

$$\Phi b + 1 \equiv \lambda x_{<b} Fx + 1\,(\phi x + 1),$$
$$\phi 0 \equiv \lambda x Fx + 1\,(\phi x + 1).$$

Let $\chi b \equiv \lambda x_{<b}\phi x+1$. Then χ is defined by the primitive recursion

$$\chi 0 \equiv 0_\tau,$$
$$\chi b + 1 \equiv \lambda x_{\leq b}\lambda y_{<x} Fy + 1\,(\chi by),$$

where τ is the appropriate type. Then

$$\phi 0 \equiv \lambda x\ Fx + 1\,(\chi x + 1x),$$
$$\phi b + 1 \equiv \chi b + 1b.$$

An arithmetical interpretation of the theory $\mathcal{T}$ is obtained by arithmetizing the theory of combinators: $N_0 x$ is a decidable predicate, and

$$N_{(\sigma,\tau)}x \leftrightarrow \bigwedge y\,(N_\sigma y \to N_\tau xy).$$

Each theorem of $\mathcal{T}_0$ transforms into a theorem of intuitionistic arithmetic $\mathcal{U}_0$. This is essentially proved in TAIT [1967], except that the N_σ are restricted in that paper to (Gödel numbers of) terms which form a minimal model for $\mathcal{T}$. The present interpretation, which is the intended one under Church's thesis, is simply a reformulation of KREISEL's [1959] interpretation in terms of effective operations. But, by formulating mechanical computability in terms of combinators instead of the equational calculus, we are able to

---

^{6} The above reduction of recursion up to 2^α to recursion up to α was obtained by applying Gödel's interpretation to the reduction given in TAIT [1961], Fn. 3, of proof by induction up to 2^α to proof by induction up to α.

interpret Gödel's concept of definitional equality, and so, the full theory $\mathcal{T}$, instead of simply the part of $\mathcal{T}$ consisting only of numerical equations. (This is mentioned as a problem for the interpretation by effective operations in TAIT [1967], p. 200.) In any case, it easily follows from any of these interpretations that, if $\mathcal{T}$ is closed under recursive definition of numerical functions up to α – i.e., if $\mathcal{U}_0$ is closed under proof by induction up to α, then $\alpha < \varepsilon_0$. Thus, to go beyond arithmetic simply by iterating the logical concept of a function, we have to go to transfinite types. It would be interesting to have a neat formulation of the extension of $\mathcal{T}$ to transfinite types; but the principal result of TAIT [1965a] shows that Γ_0, the bound on predicative ordinals (as analyzed in FEFERMAN [1964] and this volume), is a bound on the α up to which recursion can be obtained, providing that we do not introduce transfinite types of ordinal $\geq \Gamma_0$.

The constructive theory of ordinals (cf. BROUWER [1913]) introduces a kind of reasoning which goes beyond predicative mathematics. Let U and V be species of nt, and let $\mu st = \langle s, t \rangle$ denote some standard pairing operation. The species $T = [U, V]$ of well-founded trees over V terminating in U is "inductively defined" by the conditions

$$T \langle 0, b'' \rangle$$

and

$$\frac{T(sb^v)}{T \langle 1, s \rangle}.$$

In referring to this definition as *inductive*, I mean this: In a proof of Ts, nothing about T should be used other than that it satisfies the above conditions. Thus, if any species Z satisfies these conditions, a proof of Ts immediately yields a proof of Zs; and so, we have the principle

$$\frac{Z \langle 0, b'' \rangle \; Z \langle 1, c \rangle}{Za^t} \quad (c \text{ over } Z^v)$$

of *induction over T*. Here, the species Z may be constructed from T, itself; and that is why the introduction of inductive definitions goes beyond predicative mathematics.

BROUWER (cf. [1913]) seems to have held that the constructive use of inductive definitions is restricted to the countable trees, e.g., $T_0 = [N, N]$; but I have been unable to arrive at any conception of inductive definitions which distinguishes the countable case from the more general one, $T = [U, V]$

for arbitrary species U and V. Let $0 = \langle 0, 0 \rangle$ and $\overline{n+1} = \langle 1, \bar{n} \rangle$, and then set $\omega = \langle 1, \lambda x . \bar{x} \rangle$ (where the operation $\bar{s}$ is extended in an obvious way). Then $T_0 \omega$ follows from a proof of $T_0 \bar{b}$. But this should not be regarded extensionally as consisting of all the proofs of $T_0 \bar{0}, T_0 \bar{1}, \ldots$. Rather, it is a proof that $\bar{b}$ is in T_0 for an arbitrary number b – based on what is involved in proving that a nt is in N. But this is precisely what is involved in proving $T \langle 1, s \rangle$ from $T(sb^v)$ in the general case. There is no question of having to visualize all the cases $T(st)$ for all t in V.[7]

Let δ be a nt with

$$\delta st \langle 0, r \rangle \equiv sr, \; \delta st \langle 1, r \rangle \equiv t \langle 1, r \rangle \big(\lambda x . \delta st (rx) \big),$$

when r, s and t are nt and the right hand sides are defined. Then, we also have the principle

$$\frac{Z(sb^u) \, Z(ta^t c)}{Z(\delta sta^t)} \qquad (c \text{ over } Z^v)$$

of *recursion over* T. In the special case that $tab \equiv t_0 b$, this principle follows by induction over T applied to the species Z_0 with $Z_0 r \leftrightarrow Z(\delta str)$. On the other hand, the general case reduces to this special case. Let $\langle s, t \rangle_0 = s$ and $\langle s, t \rangle_1 = t$. Set $\phi r \equiv \langle r, \delta str \rangle$. Then, $\phi \langle 0, b^u \rangle \equiv \langle \langle 0, b^u \rangle, sb^u \rangle \equiv s'b^u$, and $\phi \langle 1, c \rangle \equiv \langle \langle 1, c \rangle, t \langle 1, c \rangle \; (\lambda x . \delta st(cx)) \rangle \rangle \equiv \langle \langle 1, \lambda x . (\phi(cx))_0 \rangle, t \langle 1, \lambda x . (\phi (cx))_0 \rangle \; (\lambda x . (\phi(cx))_1) \rangle \equiv t'(\lambda x . \phi(cx))$.

Brouwer's ordinals are represented by trees in $[\{0\}, N]$. $\langle 0, 0 \rangle$ is the least ordinal; $\langle 1, \pi r \rangle$ is the successor of r; and if s is not of the form πr, $\langle 1, s \rangle$ is the ordinal sum $s0 + s1 + \cdots$. BROUWER (e.g., [1927]) applied the theory of ordinals to his non-atomistic theory of non-discrete spaces such as Baire space and the continuum. But, it is just as convenient to work directly with trees, rather than with their ordering as ordinals. In fact, it is simpler to use the trees in $[N, N]$, which I will call the *countable* trees.[8] Let $\vec{t} = \lambda x . t (\pi x)$. There is a nt η such that, writing $s't$ for ηst, $\langle 0, s \rangle' t \equiv s$ and $\langle 1, s \rangle' t \equiv (s(t0))' \vec{t}$ (when s and t are nt and the right hand sides are defined). Let p range over

---

[7] BROUWER (cf. [1927]) does want to regard proofs as infinite structures. But, if the proof of $T_0 \omega$ is so regarded, we see that it has the same structure as ω; and so it would be circular to infer the well-foundedness of ω (i.e., $T_0 \omega$) from the well-foundedness of this proof.

[8] Let $<$ denote the partial ordering of $[U, V]$ generated by $sb^u < s$. The trees s in $[N, N]$ are countable in the sense that the $t < s$ can be enumerated. Of course, the species of all nt is countable; and so, classically, every $[U, V]$ is countable. But, I am using this term in its constructive sense.

the countable trees and f over the functions of type $1 = (0,0)$. Then by induction on p,

$$N(p'f);$$

i.e., the countable trees operate as functions of type $2 = (1,0)$.[9] On BROUWER'S [1927] analysis, a numerical valued function which is defined for all "elements" of Baire space, i.e., all free choice sequences of numbers, is simply a function of type 2 of the form $\lambda f . p' f$. Thus, if α ranges over free choice sequences of numbers, then

$$\wedge \alpha \vee b \, R\big(\bar{\alpha}(b)\big) \leftrightarrow \vee p \wedge f \, R\big(\check{f}(p'f)\big),$$

where $\bar{\alpha}(b)$ denotes the sequence $\langle \alpha 0, ..., \alpha(b-1) \rangle$. If s is such a finite sequence, $s^\wedge b$ is the result of adding b to the end of it. On Brouwer's analysis, the principle

$$\wedge \alpha \vee b \, R\big(\bar{\alpha}(b)\big)$$
$$R(s) \vee \neg R(s)$$
$$\wedge b \, Q(s^\wedge b) \to Q(s)$$
$$\frac{R(s) \to Q(s)}{Q(\langle \rangle)}$$

of *Bar Induction* (cf. Kleene-Vesley), where s ranges over finite sequences of numbers and $\langle \rangle$ is the empty sequence, is an almost immediate consequence of induction on the p such that $\wedge f R(\check{f}(p'f))$. Kreisel and Troelstra (cf. Troelstra's paper in this symposium) have shown, further, that *every* formula of intuitionistic analysis (involving quantification over N, N_1, $[N, N]$ and Baire space) – and not just those of the form $\wedge \alpha \vee b \, R(\bar{\alpha}(b))$ – is equivalent intuitionistically to one which contains no quantifiers over Baire space.[10]

It is not the case, of course, that every function of type 2 is of the form $\lambda f . p' f$. In classical terms, there are partial recursive functions of type 2 which are defined for all recursive numerical functions, but cannot be recursively extended to all $\varPi_1^0$ numerical functions. Constructively, we can put it this way: Let $\prec$ denote the partial ordering of the unsecured sequences

---

[9] The same functions of type 2 are obtained from trees in $[\{0\}, N]$ if the definition of

$\langle 1, s \rangle' t$ is changed: $\langle 1, \pi r \rangle' t \equiv \pi(r' \, t)$; and if s is not of the form πr, $\langle 1' \, s \rangle$, $t \equiv (s(t0))'\vec{t}$. But, by using $[N, N]$, the extra case is avoided.

[10] Kreisel and Troelstra do not use quantification over $[N, N]$. Instead, they inductively define the species of "representing functions" of type 1 of the functions of the form $\lambda f . 1' f$.

of a function ϕ of type 2. Then *simple* recursive definitions of numerical functions, of the form

$$\psi ab \equiv \begin{cases} Fab & \text{if } \theta ab \nprec b \\ Gab(\psi a(\theta ab)) & \text{if } \theta ab \prec b, \end{cases}$$

are valid. For, this only requires that there be no infinite sequences $b \succ \theta ab \succ \theta a(\theta ab) \succ \ldots \succ \theta^n ab \succ \ldots$, which follows from the fact that $\phi(\lambda x.(\theta^x ab)_x)$ is defined, where $(b)_x$ denotes the xth element in the sequence coded by b. But, we cannot infer the validity of the general (course-of-values) form of recursion

$$\psi b \equiv Fb(\lambda x_{\prec b} \psi x)$$

when ϕ is not of the form $\lambda f.p'f$. For, if $\subset$ is defined as above from $\prec$, we have seen how recursion on $\subset$ can be reduced to course-of-values recursion on $\prec$. But, even though $\prec$ may have no (computable) infinite descending sequences, $\subset$ may have (cf. PARIKH [1966]). Nevertheless, if we have proved $N(\phi f)$ using only the kind of principles (including transfinite recursions) which we have so far discussed, which make no use of the fact that f is restricted to computable functions, then it is reasonable to suppose that ϕ is of the form $\lambda f.p'f$. In particular, we should expect the system $\mathcal{T}_1$, obtained by adding bar recursion of type 0 (cf. SPECTOR [1962]) to Gödel's theory $\mathcal{T}$, to be valid when we interpret functions of type 2 as countable trees $\lambda f.p'f$ (since Spector's extensional form of bar recursion on $\lambda f.p'f$ can be reduced to recursion on p). That this is so follows from TAIT [1967], which interprets $\mathcal{T}_1$ in intuitionistic analysis, and Troelstra's paper: A function constant of type 2 in $\mathcal{T}_1$ is interpreted as a term t for which $\bigwedge \alpha \bigvee b(t\alpha \equiv b)$ is a theorem of intuitionistic analysis, and so, $tf \equiv p'f$ for some tree p.

Brouwer's argument for identifying the numerical valued functions on Baire space with the functions $\lambda f.p'f$ is based on a consideration of what it would mean to prove that a function is defined for all free choice sequences. A general theory of such proofs (as mental objects) would be required to make his argument rigorous. Yet, as it stands, it seems to me to have much the same kind (whether or not degree) of status as Turing's analysis of computability: It presents plausible considerations for accepting a particular definition of what we should mean by a numerical valued function on Baire space.

In terms of the functions $\lambda f.p'f$, it is possible to give a very simple treatment of the Hilbert-Ackermann substitution method. By TAIT [1965b], the crux of this method is this: Let ϕ be of type $(0, 1)$ with

(*) $$\phi ab \equiv 0.v.\phi(\pi a)\, b \equiv \phi ab,$$

and let F, of type $(1, (1, 0))$, be defined by (explicit definitions and) simple recursion up to some ordinal $<\alpha$. Then there is a G of type 2, defined by simple recursion up to some $\beta < 2^{\alpha}$ such that, for $k = Gf$,

$$Ff(\phi k) \equiv Ff(\phi k + 1).$$

Suppose that F is $\lambda fg.p'\langle f, g\rangle$, where $\langle f, g\rangle = \lambda x.\langle fx, gx\rangle$. We define ψp by recursion on p so that, when ϕ satisfies (*), $Gf = \psi pnf\phi$ satisfies the above equation and $Gf \geq n$.

$$\psi\langle 0, m\rangle\, bf\phi \equiv b$$

$$\psi\langle 1, s\rangle\, bf\phi \equiv \begin{cases} k = \psi(s\langle f0,\phi 00\rangle\, b\vec{f}\lambda x.\vec{\phi x}, \text{ if } \phi k + 10 \equiv \phi 00 \\ \psi(s\langle f0, \phi k + 10\rangle \max(k + 1, b)\, \vec{f}\lambda x.\vec{\phi x}, \text{ otherwise}. \end{cases}$$

By induction on p, $\psi pbf\phi \geq b$ always holds. If $F \equiv \lambda fg.\langle 0, m\rangle'\langle g.f\rangle$, then it is immediate that $Gf = \psi\langle 0, m\rangle\, nf\phi$ satisfies the equation. Let $F \equiv \lambda fg.$ $\langle 1, s\rangle'\langle f, g\rangle$, and set $F_m = \lambda fg.(sm)'\langle f, g\rangle$. If ϕ satisfies (*), then so does $\lambda x.\vec{\phi x}$; and so, if $k_m = \psi(sm)\, nf\lambda x.\vec{\phi x}$,

$$F_m\vec{f}\,\vec{\phi k_m} \equiv F_m\vec{f}\,\overrightarrow{\phi k_m + 1}.$$

Choose $m = \langle f0, \phi 00\rangle$. If $\phi k_m + 10 \equiv \phi 00$, then $k_m = \psi\langle 1, s\rangle\, nf\phi$; and $\phi k_m 0 \equiv \phi 00$ by (*), so that $m \equiv \langle f0, \phi k_m 0\rangle \equiv \langle f0, \phi k_m + 10\rangle$. Hence, $Ff(\phi k_m) \equiv F_m\vec{f}\,\vec{\phi k_m} \equiv F_m\vec{f}\,\overrightarrow{\phi k_m + 1} \equiv Ff(\phi k_m + 1)$. If $\phi k_m + 10 \not\equiv \phi 00$, then for all $b < k_m + 1$, $\phi b0 \equiv \phi k_m + 1$. Let $m' = \langle f0, \phi k_m + 10\rangle$. Then $\psi\langle 1, s\rangle\, nf\phi \equiv \psi$ $(sm') \max(k_m + 1, n)\vec{f}\lambda x.\vec{\phi x}$, which we set $= k$. $F_{m'}\vec{f}\vec{\phi k} \equiv F_{m'}\vec{f}\overrightarrow{\phi k + 1}$, and, since $k \geq k_m + 1$, $m' \equiv \langle f0, \phi k0\rangle \equiv \langle f0, \phi k + 10\rangle$. So, $Ff(\phi k) \equiv F_{m'}\vec{f}\vec{\phi k_m} \equiv$ $F_{m'}\vec{f}\overrightarrow{\phi k + 1} \equiv Ff(\phi k + 1)$.

The rest of the treatment of the substitution method would consist in showing that if p is of rank $<\alpha$, then $G = \lambda f.q'f$ for some q of rank $<2^{\alpha}$. But I will not do this here.[11]

---

[11] This discussion applies to the substitution method for systems with mathematical induction. For systems with induction up to β, the condition (*) on ϕ is replaced by $\phi ab \equiv 0.v.\phi(\pi a)b \prec \phi ab$, where $\prec$ is the given ordering of type β. The definition of ψ must be modified in the last case; and, instead of the bound 2^{α} on the rank of q such that $\lambda f.q'f$, we get the bound $(\beta + 1)^{\alpha}$. See footnote 12.

Now, let p range over $[U, V]$ for arbitrary species U and V, and let f range over V^N. Then by recursion on p,

$$U(p'f);$$

so that the trees in $[U, V]$ operate as U-valued functions on V^N. Again, if we try to see what should be meant by a U-valued function defined for all free choice sequences of elements of V (where the nth choice is made only after it has been shown to be in V), it seems to me that we are led to the functions $\lambda f.p'f$. Thus, if α ranges over such sequences, $\bigwedge \alpha \bigvee b \, R(\bar{\alpha}(b))$ should again be interpreted by $\bigvee p \bigwedge f R(\bar{f}(p'f))$; and so, bar induction with respect to formulae $\bigwedge \alpha \bigvee b \, R(\bar{\alpha}(b))$ follows by induction over $[U, V]$.

In 1962, Gödel suggested that one might obtain a consistency proof for classical analysis by introducing such inductively defined species into intuitionistic mathematics. In view of SPECTOR'S [1962] interpretation of classical analysis in Σ_4 (i.e., Gödel's theory $\mathcal{T}$ with bar recursion of each finite type added), this seems very plausible. For, if the functions of type $((0, \sigma), 0)$ are all of the form $\lambda f.p'f$, then bar recursion of type σ is an immediate consequence of recursion on p. But, one must show that the definitional axioms of Σ_4 do not lead to functions of type $((0, \sigma), 0)$ which are not of the form $\lambda f.p'f$.

It is clear that this cannot be shown using only the constructive principles which have been discussed here. For, arithmetizing the theory of combinations, U^V is arithmetic in U and V and $[U, V]$ is Π_1^1 in U and V, and all the principles which have been mentioned are formalized in Π_1^1 analysis (i.e,. with the comprehension axiom restricted to Π_1^1 formulae). To see this, one need only note that induction over U^V is used only for species which are (classically) Π_1^1 in Π_1^1 in ... in Π_1^1 formulae. So, to carry out Gödel's suggestion, stronger kinds of inductive definitions must be found – or more generally, stronger constructive principles.

However, the present methods do suffice to interpret Σ_4 in this way if bar recursion is restricted to types θ_m, where $0_0 = 0$ and $\theta_{m+1} = ((\theta, \theta_m), \theta)$. An examination of Spector's interpretation of classical analysis in Σ_4 shows that bar recursion of types $\theta_0 = 0$ and $\theta_1 = 2$ suffice for Π_1^1 analysis. I will save the details of this foundation for bar recursion of types θ_m for another occasion. At the present time, I have no idea how to extend this foundation to bar recursion of finite types other than the θ_m, so as to obtain a foundation for other instances of the comprehension axiom. But, using proof theory for infinitary formulae, it is possible to prove the consistency of the Δ_2^1 comprehension rule (i.e., if the formula has been proved to be Δ_2^1, we take as an axiom that its extension is a set). Here, we need the species T_z of trees built up by: $T_0 = [N, N]$. If z has been obtained already in some T_u, then $T_z = [N, \bigcup_v T_{zv}]$, where v ranges over the appropriate species. T_ω already suffices for the Π_1^1 comprehension axiom. Again, I will present the details another time. Actually, for the consistency of specific formal systems, the species T_z are not needed, but only their relativizations to specific decidable sets M of functions (i.e., $\langle 1, t \rangle \in T_z$ only if $t \in M$). These relativized T_z consist of countable trees, and are themselves countable. I have not determined the rank[12], say, of the relativized T_ω, since, because I have been working with infinitary systems rather than the formal system of Π_1^1 analysis, I have not determined the class M of functions needed. It is reasonable to suppose that the rank of the relativized T_ω is the upper bound in the ordinal diagrams of order $\omega + 1$, since these are the ordinals TAKEUTI [1967] used to prove the consistency of Π_1^1 analysis.

References

ACKERMANN, W., 1928, Zum Hilbertchen Aufbau der reelen Zahlen, Math. Ann. **99**, 118–133.

BROUWER, L. E. J., 1913, Intuitionism and formalism, Bull. Am. Math. Soc. **20**, 81–96.
   1927, Über Definitionsbereiche von Funktionen, Math. Ann. **97**, 60–75.

CURRY, H., 1930, Grundlagen der kombinatorischen Logik, Am. J. Math. **52**, 509–536, 789–834.

FEFERMAN, S., 1964, Systems of predicative analysis, J. Symb. Logic **29**, 1–30.

GENTZEN, G., 1943, Beweisbarkeit und Unbeweisbarkeit von Anfangsfällen der transfiniten Induktion in der reinen Zahlentheorie, Mat. Ann. **119**, 140–161.

GÖDEL, K., 1958, Über eine bisher noch nicht benützte Erweiterung des finiten Standpunktes, Dialectica **12**, 280–287.

HILBERT, D., 1925, Über das Unendliche, Math. Ann., **95**, 161–190.

HOWARD, W., 1964, Transfinite induction and transfinite recursion, unpublished.

KLEENE, S. and R. VESLEY, 1965, The foundations of intuitionistic mathematics (Amsterdam, North-Holland Publ. Co.).

KREISEL, G., 1959, Inessential extensions of Heyting's arithmetic by means of functionals of finite type, J. Symbolic Logic, **24**, abstract, 284.
   1965, Mathematical logic, in: Lectures on modern mathematics, ed. T. L. Saaty, III.

PARIKH, R., 1966, Some generalizations of the notion of a well ordering, Z. math. Logik und Grundl. der Math. **12**, 333–340.

SPECTOR, C., 1962, Provably recursive functionals of analysis, in: Recursive function theory, Proc. Symp. in pure mathematics, Am. Math. Soc. (Providence, R.I.) 1–27.

TAIT, W., 1961, Nested recursion, Math. Ann. **163**, 236–250.
   1965a, Infinitely long terms of transfinite type, in: Formal systems and recursive functions, eds. J. Crossley and M. Dummett (Amsterdam, North-Holland Publ. Co.) 176–185.

---

[12] E.g., the rank of $\langle 0, s \rangle$ is $\leq$ any ordinal. The rank of $\langle 1, s \rangle$ is $\leq$ the ordinal z just in case st^σ has rank $\leq z_t < z$ for all t in R_σ.

1965b, The substitution method, J. Symb. Logic **30**, 175–192.

1967, Intensional interpretations of functionals of finite type I, J. Symb. Logic **32**, 198–212.

TAKEUTI, G., 1967, Consistency proofs of subsystems of classical analysis, Ann. Math. **86**, 299–348.

TURING, A., 1936–7, On computable numbers, with an application to the Entscheidungs-problem, Proc. London Math. Soc. 2, **42**, 230–265; corrections, ibid., **43**, 544–546.

THE THEORY OF CHOICE SEQUENCES

A. S. TROELSTRA[1]

University of Amsterdam, Amsterdam, Netherlands

This paper consists of two parts. In the first part we describe a formal system for intuitionistic analysis, in the second part of the paper we discuss the intuitive justification of this system.

The system to be discussed shall be called CS (CS from Choice Sequence). CS contains numerical variables, two kinds of variables for constructive functions and variables for choice sequences. The subsystem of CS obtained by restricting the language, axioms and rules of CS to expressions not involving variables for choice sequences, shall be called IDK. (IDK, because the main feature of the subsystem is an Inductive Definition of a class of constructive functions called K.)

The main result concerning the relation between CS and IDK can be stated as follows. With every formula A of CS not containing free variables for choice sequences a translation $\mathscr{A}$ which is a formula of IDK can be associated, such that $\vdash_{CS} A \leftrightarrow \mathscr{A}$. In fact, a much stronger result can be obtained, since we can prove finitistically $\vdash_{CS} A$ iff $\vdash_{IDK} \mathscr{A}$.

This paper does not contain a proof of this result; full details of the formal work concerning CS will appear in KREISEL and TROELSTRA.

The formal work on the system CS was started some years ago by KREISEL [1963] (which was privately circulated only) and was recently improved and rounded off to a certain extent by a joint effort of Kreisel and the author.

1. Some notations and conventions

1.1. In this section we describe some notations and conventions for use in informal discussions. As logical symbols we use $\wedge$, $\vee$, $\neg$, &, $\vee$, $\rightarrow$,

---

[1] Research for, and preparation of this paper was made possible by a fellowship from the Netherlands Organization for the advancement of Pure Research (Z.W.O.).

$\leftrightarrow$. In this sequence each symbol binds stronger than all symbols to the right of it; we can omit parentheses accordingly. In general, we shall omit parentheses whenever it is possible to do so without confusion.

In writing terms we adopt association to the left: $\alpha\beta x = \alpha(\beta(x))$.

1.2. N indicates the set of natural numbers. Natural numbers are denoted by letters x, y, z, u, v, w, n, m. We shall suppose that we have an enumeration of all finite sequences of natural numbers, such that 0 corresponds to the empty sequence. The sequence number of a sequence $x_0, x_1, x_2, ..., x_u$ under this enumeration without repetition is written as $\langle x_0, ..., x_u \rangle$.

We write as a shorthand $\langle x \rangle = \hat{x}$ for the one-element sequence with only element x.

n, m are reserved to denote (on the intended interpretation of the formulae considered) sequence numbers. Concatenation of sequences corresponds to the operation $*$ on sequence numbers.

Furthermore we have a pairing function $\{\ \ \}$ with two inverses indicated by superscripts i.e. $\{x, y\}^1 = x$, $\{x, y\}^2 = y$.

Successor and predecessor are written as x^+ or $x + 1$, x^- or $x \div 1$.

1.3. S always denotes a species containing at least two different objects.

A process which assigns to every natural number $x \in N$ an element of S, is called a *sequence* or *function* (from N into S). χ, χ', χ'' will be used to denote sequences in general. Equality between sequences will always be interpreted extensionally, i.e.

$$\chi = \chi' \leftrightarrow \wedge x(\chi x = \chi' x).$$

The species of sequences from N into S is denoted by S^N.

The *constructive functions* (or *sequences*) of S^N are those sequences which are completely fixed in advance by some law for generating the elements.

a, b, c, d are letters used for constructive functions of N^N. (Sub- or superscripts can be added if necessary.) The notion of *choice sequence* will be explained later; $\alpha, \beta, \gamma, \delta, \varepsilon$ are used for choice sequences.

We use the λ-notation to define functions, λ' for abstraction of constructive functions, λ for abstraction of choice sequences.

If χ is a function, $\bar{\chi}$ is the corresponding course-of-values function defined by

$$\bar{\chi}0 = 0, \quad \bar{\chi}x = \langle \chi 0, ..., \chi(x \div 1) \rangle \quad \text{for} \quad x > 0.$$

1.4. A, B, C, D, P, Q denote arbitrary predicates of sequences and numbers. We shall in general suppose all predicates to be extensional with respect to functions, i.e.

$$A\chi \& \chi = \chi' \to A\chi'\,.$$

K is a predicate constant for constructive functions of N^N; e, f are reserved for elements of K, hence we are permitted to introduce $\bigwedge e$, $\bigvee e$ as abbreviations of $\bigwedge e \in K$, $\bigvee e \in K$.

We define a special constructive function $k^{(n)}$ for every number n. Let $n = \langle x_0, \ldots, x_u \rangle$; then, if $m = \langle w, y_0, \ldots, y_v \rangle$,

$$k^{(n)}m = \begin{cases} x_w + 1 & \text{if} \quad w \leq u\,, \\ y_w + 1 & \text{if} \quad v > u, u < w \leq v\,, \\ 0 & \text{if} \quad w > v, u < w\,. \end{cases}$$

2. Basic principles of IDK

2.1. In order to illustrate the significance of the main result announced above, we shall discuss the intuitive justification of the basic principles of IDK first.

In the first place IDK contains an axiom of choice:

$$\bigwedge x \bigvee a A(x, a) \to \bigvee b \bigwedge x (x, \lambda' y.\, b\,\{x, y\}) \tag{1}$$

(A not containing free choice variables).

On account of the intuitionistic interpretation of the quantifier combination $\bigwedge x \bigvee a$, this seems to be evident.

2.2. The most important feature of IDK is an inductive definition of a certain class K of constructive functions. We make a few general remarks about generalized inductive definitions (g.i.d.) first.

Let $A(P, s)$ be an expression in a certain formal language. P is a predicate variable (i.e. a letter standing for an arbitrary predicate in the formal expression). Then, under suitable conditions on A, one can assert the existence of a minimal class or a minimal predicate P_A, which satisfies $A(P_A, s) \leftrightarrow P_A s$ for all s. This amounts to introducing a new predicate constant P_A in our language, together with the axiom

$$A(P_A, s) \leftrightarrow P_A s \tag{2}$$

and the axiom scheme expressing minimality (for any predicate Q in the *extended* language)

$$\bigwedge s [A(Q, s) \to Qs] \to \bigwedge s [P_A s \to Qs]\,. \tag{3}$$

Using classical set theory, we can prove the existence of P_A under a very general condition on A, namely monotonicity:

$$A(P, s) \& P \subseteq P' \rightarrow A(P', s). \tag{4}$$

In this case, (2) can be weakened to

$$A(P_A, s) \rightarrow P_A s \tag{5}$$

since $\lambda s.\ A(P_A, s) \subseteq P_A$, and hence by (5) $A(\lambda s.\ A(P_A, s), t) \rightarrow A(P_A, t)$ and therefore by (3) we can conclude to (2).

Although the existence of P_A in case A satisfies monotonicity can be justified in the general theory of constructive proofs (compare e.g. section 2 of KREISEL [this volume]) it is worthwhile looking for special cases which can be justified by means of less abstract intuitive notions. In fact for IDK we need only one very special class introduced by g.i.d..

Let us think of a predicate or a class K of constructive functions P which satisfies two closure conditions:

$1°)$ P contains all non-zero constant functions:

$$\bigvee x(a = \lambda'n.x + 1) \rightarrow Pa,$$

$2°)$ If $a0 = 0$, and for every y $\lambda'n.a(\hat{y} * n)$ belongs to P, then a belongs to P:

$$a0 = 0 \ \& \ \bigwedge y\, P(\lambda'n.a(\hat{y} * n)) \rightarrow Pa.$$

If we write

$$A_K(P, a) = \bigvee x(a = \lambda'n.x + 1) \vee (\bigwedge y\, P(\lambda'n.a(\hat{y} * n)) \ \& \ a0 = 0)$$

the closure conditions for P can be expressed by

$$A_K(P, a) \rightarrow Pa. \tag{6}$$

The minimal class K satisfying (6) is such that Ka is proved using (6) only; in other words, the proof conditions for Ka are: Ka is proved using $1°$ and $2°$ only.

It seems natural and evident that these proof conditions determine the minimal class satisfying (6); but we shall elaborate this a little more.

The natural, "direct" proof of Ka can be visualized as a (in general infinite) well-founded tree with a topmost node corresponding to the conclusion Ka. Terminal nodes correspond to inferences on account of condition $(1°)$. Passing from a row of immediate descendants of a node v to v itself corresponds to an inference on account of condition $(2°)$. The elements of K occurring in such a proof of Ka are all of the form $\lambda'n.a(m*n)$.

In this way a itself codifies the natural proof of Ka.

On account of the minimality of K, we expect the following scheme to be valid

$$\bigwedge a\left[A_K(Q, a) \to Qa\right] \to \bigwedge a\left[Ka \to Qa\right]. \tag{7}$$

Proof-theoretically, we can convince ourselves of the validity of (7) as follows. Suppose $\bigwedge a[A_K(Q, a) \to Qa]$ holds. This means that Q is closed under conditions $1°, 2°$.

Let Ka. With every inference of type $1°$ or $2°$ in the natural proof of Ka we can associate inferences of type $3°$ and $4°$ respectively:

$3°)$ $\bigvee x(b = \lambda'n.x+1) \to Kb \& Qb.$

$4°)$ $b0 = 0 \& \bigwedge yK(\lambda'n.\, b(\hat{y}*n)) \& \bigwedge yQ(\lambda'n.\, b(\hat{y}*n)) \to Kb \& Qb.$

In this way we obtain a proof of $Ka \& Qa$ by replacing in the natural proof of K every inference of type $1°$ or $2°$ by the corresponding inference of type $3°, 4°$. This justifies (7).

This line of argument closely parallels the intuitive argument which convinces us of the validity of induction for the natural numbers.

The elements of K can serve to represent continuous functionals of types $N^N \to N$ and $N^N \to N^N$, as follows.

One proves easily

$$\bigwedge a \in K \bigwedge \chi \bigvee x(a(\bar{\chi}x) \neq 0), \tag{8}$$

$$\bigwedge a \in K \bigwedge n \bigwedge m(an \neq 0 \to a(n*m) = an). \tag{9}$$

Let a be a function of K. Then a functional Φ_a of type $N^N \to N$ is determined by:

$$\Phi_a\chi = y \leftrightarrow \bigvee x(a(\bar{\chi}x) = y + 1). \tag{10}$$

(8) proves that some y satisfying (10) always can be found, (9) proves uniqueness of this value. Clearly Φ_a is continuous. By looking at a function a as a sequence $\lambda'n.\, a(\hat{x}*n)$, $x = 0, 1, 2, \ldots$ we see that we also can codify a functional Ψ_a of type $N^N \to N^N$ by stipulating

$$(\Psi_a\chi)\, x = y \leftrightarrow \bigvee z(a(\hat{x}*\bar{\chi}z) = y + 1).$$

(Later on, we shall argue that every continuous functional of type $N^N \to N$ or $N^N \to N^N$ has a representative in K.)

To indicate $\Phi_e\alpha = x$ we write $e(\alpha) = x$, to indicate $\Psi_e\alpha = \beta$ we write $e|\alpha = \beta$. For $k^{(n)}|\alpha$ we write shortly $n|\alpha$.

3. The systems CS and IDK

3.1. Conventions

Our conventions in the description of CS are in principle independent of the conventions for informal use, but in most cases the conventions are closely parallel to the informal language. We have four[2] sorts of variables:

numerical variables: x, y, z, u, v, w, n, m (n-Var)

variables for constructive functions: a, b, c, d (c-Var)

variables for K-functions: e, f (K-Var)

variables[3] for choice functions: $\alpha, \beta, \gamma, \delta, \varepsilon$ (choice-Var).

t, s are used to denote terms (Tm). Terms not involving choice variables are called constructive terms (c-Tm). There are three kinds of functors, constructive functors (c-Fn), K-functors (K-Fn), and choice functors (Fn). ϕ, ϕ' denote arbitrary functors.

We have three abstraction operators: λ for choice-functor abstraction, λ' for abstraction of constructive functors, λ'' for abstraction of K-functors. The logical symbols are $\&, \vee, \bigvee, \bigwedge, \rightarrow; \neg, \leftrightarrow$ are conceived as abbreviations. For successor and predecessor we write $^+, {}^-$; other functions are written as in the informal case. Furthermore we adopt the usual bracketing conventions.

3.2. Simultaneous definition of Tm, c-Tm, Fn, c-Fn, K-Fn

(1) If $t \in$ Tm, and t does not contain choice variables, then $t \in$ c-Tm.

(2) $0 \in$ Tm.

(3) Numerical variables are terms.

(4) If $t, s \in$ Tm, then $t^+, t^-, \{t, s\}, t^1, t^2, \langle t \rangle, t * s \in$ Tm (possibly some functions are added).

(5) Choice variables belong to Fn.

(6) Constructive variables belong to c-Fn.

(7) K-variables belong to K-Fn.

(8) If $t(x) \in$ c-Tm, then $\lambda' x. t(x) \in$ c-Fn.

(9) If $t(x) \in$ Tm, then $\lambda x. t(x) \in$ Fn.

(10) If $t \in$ c-Tm, then $k^{(t)} \in K$-Fn, $\lambda'' n.t^+ \in K$-Fn.

(11) If $t \in$ c-Tm, $\phi \in K$-Fn, then $\lambda'' n. \phi(t * n) \in K$-Fn.

---

[2] Separate variables for the elements of K are added solely for the purpose of obtaining a suitable definition of terms and functors.

[3] We have replaced "free choice sequence" by "choice sequence", henceforth "free choice variable" must be interpreted as "free choice-variable" not as "free-choice variable".

(12) If $\phi \in K$-Fn, $\phi' \in$ Fn, then $\phi(\phi') \in$ Tm, $\phi | \phi' \in$ Fn. Likewise with Fn replaced by c-Fn.

(13) If $\phi \in$ Fn $\cup K$-Fn $\cup$ c-Fn, and $t \in$ Tm, then $\phi(t)$, $\bar{\varphi}(t) \in$ Tm. We write $t | \phi$ for $k^{(t)} | \phi$.

3.3. Definition of the class of well formed formulae (Fm)

(1) If $t, s \in$ Tm, then $t = s \in$ Fm.

(2) If $A, B \in$ Fm, then $(A) \& (B)$, $(A) \rightarrow (B)$, $(A) \vee (B)$,
$\wedge x(A)$, $\vee x(A)$, $\wedge a(A)$, $\vee a(A)$, $\wedge e(A)$, $\vee e(A)$,
$\wedge \alpha(A)$, $\vee \alpha(A) \in$ Fm.

Formulae according to clause (1) are called *atomic* formulae.

3.4. Logical axioms and rules, equality axioms

Our system contains axioms and rules for four-sorted intuitionistic predicate logic; $\neg P$ is conceived as $P \rightarrow 0^+ = 0$. As equality axioms and rules of λ-conversion we have

E1. $x = x$; E2. $x = y \rightarrow y = x$; E3. $x = y \& y = z \rightarrow x = z$. E4. $x = y \rightarrow t(x) = t(y)$.

E5. $(\lambda x. t(x))(t') = t(t')$; likewise for λ', λ''.

$\phi = \phi'$ is an abbreviation for $\wedge x(\phi x = \phi' x)$;

$s \neq t$ is an abbreviation for $s = t \rightarrow 0^+ = 0$.

3.5. Axioms for function constants and constant terms .

D1. $\neg 0 = x^+$; D2. $x^+ = y^+ \rightarrow x = y$; D3. $\{x, y\}^1 = x, \{x, y\}^2 = y, \{x^1, x^2\} = x$.

D4. Defining equations for the introduced primitive recursive functions: $\bar{\ }, *, k^{(x)}, \langle \ \rangle$ and possibly some others. (For $\langle t \rangle$ we also write $\hat{t}$).

D5. $\bar{\alpha} 0 = 0$, $\bar{\alpha} x^+ = \bar{\alpha} x * \langle \alpha x \rangle$. Likewise for a, e instead of α.

D6. $e(\alpha) = x \leftrightarrow \vee y(e(\bar{\alpha} y) = x^+)$. Likewise for a, f instead of α.

D7. $(e | \alpha) x = y \leftrightarrow (\lambda'' n. e(\langle x \rangle * n))(\alpha) = y$. Likewise for a, f instead of α.

3.6. Induction scheme

For arbitrary formulae Bx:

$$\text{I.} \quad [B0 \& \wedge x(Bx \rightarrow Bx^+)] \rightarrow \wedge x\, Bx.$$

3.7. Axioms for constructive functions

C1. Let $A(x, a)$ be a formula without free choice variables. Then

$$\wedge x \vee a A(x, a) \rightarrow \vee b \wedge x A(x, \lambda' y . b \{x, y\}).$$

C2. Define Ka as an abbreviation of $\bigvee e(a=e)$ and let
$$A_K(P, a) = \bigvee x[\lambda'n.\ x^+ = a] \vee [a0 = 0 \ \& \ \bigwedge xP(\lambda'n.a(\langle x\rangle * n))].$$
Then C2.1. $A_K(K, a) \to Ka$.

      C2.2. For arbitrary predicates for constructive functions in our notation:

$$\bigwedge a[A_K(Q, a) \to Qa] \to \bigwedge a[Ka \to Qa].$$

3.8. Axioms for choice sequences

In these axioms A contains no other free choice variables besides those exhibited.

F1. $\bigwedge x \vee \alpha B(x, \alpha) \to \bigvee \beta \wedge x \ B(x, \lambda y.\beta\{x, y\})$.

F2. $A\alpha \leftrightarrow \bigvee e[\bigvee \beta(\alpha = e|\beta) \ \& \ \bigwedge \beta \ A(e|\beta)]$.

F3. $\bigwedge \alpha \vee a \ A(\alpha, a) \to \bigvee e \vee b \wedge n(en \neq 0 \to \bigwedge \alpha \ A(n|\alpha, \lambda'y.b\{(en)^-, y\}))$.

F4. $\bigwedge \alpha \vee \beta \ A(\alpha, \beta) \to \bigvee e \wedge \alpha \ A(\alpha, e|\alpha)$.

F2 is the analogon of F3 in Kreisel [1963], F3 and F4 correspond to F5, F6 in Kreisel [1963].

3.9. CS and IDK

3.1–3.8 describe CS. IDK is obtained by restricting all axioms and rules to those not containing choice variables.

If we replace in a formula A a c-functor or a choice functor by any other functor, the formula remains well-formed. A K-functor however, cannot always be replaced by another functor since $\phi|\alpha$ etc. only make sense if $\phi \in K\text{-Fn}$.

3.10. Consequences of the axioms

The following theorem enumerates some consequences of the axioms which can be proved straightforwardly and without difficulty.

THEOREM 1. A', A do not contain other choice variables besides those shown.

(1) In CS we can replace F2 by the axiom
$$\bigwedge e[\bigwedge \alpha \ A(e|\alpha) \to \bigwedge \alpha \ A'(e|\alpha)] \leftrightarrow \bigwedge \alpha[A\alpha \to A'\alpha].$$

(2) $\bigwedge e \vee a[e=a]$, $\bigwedge a \vee \alpha[a = \alpha]$
$$\bigwedge \alpha \vee x \ A(\alpha, x) \leftrightarrow \bigvee e \wedge n(en \neq 0 \to \bigwedge \alpha \ A(n|\alpha, (en)^-))$$
$$\bigwedge \alpha \vee a \ A(\alpha, x) \leftrightarrow \bigvee e \vee b \wedge n(en \neq 0 \to \bigwedge \alpha \ A(n|\alpha, \lambda'y.b(\langle (en)^-\rangle * y)))$$
$$\bigwedge \alpha \vee f \ A(\alpha, f) \leftrightarrow \bigvee e \vee f \wedge n(en \neq 0 \to \bigwedge \alpha \ A(n|\alpha, \lambda''y.f(\langle (en)^-\rangle * y)))$$
$$\bigwedge \alpha \vee \beta \ A(\alpha, \beta) \leftrightarrow \bigvee e \wedge \alpha \ A(\alpha, e|\alpha).$$

(3) $\bigwedge \alpha \bigwedge x\, B(\alpha, x) \leftrightarrow \bigwedge x \bigwedge \alpha\, B(\alpha, x)$

$\qquad \bigwedge \alpha \bigwedge a\, B(\alpha, a) \leftrightarrow \bigwedge a \bigwedge \alpha\, B(\alpha, a)$

$\qquad \bigwedge \alpha \bigwedge e\, B(\alpha, e) \leftrightarrow \bigwedge e \bigwedge \alpha\, B(\alpha, e).$

(4) $\bigvee \alpha\, A\alpha \leftrightarrow \bigvee a\, Aa.$

(5) If $A\alpha$ is an atomic formula, then $\bigwedge \alpha\, A\alpha \leftrightarrow \bigwedge a\, Aa.$

(6) $\bigwedge \alpha \bigwedge \beta\, A(\alpha, \beta) \leftrightarrow \bigwedge e \bigwedge f \bigwedge \alpha\, A(e|\alpha, f|\alpha).$

3.11. *Definitions*

Quantifiers $\bigvee \alpha$, $\bigwedge \alpha$ are called *choice quantifiers*. An *outermost* choice quantifier is a choice quantifier which does not occur within the scope of another choice quantifier. The number of logical symbols occurring within the scope of an outermost choice quantifier is called the *degree* of the formula considered.

3.12. *Description of the translation*

To begin with, $A \vee B$ is everywhere replaced by

$$\bigvee x \{(x = 0 \to A)\,\&\,(x \neq 0 \to B)\}\,.$$

Now let $F = F^1$ be a formula of CS without free choice variables, and without $\vee$. The translation is carried out in a number of successive steps. The formula F^n, obtained at stage n from the initial formula F^1 is transformed into F^{n+1} at stage $n+1$, by replacing a subformula X of F^n with an outermost choice quantifier in front by a formula X', according to one of the clauses (a)–(j) below.

(a) When $X = \bigwedge \alpha\, A\alpha$, A atomic, take $X' = \bigwedge a\, Aa.$

(b) When $X = \bigwedge \alpha \bigwedge x\, A(\alpha, x)$, $\bigwedge \alpha \bigwedge a\, A(\alpha, a)$ or $\bigwedge \alpha \bigwedge e\, A(\alpha, e)$

$\qquad$ take $X' = \bigwedge x \bigwedge \alpha\, A(\alpha, x)$, $\bigwedge a \bigwedge \alpha\, A(\alpha, a)$, $\bigwedge e \bigwedge \alpha\, A(\alpha, e)$ respectively.

(c) When $X = \bigwedge \alpha \bigwedge \beta\, A(\alpha, \beta)$, take $X' = \bigwedge e \bigwedge f \bigwedge \alpha\, A(e|\alpha, f|\alpha).$

(d) When $X = \bigwedge \alpha \bigvee x\, A(\alpha, x)$, take $X' = \bigvee e \bigwedge n(en \neq 0 \to$

$\qquad \qquad \bigwedge \alpha\, A(n|\alpha, (en)^-)).$

(e) When $X = \bigwedge \alpha \bigvee a\, A(\alpha, a)$, take $X' = \bigvee e \bigvee b \bigwedge n(en \neq 0 \to$

$\qquad \qquad \bigwedge \alpha\, A(n|\alpha, \lambda' y.b(\langle (en)^- \rangle * y))).$

(f) When $X = \bigwedge \alpha \bigvee f\, A(\alpha, f)$, take $X' = \bigvee e \bigvee f \bigwedge n(en \neq 0 \to$

$\qquad \qquad \bigwedge \alpha\, A(n|\alpha, \lambda'' y. f(\langle (en)^- \rangle * y))).$

(g) When $X = \bigwedge \alpha \bigvee \beta\, A(\alpha, \beta)$, take $X' = \bigvee e \bigwedge \alpha\, A(\alpha, e|\alpha).$

(h) When $X = \bigwedge \alpha(A\alpha\,\&\,B\alpha)$, take $X' = \bigwedge \alpha\, A\alpha\,\&\,\bigwedge \alpha\, B\alpha.$

(i) When $X = \bigwedge \alpha(A\alpha \to B\alpha)$, take $X' = \bigwedge e[\bigwedge \alpha\, A(e|\alpha) \to \bigwedge \alpha\, B(e|\alpha)].$

(j) When $X = \bigvee \alpha\, A\alpha$, take $X' = \bigvee a\, Aa.$

Remarks. In the application of the foregoing clauses, the newly introduced variables are always supposed to be fresh. The translation of a formula A is indicated by writing the formula in script: $\mathscr{A}$.

With every transition to the next stage, either the degree or the total number of outermost choice quantifiers diminishes.

4. Some theorems concerning CS and IDK

THEOREM 2. For every formula A of CS not containing free choice variables: $\vdash_{CS} A \leftrightarrow \mathscr{A}$.

The proof is immediate from 3.12. We can prove more, however:

THEOREM 3. Finitistically we can prove for any A of CS not containing free choice variables:

$$\vdash_{CS} A \leftrightarrow \vdash_{IDK} \mathscr{A}.$$

The proof of this theorem consists in a detailed verification that axioms and rules under the translation are carried over into theorems and derived rules of IDK. (A full proof will be presented in KREISEL and TROELSTRA.)

Theorem 3 is the main result concerning CS. As a corollary to Theorem 3 we obtain the result that CS is a conservative extension of IDK. Since IDK is a subsystem of classical analysis, we also have obtained a consistency proof for CS relative to classical analysis.

Kleene's system (KLEENE and VESLEY [1965]) is essentially contained in CS (modulo some differences in the set of explicitly introduced recursive functions).

The strength of IDK is greater than it may appear at first sight; in fact, many predicates which can be introduced by a generalized inductive definition can be defined explicitly in terms of K. As an example we state a theorem.

DEFINITION. $A(P, a)$ is *positive*, if $A(P, a)$ is of the form

$$\bigvee b \bigwedge x \sum_{i=1}^{n} \prod_{j=1}^{m} A_{ij}(b, x, a),$$

where each A_{ij} is either a formula of IDK or a formula $P(\varphi(b, x, a))$, φ a constructive functor of IDK ($\sum, \prod$ are used for disjunction, conjunction respectively).

THEOREM 4. If $A(P, a)$ is positive, then a predicate P_A can be explicitly defined in IDK such that $A(P_A, a) \to P_A a$, and the scheme $\bigwedge a[A(Q, a) \to Qa] \to \bigwedge a[P_A a \to Qa]$ are satisfied.

Remark. This theorem can still be generalized considerably (KREISEL and TROELSTRA). Remark that an $A(P, a)$ of the form

$$Q_1 \ldots Q_m \sum_{i=1}^{n} \prod_{j=1}^{u} A_{ij}(\ldots, a)$$

where the Q_i are quantifiers of the types $\bigvee x$, $\bigwedge x$, $\bigvee a$, and the A_{ij} as in the definition of "positive", is equivalent to a positive A. This can be seen by repeated application of C1 and contraction of variables by means of the pairing function.

5. Intersubjective and solipsist situations

The weakest possible way of justification for the axioms of the system CS would be an argument like this: IDK is intuitively justified; the use of choice-variables corresponds to a special "non-standard" interpretation of the logical constants in connection with functions. This interpretation is then given by the translation defined in Section 3 of this paper, and the proof of Theorem 3 is in fact a verification of the fact that the laws of logic remain valid for the non-standard interpretation.

This is not very satisfactory however. In this manner, the properties of choice sequences become a mere matter of convention. Therefore we shall endeavour to find a more satisfactory kind of justification.

The most general interpretation of the logical constants was first indicated by Heyting; a fairly elaborate description can be found in MYHILL [1967]. Take as a typical example implication: asserting $A \to B$ means that we have a construction which transforms any proof of A into a proof of B (and that we possess a proof which demonstrates this fact).

A "non-standard" interpretation of the logical constants might consist in restrictions on the kind of proofs used; the special interpretation of $A \to B$ would become: we have a construction (belonging to a class $\mathscr{C}$) which transforms any proof of A which belongs to $\mathscr{C}$ into a proof of B, taken from the class $\mathscr{C}$.

Now a more satisfactory justification of CS might consist of an intuitive description of the notions and the description of a context (an intuitive "picture" or "situation") into which the non-standard interpretation of the logical constants (if needed) would fit naturally.

To begin with, we make a distinction between two types of general situation: the solipsist and the intersubjective situation.

In *solipsist* situations we are concerned with the thoughts of a single mathematician (in Brouwer's terminology: creative subject). In his papers after 1945, Brouwer seems to argue in a solipsist situation (compare e.g. BROUWER [1948, 1952, 1954]).

In an *intersubjective* situation we have a collection of mathematicians $\Sigma_1, \Sigma_2, \Sigma_3, \ldots$ who can communicate or withhold information. We are interested in conclusions valid for every mathematician.

In the sequel we shall mainly explore intersubjective situations. In the case that all mathematicians have all information in common, the intersubjective situation reduces to the solipsist situation.

6. Empirical sequences and "Kripke's scheme"

KREISEL [1967] p. 160 formalizes some basic assumptions (for an intersubjective situation) which seem to underly Brouwer's controversial counterexamples.

Although the discussion in KREISEL [1967] is not likely to be definitive (see e.g. the remarks in VAN ROOTSELAAR) we use it here as a basis for our discussion. On the basis of the principles

$$(\Sigma \vdash_m A) \vee \neg (\Sigma \vdash_m A) \tag{11}$$

$$A \to \bigwedge \Sigma (\neg \neg \bigvee m (\Sigma \vdash_m A)) \tag{12}$$

$$\bigvee \Sigma \bigvee m (\Sigma \vdash_m A) \leftrightarrow A \tag{13}$$

((13) indicates the intended meaning of A according to Kreisel) we can derive what Myhill calls "Kripke's scheme" (MYHILL [1967], KREISEL [1967] p. 174):

$$\bigvee \chi \{ [\bigwedge x (\chi x = 0) \leftrightarrow \neg A] \& [\bigvee x (\chi x \neq 0) \to A] \}. \tag{14}$$

For if we take

$$\neg (\Sigma \vdash_x A) \to \chi x = 0, \ \Sigma \vdash_x A \to \chi x = 1$$

we see that (14) is derivable for every Σ.

If we define $A\chi' \leftrightarrow \bigvee x \bigwedge y \ (y \geq x \to \chi' y = 0)$ we obtain:

$$\bigwedge \chi' \bigvee \chi \{ [\bigwedge x (\chi x = 0) \leftrightarrow \neg A\chi'] \& [\bigvee x (\chi x \neq 0) \to A\chi'] \}. \tag{15}$$

The dependence of χ on χ' is not continuous.

We return to this question in Section 9.

In the discussion in the remainder of this paper we take a constructive operation to be an operation which is given in such a way that every mathematician obtains the same result by applying the prescription.[4]

7. Lawless sequences

By way of introduction, we discuss the notion of a lawless[5] sequence (the absolutely free choice sequences of KREISEL [1958]) before we enter on the discussion of the more complicated notion of a choice sequence. For lawless sequences it is indifferent whether we consider a solipsist or an intersubjective situation.

DEFINITION. A *lawless* sequence (for a mathematician Σ) is a sequence $\chi \in S^N$ such that at any given moment only an initial segment is known (to Σ) with no restrictions on future terms.

A lawless sequence χ can therefore be viewed as a source which produces values $\chi_0, \chi_1, \chi_2, \ldots$ while Σ does not know anything about the process according to which the values are determined. If we speak about lawless sequences χ, χ', either χ, χ' are thought to be the same source from the start, or if not, no connection between them will ever become known.

(A good illustration is provided by a die; the sequence of the casts of a die is a sequence which takes its values in the species $\{1, 2, \ldots, 6\}$; at any moment, only finitely many casts are known, about the future casts nothing can be said.)

For lawless sequences, we can therefore assert:

$$\bigwedge \chi \bigwedge \chi' (\chi = \chi' \vee \chi \neq \chi'). \tag{16}$$

For either χ, χ' are identical, i.e. they denote the same source of values, or they are intended as different sources; in the latter case, it is absurd to assume that a mathematician could ever prove $\chi x = \chi' x$ for all x, hence $\chi \neq \chi'$.

Another important property of lawless sequences is a strong kind of con-

---

[4] "Constructive sequence" in this sense seems closely related to MYHILL's [this volume] "mathematical sequence". Suppose we make two assumptions: (a) the order of the proofs which are the result of the mathematical activity of a mathematician cannot be communicated to another mathematician in a finite amount of time, (b) different mathematicians do not necessarily have all information in common. Then one might try, tentatively, to distinguish Myhill's mathematical sequences from the wider class of the empirical ones, by characterizing mathematical sequences as given by a law which can be communicated in a finite amount of time. In this case, an identification of "constructive" with "recursive" is certainly plausible.

[5] We have adopted Gödel's suggestion and replaced Kreisel's "absolutely free choice sequences" by "lawless sequences".

tinuity. For $A\chi$ not containing other free variables for functions besides χ (with the possible exception of the free variables for constructive functions) we can assert:

$$A\chi \to \bigvee\chi(\chi\in n \,\&\, (\wedge\chi'\in n)\,A\chi') \tag{17}$$

(where $\chi\in n$ is an abbreviation for $\bigvee x(\bar\chi x = n)$).

In the case of an intersubjective situation, one might take lawless sequences as to be generated for a Σ_j by communication (of a Σ_i to Σ_j) of values $\chi 0, \chi 1, \chi 2, \ldots$, and never anything more.

In the context of an intersubjective picture we can also describe a notion slightly different from "lawless"; let us call it "*free*" for the time being.

Σ_i creates free sequences χ, χ', χ'' for Σ_j by communicating values $\chi 0, \chi 1, \chi 2, \ldots; \chi'0, \chi'1, \ldots; \chi''0, \ldots$. Moreover, at some moment, Σ_i might decide to communicate information of the form $\chi = \chi'$ to Σ_j.

Free sequences are therefore objects which individually behave like lawless sequences, because only an initial segment is known at any time, but they can be connected by extra information of the form $\chi = \chi', \chi' = \chi''$ etc. (Remark that this extra information nevertheless for any single free χ amounts to an initial segment only.)

(17) remains valid for free sequences, but instead of (16) we obtain exactly the opposite:

$$\neg \wedge\chi\wedge\chi'(\chi = \chi' \vee \chi \neq \chi'). \tag{18}$$

An exposition of the formal theory of lawless sequences of N^N is to appear in KREISEL.

8. Choice sequences – justification of CS

8.1. The justification of the full system CS asks for a certain change in the interpretation of the logical constants, as a consequence of certain restrictions imposed on the proofs. We use $\alpha, \beta, \ldots$ for choice sequences. A *choice sequence* for any mathematician Σ_i is a sequence β about which at any moment the available facts consist of an initial segment $\bar\alpha x$ (α is a sequence about which nothing else is known) together with an equation $\beta = e|\alpha$.

To state it otherwise, a mathematician Σ_j may create a choice sequence α for Σ_i by starting communication of values $\alpha 0, \alpha 1, \ldots; \Sigma_j$ at a certain moment can add information $\alpha = e|\beta$, and then proceed with communicating values $\beta 0, \beta 1, \ldots, \beta x, \ldots$; later on, again information of the form $f|\gamma = \beta$ can be added, followed by communication of values of γ, and so on. This process must be such that more and more values of α are determined.

This notion of choice sequence is a fairly natural thing to consider if we look for a class of sequences invariant under continuous operations, while at the same time we require that operations defined on the whole class are necessarily continuous.

The axioms which need justification are especially F1–F4.

8.2. We begin with the discussion of F2; F1 will be discussed after the other axioms.

Suppose a certain mathematician Σ_i asserts $A\alpha$, at a given time (stage) τ. The information concerning α available to Σ_i at time τ can be condensed into the form $\alpha = e|\beta$, $\bar{\beta}x = n$. $A\alpha$ must be provable for Σ_i on account of this information only. Therefore

$$\alpha' = e|\beta' \;\&\; \bar{\beta}x = \bar{\beta}'x \to A\alpha'$$

and therefore

$$\wedge\beta' \in nA\,(e|\beta').$$

It is always possible to conceive a $\beta' \in n$ as a sequence $n|\gamma$. Hence

$$\wedge\gamma\,A\,(e\,(n|\gamma)).$$

We can contract the two continuous operations e, $k^{(n)}$ into one such that $\wedge\chi(e(n|\chi)=f|\chi)$, and therefore

$$\wedge\gamma A\,(f|\gamma)$$

and hence

$$A\alpha \to \vee f\,(\vee\beta\,(\alpha = f|\beta)\;\&\;\wedge\gamma\,A\,(f|\gamma)).$$

8.3. To simplify the discussion, we consider instead of F3 itself, the simpler consequence (α the only free choice variable in A)

$$\wedge\alpha\vee xA\,(\alpha, x) \to \vee e\wedge n\,(en \neq 0 \to \wedge\alpha\,A\,(k^{(n)}|\alpha, (en)^-)). \qquad (19)$$

F3 itself can be treated along the same lines.

Suppose $\wedge\alpha\vee x\,A(\alpha, x)$. On account of the intuitionistic interpretation of the logical constants, this implies: there is an algorithm Φ (constructive procedure) which assigns to every α a natural number $\Phi\alpha$ (i.e. Φ is a constructive functional of type $N^N \to N$) such that $\wedge\alpha\,A(\alpha, \Phi\alpha)$.

In general, we may suppose $\Phi\alpha$ to depend on all the information available; for example, if some Σ_i possesses information concerning α of the form $\alpha = e|\beta$, $\bar{\alpha}x$, then $\Phi\alpha$ may depend on e as well as on $\bar{\alpha}x$. Hence not necessarily $\alpha = \beta \to \Phi\alpha = \Phi\beta$.

However, Σ_i may create for another mathematician Σ_j a sequence β, by communicating values of α, and nothing more, to Σ_j: $\alpha 0, \alpha 1, \ldots$. We shall suppose all mathematicians in our picture to have the same mental abilities.

Therefore, if Σ_j computes $\Phi\beta$, Σ_i must be able to conceive (by mentally abstracting from extra information) the idea of the object β, and Σ_i must also be able to compute $\Phi\beta$.

A convenient notation to indicate the process of forming β from α by "mental abstraction" is provided by a symbol, say Ψ, for an abstraction operator (analogous to a forgetful functor): $\Psi\alpha = \beta$.

It is clear that $\Psi\alpha = \Psi\alpha'$ implies $\Phi\Psi\alpha = \Phi\Psi\alpha'$.

We certainly have $A(\Psi\alpha, \Phi\Psi\alpha)$; but Σ_i "remembering" the origin of $\Psi\alpha$ (that is, adding the extra information concerning α not contained in $\Psi\alpha$) concludes from $\alpha = \Psi\alpha$ to $A(\alpha, \Phi\Psi\alpha)$.

Here we have cheated a little. For the concept of $\Psi\alpha$ is such, that Σ_i can not prove mathematically $\alpha = \Psi\alpha$, since realizing $\alpha = \Psi\alpha$ transforms $\Psi\alpha$ into another object. Hence permitting the substitution of α for $\Psi\alpha$ imposes in fact a restriction on Φ, i.e. a restriction on the possible proofs for $\bigwedge \alpha \bigvee x\, A(\alpha, x)$. In this sense, a non-standard interpretation of the logical constants is introduced. We shall return to this crucial point in the next paragraph. In the remainder of this paragraph we shall take the permissibility of the substitution of α for $\Psi\alpha$ for granted.

$\Phi\Psi$ is clearly a continuous functional, since now only an initial segment of $\Psi\alpha$ (hence of α) is used to compute the value of the functional. We can therefore assert continuity

$$\bigwedge \alpha \bigvee x\, A(\alpha, x) \rightarrow \bigwedge \alpha \bigvee x \bigvee y \bigwedge \beta\, (\bar{\alpha}y = \bar{\beta}y \rightarrow A(\beta, x)).$$

The second part of our justification of F2 consists in making it plausible that every continuous functional can be represented by a function from K.

Let us introduce a shorthand notation: $\langle x \rangle * \chi = \hat{x} * \chi$ is to denote the sequence χ' with $\chi'0 = x$, $\chi'(y+1) = \chi y$. Likewise $n * \chi$ for finite sequences n.

"Φ is continuous" means: for every χ, $\Phi\chi$ is determined by an initial segment $\bar{\chi}x$; so if $\bar{\chi}x = n$, $\lambda\chi.\, \Phi(n * \chi)$ is a constant functional.

Now we make the assumption, that if there is any proof of "Φ is continuous" at all, then there must be a direct proof of this fact, using two kinds of inferences:

(I) Φ' is a constant functional, hence continuous.

(II) For every x, $\Phi'(\hat{x} * \chi)$ is continuous, i.e. for every x and every χ there is a y such that $\Phi'(\hat{x} * \chi)$ is determined by $\bar{\chi}y$; hence for every χ there is a y' such that $\Phi'\chi$ is determined by $\chi'y$ (and therefore Φ' is continuous).

Parallel to this proof (compare the evidence presented for the axioms for K in Section 2) we can prove that Φ is represented by an $e \in K$, starting from the fact that the constant functionals are represented by elements of K.

This type of assumption about proofs we have used is also the idea underlying Brouwer's proofs of the fan theorem and the "Wohlordnungssatz" (see BROUWER [1924, 1927]).

So now we are justified in stating

$$\bigwedge \alpha \bigvee x \, A(\alpha, x) \rightarrow \bigvee e \bigwedge \alpha \, A(\alpha, e(\alpha))$$

which is equivalent to (19).

8.4. The justification of F4 can be obtained from the justification of F3 in the following manner. $\bigwedge \alpha \bigvee \beta \, A(\alpha, \beta)$, on account of the interpretation of the logical constants, implies the existence of an algorithm Φ such that $\bigwedge \alpha \, A(\alpha, \Phi\alpha)$. In particular, $\bigwedge \alpha \, A(\Psi\alpha, \Phi\Psi\alpha)$, and using, as before, $\alpha = \Psi\alpha$, we get $\bigwedge \alpha \, A(\alpha, \Phi\Psi\alpha)$. $\Phi\Psi = \Phi'$ is extensional, i.e. $\alpha = \beta \rightarrow \Phi\Psi\alpha = \Phi\Psi\beta$. If we write $(\Phi')_x$ for $\lambda\alpha.(\Phi'\alpha)(x)$ we can rephrase our conclusion as

$$\bigwedge \alpha \, A(\alpha, \lambda x.((\Phi')_x \alpha)).$$

We have

$$\bigwedge x \bigvee e \bigwedge \alpha ((\Phi')_x \alpha = e(\alpha))$$

(applying the previous justification of (19)).

Hence with C1, C2.2:

$$\bigvee f \bigwedge x \bigwedge \alpha ((\Phi')_x \alpha = (\lambda' n.f(\hat{x} * n)(\alpha)))$$

and therefore

$$\bigvee f \bigwedge \alpha (\lambda x.(\Phi')_x \alpha = f | \alpha)$$

and this justifies F4.

8.5. Now we return to the justification of F1. First we remark, that once we have justified F2, we also have a justification of (A, B with α as only free choice variable):

$$\bigwedge \alpha [A\alpha \rightarrow B\alpha] \leftrightarrow \bigwedge e [\bigwedge \alpha \, A(e|\alpha) \rightarrow \bigwedge \alpha \, B(e|\alpha)]. \qquad (20)$$

The implication from the left to the right is immediate.

In the other direction, we argue as follows. Suppose $A\alpha$. Then by F2:

$$\bigvee e [\bigwedge \beta \, A(e|\beta) \,\&\, \bigvee \beta (e|\beta = \alpha)].$$

If we suppose $\bigwedge e [\bigwedge \alpha \, A(e|\alpha) \rightarrow \bigwedge \alpha \, B(e|\alpha)]$, it follows that

$$\bigwedge \beta \, B(e|\beta) \,\&\, \bigvee \beta (e|\beta) = \alpha$$

hence $B\alpha$.

Now we consider the case of F1 with one choice parameter γ. We have to justify:

$$\bigwedge \gamma [\bigwedge x \bigvee \alpha \, A(\alpha, x, \gamma) \rightarrow \bigvee \beta \bigwedge x \, A(\lambda y.\beta\{x, y\}, x, \gamma)].$$

On account of (20) this is equivalent to showing that

$$\bigwedge e\{\bigwedge x \bigwedge \gamma \bigvee \alpha\, A(\alpha, x, e|\gamma) \to \bigwedge \gamma \bigvee \beta \bigwedge x\, A(\lambda y.\beta\{x, y\}, x, e|\gamma)\}.$$

Suppose therefore $\bigwedge x \bigwedge \gamma \bigvee \alpha\, A(\alpha, x, e|\gamma)$. By F4, we can replace this by $\bigwedge x \bigvee f \bigwedge \gamma A(f|\gamma, x, e|\gamma)$, and hence by application of C1, C2.2:

$$\bigvee f' \bigwedge x \bigwedge \gamma A(\lambda n.f'(\hat{x}*n)\,|\gamma, x, e|\gamma).$$

The conclusion to be derived is equivalent to (on account of F4):

$$\bigvee f'' \bigwedge \gamma \bigwedge x\, A(\lambda y.(f''|\gamma)\{x, y\}, x, e|\gamma).$$

Therefore we have to show that from f' we can construct f'' such that

$$\lambda'n.f'(\hat{x}*n)\,|\gamma = \lambda y.(f''|\gamma)\{x, y\}$$

for every x, which is not hard to verify. (Full details in KREISEL and TROELSTRA.)

9. The continuity axioms

9.1. In the previous section we made use of $\Psi\alpha = \alpha$ in the justification of F3 and F4. However, although the use of $\Psi\alpha = \alpha$ seems to be essential for the justification of F4, in the case of F3 we can eliminate this aspect[6]. For we obtained in 8.3 $A(\Psi\alpha, \Phi\Psi\alpha)$. $\Phi\Psi\alpha$ is computed from an initial segment $(\overline{\Psi\alpha})\,x$. (Since no other information can be used by Σ_j.) But if we confront Σ_j with α, then Σ_j can recognize that the information about α is a (consistent) extension of the information concerning $\Psi\alpha$, and also $(\overline{\Psi\alpha})\,x = \bar{\alpha}x$. Therefore $A(\alpha, \Phi\Psi\alpha)$.

9.2. In KREISEL [1965] and MYHILL [1967] p. 173, Myhill used (15) as a counterexample to F4. It is not at all clear, however, that the χ constructed from a choice sequence χ' (in our sense) is again a choice sequence. This is also not clear for the notion of choice sequence considered by Myhill. So, although (15) certainly casts doubt on the validity of F4 if we do not make any restrictions on our proofs, it is not a conclusive counterexample.

The restriction on proofs which is implicit in the use of $\Psi\alpha = \alpha$ does not permit the deduction of (15), as is to be expected (since CS is consistent modulo IDK) and as one can see without much difficulty.

---

[6] MYHILL [1967] stresses the difference between F3 and F4. The argument as presented in MYHILL [1967] was not quite satisfactory to me, but the underlying idea is utilized in the argument in this paper.

10. Various notions of sequence

10.1. A sequence $\chi \in S^N$ is called *lawless with respect to* a predicate (condition) $R \subseteq S^N$, if our information concerning χ at any moment consists of an equation $\bar{\chi}t_1 = t_2$ (t_1, t_2 constant terms) and $R\chi$ (i.e. the assertion that χ satisfies R).

We can describe many different notions of sequence by specializing the condition R in this definition.

The notions below can either be interpreted as "lawless with respect to R" for a suitable R, or they are immediately derived from such notions. However, we shall only describe them in terms of relative lawlessness if it is convenient to do so.

We introduce a notation first. If $\chi \in (S_0 \times S_1 \times \cdots \times S_{u-1})^N$, we can introduce projection mappings $\Pi_0, \ldots, \Pi_{u-1}$ such that

$$\chi x = \langle (\Pi_0 \chi)\, x, \ldots, (\Pi_{u-1}\chi)\, x \rangle.$$

10.2. The following notions have some mathematical, didactical or historical interest.

(A) Lawless sequences of S^N.

(B) Constructive functions of S^N.

(C) Free sequences of S^N.

(D) Define the following predicate for constructive functions:

$$\mathrm{Spr}\,(a) \leftrightarrow \wedge n \vee x\, (an \neq 0 \to a\,(n * \hat{x}) \neq 0)\ \&\ a0 \neq 0.$$

Membership of a spread (a is a spread iff $\mathrm{Spr}(a)$) is expressed by $\chi \in a \leftrightarrow \wedge x (a\bar{\chi}x \neq 0)$.

If we take for R in the definition of relative lawlessness: $R\chi = \vee a[\mathrm{Spr}(a)\,\&\, \chi \in a]$, then we have a description of the sequences lawless with respect to a spread. This is the notion underlying KREISEL [1963] and KREISEL [1965] (sec. 2.521).

(E) Let $\chi \in (N \times \mathrm{Spr})^N$. We define R by

$$R\chi \leftrightarrow \wedge x(\Pi_0 \chi \in (\Pi_1 \chi)\, x)\ \&\ \wedge x((\Pi_1 \chi)\,(x+1) \subseteq (\Pi_1 \chi)\, x).$$

Spread inclusion is defined by:

$$a \subseteq b \leftrightarrow \wedge n\,(an \neq 0 \to bn \neq 0).$$

(F) Take the Π_0 projection of the sequences of type (E). This is the notion studied in MYHILL [1967].

It seems that the notion originated with Brouwer (footnote on page 245 of BROUWER [1924]). To describe it less formal: we consider the Π_0-projection of a sequence of pairs $\langle \chi 0, a_0 \rangle, \langle \chi 1, a_1 \rangle, \dots a_0, a_1, \dots$ are spreads such that $a_0 \supseteq a_1 \supseteq \dots$ and χ belongs to every a_u.

Remark. Distinguishing between (E) and (F) is merely a matter of convenience; the extensionality of predicates with respect to numerical values has to be expressed as follows for notion (E)

$$A\chi \,\&\, \Pi_0 \chi = \Pi_0 \chi' \to A\chi'$$

whereas for (F) we can take the usual formulation:

$$A\chi \,\&\, \chi = \chi' \to A\chi'.$$

(G) The most general type of sequence of N^N we can formulate within this framework will be something like this: At any moment we know about χ an initial segment and certain additional information of the form $T\chi$ i.e. χ satisfies some predicate $T \subseteq N^N$. To state it otherwise: χ is the Π_0-projection of a sequence of pairs $\langle \chi 0, T_0 \rangle, \langle \chi 1, T_1 \rangle, \dots$ such that $\bigwedge x(T_x \chi)$, and $\bigwedge x(T_{x+1} \subseteq T_x)$, $\bigwedge x(T_x \subseteq N^N)$.

This notion suffers from the indeterminateness of the intuitionistic notion of species. Perhaps some restrictions on the T_x ought to be made.

11. Discussion of some notions of sequence

11.1. It is fairly easy to see that for the notions (F) and (G) we could justify the axioms F3–4 in the same manner as for choice sequences. For the notion (F) we can assert a stronger axiom instead of F2:

$$A\chi \leftrightarrow \bigvee a \,[\mathrm{Spr}(a) \,\&\, \chi \in a \,\&\, \bigwedge \chi' \in aA\chi'], \tag{21}$$

A not containing free variables for sequences besides χ and variables for constructive sequences.

The justification can be given along the same lines as the discussion of F2 for choice sequences.

For notion (G) we cannot assert an axiom of this type unless we introduce variables for species of sequences.

11.2. If we have a formal theory for a certain notion of sequence in which we can define continuous operations on sequences, then the assumption of unrestricted rule of substitution for terms and functors requires the notion to be invariant with respect to continuous transformations. For the notions (D) and (F) this invariance is certainly not evident. In fact, we have the following formal result, which shows that these notions are not very well suited to a system of analysis in which continuity is to be a main feature.

THEOREM 5. Let CS^o be obtained from CS by replacing F2 by (21) and omitting F4. Then we can derive in CS^o:

$$\wedge a \vee d\left[\wedge y \vee x\, a\{y, x\} \neq 0 \leftrightarrow \vee x \wedge y\, d\{x, y\} \neq 0\right].$$

Remark. The result conflicts with Church's thesis, but even without acceptation of Church's thesis, the conclusion seems undesirable.

PROOF: We shall introduce explicit names for various K-functors not included in the K-functor definition in Section 3, in order to simplify the proof. The existence of functions with the desired properties can be proved using the axioms for K and axioms of choice; therefore it is possible to eliminate these names in the proof.

Let $e[a]$ denote a function of K which satisfies, in case $\mathrm{Spr}(a)$ holds:

$$\wedge \alpha(e[a]|\alpha \in a), \quad \wedge \alpha \vee \beta(e[a]|\beta = \alpha).$$

(21) can be rephrased as

$$A\alpha \leftrightarrow \vee a\left[\mathrm{Spr}(a)\,\&\,\alpha \in a\,\&\,\wedge \beta\, A(e[a]|\beta)\right]. \tag{22}$$

We apply (22) to $A\alpha = \vee \beta(\alpha = e|\beta)$ and we obtain

$$\vee a\left[\mathrm{Spr}(a)\,\&\,\alpha \in a\,\&\,\wedge \beta \vee \gamma(e[a]|\beta = e|\gamma)\right] \leftrightarrow \vee \beta(\alpha = e|\beta).$$

Now we substitute $e|\alpha$ for the free variable α and apply the rule of generalization.

The result is:

$$\wedge \alpha \vee a\left[\mathrm{Spr}(a)\,\&\,e|\alpha \in a\,\&\,\wedge \beta \vee \gamma(e[a]|\beta = e|\gamma)\right]. \tag{23}$$

We apply F4 to (23):

$$\vee b \vee f \wedge n(fn \neq 0 \to \wedge \alpha[\mathrm{Spr}(\lambda'y.b\{en \dotdiv 1, y\})\,\&\,e:n|\alpha \in \lambda'y.b\{en \dotdiv 1, y\}\,\&$$
$$\wedge \beta \vee \gamma(e[\lambda'y.b\{en \dotdiv 1, y\}]|\beta = e|\gamma)]. \tag{24}$$

(Here $e:f$ is an abbreviation for the composition function which satisfies

$$\wedge \alpha(e|(f|\alpha) = e:f|\alpha).)$$

We can enumerate the functions $\lambda'y.b\{en \dotdiv 1, y\}$ for which $en \neq 0$ by a function c, $c^x = \lambda'y.c\{x, y\}$.

We obtain therefore from (24)

$$\wedge \alpha \vee x(e|\alpha \in c^x\,\&\,\wedge x(\mathrm{Spr}(c^x))\,\&\,\wedge \alpha \wedge x(\alpha \in c^x \to \vee \beta(e|\beta = \alpha))). \tag{25}$$

Now let a be any fixed constructive function. We define a spread d from a by the conditions:

(I) For all y, $d((\overline{\lambda'x.0})\,y) \neq 0$.

(II) If $dn \neq 0$, then $d(n * \hat{0}) \neq 0$.

(III) If $d\bar{\alpha}y \neq 0$, $\alpha(y \dot- 1) \neq 0$ or $y = 0$, and $a\{y, z\} \neq 0$, then $d(\bar{\alpha}y * \langle z \rangle) \neq 0$.

Let $sgx = 1 \dot- (1 \dot- x)$.

We choose a g such that $\bigwedge \alpha \bigwedge x[(g|\alpha)\,x = sg\alpha x]$.

Substitute $g : e[d]$ for e. Then from (25) we conclude:

$$\bigvee x(\lambda'y.0 \in c^x) \leftrightarrow \bigwedge y \bigvee x(a\{y, x\} \neq 0).$$

If we define

$$d'\{x, y\} = c^x(\overline{(\lambda'z.0)}\,(y + 1))$$

we obtain

$$\bigvee d'\,(\bigvee x \wedge yd'\{x, y\} \neq 0 \leftrightarrow \bigwedge y \bigvee x\,a\{y, x\} \neq 0)$$

and hence by generalization the desired conclusion.

12. Acting on incomplete information

Instead of the intuitive pictures given so far, we could also have taken another point of view, which covers all formal facts, namely that speaking about lawless sequences, choice sequences etc. is only an expression of the fact that we are operating on certain types of incomplete information concerning sequences.

The logical background for acting on incomplete information is described in GRZEGORCZYK [1964] section 4.

However, the explanation of disjunction and existential quantification given there simply refers back to a notion of sequence, as is apparent from the use of the word "branch". See also KREISEL [1965] pp. 109–110.

It is indeed hard to see (taking a simple example) what can be asserted about lawless sequences, that cannot be obtained from the idea of proving something about sequences on account of finite initial segments only. Nevertheless, if we introduce our "notions" just by stipulating certain types of information we are acting on, our "notions" look rather arbitrary. We therefore prefer the approach of the previous sections, as being more suggestive. We certainly do not claim our analysis of the notion of choice sequence to be final; in fact, it will be clear from the discussions that there is a wide range of notions and "contexts" which deserve to be investigated.

ACKNOWLEDGEMENT. I am deeply indebted to professor Kreisel for many stimulating discussions and remarks concerning the subject matter of this paper.

References

BROUWER, L.E.J., Über Definitionsbereiche von Funktionen, Math. Annalen **97** (1927) 60–76.

BROUWER, L.E.J., Zur Grundlegung der intuitionistischen Mathematik I, Math. Annalen **93** (1924) 244–258.

BROUWER, L.E.J., Consciousness, philosophy and mathematics, Proc. Xth Intern. Congress Philosophy, Amsterdam, 1948, eds. H.J. Pos, E.W. Beth and J.H.A. Hollack (Amsterdam, North-Holland Publ. Co., 1949) 1235–1249.

BROUWER, L.E.J., Historical background, principles and methods of intuitionism, South-African J. Sci. **49** (1952) 139–146.

BROUWER, L.E.J., Points and spaces, Canad. J. Math. **6** (1954) 1–17.

GRZEGORCZYK, A., A philosophically plausible formal interpretation of intuitionistic logic, Proc. Akad. Amsterdam A **67** = Indag. Math. **26** (1964) 596–601.

HOWARD, W.A. and G. KREISEL, Transfinite induction and bar induction of types zero and one, and the role of continuity in intuitionistic analysis, J. Symb. Logic **31** (1966) 325–358.

KLEENE, S.C. and R.E. VESLEY, Foundations of intuitionistic mathematics (Amsterdam, North-Holland Publ. Co., 1965).

KREISEL, G., A remark on free choice sequences and the topological completeness proofs, J. Symb. Logic **23** (1958) 369–388.

KREISEL, G., Stanford rapport on the foundations of analysis, sections III and IV (Stanford, 1963) mimeographed.

KREISEL, G., Mathematical logic, in: Lectures on mathematics, vol. III, ed. T.L. Saaty (New York, 1965) pp. 95–195.

KREISEL, G., Informal rigour and completeness proofs, and Discussion (Y. Bar-Hillel, A. Heyting, G. Kreisel, J. Myhill) in: Problems in the philosophy of mathematics, ed. I. Lakatos (Amsterdam, North-Holland Publ. Co., 1967) pp. 138–171, and pp. 172–186.

KREISEL, G., Lawless sequences, Comp. Math., to appear.

KREISEL, G., Functions, ordinals, species. This volume, pp. 145–159.

KREISEL, G. and A.S. TROELSTRA, A formal system for intuitionistic analysis (in preparation).

MYHILL, J., Notes towards an axiomatization of intuitionistic analysis, Logique et Analyse **35** (1967) 280–297.

MYHILL, J., Formal systems of intuitionistic analysis I. This volume, pp. 161–178.

VAN ROOTSELAAR, B., Review of MYHILL [1967], Math. Rev. **36** (1968), # 35, p.q.

Section 3

Automata and Programming Languages

PROBLEMS IN THE THEORY OF
PROGRAMMING LANGUAGES

J. W. DE BAKKER

Mathematical Centre, Amsterdam, Netherlands

1. Introduction

The theory of programming languages is usually divided into three parts (see e.g. ZEMANEK [1966]):

a. Syntax.

It is investigated which formal systems can be used for the definition of grammars of programming languages. A grammar is a set of rules that defines which sequences of symbols over a given alphabet form a program in the language concerned. Two important requirements which should be fulfilled by such a system are: It should be powerful enough to allow formal expression of all syntactical rules, and it should define the structure of a program in such a way that efficient translation is possible.

b. Semantics.

Problems are investigated which deal with the meaning of programs. The ultimate goal is the development of a theory that leads to a formal definition of the semantics of programming languages and that can provide an answer to questions such as: "Are two given programs equivalent?", or "Is a compiler for a certain language correct?", or "Does a given program solve a certain problem?".

c. Pragmatics.

Here the object of study is the relation between the language and its user. Hence, the important question in this area is: "Which concepts should be included in a language to allow the programmer efficient, compact and elegant formulation of his problem?".

It is clear that for practical purposes, pragmatic problems are the most important. Consequently, most of the efforts in programming languages have been spent in this field. However, as far as we know, no theory of

pragmatics has been developed as yet. Theoretical considerations have up
to now mainly been concerned with syntax. We mention only: the theory of
context free languages with their various specializations and generalizations,
the production language of Floyd, and the syntax directed compilers. In
our talk, we shall not deal with these investigations but restrict ourselves
to semantic problems and try to give an impression of the work that has been
done in this field.

2. Semantics and the general theory of computation

For the development of semantic theories about programming languages,
it is clearly desirable to have available a "general theory of computation"
which can provide a background or framework to which semantics can be
related. However, such a general theory of computation is only in a rudi-
mentary stage. There are several ways of approaching such a theory. A
survey of the situation, as it existed several years ago, has been given by
McCARTHY [1963b]. In our opinion, no decisive progress has been made
since then. We shall now discuss a few approaches in somewhat more detail.

a. The theory of computability, i.e. the theory of Turing machines,
recursive functions, etc. It was already said by McCarthy that this theory
has as yet only resulted in the statement of the essential limits which are
imposed upon a theory of computation. Its relevance for a theory of al-
gorithmic processes, as they occur in the practical use of computers, is very
limited. However, it should be mentioned that in the past few years, research
has started into real-time aspects of Turing machines, i.e., investigations
which take into account the time factor, e.g. expressed by the number of
operations that are required for a certain calculation. This new branch of
the theory of Turing machines might eventually lead to results which are of
interest for the theory of computation. Among the many formalisms that
have been proposed for studies of computability, and that have all been
proved to be equivalent, there is one system we want to mention separately,
namely the theory of "graphschemata". It was proved by PÉTER [1958]
that these graphschemata are equivalent to recursive functions. However,
it is probable that the formalism of graphschemata shows the closest connection to the methods that are used in practice for the description of computer
algorithms. This follows from the fact that graphschemata are nothing but
flow diagrams obeying certain restrictions. Investigations in this area have
been reported by KALUZHNIN [1961] and THIELE [1966]. Related is the work
of BöHM and JACOPINI [1966], who exhibit a number of components, from

which, in a sense, each flow diagram can be made up (they need some extra formalism, for which we refer to their paper).

b. Automata theory. Here the situation is the same as above. Although automata theory has led to many results of mathematical interest, again no generally accepted system, directly useful for a theory of computation, has come forward. We think that the following quotation from WANG [1965] is still valid:

"Although there are various elegant formulations of Turing machines, they are still radically different from existing computers. To approach the latter, we should use fixed word lengths, random access addresses, accumulator, and permit internal modifications of the programs. Alternatively, we could, for example, modify computers to allow more flexibility in word lengths. Too much energy has been spent on oversimplified models, so that a theory of machines and a theory of computation which have extensive practical applications have not been born yet."

We shall give here a few examples of several automaton-like models that have been proposed in the past few years. No attempt is made at completeness, but we wish to give only an impression of the great variety that exists in this field:

b1. One of the first proposals was made by KAPHENGST [1959]. This paper introduces concepts such as register, instruction and instruction counter, etc., in an abstract machine which is then proved to be equivalent to recursive functions.

b2. A paper by RAYMOND [1966]. Emphasis is laid here upon a study of the memory of a computer.

b3. A paper by DE BACKER and VERBEEK [1966]. In this article the notion of error in a computation plays an important role.

b4. A paper by MAURER [1966]. This paper covers many aspects of existing computers: It treats the notions of memory, registers, input/output, and instructions. It appears to be an interesting contribution to a theory of computing that is more concerned with hardware aspects.

b5. The stack automata, as introduced by GINSBURG, GREIBACH and HARRISON [1967]. Here the purpose is to simulate techniques which are used in the translation of programming languages.

b6. The theory of "Random Access, Stored Program Machines", as introduced by ELGOT [1966] and ELGOT and ROBINSON [1964]. We shall return to this later, since it has played a role in the formal definition of PL/I.

c. McCARTHY's mathematical theory of computation [1963a, b], [1965]. This theory is not directly related to either the theory of computability or to automata theory. McCarthy's papers [1963a, b] and [1965] have become well known and have influenced work on the semantics of programming languages, as we shall see below.

d. Proofs about programs.

We shall make here some remarks on investigations, related to theories of computation, which are in some way concerned with proofs about programs. First of all, it is obvious that a theory intended to lead to proofs about programs, will be limited by unsolvability results from logic. We mention only the classic example concerning the impossibility of an algorithm which decides for each arbitrary program whether it will get into an infinite loop. Another difficulty that arises when one wants to develop a theory that can prove the correctness of a program, is the following:

Suppose that one wishes to prove that a given program P, written in some programming language, gives a correct description of a certain process Q. This problem only makes sense if Q can be precisely stated by means of some other formalism, e.g. some part of mathematics. Often, however, the only precise way of stating process Q is by exhibiting some program that describes it. Clearly, in these cases a proof of the correctness of this description will be very difficult or even impossible.

We now mention a few investigations that deal with proofs about programs:

d1. Well known is the work of Yanov [1960], who introduced the "logical schemes of algorithms" and derived several equivalence results about them.

d2. Less well known is the work that has been done by Igarashi [1964a, b]. See also Igarashi [1963].

d3. McCarthy [1963a] has used his technique of recursion induction for some proofs on Algolic (i.e., written in a small subset of ALGOL 60) programs. Later on, we shall mention another type of proof due to him.

d4. Naur [1966] has proposed a method to be used for the proof of algorithms, by the technique of what he calls "general snapshots", i.e., expressions of static conditions existing whenever the execution of the algorithm reaches particular points.

d5. Evans [1965] has proved the correctness of two translation algorithms. Some references to other work in this area which we found in his paper, are: Cooper [1965] and London [1964].

3. Semantic definition of programming languages

After having tried to give an impression of the background which is available for a theory of semantics, we shall now deal with one of the main goals of a semantic theory, namely the development of a system for the formal definition of programming languages. We first state some reasons for such a formal definition:

a. First of all, the wish to provide the compiler-writer with a complete, precise and unambiguous definition of the language which he has to translate. Such a definition should e.g. make it clear which parts of the language are not fully specified, so that the compiler-writer knows where he has to give his own interpretation. Experience has shown that it is almost impossible to avoid ambiguities in the definition of a programming language by means of a natural language, such as English.

b. One might require of a formal definition that it can be used as a basis for the development of a compiler. The formal definition should then be designed in such a way that it reflects in some sense the structure of the compiler. It should be remarked that it is often difficult to combine requirements a and b.

c. Recently, suggestions have been made for the introduction of programming languages which allow the programmer to include modifications or extensions of the language in his program. It is clear that it is necessary in such a situation to provide the programmer with a formalism in which he can state these modifications to the language.

d. Finally, a formal definition of a programming language should provide insight into theoretical properties of this language. It should lead to a vocabulary which can be used for discussions about the language. One might expect of such theoretical investigations e.g. the detection of incompatible, contradictory or ambiguous concepts or constructions in the language. It might also be used as a source of inspiration for new useful concepts, which would not have originated directly from practical considerations.

We shall now discuss some systems which have been proposed for the formal definition of programming languages. It will appear that the situation is the same as with the theory of computation; i.e., almost every author has his own system; there is as yet no generally accepted method, nor any indication of a convergence in opinion towards such a method. In September 1964, a conference on "Formal Language Description Languages" was held, organized by the technical committee on programming languages of the International Federation for Information Processing. The proceedings of this conference (STEEL [1966a]) show clearly how much the ideas of the several authors diverge.

First of all we mention the methods that are based upon the λ-calculus. LANDIN [1964], [1965], [1966] is the main representative of this group. BÖHM [1966a, b] uses both the λ-calculus and the combinatory logic of Curry. He calls his system CUCH, derived from CUrry and CHurch. The λ-calculus also plays an important role in the work of STRACHEY [1966]. It appears that the λ-calculus allows an elegant definition of the locality concept; the definition of assignment statements and goto statements causes more difficulties.

Well known is the state vector approach of McCARTHY [1966]. In principle, the components of the state vector are: the current values of the variables that occur in the program, and the number of the statement which is to be executed. The semantics of a program is defined by a recursive function that describes how the state vector changes as a result of the statements that occur in the program. McCarthy admits that the structure of the state vector will have to become more complicated if recursion occurs in the program. Also, the meaning of e.g. declarations and procedures cannot be defined directly in terms of this state vector.

McCarthy has applied his formalism also to give a proof of the correctness of a simple compiler for arithmetic expressions (McCARTHY and PAINTER [1966]). Again, however, he says that in order to apply the technique to proofs concerning the correctness of translation of e.g. sequences of assignment statements or goto statements, "a complete revision of the formalism will be required".

WIRTH and WEBER [1966] let the semantic description of a programming language run parallel to its syntactic definition. Whenever a syntactic rule is applied during the analysis of a program, a corresponding semantic rule is applied which changes the values of zero or more entities in a so-called environment. The semantic rules are formalized in a language which is said to correspond closely to the elementary operations of a computer. It is assumed that the concepts of this elementary language do not need further formal definition. He demonstrates his system by means of a formal definition of the programming language EULER, based upon a generalization of ALGOL 60.

FELDMAN [1966] has introduced a "Formal Semantic Language", which he has designed for the purpose of constructing compilers. For these practical purposes, FSL has proven to be of much use. However, we feel that FSL is too complicated a language to be considered a solution to the problem of the formalization of semantics.

Finally, we mention some systems which give only some principles for semantic description, from which it is not yet possible to form an opinion as to their applicability to a complete formal definition of a programming language: the papers of STEEL [1966b], GARWICK [1966], and NIVAT and NOLIN [1966].

Complete formal definitions have been given of PL/I (PL/I Definition Group of the Vienna Laboratory [1966]) and of ALGOL 60 (DE BAKKER [1967]). We shall return to the definition of ALGOL 60 below. The definition of PL/I is due to a group at the IBM Laboratory in Vienna. We quote from the introduction to their report:

"The method adopted is based on the definition of an abstract machine which is characterized by the set of its states and its state transition function. A PL/I program defines an initial state of the machine, and the subsequent behaviour of the machine is said to define the interpretation of the PL/I program...

The basis for the development of the method are the publications of McCarthy, Landin and Elgot. Especially, the notions of instruction and computation are similar to those given by Elgot. The notion of Abstract syntax is due to McCarthy."

The impressive size of the PL/I document does not allow a more detailed explanation of the techniques used.

For the sake of completeness, we mention the announcement of a paper by CHRISTENSEN and MITCHELL [1967], which will give a partly formalized definition of NICOL II, a version of PL/I.

4. A formal definition of Algol 60

In DE BAKKER [1967] we have investigated a method for the formal definition of programming languages, and applied this method to a complete formal definition of ALGOL 60. The system is based upon two papers by VAN WIJNGAARDEN [1963], [1966]. We here give only a sketch of its principles; for details we refer to our paper. The method consists essentially of a combination of Markov algorithms and context free grammars. The definition of a language is given by means of a list of rules, which are either of syntactical nature, in which case they have the form of a production rule of a context free grammar, or of semantical nature. Then they have the structure of a substitution rule, as used in Markov algorithms. In these substitution rules, use is made of the metalinguistic variables, as defined in the syntactical rules. (A combination of syntactical and semantical elements in one rule is also possible; we shall not treat this feature here.)

As an example, we exhibit the definition of the greatest common divisor of two integers, written in "unary" notation, by means of the Euclidean algorithm:

$$\langle\text{integer}\rangle :: = 1 | \langle\text{integer}\rangle\ 1$$
$$(\langle\text{integer } 1\rangle, \langle\text{integer } 1\rangle) \rightarrow \langle\text{integer } 1\rangle$$
$$(\langle\text{integer } 1\rangle\ \langle\text{integer } 2\rangle, \langle\text{integer } 1\rangle) \rightarrow (\langle\text{integer } 1\rangle, \langle\text{integer } 2\rangle)$$
$$(\langle\text{integer } 1\rangle, \langle\text{integer } 1\rangle\ \langle\text{integer } 2\rangle) \rightarrow (\langle\text{integer } 1\rangle, \langle\text{integer } 2\rangle).$$

Note the occurrence of so-called "indices" within the metalinguistic variables. The function of these indices is the following: If, in a certain rule, one of its possible productions is substituted for an indexed metalinguistic variable, then the same substitutions must be made in all places in this rule where this metalinguistic variable occurs with the same index.

An abstract machine is introduced, called the processor, which applies the rules described above, to an input sequence (in the example given above, the processor might be asked to evaluate e.g. (111,11)). When the processor has to establish whether a substitution rule is applicable to an input sequence, it uses a well-defined parsing scheme. Details of the way parsing is performed are omitted here.

A further important property of the system is the following: Whenever the value of a certain input sequence has been determined, this value is added – in the form of a new substitution rule – to the already existing list of rules. Consequently, the list of rules is continuously growing, according as more input sequences are evaluated. This last feature, i.e. the growing of the list of substitution rules, is essential for the definition of a programming language such as ALGOL 60. The definition of ALGOL 60, as given in DE BAKKER [1967], consists of a list of about 800 rules, of syntactical, semantical (or mixed) type. If the processor evaluates an ALGOL 60 program, this is performed essentially by successive evaluation of the declarations and statements that constitute the program concerned. E.g. evaluation of the assignment statement $a := 3$, will lead to the extension of the already existing list of rules with the substitution rule $a \rightarrow 3$. We cannot deal here with the way in which declarations, procedures, goto statements etc. are treated. Their treatment is explained extensively in our paper. We now give a summary of its contents: First a detailed description is given of the system of which we have sketched some principles above. Next we investigate some theoretical properties of the system, namely its relation to the theory of computability, and to a few aspects of the theory of phrase structure languages. The processor is defined by means of an ALGOL 60 program, and this program is demonstrated by a large number of examples. Then follows the definition of ALGOL 60, by means of about 800 rules, and a commentary upon this definition.

Our system has proved capable of giving a complete formal definition of ALGOL 60, from the definition of integer arithmetic to the definition of e.g. the procedure concept. However, it cannot be used directly as a basis for a compiler for the language.

5. Conclusion

From the research which has been performed up to now in the semantics of programming languages, it can be concluded that, for the treatment of the more difficult concepts, present-day mathematics is only of limited use. It appears that concepts, as nowadays current in programming languages, often have no direct counterparts in mathematics. We give a few examples: One would expect that a simple concept such as the arithmetic expression, would be clear to everyone who knows some high school algebra. However, already in this simple case anomalies are caused by the possibility of side effects in a language such as ALGOL 60, so that e.g. $a+b$ is not necessarily equal to $b+a$. More difficult is the concept of locality and the related problems of storage allocation. Although the locality concept is related to the idea of bound variables, this does not help much if one wants to investigate concepts like own dynamic arrays. The name-value relation in its simplest form is known in logic. However, the general reference structure, as present in the proposal for ALGOL 68, is again, as far as we know, without a direct counterpart. Simple data structures, such as vectors, matrices or rectangular arrays in general, or trees, are well known. This does not hold for more complicated structures, such as the records proposed by Hoare, see WIRTH and HOARE [1966]. Function designators are at first sight nothing but functions, as known in mathematics. However, a mathematician will not be confronted with the question: "What happens to the value of the function if a jump to a point outside is performed?". We know of no concept in mathematics that can be related to goto statements. We might remark here that a complete formal definition of the meaning of goto statements, at least in our system and in several others as well, is one of the most difficult tasks. Some authors consider the goto statement as a relic from the days of machine coding, and propose to abolish it (MCKEEMAN [1966]) or at least to diminish its use (DIJKSTRA [1965]). Finally we mention the notion of parallel processing, which has hardly been investigated at all in computability and automata theory.

McCarthy once expressed the hope that mathematical logic will be as fruitful for the science of computation as analysis has been for physics. We hope to have given an impression of the results which have been obtained in this direction and of the many open problems which still remain to be studied.

References

Böhm, C., The CUCH as a formal and description language, in: Formal language description languages for computer programming, ed. T. B. Steel Jr. (Amsterdam, North-Holland Publ. Co., 1966a) pp. 179–197.

Böhm, C., Introduction to CUCH, in: Automata theory, ed. E. R. Caianiello (New York, Academic Press, 1966b).

Böhm, C. and G. Jacopini, Flow diagrams, Turing machines and languages with only two formation rules, Comm. ACM 9 (1966) 366–372.

Christensen, C. and R. W. Mitchell, Reference manual for the NICOL II programming language, to appear as a report of Computer Associates, Wakefield, USA.

Cooper, D. C., The equivalence of certain computations (Computation Center, Carnegie Institute of Technology, 1965).

De Backer, W. and L. Verbeek, Study of analog, digital and hybrid computers using automata theory, I.C.C. Bulletin 5 (1966) 215–245.

De Bakker, J. W., Formal definition of programming languages, with an application to the definition of ALGOL 60, Mathematical Centre Tracts 16 (Amsterdam, Mathematisch Centrum, 1967).

Dijkstra, E. W., Programming considered as a human activity, in: Proc. IFIP Congress 1965, ed. A. Kalenich (Washington, Spartan Books, 1965) Vol. 1, pp. 213–219.

Elgot, C. C., Machine species and their computation languages, in: Formal language description languages for computer programming, ed. T. B. Steel Jr. (Amsterdam, North-Holland Publ. Co., 1966) pp. 160–179.

Elgot, C. C. and A. Robinson, Random-access, stored program machines, an approach to programming languages, J. ACM. 11 (1964) 365–399.

Evans Jr., A., Syntax analysis by a production language, Ph.D. thesis, Carnegie Institute of Technology, 1965.

Feldman, J., A formal semantics for computer languages and its application in a compiler-compiler, Comm. ACM 9 (1966) 3–9.

Garwick, J. V., The definition of programming languages by their compilers, in: Formal language description languages for computer programming, ed. T. B. Steel Jr. (Amsterdam, North-Holland Publ. Co., 1966) pp. 139–147.

Ginsburg, S., S. A. Greibach and M. A. Harrison, Stack automata and compiling, J. ACM 14 (1967) 172–201.

Igarashi, S., On the logical schemes of algorithms, Information Processing in Japan 3 (1963) 12–18.

Igarashi, S., An axiomatic approach to the equivalence problems of algorithms with applications, Ph.D. thesis, University of Tokyo, 1964a.

Igarashi, S., A formalization of the description of languages and the related problems in a Gentzen type formal system, RAAG Research Notes, Third Series, no. 80, 1964b.

Kaluzhnin, L. A., Algorithmization of mathematical problems, Probl. Cybernet. 2 (1961) 371–392.

Kaphengst, H., Eine abstrakte programmgesteuerte Rechenmachine, Z. math. Logik und Grundl. Math. 5 (1959) 366–379.

LANDIN, P. J., The mechanical evaluation of expressions, Comp. J. **6** (1964) 308–320.

LANDIN, P. J., A correspondence between ALGOL 60 and Church's lambda notation, Comm. ACM **8** (1965) 89–101; 158–165.

LANDIN, P. J., A formal description of ALGOL 60, in: Formal language description languages for computer programming, ed. T. B. Steel Jr. (Amsterdam, North-Holland Publ. Co., 1966) pp. 266–294.

LONDON, R. L., A computer program for discovering and proving sequential recognition rules for well-formed formulas defined by a Backus normal form grammar, Ph.D. thesis, Carnegie Institute of Technology, 1964.

MAURER, W. D., A theory of computer instructions, J. ACM **13** (1966) 226–236.

MCCARTHY, J., Towards a mathematical theory of computation, in: Proc. IFIP Congress 1962, ed. C. M. Popplewell (Amsterdam, North-Holland Publ. Co., 1963a) pp. 21–28.

MCCARTHY, J., A basis for a mathematical theory of computation, in: Computer programming and formal systems, eds. P. Braffort and D. Hirschberg (Amsterdam, North-Holland Publ. Co., 1963b) pp. 33–69.

MCCARTHY, J., Problems in the theory of computation, in: Proc. IFIP Congress 1965, ed. A. Kalenich (Washington, Spartan Books, 1965) Vol. 1, pp. 219–222.

MCCARTHY, J., A formal description of a subset of ALGOL, in: Formal language description languages for computer programming, ed. T. B. Steel Jr. (Amsterdam, North-Holland Publ. Co. 1966) pp. 1–12.

MCCARTHY, J. and J. PAINTER, Correctness of a compiler for arithmetic expressions, Technical Report CS 38, Computer Science Dept., Stanford University, 1966.

MCKEEMAN, W. M., An approach to computer language design, Technical Report CS 48, Computer Science Dept., Stanford University, 1966.

NAUR, P., Proof of algorithms by general snapshots, B.I.T. **6** (1966) 310–317.

NIVAT, M. and N. NOLIN, Contribution to the definition of ALGOL semantics, in: Formal language description languages for computer programming, ed. T. B. Steel Jr. (Amsterdam, North-Holland Publ. Co., 1966) pp. 148–159.

PÉTER, R., Graphschemata und rekursive Funktionen, Dialectica **12** (1958) 373–393.

PL/I DEFINITION GROUP OF THE VIENNA LABORATORY, Formal definition of PL/I, IBM Technical Report TR 25.071, 1966.

RAYMOND, F. H., Etude générale des structures de calculatrices à préfixes et à piles, I. Chiffres **9** (1966) 235–277.

STEEL JR., T. B. (editor), Formal language description languages for computer programming, Proceedings IFIP Working Conference, Vienna, 1964 (Amsterdam, North-Holland Publ. Co. 1966a).

STEEL JR., T. B., A formalization of semantics for programming language description, in: Formal language description languages for computer programming, ed. T. B. Steel Jr. (Amsterdam, North-Holland Publ. Co., 1966b) pp. 25–36.

STRACHEY, C., Towards a formal semantics, in: Formal language description languages for computer programming, ed. T. B. Steel Jr. (Amsterdam, North-Holland Publ. Co., 1966) pp. 198–220.

THIELE, H., Wissenschaftstheoretischen Untersuchungen in Algorithmische Sprachen (Berlin, VEB, 1966).

VAN WIJNGAARDEN, A., Generalized ALGOL, Proc. ICC Symp. on Symbolic languages in data processing (New York, Gordon and Breach, 1962) pp. 409–419; Also in: Annual review in automatic programming, ed. R. Goodman (New York, Pergamon Press, 1963) vol. 3, pp. 17–26.

VAN WIJNGAARDEN, A., Recursive definition of syntax and semantic, in: Formal language description languages for computer programming, ed. T. B. Steel Jr. (Amsterdam, North-Holland Publ. Co., 1966) pp. 13–24.

WANG, H., Machines, sets and the decision problem, in: Formal systems and recursive functions, eds. J. N. Crossley and M. A. E. Dummett (Amsterdam, North-Holland Publ. Co., 1965) p. 306.

WIRTH, N. and C. A. R. HOARE, A contribution to the development of ALGOL, Comm. ACM **9** (1966) 413–432.

WIRTH, N. and H. WEBER, EULER, a generalization of ALGOL, and its formal definition, Comm. ACM **9** (1966) 13–23; 89–99.

YANOV, Y. I., The logical schemes of algorithms, Probl. Cybernet. **1** (1960) 82–140.

ZEMANEK, H., Semiotics and programming languages, Comm. ACM **9** (1966) 139–143.

COMPUTABLE AND UNCOMPUTABLE ELEMENTS OF SYNTAX

H. HIŻ

University of Pennsylvania, Philadelphia, USA

The simplicity with which the syntax of formal languages is often presented has been for some time looked on with envy by linguists. The attempts to formulate the syntax of a natural language indicate a far greater degree of complexity .The syntax of a language of mathematics seems computable. There is a decision procedure for the well-formedness of a string of symbols. And there is a decision procedure which assigns the proper structure to any well-formed string, i.e., to any formula, so that the set of all formulas for that language is recursive and the set of the structures assigned to the formulas is recursive. In other words, the set of ordered pairs of formulas and their structures is presented as a recursive set. A well known procedure for the generation of formulas is reversible, so that from the formula itself one can reconstruct its generation, and the generation is taken to be the structure of the formula. If, on the other hand, one cannot reconstruct the generation of a given string, the string is not a well-formed formula. Such procedures are well known and some cases of them will be given instantly. But first one may ask two relevant questions. Is it reasonable to expect that a natural language will have a similarly computable syntax, a syntax which will make the set of admissible texts in the language recursive and which will assign the relevant structures to each text in a reversible manner? And secondly, what should be the relevant structure or structures which we assign to a formula or to a sentence? With regard to the first question, it is relevant to note that a language of mathematics is set up with some degree of arbitrariness, and that to some extent it may be, and often is, changed according to the demands of simplicity of syntax. However, a natural language cannot be changed by a grammarian but must be taken as given. A closer examination of the second question, the question of relevant structures, will reveal that the simplicity with which the syntax of a mathematical language is usually presented is deceptive.

The following standard rules generate all and only well-formed formulas of the arithmetic of addition:

Rule 1. 0, 1, 2, 3, 4, 5, 6, 7, 8, 9 are elementary numerals.

Rule 2. If α and β are elementary numerals, then $\alpha\beta$ is an elementary numeral.

Rule 3. If α is an elementary numeral, then α is a numeral.

Rule 4. If α and β are numerals, then $(\alpha+\beta)$ is a numeral.

Rule 5. If α and β are numerals, then $\alpha=\beta$ is a well-formed formula.

These rules assign a structure to every formula by the very application of the rules. The formula shows traces of how it was obtained by the rules. But it does show such traces only up to some relevant details. $((142+5)+(2+7))=(772+1)$ can be obtained in several different ways. (First combine 2, + and 7, then 772, + and 1; or first combine 142 with + and 5, then 77 with 2, etc.) If those orders of the applications of the rules are left unspecified, whereas other orders of applications of the rules are strictly prescribed (e.g. Rule 5 is always to be used last), then some derivations are considered equivalent. All derivations of elementary numerals are equivalent. This fact reflects a particular way in which we treat elementary numerals. Had we wanted to call attention to the fact that $772=7\times10^2+7\times10^1+2\times10^0$, we would have found it useful to assign an additional structure to the elementary numerals, for instance, by changing Rule 1 and Rule 2:

Rule 1'. 0, ..., 9 are digits.

Rule 2a. If α is a digit, then it is an elementary numeral.

Rule 2b. If α is a digit, and β is an elementary numeral, then $\alpha\beta$ is an elementary numeral.

One more concept, that of digit, and more restricted ways of producing formulas will assign more refined structures to arithmetic formulas, although the new set of rules will generate exactly the same formulas as did the first set. The freedom of generation granted by the first set is acceptable only if other, later rules of generation or of inference, or some other rules which in any way operate on the strings, do not refer to the structure imposed by the derivation of the elementary numerals. The derivation of a formula is computable from the formula itself only up to equivalent derivations. Which derivations to consider equivalent depends upon what groupings and structures, what categorizations, are needed to be assigned. We need to assign exactly those structures to which we will refer in further operations on the formulas. Our syntax should, therefore, not only generate all and only formulas of arithmetic but also it should assign exactly those segmentations, groupings and categorizations to a formula which will be required when the rules of inference will be applied to the formula as a premise, or which will in some other way deal systematically with the formula. It is easy to construct a syntax, a set of rules of derivation, which will generate all and only well-formed formulas of the language but which will assign to the formulas irrelevent structures. For arithmetic, a queer syntax may, for instance, take as a relevent segment $+($ and combine it with a numeral to the left and a numeral followed by $)$ to the right. But no reasonable rule of inference for arithmetic refers to such strings as $+($. Therefore, such a syntax would be irrelevent, queer and inadequate.

As an example of a queer syntax, take the following syntax of a simple calculus of implication in the Polish notation. To obtain a well-formed formula, insert in a string of n occurrences of variables $n-1$ occurrences of C, provided that each occurrence of a variable, except the last one, is preceded, not necessarily immediately, by more occurrences of C than occurrences of variables. In other words, if there are m occurrences of C between the beginning of the string and the k-th occurrence of variables, and if $k < n$, then $m > k-1$. This rule generates, exactly, the well-formed formulas of the C-calculus. It also states some interesting properties of the formulas. But it does not deal with other segments than variables, C and strings which start from the beginning of the formula and end with an occurrence of a variable. Thus, following this rule, it is easy to write a program which will generate for $n=4$: CCCppp, CCpCppp, CCppCpp, CpCCppp and CpCpCpp, with p replaced at different occurrences by whatever variables. The fragments of the formula CCpCppp which this generation will use and, therefore, the structure which it imposes is, roughly, this:

CCpCppp.

This syntax does not treat C as a functor of two arguments. Nor does it state whether a string which on its own can be a well-formed formula is a well-formed formula when imbedded in another well-formed formula. It happens that this last property is needed to state the usual rules of inference, whereas the segments of the sort of CCp are not used in the formulation of the rules. It happens, however, that the structure

CCpCppp

may be useful in some higher order sentential logics, like protothetics, in which CCp will be treated as a functor of two sentential arguments and

CCpCpp as a functor of one sentential argument. It is not incorrect, therefore, to assign the above structure to the formula. But it is irrelevent for the purpose of constructing the elementary C-calculus. For a higher order logic we may need ordinary syntax, the syntax given by this queer rule of generation, and, perhaps, still other syntactic assignments to the same formula.

This point may be well illustrated if we return to the formulas of arithmetic. Let the formulas with addition as the only operation be generated by the normal syntax outlined in Rules 1–5. So that $=$ is (according to Rule 5) of the grammatical category of a functor which forms a formula, or a sentence, when flanked by two numerals; symbolically $(S; n\_n)$. Addition, according to Rule 4, is of the grammatical category $(n; n\_n)$. (If one considers the parentheses: $(n; (n\_n))$.) Now, the usual definition of substraction states: $x-y=z$, if and only if $y+z=x$. What should be the structure of $x-y=z$? Definitions are a usual way of generating new formulas and new syntactic structures into a language. The syntactic structure of $x-y=z$ should, therefore, also be given by the definition. Usually it is not explicitly stated. If the grammatical categories of variables in the definiendum are kept the same as when they occur in the definiens, and if the grammatical category of $=$ is everywhere $(S;n\_n)$, then $x-y=z$ may still have a structure which is not the one usually intended. For instance, it could be of the following structure:

$$
\begin{array}{ccc}
x- & y= & z \\
n(S; n\_S) & n(S; n\_n) & n \\
1\ 5\ 1\quad 4 & 2\ 4\ 2\quad 3 & 3
\end{array}
$$

The symbols in the second line of a structured string indicate the grammatical category of the phrase above, and the numerals in the third line indicate the grouping[1]. Thus, in this structured string, the category of $-$ is that of a functor which forms a sentence when flanked to the left by a numeral and to the right by a sentence. 1 and 4, in the third line, indicate which segments satisfy the requirements. By obvious reduction rules we can reduce the structured formula to S and show that it is a well-formed formula:

$$
\begin{array}{ccc}
x- & y= & z \\
n(S; n\_S) & n(S; n\_n) & n \\
1\ 5\ 1\quad 4 & 2\ 4\ 2\quad 3 & 3 \\
n(S; n\_S) & S* & * \\
1\ 5\ 1\quad 4 & 4 & \\
S* & ** & * \\
5 & &
\end{array}
$$

---

[1] The formal details of the notation used are expanded in HIŻ [1967].

(A string of asterisks indicates that the category is assigned to the entire string of symbols under which the name of the category followed by the string of asterisks appears.) The formula $x-y=z$ may have other structures yet. For instance,

$$
\begin{array}{llll}
x- & & y= & z \\
\text{n}((\text{n}; \text{n}\_); \_\text{n}) & & \text{n}(\text{S}; \text{n}\_\text{n}) & \text{n} \\
1\ \ 4\ 1 & 2 & 2\ 5\ 4\ \ 3 & 3 \\
\text{n}(\text{n}; \text{n}\_) & & *(\text{S}; \text{n}\_\text{n}) & \text{n} \\
1\ 4\ 1 & & 5\ 4\ \ 3 & 3 \\
\text{n}* & & *(\text{S}; \text{n}\_\text{n}) & \text{n} \\
4 & & 5\ 4\ \ 3 & 3 \\
\text{S}* & & *\ * & * \\
5 & & &
\end{array}
$$

or

$$
\begin{array}{llll}
x- & & y= & z \\
\text{n}((\text{n}; \text{n}\_); \_\text{n}) & \text{n}(\text{S}; \text{n}\_\text{n}) & \text{n} \\
2\ \ 3\ 2 & 1 & 1\ 5\ 3\ \ 4 & 4
\end{array}
$$

Presented in a more usual and less accurate way, three of the structures are $(x-y)=z$, $x-(y=z)$ and $x(-y)=z$. Note that $(x-y)=z$ if and only if $x-(y=z)$ and each of them if and only if $x(-y)=z$. Therefore, each of them can serve as a definition for the other. Also, the entire string $-y=z$ can be taken as a function of x: $x(-y=z)$ or

$$
\begin{array}{llll}
x- & & y= & z \\
\text{n}(\text{S}; \text{n}\_\text{S}) & \text{n}(\text{S}; \text{n}\_\text{n}) & \text{n} \\
4\ \ \ \ 4\ \ 1 & 2\ 1\ 2\ \ 3 & 3
\end{array}
$$

Again, the discontiguous phrase $x-\cdots=z$ can be a function of y:

$$
\begin{array}{lll}
x & - & y=z \\
(\text{S}; \_\text{n}\_)\ * & \text{n} \\
1\ 2 & & 1\ 2\ *
\end{array}
$$

But here $=$ does not have the usual category.

   A definition should give the intended structure in such a way that the structure of the definiendum be computable out of the structure of the definiens. For ordinary substraction it suffices to indicate that $-$ is of the same category as $+$. But the formula $x-y=z$, with other structures, plays some role in higher level mathematics where variables which range over complicated functions are used and, therefore, those functions can be substituted for variables. Note that the result of a substitution in the formula

$x - y = z$ can be restructured again. For instance, $24 - y = z$ can be restructured as a function of 4:

$$\begin{array}{cc} 2 & 4 - y = z \\ (S; \underline{\quad}n\underline{\quad}) & n \\ 1 \ 2 & 1 \ 2 *** \end{array}$$

In this way there are infinitely many structures which can be assigned to substitution instances of the formula $x - y = z$. Note also that in many mathematical formulas there will appear grammatical categories with requirements not satisfied within this formula. For instance,

$$\begin{array}{cc} \text{transitivity} & = \\ (S; \underline{\quad}(S; n\underline{\quad}n)) & (S; n\underline{\quad}n) \\ 2 \quad 1 & 1 \end{array}$$

This usually happens when one proceeds to an abstraction.

In a natural language, texts often should have many different structures. Contrary to the formulas of mathematics, however, it is hard to grasp all the structures that a text should have. The rules are not explicit; they have to be discovered in the actual practice of speakers who more or less systematically perform changes of the texts. The applicable operations determine which structures are to be assigned to the text. Some of the operations are close paraphrases, others are constant semantic changes, still others are drawing consequences. The operations involved are governed by rules; rules of paraphrase, rules of constant semantic changes, rules of consequence. An example of a close paraphrase rule is provided by a rule which allows a change of place of some adverbs in English. *Suddenly he left the room* is a close paraphrase of *He left the room suddenly*. The rule which governs this change must distinguish the structure of *He left the room* from that of *He can leave the room*. For *Suddenly he can leave the room* is not a paraphrase of *He can leave the room suddenly*. Negation, generalization, change of time, change of emphasis are typical constant semantic changes performed in a systematic way by speakers. And, according to English, the sentence *He left the room* is a consequence of the sentence *Suddenly he left the room*. The recognition of this consequence is a necessary condition for proficiency in English. An adequate syntax should state the rules of consequence which account for the speakers' feeling of consequence among texts. Paraphrasing is, of course, a particular case of drawing a consequence.

The empirical data for a syntax of a natural language are of at least eight kinds. First, some strings may be known to be acceptable texts, used or usable by speakers. Secondly, some pairs of texts may be judged by speakers to be close paraphrases, saying the same thing in other words. A set of texts, each of which is a relatively close paraphrase of each other, is called a paraphrastic set. Some paraphrastic sets are given; they can be solicited from informants. The third kind of data are sets of pairs of texts with a constant semantic difference. Paraphrasing is also a case of a constant semantic change, namely when the difference is close to zero. To collect pairs of texts with a constant semantic difference is a difficult task. Different semantic distinctions are carried out (obligatorily or naturally) by different languages. (The distinction between plural and dual is obligatory in Greek but not in English.) The fourth sort of data is provided by reports that some sentences, or some longer texts, are consequences of other texts. Just as logic systematizes the consequences used in the most formal part of science, syntax should systematize the consequences used in other kinds of discourse. In addition, and parallel to these four kinds of data, there are negative data: that some string is not a sentence, or that it is not a usable, acceptable text; that two texts are not close paraphrases of each other but convey different information; that a pair of texts is semantically differently related than another pair of texts; and that a text is not considered a consequence of a set of texts. Linguists use the negative data extensively to falsify hypotheses or to delimit other hypotheses properly.

Out of the four positive kinds of data, the first – the presence of some texts – is absolute, the rest are relative kinds of data. They relate some texts to others. We think that the relative data are far more important than the absolute ones. They reveal the internal property of utterances, whereas the absolute data state only the acceptability of the utterances. Moreover, the relative data include the absolute data. Only the usable texts are related as consequences and all the usable texts are consequences or premises for others. All the texts are paraphrasable.

A syntax of a language tries to find the general rules of paraphrasing, the general rules of consequence, and the general rules of constant semantic changes in the language. These general rules will use some general concepts, grammatical categories, and their combinations.

In what senses, then, may one say that a syntax is computable?

1. It may be claimed, and it sometimes is claimed, that the set of acceptable texts, the set of all possible utterances in the studied language, is recursive and that the set of relevant structures for each text is also recursive. For demonstration one may accept a finite set of elementary segments, a finite set of elementary structures, and a finite number of rules which will generate all the texts with their relevant structures and which will not generate anything

else. It will be decidable about each string whether it is an acceptable text or whether it has a given structure. This plan is similar to the way the syntax of elementary arithmetic or of elementary logic is often presented.

2. A less demanding requirement asks for rules which make the set of texts and the set of relevant structures of the text only recursively enumerable rather than recursive. If a string is not a usable text or if a structure does not apply to a text, the rules may not give us that information. But if a string is a text and if it has a given structure, the rules will tell us so in a finite number of steps. It seems that linguists frequently aim at meeting this requirement. But, at present, they are far from that goal, and it may be that it is too ambitious an aim.

3. A syntax of a language may be said to be computable in a different sense when it assigns, in a computable way, for each given usable text, all its relevant structures. It may be the case that the rules of paraphrasing, the rules of consequence and the rules of constant semantic changes all require only a small number of structures, that the structures imposed by some of them are already all the structures which may be imposed by any rules. However, even if one can assign to a text all its relevant structures, one may not necessarily find all the texts immediately generated by the given text. There may be many unknown rules which generate various texts though they operate on the same known structures. On the other hand, a text may be an immediate consequence of infinitely many different texts. *Peter is a student* is a consequence of *Peter studies* and of *Peter is a good student* and of *Peter needs money since he is a student,* etc. The computability of syntax in this sense requires that the structures of the sentence *Peter is a student* which will be involved in its derivation from any text are imposed by some of the derivations, and that after deriving this sentence in a few ways we will know that no new structure of this sentence will ever be used.

4. One also may call a syntax computable if all its rules are decidable, in the sense that for each pair of texts it is decidable whether they are linked by the rule.

5. What was said before (under 1. or under 2.) about texts may be, in addition, required of rules. The set of rules must be recursive or may be only recursively enumerable in order that the syntax be called computable.

6. A syntactic theory may be said to be computable, not absolutely, as in all the preceding senses, but relatively, namely relative to a subset of texts. As it is more plausible to produce a syntax computable in this sense than in the previous senses, a more detailed description of the claim is proper here.

Among all acceptable texts, A, of a language under study, there are some texts which will be called elementary texts, el(A). The elementary texts are characterized by having a property, P, which is recursive, i.e., there is a decision procedure which tells us which of the texts of the language are elementary texts. This does not mean that there is a procedure which tells us which of the arbitrary strings are elementary texts. The set of elementary texts is recursive relative to the set of all texts. If a string is a text, then we can find automatically whether or not it possesses property P and, therefore, whether or not it is an elementary text. This point is of some importance when one compares what is here proposed with other grammatical theories. In contemporary attempts at syntax, there are concepts which refer to elementary texts in this sense. In Harris' theory (HARRIS [1965] in particular p. 384), it is possible to compute whether or not a sentence is in the kernel form. In Chomsky's theory (CHOMSKY [1964]), it is possible to compute whether or not a sentence is obtainable within the base. Again, in the theory sketched below, it is possible to compute whether or not a sentence or a longer utterance is regular. But all claims, if ever made, that there is a procedure which, for an arbitrary string, decides whether it is a sentence in the kernel form, or whether it is obtainable within the base, or whether it is a regular utterance, remain disappointingly unfulfilled.

There are many essential reasons for this. Among them an important one is that the language allows only some co-occurrences of words. *He got a persistent cold* and *He got a sketchy knowledge of farming* are English sentences, but *He got a sketchy cold* presumably is not an English sentence. Furthermore, for longer sentences, and for texts longer than a sentence, the co-occurrence restrictions become more involved. *Oak is hard, This winter is hard* are acceptable but *Oak is hard but this winter is harder* is a doubtful utterance. If one wants to understand it, one must assume that *harder* here is not short for *harder than oak* but is short for some phrase like *harder than the other winter*. Therefore, in the surrounding text there should be a phrase to which the comparison refers. One must note also that the structure of a sentence often depends on its environment. *But John reads more than Peter* has different readings depending on whether it appears in *Peter talks more than John. But John reads more than Peter* or in *Peter reads a lot. But John reads more than Peter*. In the first case we may freely add *But so far as reading is concerned....* In the second case we would paraphrase rather by *But so far as John is concerned....*

A text has references to itself. Pronouns, classifiers, and comparatives are among the instruments for referring, in an English text, to other parts of itself. One may suppose that there is a general procedure which for any given acceptable text decides the references of the text to itself. (One may add that such a procedure may resolve the references only up to involved ambiguities, and up to the clarity of the text, in this respect.) But from the existence of a procedure to decide the referential structure of a text does not follow the existence of any procedure to construct all the referential structures of the language. As in many other aspects of syntax, here semantics plays an essential role. In order to construct an acceptable text, one has to know that some sentences are true. In the text *My brother and his wife went to the theater. The man bought the tickets* the phrase *the man* refers to *my brother* and the phrase *the tickets* is short for *the tickets for it* where *it* is a referential for *going to the theater*. In order to construct this text one has to know some facts, namely that my brother and not his wife, nor a theater, is a man, and that going to a theater requires tickets. No syntax can give these facts, though a syntactic analysis of texts may discover many of the facts which are explicitly or tacitly assumed by the speakers. It is implausible that the set of assumed true sentences be recursive. It depends on our changing knowledge, and our opinion, which does not change our language though it does change its use.

From the set of elementary texts, every text of the language is obtainable by application of a finite subset of the relevant rules. There are many, presumably infinitely many, rules which govern paraphrase, consequence and constant semantic changes in language. It may be assumed that all of these rules are derived from some elementary rules; that every application of a relevant rule can be viewed as a finite combination of applications of elementary, primitive rules in such a way that for each rule there is a procedure which prescribes for each of its uses which primitive rules and in what order are to be used. The set R of all relevant rules is, therefore, recursively enumerable relative to the set el(R) of elementary rules, and the set of all texts is recursively enumerable relative to the set el(A) of elementary texts by the set el(R) of elementary rules. In addition, we can assume about elementary rules that they are decidable in the sense (like in 4. above) that there is a procedure which decides for each set of strings whether they are linked by one of the rules.

This sixth sense of computability of syntax, the sense in which it seems plausible that one can eventually produce a computable syntax, can be summarized as follows:

There are A, el(A), R, el(R) and P, such that

(i) A is the set of texts in the language,

  (ii) $el(A) \subset A$,

(iii) P is a recursive property,

 (iv) $\alpha \in el(A) \equiv . \, P(\alpha) \wedge \alpha \in A$,

  (v) R is the set of relevent rules for the language,

 (vi) $el(R) \subset R$,

(vii) $el(R)$ is finite,

(viii) ρ is $el(R) \supset \rho$ is decidable,

 (ix) A is recursively enumerable relatively to $el(A)$ by $el(R)$,

  (x) R is recursively enumerable relatively to $el(R)$.

To illustrate some of the kinds of rules which may be relevant for a natural language, we will assume a short text and derive from it a few other texts. It is to be stressed, however, that this is a simple and simplified case, and that any adequate syntax of English would have to be much more involved. Let the assumed text be *The teacher examined the students*. Here we will not enter the problem that *teacher* is a nominalization of *teaches* and *students* a a nominalization of *study*. One, of course can go into these further details, as well as into the fact that *teacher* and *students* is a pair of relative terms (like *father* and *daughter*, or like *master* and *servant*, to use Aristotle's example). But, for simplicity, we will treat *the teacher* and *the students* as noun phrases (N). Similarly, we will not use the referential nature of the definite articles in these phrases.

The structure which we will assign to this sentence will be used by the rules to derive other sentences. (The notation: N – a noun phrase; S – a sentence; (S; N__N) – a phrase which forms a sentence when flanked on both sides by noun phrases; Q – a quantifier, including an article; A – an adjective; vrbn[N] – a verb number mark in agreement with a noun phrase; t – a tense mark. Thus, in the structures exhibited below, *the teacher* is a noun phrase marked by Σ, *ed* is both a tense mark and verb number mark in agreement with *the teacher*, *examin* is a phrase which when followed by a tense mark and a verb number mark in agreement with Σ forms a phrase, which in turn froms a sentence when flanked by two noun phrases.) Some of the rules will be paraphrase rules, others will be rules of consequence, sometimes applied in reversed order so that from a consequence we will obtain its premiss. Still other rules may not have a clear semantic role yet but are useful technical aids.

(a)   The teacher examin   ed   *   the students

       N   * $((S; N\_\_N); \_\_t \; vrbn[N])$ t vrbn N   *

      Σ Σ Ω 1 Σ 1 Ω

Because *examin* is indeed followed by a tense mark and by a verb number mark, the structure reduces to a more global structure

(a')   The teacher examin   ed the students
                      N   *   (S; N__N) * N   *
                      Σ   Σ   Ω   Ω

which in turn reduces to S. For some derivations it may suffice to know that the string is a sentence; for other derivations a more refined structure may be required. For the derivation which follows, the structure (a) will be used. First we will obtain *The teacher gave an examination to the students* and *The students took an examination from the teacher* which are relatively close paraphrases of (a). It is a frequent English procedure to obtain new paraphrases by nominalizing the verb and preceding it by an appropriate modal verb, with the same tense mark, and with a verb number mark in agreement with the noun phrase which is the subject of the new sentence. Different verbs take different modals in the form when the subject and the object are in the same positions as before, and different modals in the form in which the subject and the object are interchanged. Thus *Oxford published Woodger, Oxford made a publication of Woodger, Woodger got a publication at Oxford*; *John will address the government, John will give an address to the government, The government will get an address from John.* Some of the sentences receive a fluent modal with the original object before the nominalized verb: *Peter called me, Peter gave me a call, I got a call from Peter* or *I received a call from Peter.* Similarly: *The teacher gave the students an examination.* The details of the transformations involved in these and similar cases vary slightly, depending on the choice of words. In the case of (a) the subject modal transformation goes from a sentence of the form

(1)   α β   γ δ   ε
                 N ((S; N__N); __t vrbn) t vrbn [N] N
                 Σ   Σ   Ω   1 2   1 2   Σ   Ω

to a sentence of the form

(ΣM1)   α η γ   δ   an β   tion ζ ε
        N t vrbn   ((S; N__N); __t vrbn)   N
        Σ 1 2   Σ   Ω   1 2   Ω

Here η and ζ are new phrases which must be specified for each β. In our case, for $\beta = examin$, $\eta = give$ and $\zeta = to$. So that applying the rule of subject modal to (a) we obtain

(ΣMa) The teacher give ed   *   an examin
           N   *   t vrbn $((S; N\_N);$
           Σ 1 2 Σ Ω

                   ation to the students
     _t vrbn)   N   *
      1 2 Ω

The phrases *an* and *ation* are constants of the transformation (1) to $(\Sigma M1)$. Instead of *ation* we sometimes have a different constant (*ment* as in *enlightenment*, zero as in *call*). We have to use an auxiliary rule which changes *give ed* to *gave*.

Parallelly, the rule of the object modal transformation goes from (1) to

$(\Omega M1)$ ε η' γ δ' an β ation ζ' α
         N t vrbn $[N]$ $((S; N\_N);$ _t vrbn $[N])$ N
         Ω 1 Ω Σ Ω 1 Σ Σ

In our case

(ΩMa) The students take ed *   an examin
           N   *   t vrbn $[N]$ $((S; N\_N);$
           Ω 1 Ω Σ Ω

                   ation from the teacher
     _t vrbn $[N])$ N   *
      1   Σ Σ

In (ΣMa) and in (ΩMa) there are phrases, *give, an, ation, to, take, from* which are not parts of phrases to which grammatical categories are assigned in the second line. The structures which these transformations impose on the resulting sentences are partial only. The situation is similar to an arithmetic definition which does not specify exactly the grammatical categories of all the phrases of the definiendum. And just as in arithmetic we cannot use the definiendum without deciding its full grammatical structure, so for applying further transformations to (ΣMa) or to (ΩMa) we have to complete their structures. It is natural to treat *an* as a quantifier and *examination* as a phrase which together with a preceding quantifier forms a noun phrase. (This ammounts to treating *ation* as $((N; Q\_); ((S; N\_N); \_t vrbn\_)\_).)$ Similarly, *give* is to be taken as a phrase which, together with a tense mark and a verb number mark, forms a "verb with N to N object", i.e., (S; N_N to N). These new assignments are done with a view of using some specific further transformations. By and large, however, some assignments are much more fruitful than others, and one can suggest "local" rules for fruitful completions of grammatical structures. Using appropriate rules of that kind we obtain from (ΣMa)

(ΣMa1)   The teacher give   ed
   N   *   ((S; N__N to N); __t vrbn [N]) t
   Σ Σ 4 5 Ω 1 2 Σ 1

        *   an examin   ation to the students
   vrbn [N] Q (N; Q__)   *   N   *
   2   Σ 3 Ω

The form of the structure (ΣMa1) lost the fact that *examination* is a nominalized verb. For several further operations it may be relevant, however, to recall this fact. We cannot, therefore, say that (ΣMa1) reveals all the relevant structure of *The teacher gave an examination to the students*. (ΣMa) shows something important which (ΣMa1) does not. (ΣMa1) stresses the connection between *give* as a modal verb and *give* as a transitive verb. The transformation which applies to *give* as a transitive verb is applied here as well:

(ΣMa2)   The teacher give   ed
   N   *   ((S; N__N to N); __t vrbn [N]) t
   Σ Σ 4 5 Ω 1 2 Σ 1

        *   the students an examination
   vrbn [N] N   *   Q (N; Q__)
   2   Σ Ω 3 4 3

The sentence *The teacher gave the students an examination* can be treated as a function of *the teacher*. It is so treated when it leads to the sentence *I talked to the teacher who gave an examination to the students*. We can also take it as a function of *the students* or as a function of *the examination* depending on how we combine it with other sentences: *The students whom the teacher gave an examination did not like it, We have read the examination which the teacher gave the students*. In each case, out of the sentence a noun phrase is formed, by extracting from the sentence a noun, and by adjoining to the noun the remainder of the sentence by an appropriate relative pronoun. The general rule is this: If

$$\alpha\ \beta\ \gamma \qquad\qquad \delta$$
$$Q\,(N; Q\text{__})$$
$$1 \qquad\quad 1$$

is a sentence, then

$$
\begin{array}{cccc}
\text{the } \gamma & \text{wh } \varepsilon & \alpha\,\delta \\
Q & (N;Q\_) & \text{wh}\,(N) \\
2 & 3\quad 2 & 3
\end{array}
$$

is a noun phrase.

In this sentence $\alpha\beta\gamma\delta$ we, therefore, take the discontinous phrase $\alpha...\delta$ as a function of the noun phrase $\beta\gamma$:

$$
\begin{array}{cccc}
\alpha & \beta\ \gamma & & \delta \\
(S;\ \_N\_) & Q\,(N;Q\_) & \_ \\
2\quad 3 & 1\quad 2\quad 1 & 3
\end{array}
$$

This is a standard way of combining sentences. The combining of sentences is one of the procedures for obtaining from some texts new texts. As stated above, it is expected that all texts are obtainable from some texts which are called 'elementary', and that the elementary texts are characterized by a computable property P. The problem remaining is what are the elementary texts, and what should be the property P by which we recognize them. English may be reducible to more than one set of such texts, each with a different characteristic property. A reasonable assumption seems to be that an elementary text is a conjunction of sentences, each with a structure where every requirement is satisfied, i.e., if to a phrase the catagory (a; b__c) is assigned, then the phrase is within this sentence indeed flanked by phrases of categories b and c respectively. And similarly for more involved requirements. Moreover, the sentences of an elementary text do not involve each other explicitly or implicitly except by conjunctions and by referentials. Such texts are called *regularized. I talked to the teacher who gave an examination to the students* is not regularized in this sense, for it implicitly involves the sentence *The teacher examined the students. The teacher examined the students. I talked to him* is a regularized text from which the irregular one is obtainable by rules like those shown above. *Him* is a referential for *the teacher* and the period between the two sentences of the text serves as a conjunction. The text *The students whom the teacher gave an examination did not like it* is not regularized. Its regularized form is perhaps: *The teacher examined the students. The students did not like it. It* is here a referential for the first sentence and *The students* for *the students*. The non-regularized text *We have read the examination which the teacher gave the students* involves a typical complication. The difficulty lies in the ambiguity of the phrase *the examination*. Either it is a referential for *examined* or it is short for *the text of the examination*. In our case it is certainly not a referential for *examined* as we do not read an activity of examining. If we consider that the text *The teacher examined the students. We have read the examination* is regularized, we must take *the examination* as a higher order referential, a phrase which refers not directly to *examined* but to an understood feature of *examined*, namely that the teacher examined by asking a question and we have read only the question. What higher order referentials are admissible in each case must be given empirically. We use referentials in agreement with tacitly assumed sentences, sentences which are not explicitly stated because they are commonly known. No syntax can be expected to enumerate recursively all commonly known sentences which are implicitly used in referentials. Syntax, however, can to some extent find out what sentences were implicitly used for the referentials of given texts. Syntax and semantics merge. The use of a language presupposes the facts which are too trivial or too well known to be stated, though they are used for more involved locutions. The facts must be supplied independently of the syntactic theory and they constitute the recurrent anchorage of the theory in empirical linguistic data.

References

CHOMSKY, N., Aspects of the theory of syntax (1964).
HARRIS, Z. S., Transformational theory, Language **41** (1965) 363–401.
HIŻ, H., Grammar logicism, The Monist **51** (1967) 110–127.

ON THE NOTION OF A COMPUTER

Z. PAWLAK

Institute of Mathematics, Polish Academy of Sciences, Warsaw, Poland

In the theory of mathematical machines various machines are considered, such as Turing machines, push-down machines, finite automata, etc. but little attention is given to formal definition of digital computers, programs and the study of their properties.

The author's belief as well as that of many other people working in computer field is that a further development of this field requires more close relations with the existing computers.

The paper contains formal definitions of a computer, a universal computer and a program. In the proposed language one can define and study machines which seem to be fairly good models of real computers. Some elementary theorems concerning computers are stated. One can find more details concerning the outlined topics in PAWLAK [1967].

1. Computers

1.1. *Memory*

Let A, Σ, V, be sets. Elements of A are called *addresses*, Σ is refered to as an *alphabet* and elements of Σ are called *symbols*. Elements of V are called *markers*. We allow the sets A, Σ to be finite or infinite and the set V is assumed to be always finite. By Λ we denote the distinguished symbol of Σ called the *empty* symbol.

Let C and L be the sets of functions with domain and codomain as given below

$$C \subseteq \Sigma^A \qquad L \subseteq A^V.$$

Every $c \in C$ is called *content* of the memory and every $l \in L$ is called *location* of the memory. We assume that for every $c \in C$, $c(x) \neq \Lambda$ for almost all $x \in A$.

DEFINITION 1. The memory is a system $P = \langle M, I, O \rangle$, where $M = C \times L$

is referred to as a set of *memory states*, and I, O are *input* and *output functions* of a memory with domain and codomain as follows:

$$I: \Sigma \times A^n \times M \to M, \qquad O: A^n \times M \to M \times \Sigma,$$

where $n = 0, 1, 2, \ldots$ is fixed for given memory.

The function O may be considered as a pair of functions

$$O_1: A^n \times M \to M \quad \text{and} \quad O_2: A^n \times M \to \Sigma.$$

We can extend functions I and O for finite sequences of symbols and obtain new input and output functions I^*, O^*:

$$I^*: \Sigma^k \times A^n \times M \to M \quad \text{and} \quad O^*: A^n \times M \to M \times \Sigma^k,$$

where $k = 0, 1, 2, \ldots$ is some fixed number for given memory.

Thus with every memory P we can associate the *memory function*

$$\Pi_P: \Sigma^k \times A^n \times M \to \Sigma^k$$

defined as follows

$$\bar{y}_k = \Pi_P(\bar{x}_k, \bar{a}_n, m) = O_2^*(\bar{a}_n, I^*(\bar{x}_k, \bar{a}_n, m)),$$

where $\bar{y}_k = y_1, \ldots, y_k$, $\bar{x}_k = x_1, \ldots, x_k$, $\bar{a}_n = a_1, \ldots, a_n$ and $y_i, x_i \in \Sigma$, $a_i \in A$, $m \in M$.

Two memories P and P' are said to be equivalent if and only if

$$\Pi_P = \Pi_{P'}.$$

If the memory function does not depend on some arguments we shall omit those arguments and write simple for example $\Pi_P(\bar{x}_k)$.

Example 1. One address memory. Let N denote the set of natural numbers $0, 1, 2, \ldots$. We assume for this memory $A = N$, $\Sigma = N \cup \Lambda$ and the set of markers V consists of only one element v. Input function for one address memory is as follows

$$I(x, a, m) = m_1 = \langle c_1, l_1 \rangle, \quad \text{where}$$
$$c_1(z) = \begin{cases} x & \text{if} \quad z = l_1(v), \\ c(z) & \text{if} \quad z \neq l_1(v), \end{cases}$$
$$l_1(v) = a,$$

and $a, z \in A$, $x \in \Sigma$, $m \in M$, $m = \langle c, l \rangle$.

The output function for this memory is

$$O(a, m) = \langle m_2, c(a) \rangle, \quad \text{where} \quad m_2 = \langle c_2, l_2 \rangle \quad \text{and} \quad c_2 = c,$$
$$l_2(v) = a.$$

The extended input and output functions for one address memory are

$$I^*(\bar{x}_k, a, m) = m_1 = \langle c_1, l_1 \rangle, \quad \text{where}$$
$$c_1(z) = x_i \quad \text{if} \quad z = a + i - 1 \quad \text{and} \quad c_1(z) = c(z) \quad \text{otherwise},$$
$$l_1(v) = a, \quad 1 \leq i \leq k.$$
$$O^*(a, m) = \langle m_2, \bar{x}_k \rangle, \quad \text{where} \quad m_2 = \langle c_2, l_2 \rangle \quad \text{and} \quad c_2 = c,$$
$$l_2(v) = a,$$
$$x_i = c(a + i - 1).$$

One can easily show that for one address memory $\Pi_P(X) = X$ for all $X \in \Sigma^k$.

Example 2. Stack memory. The sets A, Σ, V are the same as in the Example 1. Input function for stack memory is the following

$$I(x, m) = m_1 = \langle c_1, l_1 \rangle, \quad \text{where}$$
$$c_1(z) = \begin{cases} x & \text{if} \quad z = l_1(v), \\ c(z) & \text{if} \quad z \neq l_1(v), \end{cases}$$
$$l_1(v) = l(v) + 1.$$

Output function for this memory is

$$O(m) = \langle m_2, c(l(v)) \rangle, \quad \text{where} \quad m_2 = \langle c_2, l_2 \rangle \quad \text{and} \quad c_2 = c,$$
$$l_2(v) = l(v) - 1 \quad \text{for} \quad l(v) > 0 \quad \text{and undefined for} \quad l(v) = 0.$$

The extended input and output functions for stack memory are as follows

$$I^*(\bar{x}_k, m) = m_1 = \langle c_1, l_1 \rangle, \quad \text{where}$$
$$c_1(z) = \begin{cases} x_i & \text{if} \quad z = l(v) + i \quad (1 \leq i \leq k) \\ c(z) & \text{otherwise}, \end{cases}$$
$$l_1(v) = l(v) + i.$$
$$O^*(m) = \langle m_2, \bar{x}_k \rangle, \quad \text{where} \quad m_2 = \langle c_2, l_2 \rangle \quad \text{and} \quad c_2 = c,$$
$$l_2(v) = l(v) - (k - 1),$$
$$x_i = c(l(v) - i + 1).$$

One can easily verify that $\Pi_P(X) = X^{-1}$ for all $X \in \Sigma^k$, where X^{-1} is to mean $x_k, \ldots, x_1$.

1.2. *Instructions*

With every computer there is associated the finite set of *instructions*, $R = \{r_0, r_1, \ldots, r_s\}$. Instruction $r \in R$ is a function $r: A^n \times M \to M$, where $n \geq 0$ is some fixed number for a given computer.

Two instructions r and r' are said to be *equivalent* if and only if for all

$\bar{a}_n \in A^n$ and for all $m \in M$

$$r(\bar{a}_n, m) = r'(\bar{a}_n, m).$$

If for all $\bar{a}_n \in A^n$ and for all $m \in M$

$$r(\bar{a}_n, m) = m$$

then r is called *identity instruction* and will be denoted by r_0.

Composition of instructions r_1 and r_2 is the instruction r such that

$$r = r_1(\bar{b}_n, r_2(\bar{a}_n, m)), \qquad \bar{a}_n, \bar{b}_n \in A^n$$

written short as $r = r_1 r_2$.

The instruction

$$r' = \underbrace{r \dots r}_{p}$$

is called an *iteration* of the instruction r and is written $r' = r^p$.

With every computer there is associated a finite set of *operations*, $F = \{f_0, f_1, \dots, f_p\}$. Operation $f \in F$ is a function

$$f: \Sigma^{n_1} \to \Sigma^{n_2}, \qquad n_1, n_2 > 0.$$

Instruction r is called *admissible* for the memory P and the set of operations F if r can be represented in the form

$$r(\bar{a}_n, m) = I^*\{f[O_2(\bar{a}_n, m)], \bar{a}_n, O_1^*(\bar{a}_n, m)\},$$

where f is some operation from F and I^*, O^* are the extended input and output functions of the memory P.

Example 1. Transfer instruction. Let P be the memory for which $A = N$, $\Sigma = N \cup \Lambda$, $V = \{v_1, v_2\}$. Let us assume the following input and output functions for the memory P:

$$I^*(x, a, b, m) = m_1 = \langle c_1, l_1 \rangle, \quad \text{where} \quad x \in \Sigma, \qquad a, b \in A, \qquad m, m_1 \in M$$
and

$$c_1(z) = \begin{cases} x & \text{if} \quad z = l(v_2) = b, \\ c(z) & \text{if} \quad z \neq l(v_2), \end{cases}$$

$$l_1(y) = \begin{cases} b & \text{if} \quad y = v_2, \\ l(y) & \text{if} \quad y \neq v_2. \end{cases}$$

$$O^*(a, b, m) = \langle m_2, x \rangle, \quad \text{where} \quad m_2 = \langle c_2, l_2 \rangle \quad \text{and} \quad c_2 = c,$$

$$l_2(y) = \begin{cases} a & \text{if} \quad y = v_1, \\ l(y) & \text{if} \quad y \neq v_1, \end{cases}$$

$$x = c(l_2(v_1)) = c(a).$$

Let us denote the transfer instruction by $T(a, b, m)$ and assume that the set of computer operations F contains the identity operation $i(x) = x$. We define transfer instruction as

$$T(a, b, m) = m' = \langle c', l' \rangle, \quad \text{where}$$

$$c'(z) = \begin{cases} c(a) & \text{if} \quad z = l(v_2), \\ c(z) & \text{if} \quad z \neq l(v_2), \end{cases}$$

$$l'(y) = \begin{cases} a & \text{if} \quad y = v_1, \\ b & \text{if} \quad y = v_2. \end{cases}$$

One can easily see that so defined transfer instruction is admissible for the assumed set of operations and assumed memory because

$$T(a, b, m) = I^* \{ i \, [O_2^*(a, b, m)], a, b, O_1^*(a, b, m) \},$$

for any a, b, m.

Example 2. Two address addition instruction. Let us consider memory with A, Σ, V and I^* the same as in the Example 1 but the output function defined as follows

$$O^*(a, b, m) = \langle m_2, \bar{x}_2 \rangle, \quad \text{where} \quad m_2 = \langle c_2, l_2 \rangle \quad \text{and} \quad c_2 = c,$$

$$l_2(y) = \begin{cases} a & \text{if} \quad y = v_1, \\ b & \text{if} \quad y = v_2, \end{cases}$$

$$x_1 = c(l_2(v_1)) = c(a),$$

$$x_2 = c(l_2(v_2)) = c(b).$$

Let $A(a, b, m)$ denote a two address addition instruction, defined as $A(a, b, m) = m' = \langle c', l' \rangle$ where

$$c(z) = \begin{cases} c(a) + c(b) & \text{if} \quad z = l(v_2) = b, \\ c(z) & \text{if} \quad z \neq l(v_2), \end{cases}$$

$$l(y) = \begin{cases} a & \text{if} \quad y = v_1, \\ b & \text{if} \quad y = v_2. \end{cases}$$

One can easily verify that if the computer operations set contains addition, then the instruction $A(a, b, m)$ is admissible

$$A(a, b, m) = I \{ + [O_2(a, b, m)] \, a, b, O_1(a, b, m) \}.$$

In the sequel it will be assumed that all the instructions are admissible, thus "instruction" will always mean "admissible instruction".

DEFINITION 2. Instruction which changes the content of at most one address in the memory or changes the location of at most one marker in the memory is called *simple*.

THEOREM 1. Every instruction can be represented as a composition of simple instructions.

1.3. Conditions

With every computer we associate a finite set $W = \{W_1, W_2, ..., W_t\}$, $W_i \subset M$. The elements of W are called *conditions*. We say that the memory state $m \in M$ satisfies the condition W_i if and only if $m \in W_i$.

We say that a condition W_i is admissible for the memory P if and only if

$$W_i = \{m : m \in M \quad \text{and} \quad O_2^*(\bar{a}_n, m) = x\}$$

for some $\bar{a}_n$, where O_2^* is the output function of the memory P and x is some fixed symbol of the alphabet Σ. We shall consider only admissible conditions in this paper. For example for one address memory the condition may be the set

$$W_i = \{m : m \in M \quad \text{and} \quad c(a) = 0\}, \qquad 0 \in \Sigma,$$

for some $a \in A$.

1.4. Control

Let Q be a finite set of numbers $\{1, 2, ..., s\}$. A *graph* will be defined as the system $G = \langle Q, Q', h_0, h_1 \rangle$, where $Q' \subset Q$ and $h_0 : Q - Q' \to Q$, $h_1 : Q - Q' \to Q$. Q is referred to as the set of *points* of G and Q' is referred to as the set of *end* points of G. $q \in Q - Q'$ is called *initial* point of G, if for every $q' \in Q$, $q \neq h_i(q')$, $i = 0, 1$.

The sequence $q_1, ..., q_r$, $q_i \in Q$ is called the *path* from q_1 to q_r in G, if for all i, $1 \leqslant i < r$, $q_{i+1} = h_j(q_i)$, $j = 0, 1$.

By the *flow graph* we shall mean the graph G which satisfies the following conditions:

1°. G contains exactly one initial point, written q_0.

2°. The set of end points is not empty.

3°. For every point $q \in Q - q_0$ there is a path from q_0 to q in G.

4°. For every point $q \in Q - Q'$ there is a path from q to q', where $q' \in Q'$.

DEFINITION 3. The control S of the computer is a system $S = \langle G, \varphi, \psi, \nu \rangle$ where G is the flow graph and φ, ψ, ν are functions with domains and codomains as given below

$$\varphi : Q \to R, \qquad \psi : Q \to W, \qquad v : M \times Q \to M \times Q,$$

and R, W are some fixed sets of instructions and conditions respectively, M is the fixed set of memory states and Q is the set of points of the graph G. We assume that for every end point of Q we associate the identity instruction r_0.

Elements of Q are also called *control states*. Elements of the set $T = M \times Q$ are called *computer states*. The function v is called *transition* function. If q_0 is the initial state of the control then $\langle m, q_0 \rangle$ is called the *initial state of the computer*; if q is the end state of the control, then $\langle m, q \rangle$ is called the *end state of* the computer, where $m \in M$ is some state of the memory. Let $t = \langle m, q \rangle$ and $t' = \langle m', q' \rangle$.

Transition function will be defined as follows

$$v(t) = t', \quad \text{where}$$
$$m' = [\varphi(q)] (\bar{a}_n, m)$$
$$q' = \begin{cases} h_0(q) & \text{if} \quad m' \in \psi(q), \\ h_1(q) & \text{if} \quad m' \notin \psi(q). \end{cases}$$

1.5. *Computers*

DEFINITION 4. Computer is a system $\mathcal{M} = \langle P, R, W, S \rangle$, where P, R, W, S are the memory, the set of instructions, the set of the conditions and the control of the computer respectively.

The sequence $t_0, t_1, \ldots, t_k$ is called the *computation* of the computer $\mathcal{M}$ if and only if for each $t_i \in T$ (where T is the set of states of $\mathcal{M}$), and for every i, $1 \leqslant i < k$, $t_{i+1} = v(t_i)$ and t_0, t_k are the initial state and the end state of the computer $\mathcal{M}$ respectively. t_i are called *steps* of the computation.

t_k will be denoted by $\text{Com}(t_0)$. The function Com may be considered as a pair of functions Com_1 and Com_2 such that $\text{Com}_1(t_0) = m$ and $\text{Com}_2(t_0) = q$, and $\text{Com}(t_0) = t_k = \langle m, q \rangle$.

Thus with every computer $\mathcal{M}$ there is associated the function

$$\phi_{\mathcal{M}}(\bar{x}_k, \bar{a}_n, m) = O_2^* \{ \bar{a}_n, \text{Com}_1 [I^*(\bar{x}_k, \bar{a}_n, m), q_0] \},$$

where I^* and O^* are input and output functions of the memory of the computer $\mathcal{M}$.

DEFINITION 5. We say that the function $f(x_1, \ldots, x_k)$ is *computable* by the computer $\mathcal{M}$ if and only if $f = \phi_{\mathcal{M}}$ for some $\bar{a}_n$ and m.

DEFINITION 6. The set $\Sigma' \subset \Sigma^*$ is *decidable* on the computer $\mathcal{M}$ if and only if for all $x \in \Sigma^*$ there exist such $\bar{a}_n$ and m that

$$\phi_{\mathcal{M}}(x, \bar{a}_n, m) = \begin{cases} 0 & \text{if} \quad x \in \Sigma' \\ 1 & \text{if} \quad x \notin \Sigma', \end{cases}$$

where 0, 1 are some distinguished elements of Σ.

DEFINITION 7. The set $\Sigma' \subset \Sigma^*$ is *generable* on $\mathcal{M}$ if and only if for all $x \in \Sigma'$ there is a sequence $\bar{x}_k = x_1, \ldots, x_k$, $x_i \in \Sigma$ such that

$$\phi_{\mathcal{M}}(\bar{x}_k, \bar{a}_n, m) = x \quad \text{for some} \quad \bar{a}_n \quad \text{and} \quad m.^*$$

Computers $\mathcal{M}$ and $\mathcal{M}'$ are equivalent if and only if $f_{\mathcal{M}} = f_{\mathcal{M}'}$, where $f_{\mathcal{M}}$ denotes the function computable by the computer $\mathcal{M}$, and similar $f_{\mathcal{M}'}$.

Note. If the function f is given and we search for the computer $\mathcal{M}$ such that $f = \phi_{\mathcal{M}}$ one may speak of *synthesis* of computer $\mathcal{M}$. If computer $\mathcal{M}$ is given and we search for the function $\phi_{\mathcal{M}}$ one can speak about the *analysis* of the computer $\mathcal{M}$.

2. Universal computers

2.1. *Classes of computers*

DEFINITION 8. Two computers $\mathcal{M}$ and $\mathcal{M}'$ are of the same class if and only if the memories, the instructions and the conditions of both computers are identical.

In other words the computers belonging to the same class may differ at most in the control.

Let $\mathcal{K} = \{\mathcal{M}_1, \mathcal{M}_2, \ldots\}$ be the class of computers. Then by $f_{\mathcal{K}} = \{f_{\mathcal{M}_1}, f_{\mathcal{M}_2}, \ldots\}$, where $f_{\mathcal{M}_i}$ is the function computable by the computer $\mathcal{M}_i$ – we denote the class of functions computable by the computers of the class $\mathcal{K}$. Two classes of computers $\mathcal{K}, \mathcal{K}'$ are equivalent if and only if $f_{\mathcal{K}} = f_{\mathcal{K}'}$.

One can easily define the class of one address computers, the class of two address computers etc. and show that these classes are equivalent.

2.2. *Universal computer*

Let $\mathcal{K}$ be the class of computers with alphabet Σ. Computers from $\mathcal{K}$ are denoted by $\mathcal{M}$. Let $\mathfrak{M}$ be the following computer not belonging to the class $\mathcal{K}$. For the sake of simplicity we assume that the computer $\mathfrak{M}$ has the same

---

* Definitions 5, 6 and 7 are modified versions of definitions given in SCOTT [1967].

set of addresses and the same alphabet as the computers from the class $\mathscr{K}$, i.e. $A = 0, 1, 2, \ldots$ and $\Sigma = 0, 1, 2 \ldots$. The input and output functions for the computer $\mathfrak{M}$ we assume as follows

$$\mathbf{I}^*: \mathscr{K} \times \Sigma^k \times \mathbf{M} \to \mathbf{M} \quad \text{and} \quad \mathbf{O}^*: \mathbf{M} \to \mathbf{M} \times \Sigma^k,$$

where $\mathbf{M}$ denotes the set of memory states of the computer $\mathfrak{M}$.

DEFINITION 9. The computer $\mathfrak{M}$ is a universal computer for the class of computers $\mathscr{K}$ if and only if for all $\bar{x}_k \in \Sigma^k$, $\mathscr{M} \in \mathscr{K}$ there exist $\mathbf{m} \in \mathbf{M}$ such that

$$\mathbf{O}_2^* \{ \mathrm{Com}_1 [I^*(\mathscr{M}, \bar{x}_n, \mathbf{m}), \mathbf{q}_0] \} = f_{\mathscr{M}}(\bar{x}_n),$$

where $\mathbf{q}_0$ is the initial control state of $\mathfrak{M}$.

2.3. *Synthesis of universal computer*

Let $\mathscr{M} = \langle P, R, W, S \rangle$ be any computer which belongs to $\mathscr{K}$. We shall now define computer $\mathfrak{M} = \langle \mathbf{P}, \mathbf{R}, \mathbf{W}, \mathbf{S} \rangle$ in terms of computers of the class $\mathscr{K}$ and then we show that $\mathfrak{M}$ is universal computer for the class of computers $\mathscr{K}$. In order to define $\mathfrak{M}$ we have to give $\mathbf{P}, \mathbf{R}, \mathbf{W}, \mathbf{S}$. Let us start with the construction of $\mathbf{P}$.

2.3.1. *Memory of the computer $\mathfrak{M}$*

We recall that as the set of addresses for $\mathbf{P}$ we assumed the set of natural numbers $N = 0, 1, 2, \ldots$. Let $\mathbf{C}$ be the set of content functions of $\mathbf{P}$, and let Q be the set of control states of $\mathscr{M}$. By $\mathbf{C}_r = \mathbf{C}|(N - Q)$ we denote the set of partial content functions with domain restricted to the set $N - Q$. We shall call functions from $\mathbf{C}_r$ the *reduced content functions*. The set of markers $\mathbf{U}$ in $\mathbf{P}$ consists of one element $\mathbf{u}$. In order to define the input and output functions for $\mathbf{P}$ we have to introduce some additional notions.

Let M be the set of memory states of $\mathscr{M}$, and let $S = \langle G, \varphi, \psi, v \rangle$ be the control of $\mathscr{M}$, where $G = \langle Q, Q', h_0, h_1 \rangle$. We introduce 1–1 mappings $\kappa: M \to \mathbf{C}_r$, $\rho: R \to \mathbf{R}$, where $R = \langle r_0, r_1, \ldots, r_s \rangle$ is the set of instructions of the computer $\mathscr{M}$ and $\mathbf{R} = \langle \mathbf{r}_0, \mathbf{r}_1, \ldots, \mathbf{r}_s \rangle$, $\mathbf{r}_i: A^n \times \mathbf{C}_r \to \mathbf{C}_r$ – such that for all $m \in M$, $\bar{a}_n \in A^n$ and $r \in R$

$$\kappa(r(\bar{a}_n, m)) = [\rho(r)](\bar{a}_n, \kappa(m)).$$

By φ_ρ is to mean the function $\varphi_\rho: Q \to \mathbf{R}$ such that $\varphi_\rho(q) = \rho(\varphi(q))$, for all $q \in Q$.

Let us denote by $W = \{W_1, \ldots, W_p\}$ the set of conditions of $\mathscr{M}$. By ω is to mean 1–1 mapping $\omega: W \rightarrow \mathbf{W}$, where

$$\mathbf{W} = \{\mathbf{W}_1, \mathbf{W}_2, ..., \mathbf{W}_p\}, \qquad \mathbf{W}_i \subset \mathbf{C}_r$$

such that for all $m \in M$

$$\kappa(m) \in \omega(W_i) \quad \text{if and only if} \quad m \in W_i.$$

ψ_ω denotes the function $\psi_\omega: Q \rightarrow \mathbf{W}$ such that $\psi_\omega(q) = \omega(\psi(q))$, for all $q \in Q$. The set of functions $\langle \varphi_\rho, \psi_\omega, h_0, h_1 \rangle$ we shall denote by Θ. Let δ be 1–1 mapping

$$\delta: \Theta \rightarrow \Sigma',$$

where $\Sigma' \subset \Sigma$ and Σ' is finite. δ will be called the *encoding function*. Thus we are able now to represent $\Theta = \langle \varphi_\rho, \psi_\omega, h_0, h_1 \rangle$ in the alphabet of $\mathfrak{M}$.

The input function $\mathbf{I}^*$ of $\mathbf{P}$ we define as follows

$$\mathbf{I}^*(\mathscr{M}, \bar{x}_k, \mathbf{m}) = \mathbf{m}' = \langle \mathbf{c}', \mathbf{l}' \rangle, \quad \text{where}$$

$$\mathbf{c}'(z) = \begin{cases} \delta(\Theta(z)) & \text{if } 0 < z \leqslant |Q|, \\ \kappa(I^*(\bar{x}_k, \bar{a}_n, m)) & \text{if } z > |Q|, \end{cases}$$

$$\mathbf{l}'(\mathbf{u}) = q_0,$$

and I^* is the input function of $\mathscr{M}$, $|Q|$ denotes the number of elements of Q. The output function $\mathbf{O}^*: \mathbf{M} \rightarrow \mathbf{M} \times \Sigma^k$ of $\mathfrak{M}$ satisfy the condition: for all $m \in M$ there exists such $\mathbf{l} \in \mathbf{L}$ that $O_2^*(m) = \mathbf{O}_2^*(\kappa(m), \mathbf{l})$.

Thus we defined the memory of $\mathfrak{M}$.

2.3.2. Instructions of the computer $\mathfrak{M}$

Now we have to define the instructions of $\mathfrak{M}$. The set of instructions of $\mathfrak{M}$ will consist of two instructions $\mathscr{R}_0, \mathscr{R}$. $\mathscr{R}_0$ is the identity instruction and $\mathscr{R}$ is defined in the following way:

$$\mathscr{R}(\mathbf{m}) = \mathbf{m}' = \langle \mathbf{c}'_r, \mathbf{l}' \rangle, \quad \text{where} \quad \mathbf{m} = \langle \mathbf{c}_r, \mathbf{l} \rangle \quad \text{and}$$

$$\mathbf{c}'_r = [\varphi_\rho(\mathbf{l}(\mathbf{u}))](\mathbf{c}_r),$$

$$\mathbf{l}'(\mathbf{u}) = \begin{cases} h_0(\mathbf{l}(\mathbf{u})) & \text{if } \mathbf{c}'_r \in \psi_\omega(\mathbf{l}(\mathbf{u})) \\ h_1(\mathbf{l}(\mathbf{u})) & \text{if } \mathbf{c}'_r \notin \psi_\omega(\mathbf{l}(\mathbf{u})). \end{cases}$$

2.3.3. Conditions of the computer $\mathfrak{M}$

In the computer $\mathfrak{M}$ we shall consider only one condition $\mathscr{W}$

$$\mathscr{W} = \{\mathbf{m}: \mathbf{m} \in \mathbf{M} \quad \text{and} \quad \mathbf{l}(\mathbf{u}) \in Q' \quad \text{and} \quad \psi_\omega \mathbf{l}(\mathbf{u}) = r_0\},$$

where Q' is the set of end states of M and r_0 is the identity instruction of $\mathfrak{M}$. The condition $\mathscr{W}$ will be written STOP.

2.3.4. Control of the computer $\mathfrak{M}$

The control of $\mathfrak{M}$ we shall simply give in the form of a table

	$\bar{\varphi}$	$\bar{\psi}$	$\bar{h}_0$	$\bar{h}_1$
$\mathbf{q}_0$	$\mathscr{R}_0$	STOP	$\mathbf{q}_1$	$\mathbf{q}_1$
$\mathbf{q}_1$	$\mathscr{R}_0$	STOP	$\mathbf{q}_2$	$\mathbf{q}_3$
$\mathbf{q}_2$	$\mathscr{R}_0$	STOP	$-$	$-$ END
$\mathbf{q}_3$	$\mathscr{R}$	STOP	$\mathbf{q}_1$	$\mathbf{q}_1$

In the table the control states are $\mathbf{q}_0, \mathbf{q}_1, \mathbf{q}_2, \mathbf{q}_3$ and $\mathbf{q}_2$ being the end state. $\bar{\varphi}, \bar{\psi}, \bar{h}_0, \bar{h}_1$ are the corresponding functions of the computer $\mathfrak{M}$.

Thus we completed the definition of the computer $\mathfrak{M}$. Now we are able to prove the following theorem

THEOREM 2. The computer $\mathfrak{M}$ is universal computer for the class of computer $\mathscr{K}$.

PROOF. In order to prove this theorem we have to show that for every function $f_{\mathscr{M}}$ and for all $\bar{x}_k$ there is a computation in $\mathfrak{M}$ such that

1) $$\mathbf{O}_2^* \{\mathrm{Com}_1 [\mathbf{I}^* (\mathscr{M}, \bar{x}_n, \mathbf{m}), \mathbf{q}_0]\} = f_{\mathscr{M}}(\bar{x}_n)$$

for some $\mathbf{m} \in \mathbf{M}$. Because $f_{\mathscr{M}}$ is computable by $\mathscr{M}$ therefore there is in $\mathscr{M}$ the computation such that

2) $$O_2^* \{\mathrm{Com}_1 [I^* (\bar{x}_k, \bar{a}_n, m), q_0]\} = f_{\mathscr{M}}(\bar{x}_k)$$

for some $\bar{a}_n$ and m. From the definition of $\mathbf{I}^*$ it follows that to the initial state of the computer $\mathscr{M}$ corresponds exactly one initial computer state of M, which is

$$\mathbf{t}_0 = \langle \mathbf{I}^* (\mathscr{M}, \bar{x}_k, \mathbf{m}), \mathbf{q}_0 \rangle .$$

From the definition of the control of $\mathfrak{M}$ results that to each step of the computation in $\mathscr{M}$ corresponds exactly one step in the computation in $\mathfrak{M}$ – such that $\mathbf{t}_{i+1} = \bar{v}(\mathbf{t}_i)$ if and only if $t_{i+1} = v(t_i)$, where $\bar{v}$ is the transition function of $\mathfrak{M}$. Further from the definition of the control of $\mathfrak{M}$ it follows that $\mathfrak{M}$ is in final state if and only if $\mathscr{M}$ is in its final state. By the definition of ρ we have

$$\langle \kappa \{\mathrm{Com}_1 [I^* (\bar{x}_k, \bar{a}_n, m), q_0]\}, 1 \rangle = \mathbf{Com}_1 [\mathbf{I}^* (\mathscr{M}, \bar{x}_k, \mathbf{m}), \mathbf{q}_0] .$$

By the definition of the output function $\mathbf{O}^*$ and by 2) we obtain 1) which completes the proof.

In this manner one can define various universal computers, for example one address universal computer, two addresses universal computer etc. and prove some properties of this computers.

3. Programs

Let $\mathscr{P} = \mathbf{C} | Q$ be the set of the partial content functions of the universal computer $\mathfrak{M}$ with domain restricted to the set Q, such that for all $q \in Q$, $\mathscr{M} \in \mathscr{K}$,

$$\not{p}(q) = \delta(\Theta(q)), \qquad \not{p} \in \mathscr{P}.$$

DEFINITION 10. Each function $\not{p} \in \mathscr{P}$ is called a *program* in $\mathfrak{M}$; $\Theta(q)$ is called a *program instruction* (which is to be distinguished from *machine instructions* considered in the first section of this paper); q is called *label* or an *address* of the program instruction $\Theta(q)$; $\delta(\Theta(q))$ is called a *code* of $\Theta(q)$.

With every program $\not{p} \in \mathscr{P}$ in $\mathfrak{M}$ we can associate a function $f_{\not{p}}$ computable by the program $\not{p}$ on the machine $\mathfrak{M}$. Two programs $\not{p}$ and $\not{p}'$ are said to be equivalent if and only if $f_{\not{p}} = f_{\not{p}'}$.

It seems very important to study in detail the question of equivalence of programs but this is not the aim of this paper. We are going now to state without proof theorem concerning the form of program instructions in universal computers.

THEOREM 3. For every universal computer $\mathfrak{M}$ there exists an equivalent universal computer $\mathfrak{M}'$ such that for each program instruction

$$\Theta(q) = \langle \varphi_\rho(q), \psi_\omega(q), h_0(q), h_1(q) \rangle$$

of $\mathfrak{M}'$, any of below given properties may hold
a) $h_0(q) = q + 1$ for all $q \in Q$,
a') $h_1(q) = q + 1$ for all $q \in Q$,
b) if $\varphi_\rho(q) \neq \mathbf{r}_0$ then $h_0(q) = h_1(q) = q + 1$ for all $q \in Q$,
c) if $\varphi_\rho(q) = \mathbf{r}_0$ then $h_0(q) = q + 1$ for all $q \in Q$,
c') if $\varphi_\rho(q) = \mathbf{r}_0$ then $h_1(q) = q$ for all $q \in Q$.

Much attention has been recently paid to the semantics of programming languages. It seems that the presented formalization of computers and programs contribute to this problem. The meaning of the program $\not{p}$ can be defined as the computation carried out on the universal computer $\mathfrak{M}$ according to the program f_μ. Thus we can define the valuation of programs in the computer states in such a manner that the computation associated with the program yields the value of the computed functions. Thus we have the method for solving the following problem: let f_μ be program of a universal computer $\mathfrak{M}$, and let h be a computable function. We ask whether $h = f_\mu$. This seems to be of some interest not only for the theory of programming but also for practical computation.

Acknowledgement

The author gratefully acknowledges many helpful suggestions of Dr. A. Mazurkiewicz and Dr. A. Wakulicz.

References

DAVIS, M., Computability and unsolvability (New York, McGraw Hill, 1958).

ELGOT, C.C. and A. ROBINSON, Random-access stored-program machines, an approach to programming languages, J. ACM **11** (1964) 365–399.

HERMES, H., Aufzählbarkeit, Entscheidbarkeit, Berechenbarkeit (Berlin, Springer, 1961)

KALMÁR, L., On an algebraic theory of automatic digital computers, Colloq. Foundations of Mathematics, Mathematical Machines and their Applications, Tihany, Sept. 1962, p. 129.

PAWLAK, Z., Organization of digital computers (in polish). Manuscript of lectures held at Warsaw University in 1966/67.

SCOTT, D., Some definitional suggestions for automata theory (Stanford University, 1967).

Philosophy of Logic and Mathematics

INTERPRETATION OF QUANTIFIERS

D. FØLLESDAL

University of Oslo, Oslo, Norway

1. Quantification theory might seem to be a well defined province of logic. Its syntactical and semantical features are quite well known to us, thanks to the work of Löwenheim, Skolem, Herbrand, Gödel, Church and numerous others.

One of the notable features of quantification, according to QUINE [1943, pp. 123–127; 1953a, p. 150; 1953b, pp. 79–80; 1960, pp. 166–168] is its close connection with the substitutivity of identity: any interpretation of quantifiers requires the traditional substitutivity axioms of identity, that is statements of the form:

(1) $$(x)(y)(x = y \supset \cdot Fx \supset Fy)$$

to be true (*Quine's thesis*), cf. esp. QUINE [1953b, p. 79, formula (51)]. Here 'F' stands for any predicate, simple or complex.

Note that it is the *interpretation* of the quantifiers that requires statements of form (1) to be true. Quine's thesis is therefore not refuted by merely exhibiting a system of quantification theory in which (1) is not a theorem. If Quine is right, such a system would be *semantically* incomplete, there would be formulas in the system, like (1), which are valid, that is, true under every interpretation, but not provable.

Quine has pointed out that as a consequence of this, the prospects of a quantified modal logic seem dim (QUINE [1943, p. 127; 1953a, pp. 150–156; 1953b, pp. 80–81; 1960, pp. 197–198]). However, one of the foremost proponents of quantified modal logic, Jaakko Hintikka, has rejected Quine's thesis and argued that there is no such connection between substitutivity and quantification. To quote the closing sentence of HINTIKKA [1961]: "... our considerations serve to show that the principle of substitutivity of identicals is normally unacceptable in modal logic."

Hintikka has not only rejected Quine's thesis. He has constructed a system of quantified modal logic in which (1) is not a theorem and, what is more important, he has developed a semantics for these systems which does not require (1) to be true.[1]

What better evidence could there be against Quine's thesis?

In view of all this evidence it might seem foolhardy not to give up the thesis. Yet in a paper, "Quantification into causal contexts" which I read to the previous Congress for Logic, Methodology and Philosophy of Science, in Jerusalem 1964 (FØLLESDAL [1965]) I gave an argument in support of Quine's thesis, and I also indicated how one may get a semantics for quantified modal logic that is compatible with the thesis.

In that paper, I concentrated on arguing for the thesis and did not discuss how the seemingly so overwhelming evidence against it could be disposed of. The present paper is an attempt to do this. I shall first outline briefly a semantics for quantified modal logic that is compatible with Quine's thesis, and then go on to consider Hintikka's semantic proposal in order to see whether it does actually constitute counterevidence to Quine's thesis.

2. The formulas of quantified modal logic are constructed by help of a finite or denumerable set of primitive predicates. An n-place predicate with its variable places filled with variables or other singular terms that satisfy a condition that will be stated in section 3 is called an *atomic formula*. Atomic formulas are formulas and so are all and only those closed and open sentences which can be obtained from formulas by help of truth-functional connectives, quantifiers, and the symbols '$\Box$' and '$\Diamond$'.

Let us now see how these formulas can be given an interpretation that is compatible with Quine's thesis. There are several ways of giving such interpretations, the semantic proposals of KRIPKE [1959, 1963 a, 1963 b, 1965], MONTAGUE [1960, 1967 a, 1967 b] and SCOTT [1967] are examples. They all have in common that (1) comes out valid in them.

In non-modal quantification theory the formulas are usually interpreted by specifying a universe and assigning extensions to the general terms and references to the singular terms.

Modal quantification theory may be interpreted in a similar fashion, except that here more than mere extensions matter. One has to consider other possible situations, states of affairs, courses of events, points of view, worlds, etc. and determine what extensions the terms have in them.

Formally, what one may do, is to consider a set **K** of such situations, states, courses of events, points of view, or worlds **H**. With each **H** is as-

---

[1] See the articles and book by Hintikka listed in the bibliography at the end of this paper.

sociated a set $\Psi(\mathbf{H})$, intuitively the set of individuals in $\mathbf{H}$, and to each n-adic predicate π^n is assigned an extension $\Phi(\pi^n, \mathbf{H})$ in each $\mathbf{H}$, where $\Phi(\pi^n, \mathbf{H})$ is a subset of $(\Psi(\mathbf{H}))^n$ (the nth Cartesian product of $\Psi(\mathbf{H})$ with itself). To the identity predicate, I, in particular, Φ assigns in each $\mathbf{H}$ the set of ordered pairs of members of $\Psi(\mathbf{H})$ whose first and second members are identical, thus $\Phi(I, \mathbf{H}) = \{\langle x, y \rangle : x \in \Psi(\mathbf{H}) \cdot y \in \Psi(\mathbf{H}) \cdot x = y\}$. The function Φ is called a *model*.

A more or less complicated structure may be imposed upon the set $\mathbf{K}$; in the following we shall assume that a dyadic relation R is defined on $\mathbf{K}$, and that one particular member of $\mathbf{K}$, which we shall call $\mathbf{G}$, is given a preferred position; intuitively $\mathbf{G}$ is the actual situation, state, course of events, point of view, or world. An ordered triple $\langle \mathbf{G}, \mathbf{K}, R \rangle$ will be called a *model system*.

The truthvalue $\Phi(\ulcorner \pi^n(\alpha_1, ..., \alpha_n) \urcorner, \mathbf{H})$ of an atomic formula $\ulcorner \pi^n(\alpha_1, ..., \alpha_n) \urcorner$ in $\mathbf{H}$ relative to an assignment of objects $a_1, ..., a_n$ of $\bigcup_{\mathbf{H} \in \mathbf{K}} \Psi(\mathbf{H})$ to $\alpha_1, ..., \alpha_n$ can now be defined as follows:

(i) $\Phi(\ulcorner \pi^n(\alpha_1, ..., \alpha_n) \urcorner, \mathbf{H}) = \mathbf{T}$ if the n-tuple $\langle a_1, ..., a_n \rangle \in \Phi(\pi^n, \mathbf{H})$.

(ii) $\Phi(\ulcorner \pi^n(\alpha_1, ..., \alpha_n) \urcorner, \mathbf{H}) = \mathbf{F}$ if $\langle a_1, ..., a_n \rangle \notin \Phi(\pi^n, \mathbf{H})$ and $\langle a_1, ..., a_n \rangle \in (\Psi(\mathbf{H}))^n$.

(iii) If $\langle a_1, ..., a_n \rangle \notin (\Psi(\mathbf{H}))^n$, then $\ulcorner \pi^n(\alpha_1, ..., \alpha_n) \urcorner$ is without a truth value in $\mathbf{H}$.[2]

Given these assignments for atomic formulas, the assignments for complex formulas can be built up by induction as follows:

I. A compound is without a truth value in $\mathbf{H}$ if and only if it has a component which is without a truth value in $\mathbf{H}$.

II. If all components of a compound have a truth value in $\mathbf{H}$ then the truth value of the compound is determined as follows:

$\Phi(\ulcorner \sim \varphi \urcorner, \mathbf{H}) = \mathbf{T}$ if and only if $\Phi(\varphi, \mathbf{H}) = \mathbf{F}$; otherwise $\Phi(\ulcorner \sim \varphi \urcorner, \mathbf{H}) = \mathbf{F}$,

$\Phi(\ulcorner \varphi \cdot \psi \urcorner, \mathbf{H}) = \mathbf{T}$ if and only if $\Phi(\varphi, \mathbf{H}) = \mathbf{T}$ and $\Phi(\psi, \mathbf{H}) = \mathbf{T}$; otherwise $\Phi(\ulcorner \varphi \cdot \psi \urcorner, \mathbf{H}) = \mathbf{F}$ etc. for the other truth functional connectives,

$\Phi(\ulcorner \Box \varphi \urcorner, \mathbf{H}) = \mathbf{T}$ if and only if $\Phi(\varphi, \mathbf{H}') = \mathbf{T}$ for every $\mathbf{H}' \in \mathbf{K}$ such that $\mathbf{H}R\mathbf{H}'$; otherwise $\Phi(\ulcorner \Box \varphi \urcorner, \mathbf{H}) = \mathbf{F}$,

$\Phi(\ulcorner \Diamond \varphi \urcorner, \mathbf{H}) = \mathbf{T}$ if and only if $\Phi(\varphi, \mathbf{H}') = \mathbf{T}$ for at least one $\mathbf{H}' \in \mathbf{K}$ such that $\mathbf{H}R\mathbf{H}'$, otherwise $\Phi(\ulcorner \Diamond \varphi \urcorner, \mathbf{H}) = \mathbf{F}$.

---

[2] This idea of letting some formulas be without a truth value in some possible worlds is reminiscent of Frege's and several others' treatment of names without a reference (cf. Frege's informal writings, especially "Über Sinn und Bedeutung"). As far as I know, the first to use it in modal logic was Prior in his system Q in PRIOR [1957], cf. also PRIOR [1967].

(Note that according to the general rule I, $\ulcorner \Box \varphi \urcorner$ and $\ulcorner \Diamond \varphi \urcorner$ are without truth values in **H** if and only if φ is without truth value in **H**.)

If $\alpha, \beta_1, ..., \beta_n$ are all the free variables in a formula φ, then $\Phi(\ulcorner(\alpha)\varphi\urcorner, \mathbf{H}) = \mathbf{T}$ relative to an assignment of $b_1, ..., b_n$ to $\beta_1, ..., \beta_n$ (where the b_i are members of $\Psi(\mathbf{H})$) if and only if $\Phi(\varphi, \mathbf{H}) = \mathbf{T}$ relative to every assignment of a, $b_1, ..., b_n$ to $\alpha, \beta_1, ..., \beta_n$, where $a \in \Psi(\mathbf{H})$. Otherwise, $\Phi(\ulcorner(\alpha) \varphi\urcorner, \mathbf{H}) = \mathbf{F}$ relative to the given assignment. (The formula $\ulcorner(\alpha) \varphi\urcorner$ is without a truth value in **H** relative to an assignment of $b_1, ..., b_n$ to $\beta_1, ..., \beta_n$ if not all the b_i are members of $\Psi(\mathbf{H})$.)

We now define *validity* as follows: Let φ' be the universal closure of φ; then φ is valid if and only if $\Phi(\varphi', \mathbf{G}) = \mathbf{T}$ for every model Φ on every model system $\langle \mathbf{G}, \mathbf{K}, \mathbf{R} \rangle$.

This completes the presentation of a semantics of quantified modal logic.

The notion of possible situations, states of affairs, courses of events, points of view, or worlds is of course at least as vague and problematic as the ideas of necessity and possibility themselves, and I want to emphasize that here I am concerned solely with certain formal, model theoretic structures. These show, I hope, how quantified modal logic can be made *formally* respectable, free from logical difficulties. They do not suffice to make it *philosophically* respectable. Their main relevance for philosophic discussion seems to be that they show that if one is to take exception to quantified modal logic, it has to be on philosophic grounds, and not on logical ones.

3. In this semantics, (1) is valid. One might wonder what then happens in the cases that have caused difficulties for modal logic, as for example in connection with '9 = the number of planets'. The answer is that this all depends upon what the singular terms of our modal theory are. Terms that behave like singular terms in ordinary extensional contexts often cease to do so in modal contexts. Thus for example 'the number of planets' behaves like a good singular term in extensional contexts, it has its fixed and unique reference. However, in modal contexts it attaches now to one object, now to another. Other terms, like 'the moon of the earth' presently attach to one definite object, in other possible worlds there might, conceivably, be several moons of the earth, or none. Russell, when he created his theory of descriptions, pointed out that in extensional contexts, a description '$(\imath x) Fx$' can be treated as a definite singular term only when there is a unique object satisfying 'Fx', that is only when $(\exists y)(x)(Fx \equiv .x = y)$, and that words like 'Pegasus' which cause difficulties in extensional logic, should be regarded as disguised descriptions, that can be eliminated by help of his theory. Similarly in modal logic, the descriptions that cause difficulties are those that fail to satisfy a condition stronger than but similar to Russell's, viz. '$(\exists y)\square\cdots\square(x)$ $(Fx\equiv.x=y)$', where the number of '$\square$'s depends upon the number of layers of modal operators within whose scope the description occurs. If terms that cause difficulties are treated as disguised descriptions and eliminated (with due regard to the scopes of these descriptions) our difficulties vanish. (Cf. e.g. CHURCH [1942] and FITCH [1949].)

The simplest, and also most satisfactory solution, for reasons having to do with tests for well-formedness, would be to eliminate all singular terms, as suggested by Russell and Quine, in favor of variables and general terms. These variables of quantification would then be our only singular terms; and this is the point I made in my above-mentioned paper: in order to get a satisfactory semantics for quantified modal logic these variables of quantification have to obey the universal substitutivity of identity, so that if 'x' and 'y' are quantifiable variables, and $x=y$, then 'x' can be substituted for 'y' in any context, *salva veritate*.

The terms that cause trouble, like 'the number of planets', can, if we want, be retained in our vocabulary, but we must treat them as a special category of terms that have the same position within modal logic as that which definite descriptions lacking a descriptum have within extensional logic: they do not obey the usual rules of inference for singular terms, like substitution, existential generalization and universal instantiation.

As is often done with descriptions in extensional logic, we may also, if we want, put the restricting conditions into the rules of inference, thereby restricting them rather than our vocabulary. This is to some extent a matter of taste. What is important is that whatever we do, our variables of quantification, our *bindable* variables, obey the universal substitutivity of identity.

The *expressive power* of our system is not affected by whether we put our restrictions upon the class of singular terms or into the rules of inference.

Thus, for example[3], the distinction between

it is necessary that the next president of Brazil, whoever he may be, is an F

and

it is necessary of the individual who as a matter of fact will be the next president of Brazil, that he is an F

---

[3] I choose this particular example, since Hintikka has argued, in [1967 b, p. 143], that on this approach the distinction between the two sentences in this example cannot be made. (Cf. also HINTIKKA [1966 a, p. 7, and 1967 a, pp. 46 ff.].)

is expressed in the following way if we retain in our vocabulary of singular terms "irregular" terms like 'the next president of Brazil', or for short 'b':

$$\Box Fb$$

and

$$(\exists x)(x = b.\Box Fx)$$

while the distinction will be expressed in the following way if we restrict our vocabulary of singular terms and write 'B' for 'is a next president of Brazil':

$$\Box(\exists y)[(x)(Bx \equiv .x = y).Fy]$$
$$(\exists y)[(x)(Bx \equiv .x = y).\Box Fy].$$

As we see, and might expect, the paraphrases become more complicated when we choose to restrict our vocabulary. On the other hand, these paraphrases make explicit what exactly is meant by our two original statements, so explicit indeed that we do not have to make any restriction on our rules of inference. When we choose to leave the vocabulary unrestricted, the paraphrases become, as we have seen, simpler, but on the other hand they do not carry on the face of them exactly what was meant by the original statements. Their meaning becomes fully explicit only when we start applying the rules of inference for singular terms and find that 'b' does not fulfill the restrictions that have been put into those rules.

4. Now, after we have seen one way of constructing a semantics for quantified modal logic, let us examine Hintikka's semantic proposal.

Hintikka's semantics is in many respects similar to the semantics that has been outlined in the preceding pages. In fact, the latter is modelled on the former and is nothing but an attempt to keep Hintikka's basic ideas and modify them so as to overcome the difficulties that will be discussed in this section.

One main difference between the two semantics is that Hintikka's models are sets of formulas, an extension of Carnap's state descriptions, and not algebraic structures of the kind considered here.

A *model set* μ of formulas may be thought of as a partial description of a possible state of affairs or a possible course of events, a description that is just large enough to show that the described state of affairs is logically possible: A set of (quantificational) formulas is satisfiable if and only if it is imbeddable in a model set, cf. e.g. HINTIKKA [1963, p. 66, 1966 b, p. 58]. The conditions that a model set has to satisfy, are designed to insure this. Complete lists of conditions are given in several of Hintikka's works, for example in HINTIKKA [1957 a, 1961, 1962 and 1963]. In this paper our concern is with the following conditions for identity:

(C. self=) μ does not contain any formula of the form $\sim(a=a)$;

(C.=)   If $F\in\mu$, $(a=b)\in\mu$, and if G is like F except for the interchange of a and b at some (or all) of their occurrences, then $G\in\mu$ provided that F and G are atomic formulas or identities,

and the conditions for the quantifiers, which in the first presentation of the semantics (HINTIKKA [1957a, p. 10]) had the following form:

(C.E)   If $(\exists x)\,F\in\mu$, then $F(a/x)\in\mu$ for some free variable a;

(C.U)   If $(x)\,F\in\mu$, then $F(b/x)\in\mu$ for every free variable b occurring in the formulas of μ.

The modal operators are interpreted in terms of *model systems*: A model system is a set Ω of model sets, ordered by a dyadic relation R and satisfying the following conditions:

(C.N)   If $\square F\in\mu\in\Omega$, then $F\in\mu$;

(C.M)   If $\Diamond F\in\mu\in\Omega$, then there is in Ω at least one μ^* such that $\mu R\mu^*$ and $F\in\mu^*$;

(C.N$^+$)   If $\square F\in\mu\in\Omega$, then for every $\mu^*\in\Omega$ such that $\mu R\mu^*$, $F\in\mu^*$.

A set of formulas is now satisfiable if and only if it is imbeddable in a member of a model system.

Condition (C. self=) expresses the reflexivity of identity. Condition (C.=) expresses the *restricted* substitutivity of identity, substitutivity restricted to atomic, i.e. non-modal contexts. The unrestricted substitutivity of identity, advocated by Quine, is of course compatible with this condition; (C.=) continues to hold if one adds a condition that requires identity to be universally substitutive. However, the two sets of conditions would lead to incompatible decisions concerning satisfiability. Thus, for example, the negation of (1) viz:

(2) $(\exists x)\,(\exists y)\,(x = y \cdot Fx. - Fy)$

where 'F' may be non-atomic and e.g. contain modal operators, is satisfiable in Hintikka's semantics, but it is not satisfiable if the restriction in (C.=) to atomic contexts is removed.

Hintikka's semantics as it stands is therefore incompatible with Quine's thesis; it offers an interpretation of the quantifiers which does not require (1) to be valid.

Our problem now is: how is it possible for Hintikka to interpret the quantifiers so as to make (1) invalid, i.e. (2) satisfiable?

To get some insight into this, let us see how the following instance of (2) is interpreted in Hintikka's semantics:

(3) $(\exists x)(\exists y)(x = y \cdot \square Gx. - \square Gy).$

This formula is imbeddable in the following model system:

μ: $(\exists x)(\exists y)(x = y \cdot \square Gx. - \square Gy)$
$(\exists y)(a = y \cdot \square Ga. - \square Gy)$
$a = b \cdot \square Ga. - \square Gb$
$a = b \cdot \square Ga. - \square Gb$
Ga
Gb
μ^* (where $\mu R \mu^*$): $- Gb$
Ga.

As explained in HINTIKKA [1957b], this means intuitively that the two terms 'a' and 'b', which happen to refer to the same object in our actual world μ, refer to distinct objects in some possible world μ^*, in which one of these objects is G, the other non-G.

The situation is clear as long as we consider only the terms. However, ordinarily a quantifier is interpreted as saying something not about terms, but about objects referred to by terms, and one might wonder what happens to the object which in our actual world is the common reference of 'a' and 'b' when we pass into the possible world μ^*. Is this object G or is it non-G in μ^*?

Hintikka insists that his quantifiers range not over terms, but over objects referred to by such terms: "... the values of the variables have to be real, fullfledged individuals – which seems to me the only way of making satisfactory sense of quantification." HINTIKKA [1967 a, p. 38, cp. also e.g. 1957 b]. However, although this may be Hintikka's intention, his semantic conditions do not adequately reflect this. They are conditions on expressions, not on objects referred to by these expressions. And, as we have just observed, it is hard to see how Hintikka's "substitutional" conditions for the quantifiers can be regarded as conditions on the objects referred to. (Cf. also my argument on p. 269 of FØLLESDAL [1965].)

In Hintikka's later writings, the conditions for the quantifiers are changed to

(C.E′)   If $(\exists x) F \in \mu$, then $F(a/x) \in \mu$ and $(\exists x) \square (a = x) \in \mu$ for some free individual symbol a;

(C.U′)   If $(x) F \in \mu$ and $(\exists y) \square (b = y) \in \mu$, then $F(b/x) \in \mu$,

for the case where the variable 'x' occurs within the scope of just one modal operator in F, and to more complicated conditions where 'x' occurs within the scope of several modal operators, cf. HINTIKKA [1962, pp. 146–147] and later works.

After this change, formula (3) is still imbeddable in a model system, namely the same system as before, with the following formulas added:

Additions to μ: $(\exists x) \square (a=x)$

$\qquad\qquad (\exists x) \square (b=x)$

$\qquad\qquad \square (a=c)$

$\qquad\qquad \square (b=d)$

$\qquad\qquad a=c$

$\qquad\qquad b=d$

$\qquad\qquad Gc$

$\qquad\qquad Gd;$

Additions to μ^*: $a=c$

$\qquad\qquad b=d$

$\qquad\qquad -Gd$

$\qquad\qquad Gc.$

So this semantics, too, is incompatible with Quine's thesis. And, since the fate of the object referred to by 'a' and 'b' in μ remains in the dark, the same difficulties as before arise in connection with the interpretation of the quantifiers.

In addition, the revised rules introduce another anomaly in the interpretation of the quantifiers; the quantifiers now become *context dependent*: in order to see what a quantifier means one has to look at all the occurrences of the variable that is bound by it; the interpretation of the quantifier comes to depend on the number and kind of modal operators within whose scope the variable occurs.

Thus, for example, the formula '$(x) \square Fx$' does not read, as one might expect, 'every object is necessarily F', but rather something like 'every object *that is referred to by a free individual symbol that attaches to it in every possible world* is necessarily F'.

There are other difficulties in connection with Hintikka's interpretation of the quantifiers. For example, as in other "substitutional" approaches, the universe is assumed to have no more objects than there are expressions, i.e. it is apparently supposed to be finite or denumerable. No sense is given to the notion of interpretation in a non-denumerable domain. For this reason, deep semantical results, like the Löwenheim-Skolem theorem, become pointless trivialities on this approach. Thanks to this theorem, however, Hintikka's semantics supplies an interpretation, of sorts, in a finite or denumerable domain for every formula that is satisfiable. But it does not provide us with a more general notion of interpretation. In my opinion, Hintikka's approach is therefore of interest and importance as a test for satisfiability, a proof procedure, but not as a general semantics for quantified modal logic.

The limitation to denumerable universes can be lifted if one uses a language with non-denumerably many constants. However, the other, more serious difficulties that have been discussed earlier, remain. So why then use a "substitutional" interpretation at all, why not use an interpretation in terms of models, for example of the kind outlined in part 2 of this paper.

I hope that it is clear from what I have said that my objection against Hintikka's semantics for quantified modal logic is not that it gives rise to inconsistencies, it does not; but that it is based on what I have called a *substitutional*, or *expressional* interpretation of the quantifier. The difference between this interpretation and the standard interpretation might seem insignificant, particularly when one confines one's attention to extensional contexts. But here, as in many other cases, consideration of what happens in non-extensional contexts brings out the differences. The differences, and the ensuing difficulties in Hintikka's interpretation of the quantifiers, seem to me to be so decisive as to make Hintikka's interpretation evidence for, rather than evidence against, Quine's thesis concerning the intimate connection between quantification and the substitutivity of identity.

References

CHURCH, Alonzo
    1942   Review of Quine, 'Whitehead and the rise of modern logic'. *Journal of Symbolic Logic* 7, pp. 100–101.
FITCH, Frederic B.
    1949   The problem of the Morning Star and the Evening Star. *Philosophy of Science* 16, pp. 137–141.
FØLLESDAL, Dagfinn
    1965   Quantification into causal contexts. *Boston Studies in the Philosophy of Science*, Vol. II (Humanities Press, New York, N.Y.) pp. 263–274.
HINTIKKA, Jaakko
    1957a Quantifiers in deontic logic. *Societas Scientiarum Fennica, Commentationes Humanarum Litterarum* 23, no. 4.
    1957b Modality as referential multiplicity. *Ajatus* 20, pp. 49–64.
    1961   Modality and quantification. *Theoria* 27, pp. 119–128.
    1962   *Knowledge and Belief. An Introduction to the Logic of the Two Notions* (Cornell University Press, Ithaca, N.Y.).
    1963   The modes of modality. *Acta Philosophica Fennica* 16, pp. 65–81.
    1966a 'Knowing oneself' and other problems in epistemic logic. *Theoria* 32, pp. 1–13.
    1966b Studies in the logic of existence and necessity. *The Monist* 50, pp. 55–76.
    1967a Individuals, possible worlds, and epistemic logic. *Noûs* 1, pp. 33–62.

1967b Existence and identity in epistemic contexts: A comment on Føllesdal's paper. *Theoria* 33, pp. 138–147.

KANGER, Stig

1957 *Provability in Logic.* Stockholm studies in philosophy, Vol. 1 (Almqvist & Wiksell, Stockholm).

KRIPKE, Saul

1959 A completeness theorem in modal logic. *Journal of Symbolic Logic* 24, pp. 1–14.

1963a Semantical analysis of modal logic, I. Normal modal propositional calculi. *Zeitschrift für mathematische Logik und Grundlagen der Mathematik* 9, pp. 67–96.

1963b Semantical considerations on modal logic. *Acta Philosophica Fennica* 16, pp. 83–94.

1965 Semantical analysis of intuitionistic logic I, in: *Formal Systems and Recursive Functions,* eds. J. Crossley and M. Dummett (North-Holland, Amsterdam) pp. 92–130.

MONTAGUE, Richard

1960 Logical necessity, physical necessity, ethics, and quantifiers. *Inquiry* 3, pp. 259–269.

1967a Pragmatics and intensional logic. Mimeographed, UCLA, forthcoming in *Dialectica.*

1967b Pragmatics. Mimeographed, UCLA.

PRIOR, A. N.

1957 *Time and Modality* (Clarendon Press, Oxford).

1967 *Past, Present and Future* (Clarendon Press, Oxford).

QUINE, W. V.

1943 Notes on existence and necessity. *Journal of Philosophy* 40, pp. 113–127.

1953a, *From a Logical Point of View* (Harvard University Press, Cambridge, Mass.).
1961

1953b Three grades of modal involvement. *Proceedings of XIth International Congress of Philosophy,* Brussels, Vol. 14, pp. 65–81.

1956 Quantifiers and propositional attitudes. *Journal of Philosophy* 53, pp. 177–187.

1960 *Word and Object* (Harvard University Press, Cambridge, Mass.).

SCOTT, Dana

1967 *An Outline for Quantified Intensional Logic.* Mimeographed, Stanford, June 1967.

THOMASON, Richmond H.

1967 *Some completeness results for modal predicate calculi* Mimeographed, Yale University.

AN APPROACH TO CONSTRUCTIVE MATHEMATICAL LOGIC

A. A. MARKOV

Academy of Science, Moscow, USSR

According to the fundamental thesis of constructive mathematics we consider in this science merely the results of our constructions (called constructive objects) and our abilities of realizing these constructions. We admit the abstraction of potential realizability, i.e. we abstract from practical limitations of our abilities in space, time and material and we argue as if such limitations were absent.

In constructive mathematical logic our first aim is to explain logical connectives applied to propositions in terms of logical connectives applied to actions. This presents no difficulties for conjunction, disjunction and existential quantifiers, since the applications of these connectives to actions are almost immediately clear. But the situation is different for implication: it is not immediately clear what we must do when we receive the order: "if you make action A then make action B" or something like that.

In fact there are several possibilities of defining the meaning of implication. Two of them will be considered here.

1. We can explain "$\mathscr{F}$ implies $\mathscr{G}$" $[\supset \mathscr{F}\mathscr{G}]$[1] as admissibility of the rule of passing from $\mathscr{F}$ to $\mathscr{G}$ in a certain calculus[2].

2. We can explain "$\supset \mathscr{F}\mathscr{G}$" as the deducibility of $\mathscr{G}$ from $\mathscr{F}$ by means of a certain system of inference rules.

Both these ways correspond to the naive use of implication in mathematics.

The rigorous realizations of both these ideas are connected with extensions of the language used to formulate $\mathscr{F}$ and $\mathscr{G}$: if even this language contains already the implication sign, this sign is now introduced in an essentially new sense. A stairwise construction of mathematical logic is thus expedient.

---

[1] We use here the polish notation.
[2] This idea is due to LORENZEN [1955].

Difficulties of a different kind arise in connection with the generality quantifier. The natural explanation of this quantifier includes the requirement of some "unique general method" of proving every instance of the general proposition in question. This leads to the acceptation of some, possibly transfinite, hierarchy of Carnap's inference rules. If at the same time implication is introduced as deducibility, then we shall possibly have a transfinite hierarchy of implications.

In the sequel I describe an attempt to build some first few floors of a semantical system of constructive mathematical logic according to the brief outline above.

As basis we take a formal language L_1 for the so called "pure semiotics" i.e. for talking about strings of letters, their equality and inequality, their juxtaposition, their beginnings and ends etc. In L_1 we use conjunctions, disjunctions, the existential quantifier, the restricted existential quantifiers (there exists a beginning (end) of ..., there exists a string (letter) occurring in ...), the restricted generality quantifiers (for all beginnings (ends) of ..., for all strings (letters) occurring in ...).

In the description of L_1 we use the following signs: the sign of equality by definition "$\rightleftharpoons$", the sign of graphical equality of strings in the alphabet of L_1 "$\overline{=}$", the sign of graphical inequality of such strings "$\neq$". The meaning of other metalinguistic signs will be explained below.

L_1 uses the alphabet

$$A_1 \rightleftharpoons \varsigma\, abc\, (\ ) = \neq \& \vee \forall \exists \langle\ \rangle\, |\,.$$

Strings

$$(a), (aa), (aaa), \ldots$$

are called *formal letters* [Fl]; strings

$$(b), (bb), (bbb), \ldots$$

are called *lettervariables* [Lv]; strings

$$(c), (cc), (ccc), \ldots$$

are called *wordvariables* [Wv].

Fl and the letter ς are called *constants* [Cn].

Lv and Wv are called *variables* [Vr].

Vr θ and Ω are *similar* if both are Lv or both are Wv.

Cn and Vr are called *atoms* [At].

Nonempty strings composed of atoms are called terms Tr. They can also be inductively defined by means of the following two generating rules:

Tr1 $\qquad\qquad\qquad$ At $\quad$ are $\quad$ Tr.

Tr2 $\qquad\qquad\qquad \dfrac{T - \text{Tr}, A - \text{At}}{TA - \text{Tr}}$.

The signs $\forall$ and $\exists$ are called *quantifiers* [Qu].

The signs & and $\vee$ are called *junctors* [Jn].

The signs $\langle$ and $\rangle$ are called *restricters* [Rs].

The signs $=$ and $\neq$ are called *elementary signs* [Es].

Strings of the form $(T\sigma U)$, where T and U are Tr, σ is an Es, are called *elementary formulae* [Ef].

Formulae [Fr] are now inductively defined by means of the following five generating rules:

Fr1 $\qquad\qquad\qquad$ Ef $\quad$ are $\quad$ Fr.

Fr2 $\qquad\qquad \dfrac{\mathscr{F} - \text{Fr}, \mathscr{G} - \text{Fr}, \alpha - \text{Jn}}{\alpha\mathscr{F}\mathscr{G} - \text{Fr}}$.

Fr3 $\qquad\qquad \dfrac{\mathscr{F} - \text{Fr}, \Omega - \text{Vr}}{\exists\Omega\mathscr{F} - \text{Fr}}$.

Fr4 $\qquad \dfrac{\mathscr{F} - \text{Fr}, T - \text{Tr}, X - \text{Wv}, \kappa - \text{Qu}, \rho - \text{Rs}}{\kappa\rho T\rho X\mathscr{F} - \text{Fr}}$.

Fr5 $\qquad \dfrac{\mathscr{F} - \text{Fr}, T - \text{Tr}, \xi - \text{Lv}, \kappa - \text{Qu}}{\kappa|T|\xi\mathscr{F} - \text{Fr}}$.

Parameters [Pr] of Fr are inductively defined by means of the generating rules

Pr1 $\qquad\qquad \dfrac{\mathscr{F} - \text{Ef}, \Omega - \text{Vr}, \Omega \text{ occurs in } \mathscr{F}}{\Omega - \text{Pr of } \mathscr{F}}$.

Pr2 $\qquad \dfrac{\mathscr{F}, \mathscr{G} - \text{Fr}; \Omega - \text{Pr of } \mathscr{F}; \alpha - \text{Jn}}{\Omega - \text{Pr of } \alpha\mathscr{F}\mathscr{G}; \Omega - \text{Pr of } \alpha\mathscr{G}\mathscr{F}}$.

Pr3 $\qquad \dfrac{\mathscr{F} - \text{Fr}, \theta - \text{Vr}, \Omega - \text{Pr of } \mathscr{F}, \Omega \neq \theta}{\Omega - \text{Pr of } \exists\theta\mathscr{F}}$.

Pr4 $\quad \dfrac{\mathscr{F} - \text{Fr}, X - \text{Wv}, T - \text{Tr}, \kappa - \text{Qu}, \rho - \text{Rs}, \Omega - \text{Pr of } \mathscr{F}, \Omega \neq X}{\Omega - \text{Pr of } \kappa\rho T\rho X\mathscr{F}}$.

Pr5 $\quad \dfrac{\mathscr{F} - \text{Fr}, X - \text{Wv}, T - \text{Tr}, \kappa - \text{Qu}, \rho - \text{Rs}, \Omega \text{ occurs in } T}{\Omega - \text{Pr of } \kappa\rho T\rho X\mathscr{F}}$.

Pr6
$$\frac{\mathscr{F} - \text{Fr}, \; \xi - \text{Lv}, \; T - \text{Tr}, \; \kappa - \text{Qu}, \; \Omega - \text{Pr of } \mathscr{F}, \; \Omega \neq \xi}{\Omega - \text{Pr of } \kappa \, |T| \, \xi\mathscr{F}} \; .$$

Pr7
$$\frac{\mathscr{F} - \text{Fr}, \; \xi - \text{Lv}, \; T - \text{Tr}, \; \kappa - \text{Qu}, \; \Omega \text{ occurs in } T}{\Omega - \text{Pr of } \kappa \, |T| \, \xi\mathscr{F}} \; .$$

Fl and Lv are called *letterterms* [Lt].

Substituents [St] of Vr are defined as follows: Lt are St of Lv, Tr are St of Wv.

Let now Ω be a Vr, T a St of Ω. The (metalinguistic) operator of substitution of T for Ω is defined inductively by means of the following rules.

Sb1
$$\frac{A - \text{At}}{F^{\Omega}_{T} \llcorner A \lrcorner \rightleftharpoons \begin{cases} A, \text{ if } A \neq \Omega \\ T, \text{ if } A = \Omega \end{cases}} \; .$$

Sb2
$$\frac{U - \text{Tr}, \; A - \text{At}}{F^{\Omega}_{T} \llcorner UA \lrcorner \rightleftharpoons F^{\Omega}_{T} \llcorner U \lrcorner F^{\Omega}_{T} \llcorner A \lrcorner} \; .$$

Sb3
$$\frac{U, V - \text{Tr}; \; \sigma - \text{Es}}{F^{\Omega}_{T} \llcorner (U\sigma V) \lrcorner \rightleftharpoons (F^{\Omega}_{T} \llcorner U \lrcorner \sigma F^{\Omega}_{T} \llcorner V \lrcorner)} \; .$$

Sb4
$$\frac{\mathscr{F}, \; \mathscr{G} - \text{Fr}; \; \alpha - \text{Jn}}{F^{\Omega}_{T} \llcorner \alpha \mathscr{F}\mathscr{G} \lrcorner \rightleftharpoons \alpha F^{\Omega}_{T} \llcorner \mathscr{F} \lrcorner F^{\Omega}_{T} \llcorner \mathscr{G} \lrcorner} \; .$$

$\mathscr{F} - \text{Fr}, \; \theta - \text{Vr}, \; \Sigma - $ the shortest Vr similar to θ, which is not Pr of $\mathscr{F}$ and does not occur in T

Sb5
$$F^{\Omega}_{T} \llcorner \exists\theta\mathscr{F} \lrcorner \rightleftharpoons \begin{cases} \exists\theta\mathscr{F}, \text{ if } \Omega \text{ is not Pr of } \exists\theta\mathscr{F}; \\ \exists\theta F^{\Omega}_{T} \llcorner \mathscr{F} \lrcorner, \text{ if } \Omega - \text{Pr of } \exists\theta\mathscr{F} \text{ and } \theta \text{ does not occur in } T; \\ \exists\Sigma F^{\Omega}_{T} \llcorner F^{\theta}_{\Sigma} \llcorner \mathscr{F} \lrcorner\lrcorner, \text{ if } \Omega - \text{Pr of } \exists\theta\mathscr{F} \text{ and } \theta \text{ occurs in } T. \end{cases} \; .$$

Sb6

$\mathscr{F} - \text{Fr}, \; X - \text{Wv}, \; U - \text{Tr}, \; \kappa - \text{Qu}, \; \rho - \text{Rs}, \; Y - $ the shortest Wv, which is not Pr of $\mathscr{F}$ and does not occur in T

$$F^{\Omega}_{T} \llcorner \kappa\rho U\rho X\mathscr{F} \lrcorner \rightleftharpoons \begin{cases} \kappa\rho F^{\Omega}_{T} \llcorner U \lrcorner \rho X\mathscr{F}, \text{ if } \Omega \text{ is not a Pr of } \mathscr{F} \text{ different from } X; \\ \kappa\rho F^{\Omega}_{T} \llcorner U \lrcorner \rho X F^{\Omega}_{T} \llcorner \mathscr{F} \lrcorner, \text{ if } \Omega \text{ is a Pr of } \mathscr{F} \text{ different} \\ \qquad \text{from } X \text{ and } X \text{ does not occur in } T; \\ \kappa\rho F^{\Omega}_{T} \llcorner U \lrcorner \rho Y F^{\Omega}_{T} \llcorner F^{X}_{Y} \llcorner \mathscr{F} \lrcorner\lrcorner, \text{ if } \Omega \text{ is a Pr of } \mathscr{F} \text{ different} \\ \qquad \text{from } X \text{ and } X \text{ occurs in } T. \end{cases}$$

Sb7

$\mathscr{F}$ – Fr, ξ – Lv, U – Tr, κ – Qu, η – the shortest Lv, which is not Pr of $\mathscr{F}$ and does not occur in T

$$F_T^{\Omega}{}_{\llcorner}\kappa\,|U|\,\xi\mathscr{F}_{\lrcorner} \rightleftharpoons \begin{cases} \kappa\,|F_T^{\Omega}{}_{\llcorner}U_{\lrcorner}|\,\xi\mathscr{F}, \text{ if } \Omega \text{ is not a Pr of } \mathscr{F} \text{ different from } \xi; \\ \kappa\,|F_T^{\Omega}{}_{\llcorner}U_{\lrcorner}|\,\xi F_T^{\Omega}{}_{\llcorner}\mathscr{F}_{\lrcorner}, \text{ if } \Omega \text{ is a Pr of } \mathscr{F} \text{ different} \\ \qquad \text{from } \xi \text{ and } \xi \text{ does not occur in } T; \\ \kappa\,|F_T^{\Omega}{}_{\llcorner}U_{\lrcorner}|\,\eta F_T^{\Omega}{}_{\llcorner}F_\eta^{\xi}{}_{\llcorner}\mathscr{F}_{\lrcorner\lrcorner}, \text{ if } \Omega \text{ is a Pr of } \mathscr{F} \text{ different} \\ \qquad \text{from } \xi \text{ and } \xi \text{ occurs in } T. \end{cases}$$

Fr without Pr are called *closed formulae* [Cf]. Fr without Pr different from the Vr Ω are called *Ω-formulae* [ΩF].

Tr without occurrences of Vr are called *constant terms* [Ct].

Ct without occurrences of ς and the letter ς itself are called *formal words* [Fw].

We say that $\mathscr{P}$ is a *formal beginning* [Fb] of $\mathscr{Q}$, if $\mathscr{P}$ and $\mathscr{Q}$ are Fw and either $\mathscr{P}$ is a beginning of $\mathscr{Q}$ or $\mathscr{P} = \varsigma$. We say that $\mathscr{P}$ is a *formal end* [Fe] of $\mathscr{Q}$, if $\mathscr{P}$ and $\mathscr{Q}$ are Fw and either $\mathscr{P}$ is an end of $\mathscr{Q}$ or $\mathscr{P} = \varsigma$.

The *value* [Vl] $\mathfrak{z}_{\llcorner}T_{\lrcorner}$ of a Ct T is obtained from T by successive shortenings of ςs with the restriction that, when a bare ς is obtained, it must not be shortened. The (metalinguistic) operator $\mathfrak{z}$ can be defined inductively by the generating rules:

Vl1 $\quad \mathfrak{z}_{\llcorner}C_{\lrcorner} \rightleftharpoons C\,[C - \text{Cn}]$.

Vl2 $\quad \mathfrak{z}_{\llcorner}TC_{\lrcorner} \rightleftharpoons \begin{cases} \mathfrak{z}_{\llcorner}T_{\lrcorner}C, \text{ if } \mathfrak{z}_{\llcorner}T_{\lrcorner} \neq \varsigma \text{ and } C \neq \varsigma \\ \mathfrak{z}_{\llcorner}T_{\lrcorner}, \text{ if } C = \varsigma \\ C, \text{ if } \mathfrak{z}_{\llcorner}T_{\lrcorner} = \varsigma \end{cases} [T - \text{Ct}, C - \text{Cn}]$.

Admissible values [Av] of Vr are defined by the stipulations: Av of Wv are Fw; Av of Lv are Fl.

The sense of Cf is now defined by the clauses

Sn1. A closed Ef$(T = U)$ expresses that $\mathfrak{z}_{\llcorner}T_{\lrcorner} = \mathfrak{z}_{\llcorner}U_{\lrcorner}$.

Sn2. A closed Ef$(T \neq U)$ expresses that $\mathfrak{z}_{\llcorner}T_{\lrcorner} \neq \mathfrak{z}_{\llcorner}U_{\lrcorner}$.

Sn3. A Cf $\&\,\mathscr{F}\mathscr{G}$, where $\mathscr{F}$ and $\mathscr{G}$ are Cf, expresses that both these formulae are true.

Sn4. A Cf $\vee\,\mathscr{F}\mathscr{G}$, where $\mathscr{F}$ and $\mathscr{G}$ are Cf, expresses the potential realizability of choosing one of these formulae, so that the chosen formula will be true.

Sn5. A Cf $\exists\Omega\mathscr{F}$, where Ω is a Vr, $\mathscr{F}$ an ΩF, expresses the potential realizability of choosing an Av $\mathscr{P}$ of Ω, so that the Cf $F_{\mathscr{P}}^{\Omega}{}_{\llcorner}\mathscr{F}_{\lrcorner}$ will be true.

Sn6. A Cf $\exists\rho T\rho X\mathscr{F}$, where X is a Wv, ρ a Rs, T a Ct, $\mathscr{F}$ an XF, expresses the potential realizability of choosing a Fb [Fe] $\mathscr{P}$ of $_3 {}_\llcorner T_\lrcorner$, so that $F_{\mathscr{P}}^X {}_\llcorner \mathscr{F}_\lrcorner$ will be true.

Sn7. A Cf $\exists |T| \, \xi\mathscr{F}$, where ξ is a Lv, T a Ct, $\mathscr{F} - \xi F$, expresses the potential realizability of choosing a Fl $\mathscr{L}$ occurring in $_3 {}_\llcorner T_\lrcorner$, so that $F_{\mathscr{L}}^\xi {}_\llcorner \mathscr{F}_\lrcorner$ is true.

Sn8. A Cf $\forall \rho T \rho X \mathscr{F}$, where X is a Wv, ρ a Rs, T a Ct, $\mathscr{F}$ an XF, expresses that every Fr $F_{\mathscr{P}}^X {}_\llcorner \mathscr{F}_\lrcorner$, where $\mathscr{P}$ is a Fb [Fe] of $_3 {}_\llcorner T_\lrcorner$, is true.

Sn9. A Cf $\forall |T| \, \xi\mathscr{F}$, where ξ is a Lv, T a Ct, $\mathscr{F}$ a ξF, expresses that every Fr $F_{\mathscr{L}}^\xi {}_\llcorner \mathscr{F}_\lrcorner$, where $\mathscr{L}$ is a Fl occurring in $_3 {}_\llcorner T_\lrcorner$, is true.

The applicability of a given normal algorithm to a given word can be expressed by a closed formula of L_1, and therefore truth is undecidable for closed formulae of L_1. At the same time a semantically complete calculus C_1 dealing with such formulae can be constructed.

C_1 has the three axiomschemes:

A1 $$(T = U) \, [T, U - \text{Ct}; \, _3{}_\llcorner T_\lrcorner \doteq \, _3{}_\llcorner U_\lrcorner].$$

A2 $$(T \neq U) \, [T, U - \text{Ct}; \, _3{}_\llcorner T_\lrcorner \neq \, _3{}_\llcorner U_\lrcorner].$$

A3 $$\forall |\varsigma| \, \xi\mathscr{F} \, [\xi - \text{Lv}; \mathscr{F} - \xi\text{F}].$$

It uses the following 20 inference rules

R1 $$\frac{\mathscr{F}, \mathscr{G}}{\& \, \mathscr{F}\mathscr{G}} \, [\mathscr{F}, \mathscr{G} - \text{Cf}].$$

R2 $$\frac{\mathscr{F}}{\vee \, \mathscr{F}\mathscr{G}}.$$

R3 $$\frac{\mathscr{G}}{\vee \, \mathscr{F}\mathscr{G}}.$$

R4 $$\frac{F_{\mathscr{P}}^\Omega {}_\llcorner \mathscr{H}_\lrcorner}{\exists \Omega \mathscr{H}} \, [\Omega - \text{Vr}; \mathscr{P} - \text{Av of } \Omega; \mathscr{H} - \Omega F].$$

R5 $$\frac{F_\varsigma^X {}_\llcorner \mathscr{I}_\lrcorner}{\exists \rho \mathscr{L} \rho X \mathscr{I}} \, [X - \text{Wv}; \mathscr{I} - XF; \rho - \text{Rs}, \mathscr{L} - \text{Fl}].$$

R6 $$\frac{F_{3{}_\llcorner T_\lrcorner}^X {}_\llcorner \mathscr{I}_\lrcorner}{\exists \rho T \rho X \mathscr{I}} \, [T - \text{Ct}].$$

R7 $$\frac{\exists < T < X \mathscr{I}}{\exists < TC < X \mathscr{I}} \, [C - \text{Cn}].$$

R8 $$\frac{\exists > T > X \mathscr{I}}{\exists > CT > X \mathscr{I}}.$$

R9 $$\frac{F^{\xi}_{\mathscr{L}\llcorner\mathscr{I}\lrcorner}}{\exists\,|\mathscr{L}|\,\xi\mathscr{I}}\;[\xi-\mathrm{Lv};\;\mathscr{I}-\xi F].$$

R10 $$\frac{F^{\xi}_{\mathscr{L}\llcorner\mathscr{I}\lrcorner}}{\exists\,|T\mathscr{L}|\,\xi\mathscr{I}}.$$

R11 $$\frac{\exists\,|T|\,\xi\mathscr{I}}{\exists\,|TC|\,\xi\mathscr{I}}.$$

R12 $$\frac{F^{X}_{\varsigma\llcorner\mathscr{I}\lrcorner}}{\forall\rho\,\varsigma\,\rho X\mathscr{I}}.$$

R13 $$\frac{F^{X}_{\varsigma\llcorner\mathscr{I}\lrcorner},\,F^{X}_{\mathscr{L}\llcorner\mathscr{I}\lrcorner}}{\forall\rho\mathscr{L}\rho X\mathscr{I}}.$$

R14 $$\frac{\forall<T<X\mathscr{I},\,F^{X}_{\partial\llcorner T\mathscr{L}\lrcorner\llcorner\mathscr{I}\lrcorner}}{\forall<T\mathscr{L}<X\mathscr{I}}.$$

R15 $$\frac{\forall>T>X\mathscr{I},\,F^{X}_{\partial\llcorner\mathscr{L}T\lrcorner\llcorner\mathscr{I}\lrcorner}}{\forall>\mathscr{L}T>X\mathscr{I}}.$$

R16 $$\frac{\forall<T<X\mathscr{I}}{\forall<T\varsigma<X\mathscr{I}}.$$

R17 $$\frac{\forall>T>X\mathscr{I}}{\forall>\varsigma T>X\mathscr{I}}.$$

R18 $$\frac{F^{\xi}_{\mathscr{L}\llcorner\mathscr{I}\lrcorner}}{\forall\,|\mathscr{L}|\,\xi\mathscr{I}}.$$

R19 $$\frac{\forall\,|T|\,\xi\mathscr{I},\,F^{\xi}_{\mathscr{L}\llcorner\mathscr{I}\lrcorner}}{\forall\,|T\mathscr{L}|\,\xi\mathscr{I}}.$$

R20 $$\frac{\forall\,|T|\,\xi\mathscr{I}}{\forall\,|T\varsigma|\,\xi\mathscr{I}}.$$

Implication applied to closed formulae of L_1 is then introduced as admissibility of a rule in C_1. This implication is formalized in a language L_2, which permits to build implications applied to formulae of L_1 and to form repeatedly conjunctions of formulae already obtained. The alphabet A_2 of L_2 is obtained from A_1 by adjoining the implication sign $\supset$: $A_2\rightleftharpoons A_1\supset$. Fl, Lv, Wv, Cn, Vr, At, Tr, Es, Qu, Ef, Lt, St, Ct, Fw, Fb, Fe, are defined as in L_1.

Fr of L_1 are now called *formulae of first degree* [Fld].

Strings of the form $\supset\mathscr{F}\mathscr{G}$, where $\mathscr{F}$ and $\mathscr{G}$ are Fld, are called *implications*.

Formulae [Fr] are now inductively defined by the three generating rules:

Fr1   Fld   are   Fr.

Fr2   Im   are   Fr.

Fr3
$$\frac{\mathscr{F} - \text{Fr}, \mathscr{G} - \text{Fr}}{\& \mathscr{F}\mathscr{G} - \text{Fr}}.$$

Parameters [Pr] of Fr are inductively defined by means of the three rules:

Pr1
$$\frac{\mathscr{F} - \text{Fld}; \Omega - \text{Pr of } \mathscr{F} \text{ in } L_1}{\Omega - \text{Pr of } \mathscr{F}}.$$

Pr2
$$\frac{\mathscr{F}, \mathscr{G} - \text{Fld}; \Omega - \text{Pr of } \mathscr{F}}{\Omega - \text{Pr of } \supset \mathscr{F}\mathscr{G}; \Omega - \text{Pr of } \supset \mathscr{G}\mathscr{F}}.$$

Pr3
$$\frac{\mathscr{F}, \mathscr{G} - \text{Fr}; \Omega - \text{Pr of } \mathscr{F}}{\Omega - \text{Pr of } \& \mathscr{F}\mathscr{G}, \Omega - \text{Pr of } \& \mathscr{G}\mathscr{F}}.$$

Let Ω be a Vr, T a St of Ω. The operator of substitution of T for $\Omega[F_T^{\Omega}]$ is defined by means of nine rules Sb1–Sb9, where:

Sb1–Sb7 are as in L_1 with Fld instead of Fr;

Sb8 is as Sb4 in L_1 with Fld instead of Fr and $\supset$ in the role of α;

Sb9 is as Sb4 in L_1 with & in the role of α.

Cf and ΩF are defined as in L_1. Vl of Ct and Av of Vr are defined as in L_1.

Let $\mathscr{F}$ and $\mathscr{G}$ be Cf of L_1. Let C′ be the calculus, obtained from C_1 by adjoining to the list of inference rules of C_1 the rule $\mathscr{F}/\mathscr{G}$ of passing from $\mathscr{F}$ to $\mathscr{G}$. We say that this rule is *admissible in* C_1 if there is an algorithm transforming every proof in C′, into a proof of the same formula in C_1.

We define now the meaning of Cf in L_2 as follows.

For Cf which are Fld: as in L_1.

An Im $\supset \mathscr{F}\mathscr{G}[\mathscr{F}, \mathscr{G} - \text{Cf of } L_1]$ expresses the admissibility of the rule $\mathscr{F}/\mathscr{G}$ in C_1.

A Cf $\& \mathscr{F}\mathscr{G}[\mathscr{F}, \mathscr{G} - \text{Cf}]$ expresses that both these Cf are true.

No semantically complete calculus is possible for L_2. A system of inference rules R′1–R′9 valid in L_2 can nevertheless be proposed.

R′1
$$\frac{\mathscr{F}, \supset \mathscr{F}\mathscr{G}}{\mathscr{G}} \quad [\mathscr{F}, \mathscr{G} - \text{Cf of } L_1].$$

R′2
$$\frac{\supset \mathscr{F}\mathscr{G}, \supset \mathscr{G}\mathscr{H}}{\supset \mathscr{F}\mathscr{H}} \quad [\mathscr{H} - \text{Cf of } L_1].$$

R′3
$$\frac{\mathscr{G}}{\supset \mathscr{F}\mathscr{G}}.$$

$$R'4 \qquad \frac{\supset \mathscr{F}\mathscr{G}, \supset \mathscr{F}\mathscr{H}}{\supset \mathscr{F}\,\&\,\mathscr{G}\mathscr{H}}.$$

$$R'5 \qquad \frac{\supset \mathscr{F}\mathscr{H}, \supset \mathscr{G}\mathscr{H}}{\supset \vee \mathscr{F}\mathscr{G}\mathscr{H}}.$$

$$R'6 \qquad \frac{\mathscr{K}, \mathscr{L}}{\&\,\mathscr{K}\mathscr{L}}\,[\mathscr{K}, \mathscr{L} - \text{Cf of } L_2].$$

$$R'7 \qquad \frac{\&\,\mathscr{K}\mathscr{L}}{\mathscr{K}}.$$

$$R'8 \qquad \frac{\&\,\mathscr{K}\mathscr{L}}{\mathscr{L}}.$$

$$R'9 \qquad \frac{\supset F_{\mathscr{P}}^{\Omega}\llcorner \mathscr{I}\lrcorner \mathscr{G} \text{ for every Av}\mathscr{P} \text{ of } \Omega}{\supset \exists \Omega \mathscr{I}\mathscr{G}}\,[\Omega - \text{Vr}, \mathscr{I} - \Omega F \text{ of } L_1].$$

In this system the rule $R'9$ is of an essentially different nature in comparison with the other rules $R'1$–$R'8$. Like Carnap's rule for the generality quantifier this rule permits to pass to the Cf below the dash as soon as we have a unique general method of establishing every instance of the Cf above the dash.

We intend now to introduce implication "$\rightarrow$" applied to closed formulae $\mathscr{I}$ and $\mathscr{K}$ of L_2 as deducibility of $\mathscr{K}$ from $\mathscr{I}$ by means of the rules $R'1$–$R'9$ with permission to use also arbitrary true closed formulae of L_2. In the exact definition it will be appropriate to separate the applications of $R'9$. The definition will be inductive.

$\overset{0}{\rightarrow}\mathscr{I}\mathscr{K}$ will mean that $\mathscr{K}$ is deducible from $\mathscr{I}$ and some true formula of L_2 by means of the rules $R'1$–$R'8$. $\overset{i+1}{\rightarrow}\mathscr{I}\mathscr{K}$ will mean that there are $\mathscr{I}$, $\mathscr{G}$ and Ω, satisfying the following conditions:

1. $\mathscr{I}$ is ΩF of L_1;
2. $\mathscr{G}$ is Cf of L_1;
3. we possess a general method of establishing $\overset{i}{\rightarrow}\mathscr{I}\supset F_{\mathscr{P}}^{\Omega}\llcorner \mathscr{I}\lrcorner\mathscr{G}$ for every Av $\mathscr{P}$ of Ω;
4. $\overset{0}{\rightarrow}\&\,\mathscr{I}\supset \exists \Omega \mathscr{I}\mathscr{G}\mathscr{K}$.

Here i is an arbitrary natural number. One can suppose that transfinite induction can also be necessary.

Happily the facts are much more simple. Even the implication "$\overset{i}{\rightarrow}$" gives nothing new in comparison with "$\overset{0}{\rightarrow}$". For an exact formulation of the corresponding result we need an algorithm $\mathscr{R}$, transforming every string of the form $\overset{i}{\rightarrow}\mathscr{I}\mathscr{K}\,[\mathscr{I},\mathscr{K} - \text{Cf of } L_2]$ into a closed formula of L_2. This algorithm can be inductively defined by the conditions:

$$\mathscr{R}_{\llcorner} \overset{i}{\to} \mathscr{FG}_{\lrcorner} \rightleftharpoons \supset \mathscr{FG},$$

$$\mathscr{R}_{\llcorner} \overset{i}{\to} \mathscr{F} \supset \mathscr{HG}_{\lrcorner} \rightleftharpoons \supset \&\mathscr{FHG},$$

$$\mathscr{R}_{\llcorner} \overset{i}{\to} \supset \mathscr{IFG}_{\lrcorner} \rightleftharpoons \& \vee \mathscr{IG} \supset \mathscr{FG},$$

$$\mathscr{R}_{\llcorner} \overset{i}{\to} \supset \mathscr{IF} \supset \mathscr{HG}_{\lrcorner} \rightleftharpoons \& \supset \mathscr{H} \vee \mathscr{IG} \supset \&\mathscr{FHG},$$

$$\mathscr{R}_{\llcorner} \overset{i}{\to} \mathscr{J} \&\mathscr{HL}_{\lrcorner} \rightleftharpoons \& \mathscr{R}_{\llcorner} \overset{i}{\to} \mathscr{JH}_{\lrcorner} \mathscr{R}_{\llcorner} \overset{i}{\to} \mathscr{JL}_{\lrcorner},$$

$$\mathscr{R}_{\llcorner} \overset{i}{\to} \&\mathscr{HLM}_{\lrcorner} \rightleftharpoons \mathscr{R}_{\llcorner} \overset{i}{\to} \mathscr{HR}_{\llcorner} \overset{i}{\to} \mathscr{LM}_{\lrcorner\lrcorner}.$$

Here $\mathscr{F}, \mathscr{G}, \mathscr{H}, \mathscr{I}$ can be arbitrary Cf of L_1; $\mathscr{J}$ can either be an arbitrary Cf of L_1 or a Fr of L_2 of the form $\supset \mathscr{FG}[\mathscr{F}, \mathscr{G} - \text{Cf of } L_1]$; $\mathscr{H}, \mathscr{L}, \mathscr{M}$ can be arbitrary Cf of L_2 such that $\&\mathscr{HL}$ is not a formula of L_1.

We see easily that the result of application of $\mathscr{R}$ to a string of the form $\overset{i}{\to}\mathscr{HL}[\mathscr{H}, \mathscr{L} - \text{Cf of } L_2]$ is everytimes a Cf of L_2 independent of i. Now we can state the

THEOREM 1. *Whatever be the closed formulae $\mathscr{H}$ and $\mathscr{L}$ of L_2 and the natural number i, we have $\overset{i}{\to}\mathscr{H}\,\mathscr{L}$ if and only if $\mathscr{R}_{\llcorner}\overset{i}{\to}\mathscr{H}\,\mathscr{L}_{\lrcorner}$ holds.*

"The deducibility of $\mathscr{L}$ from $\mathscr{H}$ of rank i" is thus expressible by a formula of L_2 independent of i. In the sequel we omit the rank index i over the arrow.

It is natural to define the *deductional negation* of a closed formula $\mathscr{H}$ of L_2 by means of

$$\mathit{1}\mathscr{H} \rightleftharpoons \to \mathscr{H} \, (\varsigma \neq \varsigma).$$

It follows from Theorem 1 that we have $\mathit{1}\neg\mathscr{F}$ if and only if $\mathscr{F}$ is true. Here $\mathscr{F}$ is an arbitrary Cf of L_1 and the meaning of the ordinary negation sign $\neg$ is defined in terms of implication $\supset$:

$$\neg \mathscr{F} \rightleftharpoons \supset \mathscr{F} \, (\varsigma \neq \varsigma).$$

Since the applicability of a normal algorithm to a word can be expressed by a closed formula of L_1, this may be considered as the proof of a form of the principle of constructive selection: if the hypothesis of the nonapplicability of a normal algorithm to a word is reduced ad absurdum by means of certain inference rules then the algorithm does apply to this word.

Another consequence of Theorem 1 is the deduction theorem which states that we have $\to\mathscr{FG}$, if and only if $\supset\mathscr{FG}$, where $\mathscr{F}$ and $\mathscr{G}$ are Cf of L_1.

The deductive implication can now be formalized in a language L_3 permitting to form implications, applied to formulae of L_2, and conjunctions of formulae already obtained. The construction of consecutive languages L_n can be so continued that implication in every language $L_n(n \geqslant 3)$ will have a deductive meaning.

The sequence of languages L_n so obtained can be incorporated into one language L_ω, in which implications and conjunctions can be formed without restrictions. The operator $\mathscr{R}$ can be extended to L_ω by means of the stipulations .

$$\mathscr{R}_{\llcorner} \to \mathscr{K} \mathscr{L}_{\lrcorner} \rightleftharpoons \mathscr{R}_{\llcorner} \to \mathscr{R}_{\llcorner} \mathscr{K}_{\lrcorner} \mathscr{R}_{\llcorner} \mathscr{L}_{\lrcorner\lrcorner},$$

$$\mathscr{R}_{\llcorner} \& \mathscr{K} \mathscr{L}_{\lrcorner} \rightleftharpoons \& \mathscr{R}_{\llcorner} \mathscr{K}_{\lrcorner} \mathscr{R}_{\llcorner} \mathscr{L}_{\lrcorner}.$$

Now this operator converts every closed formula of L_ω into a closed formula of L_2. The language L_ω is thus reduced to L_2.

Let us now introduce the generality quantifier $\forall$. In language $L_{\omega+1}$ formulae are built from formulae of L_ω by successive left adjoinings of strings of the form $\forall \Omega$ [Ω-variable]. $\forall \Omega \mathscr{K}$ where $\mathscr{K}$ is an Ω-formula means that we possess a method for proving every formula $F_{\mathscr{P}}^{\Omega} {}_{\llcorner} \mathscr{K}_{\lrcorner}$, where $\mathscr{P}$ is an arbitrary admissible value of Ω. A natural system of inference rules $R''1$–$R''13$ can be proposed for $L_{\omega+1}$: $R''1$–$R''5$ identical with $R'1$–$R'5$. $R''6$–$R''8$ as $R'6$–$R'8$ with the difference that $\mathscr{K}$ and $\mathscr{L}$ are now Cf of L_ω.

$R''9$
$$\frac{\forall \Omega \supset \mathscr{I} \mathscr{G}}{\supset \exists \Omega \mathscr{I} \mathscr{G}} \ [\Omega - \mathrm{Vr}, \ \mathscr{I} - \Omega \mathrm{F} \text{ of } L_1, \ \mathscr{G} - \mathrm{Cf} \text{ of } L_1].$$

$R''10$
$$\frac{\mathscr{K}}{\mathscr{R}_{\llcorner} \mathscr{K}_{\lrcorner}} \ [\mathscr{K} - \mathrm{Cf} \text{ of } L_\omega].$$

$R''11$
$$\frac{\mathscr{R}_{\llcorner} \mathscr{K}_{\lrcorner}}{\mathscr{K}}.$$

$R''12$
$$\frac{\forall \Omega \mathscr{N}}{F_{\mathscr{P}}^{\Omega} {}_{\llcorner} \mathscr{N}_{\lrcorner}} \ [\mathscr{N} - \Omega F \text{ of } L_{\omega+1}, \ \mathscr{P} - \mathrm{Av} \text{ of } \Omega].$$

$R''13$
$$\frac{F_{\mathscr{P}}^{\Omega} {}_{\llcorner} \mathscr{N}_{\lrcorner} \text{ for every Av } \mathscr{P} \text{ of } \Omega}{\forall \Omega \mathscr{N}}.$$

Here $R''13$ is Carnap's rule, corresponding to the semantics of the generality quantifier. In virtue of $R''13$ we could replace $R'9$ by the simpler rule $R''9$.

Now we can introduce a hierarchy of deductive implications for Cf of $L_{\omega+1}$.

$\overrightarrow{_0}\ \mathscr{J}\mathscr{K}$ will mean that $\mathscr{K}$ is deducible from $\mathscr{J}$ and a list of true formulae of $L_{\omega+1}$ by means of R''1–R''12.

$\overrightarrow{_{\alpha+1}}\mathscr{J}\mathscr{K}$ will mean that we have an Ω-formula $\mathscr{N}$ of $L_{\omega+1}$ such that $\overrightarrow{_\alpha}\mathscr{J}F_\mathscr{P}^\Omega {}_\llcorner\mathscr{N}{}_\lrcorner$ is provable for every admissible value $\mathscr{P}$ of Ω, and that $\mathscr{K}$ is deducible from $\mathscr{J}, \forall\Omega\mathscr{N}$ and a list of true formulae of $L_{\omega+1}$ by means of R'1–R'12.

$\overrightarrow{_\beta}\ \mathscr{J}\mathscr{K}$, where β is a limit ordinal, will mean that we have $\overrightarrow{_\alpha}\mathscr{J}\mathscr{K}$ for some $\alpha<\beta$. Here α and β are constructive ordinals. I don't know how great constructive ordinals are actually necessary in the general case. In some special interesting cases the situation is not so bad as one might suppose.

Let us consider first of all the case when $\mathscr{J}$ and $\mathscr{K}$ are closed formulae of L_ω, i.e. when they do not contain the unrestricted generality quantifier. It is not difficult to prove that in this case R''13 gives nothing new and that we have $\overrightarrow{_\alpha}\mathscr{J}\mathscr{K}$ if and only if $\mathscr{R}{}_\llcorner\rightarrow\mathscr{J}\mathscr{K}{}_\lrcorner$ is true. It follows that the principle of constructive selection holds even if the powerful Carnap's rule is accepted as means for the reductio ad absurdum.

The next interesting case is the case when: 1) $\mathscr{J}$ is of the form $\forall\theta\mathscr{M}$, where $\mathscr{M}$ is a θ-formula of L_1, determining a decidable predicate; 2) $\mathscr{K}$ a closed formula of L_ω. In this case $\overrightarrow{_\alpha}\mathscr{J}\mathscr{K}$ holds if and only if there is some admissible value $\mathscr{P}$ of θ such that $\mathscr{R}{}_\llcorner\rightarrow F_\mathscr{P}^\theta {}_\llcorner\mathscr{M}{}_\lrcorner\mathscr{K}{}_\lrcorner$ is true. It follows that if a formula $\forall\theta\mathscr{M}$ with decidable $\mathscr{M}$ of L_1 is refutable by means of our inference rules, then $F_\mathscr{P}^\theta {}_\llcorner\mathscr{M}{}_\lrcorner$ is refutable for some $\mathscr{P}$. Since decidable predicates are representable in L_1, this is another form of the principle of constructive selection: if it is false that a decidable predicate holds for every value of the argument, then one can indicate a value of the argument for which the predicate does not hold. Of course it is important here that the falsity of the general statement in question would be proved by definite logical means.

References

LORENZEN, P., Einführung in die operative Logik und Mathematik (Berlin, Springer, 1955).

General Problems of Methodology and Philosophy of Science

A SELF-CORRECTING OBSERVATION LANGUAGE*

MARY B. HESSE

University of Cambridge, England

1. The structure of theories

How should we understand the structure of scientific theory? The deductive account has recently come under attack from various directions, together with its accompanying apparatus of formal calculus and interpretations, observational and theoretical concepts, and correspondence rules relating theory to observation. I shall not repeat here the detail of these attacks, but merely refer to some of them, and then try to sketch the outlines of a different model of theory-structure which may at least improve upon the deductive model in some respects.

The deductive account of the relation of theory and observation inevitably gives rise to a picture of "levels", with theoretical postulates at the top, derived theorems appearing successively down the page, and putative observation statements at the bottom. With such a picture in mind it is easy to slide into the assumption that the deductive ordering from postulates to theorems is also an ordering from abstract to concrete, from general to particular, from theoretical to observational, and, because postulates are only postulated whereas observation statements are "directly" verified or falsified, also from uncertainty to certainty. But very little reflection is required to see that these further assumptions form a tissue of non-sequiturs. For in the first place they neglect the elementary logical fact that in order to pass from general postulates to particular observational conclusions, some particular premises are required. These must contain at least some observation predicates (for example: "This is a swan", "H_2O is water"), and so already destroy any exact correspondence between premises and theory on the one hand, and conclusions and observation on the other. Secondly, it

* I am greatly indebted to Professors R. B. Braithwaite and C. G. Hempel for their helpful comments on earlier versions of this paper.

is by no means obvious that the order of deduction must also be the order of increasing directness of empirical verifiability. Every time a new physical particle is "detected", there is at least a claim to have made an observation at a high level of deductive theory, and hence to have "directly verified" some theoretical statement. On the other hand, there are plenty of examples of statements "low down" in the deductive hierarchy whose verification is by no means easy or direct; consider any attempt to apply quantum mechanical theory in describing the outcome of a complex chemical process.

It is no accident that deductive theorists tend to slip into these non-sequiturs. If the deductive system is to work it is essential that its lower, or observational, levels should be regarded as comparatively firmly based and unproblematic, in particular that the meaning of the observation statements should be understood independently of the theoretical superstructure, and that the truth-value of the observation statements should be directly accessible. For the whole deductive account was originally motivated by puzzles about the meaning, reference, and justification of theories, all of which were held to require explication in terms of observation alone. Verifiability of theories was abandoned, but their falsifiability still demanded that the truth-value of observation statements be known, or at least accepted temporarily, on pain of vicious regress. Logical construction of theoretical predicates was abandoned, but their meaning and reference, if any, were still held to depend upon their relations to observation predicates whose meaning and reference were not in question. The tendency of the whole account has been towards an instrumentalism in which theories have neither truth-value, meaning nor reference, and in which the theory-observation distinction has been made sharp and irrevocable. But the further this approach to instrumentalism has gone, the less recognizable it has become as an account of how scientific theories actually work. To mention only one of its consequences, which is in the end perhaps the only decisive objection to it, it makes quite unintelligible the *predictive* power of theories, where prediction is understood not merely in terms of new putative observation statements derived from the system, but in terms of new observation statements in whose truth we can have great confidence *before they are tested*. The deductive account wholly fails to explicate this confidence, and therefore needs at least to be supplemented by some kind of inductive confirmation theory of theories and predictions *.

It is not this shortcoming of deductivism that has mainly been under attack however, but rather the thesis of truth-and-meaning invariance of

---

* Compare also the implicit demand for such a confirmation theory in Hempel's restatement of his classic deductive account of explanation: HEMPEL [1965] p. 338.

observation statements*. It is noticed, first, that the truth-value ascribed to observation statements is not independent of theory, for theory may be used to *correct* a "phenomenal law" such as, for example, Kepler's third law, which was corrected by Newton's gravitational theory. It is also noted that it often becomes very odd to say that the "meaning" of an observation statement is invariant to change of theory. The mass of a Newtonian particle is an unchanging measure of quantity of matter: in relativity it may be a relation between particles which depends upon their relative velocity. Can "mass" "mean" the same in the two theories? Again, Priestley claimed to have "carefully expelled from a quantity of minium all the phlogiston... by giving it a red heat when mixed with spirit of nitre..."**. What kind of an observation statement is this? In reply to such examples, deductive theorists take remedial action, spurred by the fear that if the essentials of deductivism are abandoned, we shall introduce intolerable circularities and self-valida- tions into the notion of a scientific theory. In rose-tinted spectacles all things are rosy; do not all these coherentist objections imply that from within a sufficiently comprehensive theoretical framework all conceivable empirical facts must inevitably fit?

I do not believe that attempts to shore up the deductive account in face of all these objections will be successful, but neither do I accept that its abandonment need result in any such vortex of relativities as just mentioned. The new model of theories required is to some extent already developed in the literature. It may in fact be regarded as an exploitation of theses of Duhem and Quine† on the systematic interrelation of hypotheses and ob- servation. Duhem's emphasis on the interdependence of hypotheses in a theoretical system has recently been the source of much dispute regarding the role of conventionalism in science, but it is less often noticed that Duhem also insisted that theoretical interpretation of *observations* is required before a raw "fact" can be incorporated into a theory, and even, he implied, before it can be expressed at all in language. Although in some respects himself a deductivist, there was for Duhem no unproblematic observation language, and no truth-and-meaning invariance of observation statements. The com- plement to his suggestion that a given hypothesis may be made comparatively immune to falsification by appropriate modification of other hypotheses is his equally clear suggestion that a so-called observation statement (which he

---

* See especially HANSON [1958] Chs I, II; FEYERABEND [1962]; and KUHN [1962].
** This highly illuminating case-history can be examined in CONANT [1957] p. 65, and in TOULMIN [1957] p. 205. The quotation from Priestley is in TOULMIN [1957] p. 209.
† Especially DUHEM [1954] Pt. II, Chs III-VI; QUINE [1953], [1960] Chs I, II.

called a "theoretical fact") may *not* be immune to falsification if it becomes convenient to modify it in the light of other parts of the theoretical network. This view of the relations of theoretical and observation statements has more recently been paralleled by Quine's discussion of the net-like relations of analytic and synthetic statements, any sub-set of which may be relatively entrenched, but any of which also may be dispensable.

The question that now arises is, can we use these suggestions to provide a model of theories sharp and definite enough to replace the deductive model? Criteria of adequacy for the new model which have so far emerged may be summarized as follows:

1. The model should make no fundamental stratification into theoretical and observational levels, but should rather be based on a multiplicity of interrelations between theoretical and observation statements, not all of them strict entailments.

2. The model should not demand that the truth-value of any of these statements is known infallibly.

3. The model should leave room for some shift of "meaning" of descriptive predicates between different theories, where the relevant sense of "meaning" remains to be clarified.

4. Empirical falsifiability of theories must be safeguarded, and in addition it must be shown how some kind of confirmation can be conveyed to theories and predictions by observational evidence.

I shall now try to show that a model based on a Carnap-type confirmation theory can be made to satisfy these conditions. Such a model will replace the entailments of the deductive account by confirmation-relations (or "partial entailments") between theoretical and observation statements. Confirmation as well as falsification will then be conveyed through the system from observation to theory; thus we may hope to satisfy requirements (1) and (4). Requirements (2) and (3) introduce the further feature of uncertainty of the evidence-statements, and this will be dealt with in the model by making a distinction between observation *statements*, which are uncertain, and observation *reports*, which are once-for-all verbal entries in the record, and which can be regarded as the irreducible and certain evidence upon which the confirmation values of the rest of the system depend.

2. The black box with loose connections

To fix ideas let us first consider the model in the form of a black box whose internal state we are trying to discover. We suppose a mechanism enclosed in a black box, to which are attached a number of keys and an output tape. About this box we know or assume the following:

(1) It consists of K two-state relays. The position of each relay will be described by a primitive statement specified by a latin capital with or without bar, thus: A or $\bar{A}$ for the A-relay, B or $\bar{B}$ for the B-relay, and so on.

(2) Any of the 2^K sets of positions of the K relays is a possible *state* of the machine. Disjunctions of more than one and less than 2^K state-descriptions will be said to describe *partial states* of the machine.

(3) The relays are not in general independent of each other. A prior probability distribution over all states of the machine is assumed to be known. This will be denoted by $c_0(A)$, $c_0(B)$, $c_0(AB)$, and so on.

(4) The box carries m external keys, where $m < K$. To each relay of a sub-set of m relays is attached just one of the keys. When a key is struck, say the A-key attached to the A-relay, the machine prints out either report 'A' or '$\bar{A}$' on an external tape. No key may be struck more than once.

(5) The printed report is not an infallible indication of the position of the corresponding relay, for the attachment to the printer is faulty inside the machine. It is assumed that if the relay is in state A there is a small non-zero probability ε that '$\bar{A}$' will be printed when the A-key is struck, and when the position is $\bar{A}$, there is a probability ε that 'A' is printed. It is assumed that ε has the same value for each relay, and that the faults in the relay-printer connections are independent of each other. Thus if a partial state of the machine is ABC, and the three corresponding keys are struck, there is a probability of $(1-\varepsilon)^3$ that 'ABC' is printed, $\varepsilon(1-\varepsilon)^2$ that '$\bar{A}$BC' is printed, and so on. Thus, whatever the prior distribution over states, the prior probability of obtaining a given report is never either zero or one.

We suppose that the state of the machine remains constant, and attempt by operating the keys to learn something about that state. What is learnt will not of course be infallible nor incorrigible by further evidence, because any state of the machine is consistent with any set of reports, although some states are much more improbable than others.

Let us denote the report 'A' by A' and the report '$\bar{A}$' by $\bar{A}'$. Suppose we strike the A-key, and A' is reported. Since $c_0(A')$ is non-zero we can calculate for any state or partial state of the machine (described by S) its posterior confirmation (c-value) given A', in terms of ε and the c_0-distribution:

$$c(S, A') = [c(A', AS)\, c(A, S) + c(A', \bar{A}S)\, c(\bar{A}, S)]\, c_0(S)/c_0(A')$$
$$= \frac{(1 - \varepsilon)\, c_0(AS) + \varepsilon c_0(\bar{A}S)}{(1 - \varepsilon)\, c_0(A) + \varepsilon c_0(\bar{A})}. \tag{1}$$

In particular we have

$$c(\bar{A}, A') > c(A, A') \quad \text{iff} \quad c_0(\bar{A}) > \frac{1 - \varepsilon}{\varepsilon} c_0(A) \tag{2}$$

$$c(B\bar{A}, A') > c(BA, A') \quad \text{iff} \quad c_0(B\bar{A}) > \frac{1 - \varepsilon}{\varepsilon} c_0(BA). \tag{3}$$

Thus under some circumstances $\bar{A}$ or a state description implying $\bar{A}$ may be more highly confirmed than A even on evidence A'.

Suppose now another key is struck. The report B' so obtained enables us to calculate a new set of c-values conditionally upon $A'B'$:

$$c(S, A'B') =$$
$$= \frac{(1 - \varepsilon)^2 c_0(ABS) + \varepsilon(1 - \varepsilon)[c_0(A\bar{B}S) + c_0(\bar{A}BS)] + \varepsilon^2 c_0(\bar{A}\bar{B}S)}{(1 - \varepsilon)^2 c_0(AB) + \varepsilon(1 - \varepsilon)[c_0(A\bar{B}) + c_0(\bar{A}B)] + \varepsilon^2 c_0(\bar{A}\bar{B})}.$$

And so on for any number of reports obtained by striking further keys.

3. A model for scientific theory

Now consider an interpretation of the black box in a highly simplified world in which we shall investigate the conditions for confirmation of scientific theories. Suppose the world consists of a finite number n individuals, whose nature need not be specified at present, but which may be situations, events, objects, processes. Let their names be $a_1, a_2, \ldots, a_n$. They are to be described by means of a fixed finite set of π primitive monadic two-valued predicates, P_1 or $\bar{P}_1$, P_2 or $\bar{P}_2, \ldots, P_\pi$ or $\bar{P}_\pi$. We now interpret the K states of the black box to be the $2^{n\pi}$ states of this world, and the primitive propositions A, B, C, ... each to be an assignment of a single P_r or $\bar{P}_r$ to a given individual a_s. The c_0-distribution over states of the machine corresponds to a c_0-distribution over states of the world. The process of striking a given key is interpreted as a singular observation of a given individual with regard to a given predicate, and the once-for-all report thus obtained is an observation report which remains for ever in the record. There is no provision in this model for the "same" observation to be repeated, so that we may have to envisage the predicates as time-linked – we never report the same property of an individual twice, although we may report very similar properties of that individual many times. What counts as a "very similar property" will be shown up in the c_0-distribution, that is to say, if a_s has property P_1 at time t_1 and P_2 is what we should call the "same" property at t_2, then in the absence of other evidence $c(P_2 a_s, P_1 a_s)$ will generally be relatively high.

The small probability ε represents the probable "observational error" in obtaining each report. I shall have more to say later about the nature of this error. Positions of relays which are directly attached to keys will be said to be described by *observation statements*, and those which are not so attached, by *theoretical statements*. Any truth-function of primitive statements will be called a *theory*, whether or not it contains any theoretical statements. Remember that the truth of even observation statements is not given for certain by observation reports.

We can now interpret the properties of the black box in the following manner. There is a certain c_0-distribution over the possible states of the world, and every time an observation report is obtained there is a change in the posterior c-distribution as determined by equation (1). The confirmation of any theory can thus be calculated on the basis of the evidence up to date. The possibility of "correcting" (or more strictly, casting severe doubt upon) any observation statement is provided for by the fact that the c-value of an observation statement on the basis of evidence *which may include its corresponding observation report* may become very low with increasing evidence. We shall not say, however, that any observation statement A, where $c_0(A) \neq 0$, has ever been shown to be *false*, for equation (1) entails that $c(A, Z')$ for any reports Z' is zero if and only if $c_0(A)$ is zero. To "detach" the conclusion 'A is false' would violate the continuity of c-distributions defined by (1). For the same reason we shall not say that any theory is ever shown to be either true or false, however highly confirmed or disconfirmed it may become on increasing evidence.

The results of the preceding section show that the success of this model depends crucially upon the c_0-distribution. Before going any further it is therefore necessary to consider the immediate objection that since we have no grounds for assigning any particular c_0-distribution to states of the world, all subsequent results are worthless. My claim is that we do in fact have some such grounds, and at this stage it is important to be clear how they should be understood.

The c_0-distribution required for an inductive confirmation theory need not be regarded as an a priori postulate from which the probabilities of inductive inferences are obtained deductively. Such a view would be open to all the Humean objections to attempts to reduce induction, even probabilistic induction, to deduction. But there is an alternative view – a confirmation-theory may be regarded rather as an *explication* of accepted kinds of inductive argument, and therefore as being justified a posteriori by its success in giving relatively high c-values on given evidence to those theories in which we would have great confidence if we followed our normally accepted inductive rules. Such a justification of course raises the question as to whether we can in fact specify any set of "normally accepted inductive rules", and this is too large a question to take up here. It will have to suffice to state that in the simple taxonomic world we are considering here, some postulate like Keynes' Principle of Limited Independent Variety is sufficient to explicate most of the interesting types of inference encountered in such a world, including Mill's methods, and inductive arguments from analogy and variety. Application to a more realistic world would require extension of the model to deal at least with relational and ordered predicates, a task which involves great mathematical difficulties, but little that is new in philosophical principle. The crucial dependence of the model upon the c_0-distribution therefore need not be an insuperable objection, for in simple cases it can already be shown that fairly liberal conditions upon the distribution are sufficient to generate quite powerful inductive inferences. In seeking to explicate the structure of scientific theory it is not, fortunately, necessary to show that such inductive inferences are absolutely justified, only that the explication reproduces closely enough the intuitively acceptable rules of theorizing. (See, for example, CARNAP [1962], ACHINSTEIN [1963], HESSE [1964], [1968].)

4. Truth-and-meaning variance

We can now consider how far this model for scientific theories satisfies the requirements laid down in Section 1.

First, it replaces the asymmetry of confirmation and falsification in the deductive account by a symmetry of high and low confirmation. No theory or system of theories is ever conclusively falsified (or verified) by any set of observation reports, because there is a finite probability that the reports may be in error. But this does not imply that we cannot compare one theory with another, for we can compare their c-values, and this comparison depends partly but essentially on observed evidence. There is no circularity of confirmation or falsification here. Also, it should be noticed that where genuine deductive relations *do* appear in the theory structure these are represented in the model by transference of minimum c-value from premises to conclusions. The logic of the model is thus in this respect an extension rather than a replacement of the logic of deductive systems.

Second, how far does the model represent what is true in the much-discussed theory-observation distinction, and the theory-ladenness of observation? The model does make a distinction between theory and observation in the sense that some relay-positions are "directly" reported and some are not, but since this does not imply in the model that observation statements are infallible, the distinction is merely pragmatic and does not enter essentially into the confirmation logic. After some evidence has been collected the initial distinction will indeed be minimised, for some observation statements may be less well confirmed than some theoretical statements even though their corresponding reports are in the record.

There remains the more difficult question of meaning variance. Proponents of this thesis are not always too clear in their expressions of it, so I shall first state what I think to be both true in the thesis, and to correspond best to the intentions of its authors. The thesis can be put in sharp paradoxical form as follows:*

(1) The meaning of a term in one theory is not the same as its meaning in another prima facie conflicting theory.

(2) Therefore no statement, and in particular no observation statement, containing the term in one theory can contradict a statement containing the term in the other.

(3) Therefore observation cannot decide between such prima facie conflicting theories.

A similar paradox can be derived from (1) with regard to explanation:**

(1a) The meaning of a term in the pre-theoretical observation language is different from its meaning in a theory which is said to explain that domain of observation.

(2a) Therefore if the theory entails some observation statement, that statement cannot be the same as any pre-theoretical observation statement, even if it is typographically similar to it.

(3a) Therefore no theory can explain the observational explanandum.

The force of both paradoxes depends on a slide in the meaning of "meaning", and in particular in the obscurity of "meaning" in assertions (1) and (1a). If we enquire what the meaning-variance philosophers have in mind in denying sameness of meaning in (1) and (1a), this is perhaps best expressed by saying that *context meaning* varies from theory to theory, where the context meaning of a predicate or a statement in a given theory is a function of all of the statements of that theory and their c-values. This suggestion

---

* This paradox is examined in FINE [1967].
** See, for instance, NAGEL [1961] p. 87 and ALEXANDER [1963] pp. 84, 95.

may sound brusque, but it does seem to be sufficient for the apparently very radical proposals contained in (1) and (1a), since it is certainly the case that when, for instance, we use the word "mass" in Newtonian mechanics, we do commit ourselves to the likely truth of a set of statements about mass which is different from the set of statements about mass in relativity mechanics, and this is the difference that seems to be in question in (1) and (1a). I now interpret the assertions (1) and (1a) to be the tautologous remarks that the set of statements contained in one theory is different from that in another, or in that partial theory which is sometimes called the set of observation statements. Context meaning understood as a function of the whole theory in which a predicate or statement occurs is then variant by definition.

It may perhaps seem to be an objection to this construal of context meaning that it follows that a predicate has as many context meanings as there are theories and partial theories in the language, and that context meaning within one theory changes with changing evidence. If this should seem counter-intuitive it should first be noted that the proposal shares this feature with the deductivist proposal to understand the "meaning" of theoretical predicates in terms of their place in the deductive system plus its observational consequences (a proposal called "contextualism" by BRAITHWAITE [1962]). More importantly, however, context meaning does not exhaust the senses of "meaning" referred to in the paradoxes, for there are at least two other senses which do not share the meaning-variance of context meaning:

(i) It does not follow from what has been said about context meaning that "the meaning of P" in theory T_1 is different from that in T_2 in the sense that *deductive* or *confirmation* relations between statements containing P are theory-dependent, indeed in merely stating that the context meaning of P varies between different theories, we are assuming the relevant identity of P for such logical relations.

(ii) Nor does it follow that the *reference* of a statement in T_1 is necessarily or even usually different from that of a typographically similar statement in T_2.

The second and third parts of the paradoxes of meaning therefore do not follow in the sense required, for it is perfectly possible for a statement in one theory to *contradict* a statement in another; for a statement to be logically the *same* in two theories; and for the empirical *reference* of a statement in one theory to be the same as its reference in another.

It is not quite clear that this account is sufficient however, for a proponent of meaning variance might reply somewhat as follows. "In speaking just now of the 'same' statement, and the 'same' reference, you are presupposing exactly what I deny, namely that observational states of affairs can be described in a theory-neutral language, and that it is perfectly clear which statements of the theory can be said to be the 'same' as these observation descriptions. Context meaning certainly cannot provide the criteria of identity here, and typographic similarity is obviously neither necessary nor sufficient. What other features of the statements of two different theories determine that they have the same reference?"

Let us try to clarify the issue here by returning to the black box. We now need to notice a feature which has been tacitly presupposed in its specification, namely that the keys are classified in a two-dimensional array, corresponding to the set of individuals and the set of predicates. We may visualize the key-board as arranged in n columns corresponding to the n individuals, and π rows corresponding to the π predicates. This assumption of course begs crucial questions which are now relevant. We may perhaps regard it as reasonable to assume in our simple world that we know the classification of relays corresponding to individuals independently of the theoretical state we are seeking, that is, we have criteria for "same" and "different" individuals which, while not making our judgments infallible (as allowed for by ε), nevertheless are not *generally* in question (perhaps the criteria depend on space-time continuity and not generally on properties). But it appears much less reasonable to assume that we know the classification of relays in terms of predicates independently of the machine state we are seeking. Indeed the meaning-variance thesis in the form just expressed seems to deny exactly this, for this thesis implies not only that predicates have different contextual meanings in different theories, but also that they have in general different *extensions*, or empirical references. To accept this thesis in terms of the black box would be to suppose in general that in one theory a given relay is said to be probably hooked up to one key, and in another theory to a key corresponding to a different predicate.

Such a possibility is to some extent already allowed for in the parameter ε, for we could certainly come to doubt in certain circumstances all reports of $P_r(a)$ on the basis of their low c-value, and to suspect that such reports should be replaced in these same circumstances by reports of $P_s(a)$ which have much higher c-value. That is to say, the error ε may be interpreted not only as indicating faulty relay-printer connections, but also miswired relays, where the relay-printer connections P_r and P_s have become crossed. It is of course built into the assumption that ε is small that this could not be the case for most reports most of the time, and therefore the radical changes of meaning which seem to be envisaged by the meaning-variance thesis are not accommodated in the model. An extreme meaning-variance position would in fact be equivalent to supposing that we were entirely in the dark as to which relays should be classified with which predicates. The problem of determining the probable state of the box in these circumstances might not be insoluble, but it would demand indifference assumptions about the prior probabilities of connections between printer and relays which could only seem arbitrary, and which do not seem to correspond to any *general* doubts we have about what predicates to report of what individuals in observed situations. To have such general doubts would in fact be to doubt both the possibility of an intersubjective descriptive language, and also the efficacy of the processes by which we come to learn it. A more moderate meaning-variance position on the other hand might demand only that *some* alternative relay-printer connections be explicitly allowed for in the c_0-distribution, a situation which seems closer to our actual uncertainties of observation, and which could be simulated in the model, though at the cost of greater complexity.

Difficulties connected with meaning-variance bring us finally to a general point regarding the use of confirmation theory in this type of model. The possibility of explicating continuity of inference relative to increasing evidence is bought at the price of never conclusively accepting or rejecting any empirical statement, and to some extent also at the price of never introducing new theoretical concepts. Just as we cannot accept or reject any state-description without violating the conditions of equation (1) and hence changing discontinuously the sequence of c-distributions, so we cannot change our language by introducing new predicates, abandoning old ones, or radically revising their occasions of correct use without similar discontinuities in this sequence. These admitted limitations on the model do not however reduce its usefulness, they merely call for a supplementation of confirmation theory by a theory of acceptance and rejection, which would undoubtedly have to take account of the distribution of c-values obtained to date. Perhaps Kuhn's conception of periods of normal science broken by changes of paradigm should be understood in terms of the occasions of acceptance or rejection of theories and of modifications of the predicate set. But these occasions may be rarer than has been supposed, for what I hope I have indicated here is that many of the significant features of theoretical inference can be explicated even within one sequence of c-distributions. To just that extent there is an inductive logic of theoretical science, which includes what is true in the deductive account, while also meeting some of the objections to that account.

References

ACHINSTEIN, P., Variety and analogy in confirmation theory, Phil. Sci. **30** (1963) 216.

ALEXANDER, P., Sensationalism and scientific explanation (London, 1963).

BRAITHWAITE, R.B., Models in the empirical sciences, in: Logic, methodology and philosophy of science, eds. E. Nagel, P. Suppes and A. Tarski (Stanford, 1962) p. 230.

CARNAP, R., Logical foundations of probability (2nd ed., Chicago, 1962).

CONANT, J.B., The overthrow of the phlogiston theory, in: Harvard case histories in experimental science I, ed. J. B. Conant (Cambridge, Mass., 1957).

DUHEM, P., The aim and structure of physical theory, transl. P. P. Wiener (Princeton, 1954).

FEYERABEND, P.K., Explanation, reduction and empiricism, in: Minnesota studies in the philosophy of science III, eds. H. Feigl and G. Maxwell (Minneapolis, 1962) p. 28.

FINE, A.I., Consistency, derivability, and scientific change, J. Phil. **64** (1967) 231.

HANSON, N.R., Patterns of discovery (Cambridge, 1958).

HEMPEL, C.G., Aspects of scientific explanation (New York, 1965).

HESSE, M., Analogy and confirmation theory, Phil. Sci. **31** (1964) 319.

HESSE, M., Consilience of inductions, in: Problems in the philosophy of mathematics, ed. I. Lakatos (Amsterdam, North-Holland Publ. Co., 1968).

KUHN, T.S., The structure of scientific revolutions (Chicago, 1962).

NAGEL, E., The structure of science (New York, 1961).

QUINE, W.V.O., Two dogmas of empiricism, in: From a logical point of view (Cambridge, Mass., 1953).

QUINE, W.V.O., Word and object (New York, 1960).

TOULMIN, S.E., Crucial experiments: Priestley and Lavoisier, J. Hist. Ideas **18** (1957) 205.

THE VARIETIES OF INFORMATION AND SCIENTIFIC EXPLANATION

J. HINTIKKA

Stanford University, Stanford, USA
University of Helsinki, Helsinki, Finland

1. The importance of information

The concept of information seems to be strangely neglected by epistemo-logists and philosophers of language. In many everyday situations, know-ledge and information are nearly exchangeable terms; yet for every score of books with the phrase "theory of knowledge" in their titles there scarcely exists a single paper by a logician or philosopher dealing with the theory of information.[1] Again, the information that a sentence yields or can yield might very well seem to an ordinary man much more important than the so-called meanings of the terms it contains, or even the meaning of the sentence itself. Yet, with but few exceptions, philosophers of language have not devoted more than a vanishingly small part of their efforts to the theory of information as compared with the theory of meaning. Why this should be so, I do not know. Perhaps the fact that mathematicians and communi-cation theorists largely succeeded in appropriating the term "information" for their special purposes a couple of decades ago has something to do with this.[2] I also suspect that it is much harder to talk persuasive nonsense about the quantitative concept of information than of the qualitative notions of knowledge and meaning. Be this as it may, the neglect is a regrettable one. In this paper, I shall try to call philosophers' attention to a few possibilities of correcting it. I have already tried to do so in some earlier papers[3]; the present one is partly a sequel to them and partly a new enterprise.

---

[1] One of the most interesting exceptions is constituted by the studies of Ernest W. Adams and his students of the role of information in certain important methodological connections. See ADAMS [1966], HANNA [1966].

[2] See e.g. SHANNON and WEAVER [1949], KHINCHIN [1957], CHERRY [1957].

[3] HINTIKKA and PIETARINEN [1966] and HINTIKKA [1968].

2. Information as the elimination of uncertainty

The philosophical study of the concept of information was started by Carnap and Bar-Hillel soon after 1950.[4] It was called by them theory of semantic information, and distinguished from the statistical information theory of communication theorists. Similar ideas had been informally expounded by Sir Karl Popper already in the thirties.[5]

The basic idea of their approach may be said to be one particular way of explicating the general idea that information equals elimination of uncertainty. In order to measure this uncertainty, a distinction is made between the different logical possibilities that we can express in a language. The more of them a statement s admits of, the more probable it is in some "purely logical" sense of probability. The more of them a statement s excludes, the less uncertainty does it leave, and the more informative will it therefore be. The probability $p(s)$ and information $inf(s)$ of a statement s are thus inversely related.

In some earlier papers, I have examined how the different cases might be distinguished from each other (and weighted) on which a purely logical measure of information might be based in certain simple languages.[6] These studies have strongly suggested to me that no absolute answer to this question is forthcoming. The weights that the different cases have to be given will depend on the order which we expect (or are entitled to expect) to obtain in the universe. Thus we are forced (it seems to me) from a purely logical conception of probability toward some form of Bayesianism.

The basic idea that underlies the concept of information nevertheless remains essentially the same in all cases. The information of s is the amount of uncertainty we are relieved of when we come to know that s is true.

3. Unexpectedness versus content

If this is all there is to be said here, any monotonically decreasing function of $p(s)$ could be thought of as a measure of the information of s. In order to pick out a particular measure, we must say a little more of how we expect the concept of information to behave vis-à-vis the concept of probability. Some important requirements of this kind are in fact quite straightforward. For instance, if it is required that $inf(s)$ be additive with respect to proba-

---

[4] See CARNAP and BAR-HILLEL [1952], BAR-HILLEL and CARNAP [1953], KEMENY [1953].
[5] POPPER [1935].
[6] See HINTIKKA [1965], [1966].

bilistically independent conjuncts, i.e. that $\inf(s_1 \& s_2) = \inf(s_1) + \inf(s_2)$ if s_1 and s_2 are independent with respect to a probability-measure p, then the inverse relation must be expressed by the definition

$$\inf(s) = -\log p(s) \tag{1}$$

provided that certain natural further assumptions are made.[7]

However, this is not the only way in which the concept of information or content can be defined, for there are other requirements which we can legitimately impose on this concept and which turn out to presuppose entirely different ways of defining information. In so far as it can be claimed that all these different requirements we can use here are part of our ordinary presystematic idea of information, the incompatibility of these requirements will show that this presystematic idea is intrinsically ambiguous.

Alternatives to (1) are in fact easy to come by. One very natural possibility here is to define the content cont(s) of s by the even simpler formula

$$\text{cont}(s) = 1 - p(s). \tag{2}$$

The justification of definition (2) will be indicated later.

It has been suggested that (1) is to be thought of as a measure of the *surprise value* or the *unexpectedness* of (the truth of) s, while (2) is a measure of the *substantive information* or *content* of s. This suggestion often helps to understand the difference between the two.[8]

The formal relation of $\inf(s)$ and cont(s) is in any case straightforward; it can be expressed e.g. by

$$\inf(s) = \log \frac{1}{1 - \text{cont}(s)}. \tag{3}$$

4. Measures of relative information

In terms of inf and cont, we can also define relative measures of unexpectedness and of content:

$$\inf_{\text{add}}(s|t) = \inf(s \& t) - \inf(t), \tag{4}$$

$$\text{cont}_{\text{add}}(s|t) = \text{cont}(s \& t) - \text{cont}(t). \tag{5}$$

---

[7] A somewhat loose sketch of an argument to this effect is given by TÖRNEBOHM [1964] pp. 49–50. Cf. Cox [1961] pp. 37–38.

[8] Cf. BAR-HILLEL [1964] p. 307. The logical basis of this distinction is clear enough. Somewhat roughly speaking, it may be said that cont measures the absolute number of possibilities which an item of information enables us to disregard, whereas inf measures the relative number of such possibilities, with respect to the total number of possibilities not previously eliminated.

These relative measures tell us simply how much information s adds to the information t has already given to us. This explains the use of the subscript. We shall also often call $\inf_{add}$ and cont_{add} *incremental* information (or unexpectedness) and *incremental* content, respectively.

It is easily seen that both these measures of relative information can be given a very natural expression, though different in the two cases:

$$\inf_{add}(s|t) = -\log p(s|t), \tag{6}$$

$$\mathrm{cont}_{add}(s|t) = \mathrm{cont}(t \supset s). \tag{7}$$

Relative unexpectedness is thus related to relative probability in the same way as absolute unexpectedness to absolute (a priori) probability. The content of s relative to t is the content of the statement that if t is true, then so is s.[9]

This last fact suggests a way of justifying definition (2). It embodies a requirement which we might very well want to impose on our concept of (informational) content in any case.[10] But if we do so, we are readily led to some such relation as (2). In fact, if we simply define

$$p^*(s) = \mathrm{cont}(\sim s)$$

then it follows easily from the requirement

$$\mathrm{cont}(s \& t) - \mathrm{cont}(t) = \mathrm{cont}(t \supset s) \tag{8}$$

that p^* satisfies some of the axioms of probability calculus. For instance, by substituting $\sim s$ and $\sim t$ for s and t in (8) we at once obtain

$$p^*(s \lor t) = p^*(s) + p^*(t)$$

for the case in which $(s \& t)$ is a contradiction, provided that logically equivalent statements are assumed to be intersubstitutable. This verifies the usual additivity requirement. By putting $s = t$ in (8) we likewise obtain

$$p^*(s) = 0 \quad \text{if} \quad s \quad \text{is a contradiction}.$$

If the normalizing conditions $\mathrm{cont}(s) \geqslant 0$ and $\mathrm{cont}(s \& \sim s) = 1$ are assumed, it follows that p^* satisfies all the axioms of the probability calculus (with the possible exception of Kolmogorov's axiom of denumerable additivity).[11]

---

[9] See BAR-HILLEL [1964] chapter 15, for a number of further results concerning incremental content and information.

[10] One way of motivating (7) is as follows: the information that s adds to the information of t must surely be the information of the weakest statement which will, when added to t, logically imply s. This statement is $(t \supset s)$; hence the validity of (7).

[11] It has been suggested by Savage that this axiom is perhaps not entirely indispensable for all interesting purposes; see DUBINS and SAVAGE [1965] p. 10 (with references to similar opinions previously aired by De Finetti).

In terms of this measure, cont can then be defined as in (2). In this sense, then, does the assumption of (8) easily lead to a definition of form (2).[12]

There is another sense in which we can speak of relative information and relative content, however, besides the incremental sense.[13] In some ways, the motivation of this sense is even more obvious. Instead of asking what information or content s adds to t, we can consider the world on the assumption that t is true, and ask how information or content could be characterized for this limited purpose. The resulting senses of information and content might be called *conditional* information and *conditional* content, in short $\inf_{cond}$ and cont_{cond}. The way to define them is obviously to substitute relative probability for absolute probability:

$$\inf_{cond}(s|t) = -\log p(s|t) \tag{9}$$

$$\text{cont}_{cond}(s|t) = 1 - p(s|t). \tag{10}$$

From (6) it is seen that $\inf_{add}(s|t) = \inf_{cond}(s|t)$. We can thus omit the subscripts $_{add}$ and $_{cond}$ in the case of inf, and speak simply of relative information or unexpectedness. However, the difference between cont_{add} and cont_{cond} is vital.

The difference between the two might be illustrated by means of the following example. Let us assume that we are dealing with the kind of languages which Carnap typically considers and in which the probability of a statement is the sum of the probabilities of all the state-descriptions compatible with it. Then cont(s) is the sum of the probabilities of all the state-descriptions excluded by s, and $\text{cont}_{add}(s|t)$ is the sum of the probabilities of all the state-descriptions excluded by s but not by t. In contrast to this, $\text{cont}_{cond}(s|t)$ is the sum of the relative probabilities of all the state-descriptions excluded by s relative to t.

5. Information relative to a subject matter. Transmitted information

An important further ambiguity in the notion of information can be found as follows[14]: What is defined by (1) or (2) may be said to be a measure of

---

[12] Notice, furthermore, that by replacing s by $s \& \sim s$ in (8) we obtain $p^*(s \lor \sim s) = p^*(t) + p^*(\sim t)$ for any t. If cont is to be nonnegative, p^*(tautology) will therefore be the maximum of all the values that p^* can have, and the assumption that $p^*(s \lor \sim s) = 1$ is thus truly a normalizing stipulation only.

[13] Somewhat surprisingly, this second sense of relative content seems not to have been discussed extensively in the earlier literature on semantic information.

[14] Ideas closely related to the one which underlies the present section have been discussed briefly in a slightly different form by Törnebohm [1964] pp. 51–52, and employed by Adams [1966] pp. 159–168 (under the title "transmitted information").

the information that a statement h carries concerning the subject matter of which it speaks. As was indicated, it is the amount of uncertainty concerning whatever h is about which we get rid of when we learn that h is true. However, very often this is not all the kind of information we are interested in. Frequently we are not interested in the subject matter of h at all. That is, frequently we are not interested in the reduction in our uncertainty concerning what h says, but rather in the reduction of uncertainty concerning certain other matters which our knowledge of h brings out. These matters may be described by some other statement, e.g. by g. Then the amount of information that h conveys (contains) concerning the subject matter of g is naturally measured by

$$\inf(g) - \inf(g|h) = \log\left[p(g|h)/p(g)\right] = \log\left[p(g \& h)/p(g)p(h)\right] \tag{11}$$

or, alternatively, by

$$\text{cont}(g) - \text{cont}_{\text{add}}(g|h) = 1 - p(g \vee h). \tag{12}$$

This may be compared with the analogous expression

$$\text{cont}(g) - \text{cont}_{\text{cond}}(g|h) = p(g|h) - p(g). \tag{13}$$

The explanation of (11) is very simple: $\inf(g)$ is precisely the uncertainty which we get rid of when we come to know g; $\inf(g|h)$ is the information g adds to that of h, i.e. the uncertainty that there remains concerning g even after we have learned that h is true. Hence $\inf(g) - \inf(g|h)$ measures the reduction of our uncertainty concerning g which takes place when we come to know, not g, but h. Similar remarks apply to (12).

In the case of (13), somewhat different explanation is called for. Here $\text{cont}(g)$ is the informative content of g a priori, whereas $\text{cont}_{\text{cond}}(g|h)$ is what the informative content of g would be in a world in which we could restrict ourselves entirely to possibilities compatible with h, i.e. in a world in which we know the truth of h. The difference (13) is thus primarily the *change in the information-carrying status of g which takes place when one comes to know h.*

The value of (13) can be either positive or negative. This is in keeping with the explanation just given of the meaning of (13), for coming to know h can obviously affect the relative information-carrying status of g positively or negatively.

It is seen that if we put $h=g$, we obtain from (11) $\inf(g)$ and from (12) as well as (13) $\text{cont}(g)$. This result is of course obvious in view of the intuitive meanings of (11)–(13), respectively. It shows that these new senses of information are generalizations of (1) and (2), respectively.

It is also seen at once that (11) can be either positive or negative, whereas

(12) cannot obtain negative values. This is natural in view of the intuitive difference between the two measures inf and cont. Our *surprise* at finding that g is the case can be greater after we have first found out that h is true than it would be a priori. Thus h may have a negative surprise value concerning the subject matter of g.

In contrast, the substantive information that h conveys concerning the subject matter of any g has to be positive (or zero), as it was found to be.

When g and h are independent (with respect to the probability measure p), (11) is zero. When $h \supset g$ is logically true, (g & h) is logically equivalent with h, and (11) therefore receives the value $-\log p(g) = \inf(g)$. As might be expected, in this case the information h carries concerning the subject matter of g is the same g itself carries. This is in fact an optimal case, for if g is constant but h varies, $\inf(g)$ is the largest value (11) can receive.

Similarly, (12) and (13) also assume their maxima (for a constant g) when g is logically implied by h. Furthermore, (13) is like (11) in that it assumes the value $= 0$ when g and h are probabilistically independent.

It is also worth noting that both (11) and (12) are symmetric with respect to g and h, whereas (13) is not.

Because of the importance of the ideas that underlie (11)–(13), a special notation may be in order. I shall use for (11) the expression transinf($h|g$), for (12) the expression transcont$_{add}$($h|g$), and for (13) the expression transcont$_{cond}$($h|g$). The suggested approximate readings are: "the information h conveys concerning the subject matter of g" for the first two and "the change in the content of g due to h" for the third. The motivation for the notation will be given later.

Examples of the distinction between the plain information inf(h) or cont(h) and one of the relative senses of information (11)–(13) abound in ordinary life. If I am told that such-and-such weather conditions obtain in San Francisco today (e.g. "it is foggy today"), what is the information this statement (call it "s") gives me? Usually, I am not impressed by the reduction of my uncertainty concerning San Francisco weather today that this statement brings about, i.e., I am not particularly interested in inf(s) or in cont(s). I am much likelier to be interested in the information this statement gives me concerning the weather conditions that might be expected to obtain on some other day, e.g. tomorrow. For instance, I might be interested in the information s conveys concerning the chances that it will be foggy in San Francisco tomorrow, too. If this is expressed by the statement t, this means that I am interested in transinf($s|t$) or perhaps in transcont$_{add}$($s|t$) or transcont$_{cond}$($s|t$) rather than in inf(s) or in cont(s).

This homely example perhaps also illustrates the ubiquitousness of the senses of information we have just characterized. Another indication of their prevalence is the role of expressions like (11) in statistical information theory, where they are said to define *transmitted information*.[15] The connection between this usage and the explanations we have given of (11) is straightforward: in the case of the transformation of messages we are interested in the amount of information carried by the statement that a certain definite message is received concerning whether what was sent or not. If h is the statement about the arrival of the message and g the statement about its being sent, then this is precisely what (11) expresses.

6. Expected information

What we have said so far does not exhaust all the senses (or kinds) of information one might legitimately be interested in. Often, in the kind of situation with which my example dealt, we are not primarily interested in the reduction of our uncertainty as to whether it will be foggy in San Francisco tomorrow. Rather, we might be interested in the reduction of our uncertainty as to *whether or not* it will be foggy. One important kind of information can be measured by measuring the reduction of this uncertainty. A way of doing so is as follows: Let $e=$ "it is foggy today" and $h=$ "it will be foggy tomorrow". Then the expected value of the information which e yields concerning the state of affairs described by h or by $\sim h$ is

$$p(h|e) \operatorname{transinf}(e|h) + p(\sim h|e) \operatorname{transinf}(e|\sim h) \qquad (14)$$

or

$$p(h|e) \operatorname{transcont}_{add}(e|h) + p(\sim h|e) \operatorname{transcont}_{add}(e|\sim h) \qquad (15)$$

depending whether we are considering unexpectedness or substantial information.

The expression analogous to (15)

$$p(h|e) \operatorname{transcont}_{cond}(e|h) + p(\sim h|e) \operatorname{transcont}_{cond}(e|\sim h) \qquad (16)$$

measures the expected change in the information of the true answer to the question: "Is h or $\sim h$ the case?" that is brought about by our knowledge of e.

More generally, if we are dealing with a number of pairwise exclusive and collectively exhaustive alternatives $h_1, h_2, ..., h_k$, then the information which

---

[15] Cf. e.g. SHANNON and WEAVER [1949] pp. 36, 110–111. The difference $\operatorname{inf}(g) - \operatorname{transinf}(h|g) = \operatorname{inf}(g|h)$ is the so-called "equivocation" of the statistical information theorists.

e carries concerning the subject matter they speak of is in the present sense of the word measured by

$$\sum_i p(h_i|e) \, \text{transinf}(e|h_i) = \sum_i p(h_i|e) \log \frac{p(h_i|e)}{p(h_i)}$$

$$= \sum_i p(h_i|e) \log [p(h_i \& e)/p(h_i) \, p(e)] \qquad (17)$$

or by

$$\sum_i p(h_i|e) \, \text{transcont}_{\text{add}}(e|h_i) = 1 - \sum_i p(h_i|e) \, p(h_i \vee e), \qquad (18)$$

respectively. An analogous expression gives the expected effect of our "evidence" *e* (as we may think of it) on the true alternative h_i:

$$\sum_i p(h_i|e) \, \text{transcont}_{\text{cond}}(e|h_i). \qquad (19)$$

Expressions of the form (17) occur in statistical information theory and also in theoretical statistics. [16] Although they have not been considered very often by logicians and philosophical methodologists, it seems to me that they ought to have been. They arise on the basis of the very general considerations which were sketched above and which are largely independent of the particular kind of probability which has been assumed to underlie our discussion. They are not due to the statistical character of the ordinary "statistical" information theory nor to any particular sense of probability employed therein.

7. Applications of the distinctions. Local versus global theorizing

The concept of relative information defined by (17) and (18) can be illustrated by means of many different examples. One of them pertains to a line of argument which I used in an earlier paper. Suppose we have a number (say *k*) of primitive predicates by means of which we can classify individuals into $K=2^k$ Q-predicates (in Carnap's sense). Assume that we are interested in the question how the individuals of our universe of discourse are distributed among the different Q-predicates. More specifically, we may ask whether they leave some Q-predicates empty, i.e. whether any true general laws can be formulated in terms of our primitive predicates and quantifiers, and also what the relative frequencies of the different Q-predicates are. In both these respects, the information conveyed by an observation-statement concerning a finite number of individuals (stating which Q-predicates belong

---

[16] See e.g. SAVAGE [1954] pp. 50, 235–238.

to them) depends on what we know (or, if we are subjectivists, what we believe) of the overall regularity of our universe.

An extreme case is one in which the universe is known to be completely regular: all individuals have the same Q-predicate, although we do not know a priori which. Then an observation-statement concerning a single individual gives us all the information we are interested in, both information concerning laws and information concerning relative frequencies.

More generally, an observation statement is clearly the more informative the more regular the universe is known to be. For instance, if we know that our individuals are likely to be concentrated heavily on a few Q-predicates, the observation of (say) just two individuals having the same Q-predicate tells us more about the universe than it would do if we knew that the universe is "disorderly" in the sense that its members are likely to be divided evenly among all the Q-predicates. In the latter case, the identity of the Q-predicates which the two individuals have is likely to be dismissed as a freak.

Elsewhere I have briefly discussed the consequences of observations of this kind.[17] Here I want to emphasize only the fact that the sense in which we are here speaking of the information of an observation-statement has to be defined by (17) or (18) rather than by (1) or (2). What is involved is the information these singular observation-statements convey concerning possible generalizations (strict or statistical generalizations). In fact, it is readily seen that the "absolute" information (defined by (1) or (2)) of the observation-statements is not what is involved, for it is low precisely when an observation-statement is highly informative about generalizations, in the sense just explained, i.e. when a high degree of regularity may be expected. This illustrates quite strikingly the difference between (1)–(2) on one hand and (17)–(18) on the other.

It also illustrates the fact that the difference between $\mathrm{inf}(e)$ and $\mathrm{trans\text{-}inf}(e|h)$ (as well as between $\mathrm{cont}(e)$ and $\mathrm{transcont}(e|h)$) is especially important in the case of a singular statement e. We are seldom interested in the information such a statement conveys concerning its own subject matter, but rather in what it tells us concerning other (unobserved) individuals or concerning different possible generalizations. In contrast, we are much likelier to be interested in the information generalizations carry concerning their own subject matter.

However, there are other important differences between different kinds of situations. One of the most important uses that our distinctions have is

---

[17] See HINTIKKA [1968].

to show that there are several different ways of looking at the relation of observational data to those hypotheses which are based on them and which perhaps are designed to explain them. In different situations the concept of information can be brought to bear on this relation in entirely different ways. There are hence no unique explications of such concepts as "explanation" and "degree of factual (evidential) support". No wonder, therefore, that a host of different explications have been offered for the latter notion in current literature.[18] In general, the scientific search for truth is much less of a single-goal enterprise than philosophers usually realize, and suitable distinctions between different senses of information perhaps serve to bring out some of the relevant differences between different goals.

Let us consider some differences between different cases. One of the most important distinctions here is between, on one hand, a case in which we are predominantly interested in a particular body of observations e which we want to explain by means of a suitable hypothesis h, and on the other hand a case in which we have no particular interest in our evidence e but rather want to use it as a stepping-stone to some general theory h which is designed to apply to other matters, too, besides e. We might label these two situations as cases of local and of global theorizing, respectively. Often the difference in question can also be characterized as a difference between explanation and generalization, respectively. Perhaps we can even partly characterize the difference between the activities of (local) explanation and (global) theorizing by spelling out (as we shall proceed to do) the difference between the two types of cases.

8. Maximum likelihood principle and its presuppositions

In the former case, we want to choose the explanatory hypothesis h such that it is maximally informative concerning the subject matter with which e deals. Since we know the truth of e already, we are not interested in the substantive information that h carries concerning the truth of e. What we want to do is to find h such that the truth of e is not unexpected, given h. This means that we want to deal with the measure of unexpectedness inf rather than with the measure cont, and to choose h such as to reduce the surprise value of e as much as possible.

Thus we arrive at the suggestion that in the case of explanation (local

---

[18] A convenient summary of a number of them is provided in the survey article by KYBURG [1964]. Cf. also GOOD [1960] and TÖRNEBOHM [1966].

theorizing) we should choose h so as to maximize

$$\text{transinf}(h|e) = \log[\text{p}(e|h)/\text{p}(e)].\tag{20}$$

Since e was assumed to be constant, to maximize (20) means to choose h so as to maximize the conditional probability $\text{p}(e|h)$, known as the likelihood of e given h. Thus we arrive at the famous maximum likelihood principle as the natural method of choosing one's explanatory hypothesis in the kind of circumstances indicated (local theorizing).[19] Thus the importance of this principle in statistics has an interesting general reason which can be brought out in terms of the concept of information.

Törnebohm has suggested using (20), suitably normalized, as a measure of the evidential strength of h vis-à-vis e.[20] In view of what we just found, it is not surprising that he should end up with the maximal likelihood principle when he applies the principle to a simple case.

At the same time our observations may indicate some of the limitations of Fisher's maximum likelihood principle. Its rationale was seen to be in terms of the concept of information. This recalls Fisher's insistence that he is not dealing with inductive behavior or with decisions under uncertainty, but with "the improvement of natural knowledge".[21] Our description above of the circumstances in which we are led to the maximum likelihood principle also recalls the kind of situation (analysis of experimental data) which Fisher typically deals with.[22] It may be that the maximum likelihood method is tied more closely than its proponents sometimes realize to cases where the explanation of the particular data predominates over other concerns. It appears that the maximum likelihood principle is a weapon of explanation rather than of generalization.

This does not mean that the maximum likelihood principle cannot occasionally be quite useful for the latter purpose, too. This is the case when we already know that any explanation of the particular data we have will serve to explain whatever other data we might be interested in. This presupposes, obviously, that the regularity of our universe is already known to be maximal (or very great) in the relevant respects – in the sense that whatever observations we make concerning a part of it can be carried over intact so as to

[19] For the principle, see e.g. CRAMÉR [1946] pp. 498–506; FISHER [1956] pp. 68–72.
[20] TÖRNEBOHM [1966].
[21] FISHER [1956] pp. 100–104.
[22] In Fisher's view, "the science of statistics is essentially a branch of Applied Mathematics, and may be defined as mathematics as applied to observational data" (FISHER [1925] p. 1).

apply to others.[23] However, to paraphrase a well-known statement of Mill's, whoever answers the question as to when this is possible, has solved the riddle of induction, and the maximum likelihood principle does not help us in that enterprise. These observations are connected with Fisher's penchant to assume, in the case of estimation, that the correct form of a law has already been discovered and that there remains only the task of estimating the numerical values of the parameters these laws involve. What I would consider the main aspect of theorizing as distinguished from explanation, viz. determining the form of these laws, is thus assumed to have been accomplished before the estimation problem is raised.

In another paper, I have studied some ways of expressing the regularity which we have been discussing by means of explicit parameters.[24] Whenever the regularity is not maximal, we have to be wary of generalizing too much from observations. The strength of this conservatism varies inversely to the regularity we are allowed to assume there is in the universe. Carnap's λ is a well-known index of conservatism of this kind. I have argued that its uses are restricted to singular inductive inference and that we need a comparable index of caution for inductive generalization, too. Be this as it may, it is interesting to see that the maximum likelihood principle results from the types of inductive logic which are calculated to be models (however oversimplified) of genuine inductive inference if and only if $\lambda \rightarrow 0$, i.e. only if the regularity of our universe is maximal. It is only then that the maximal likelihood principle is an acceptable tool of inductive inference.

In order to have a firm grasp of the nature of this principle, it is perhaps useful to have a closer look at its consequences for the kind of "Carnapian" situation which has already been used earlier as a testing ground (applied monadic first-order language). In such a situation, we can classify observed individuals into a number of classes (some of which may be empty) and which form a partition of our universe of discourse. (They may be given by the Q-predicates mentioned above.) If we have observed a random sample of individuals belonging to some of these, what hypothesis should we set up

---

[23] Is it accidental that so many of the most successful applications of Fisherian techniques have been in the field of biology? Is it perhaps the case that the presuppositions of the use of these techniques for the purpose of genuine theorizing are likelier to be satisfied there than in the social sciences? Once you have found out all the relevant features of a few well-developed members of a species, you are apt to have found out what you wanted for the whole species, one is tempted to say, and this would be precisely what the assumption of maximum regularity amounts to.

[24] See HINTIKKA [1966] and cf. Carnap's earlier work on the index of caution λ for singular inductive inference, especially CARNAP [1952].

concerning the whole universe? The answer which the maximum likelihood principle gives is known as the straight rule. [25] It tells us to assume that the actual relative frequencies of the different kinds of individuals in the whole universe are the same as the observed relative frequencies.

It is not hard to see that this is not a very realistic method of choosing our hypothesis in many cases, especially when our sample is small. (Suppose e.g. that we have observed only two individuals of different kinds. It does not appear motivated to assume on the basis of such a sample that all the individuals of the universe belong to the two kinds our pair of observed individuals exemplify, or that they are divided precisely evenly between the two.) Hence the straight rule is rejected by the majority of writers on induction as a method of generalizing from random samples. It is important to realize, however, that this rejection depends entirely on our interest in what they hypothesis we adopt says of individuals other than the observed ones, in brief, what its total information is. If our sole purpose were merely to give the best possible available explanation of our observations, we might be led to change our preferences and opt for the straight rule. And we would certainly do so in any case if we happened to know that the universe is completely regular.

An interesting interpretation of (11) is obtained by observing that

$$\mathrm{transinf}(h|g) = \inf(g) - \inf(g|h) = \inf(g) + \inf(h) - \inf(g \,\&\, h)$$

which can obviously be interpreted as the amount of information shared by h and g. Starting from this idea, Törnebohm makes the shrewd observation that the use of (20) (perhaps suitably normalized) as a measure of the acceptability of h seems to be in good agreement with the practice of historians. [26] A historian, clearly, is striving to organize his narrative so as to make the information it conveys overlap as closely as possible with the information his sources (i.e. the evidence e) contain, which is just what the maximization of (20) (for a fixed e) amounts to. It is important to realize, however, that in this respect the interests of a historian are apt to differ from those of a scientist. In the recent discussions concerning the methodology of history, it has frequently been insisted that a historian does not strive to generalize. [27] Part of what is perhaps meant by such statements can now be appreciated. A historian is in the first place trying to explain the particular data he has,

---

[25] Cf. CARNAP [1952].
[26] TÖRNEBOHM [1966] p. 85.
[27] See e.g. DRAY [1956] and the references to the subsequent discussion in PASSMORE [1966] pp. 539–540.

and is not overtly concerned with setting up theories with a view to saying something informative about individuals and events not immediately relevant to these data. [28] This is precisely why a historian can be said (very roughly of course) to be guided, in his choice of a hypothesis h, by the expression (20) for the information which h gives concerning e, rather than by some function that turns on the overall information of h.

More generally, the importance of likelihoods in statistical testing can be appreciated in the light of our observations. If two hypotheses h_i and h_j are compared with respect to their informativeness for certain particular data e, we have

$$\text{transinf}(h_i|e) - \text{transinf}(h_j|e) = \log[\text{p}(e|h_i)/\text{p}(e|h_j)]. \tag{21}$$

In other words, if this is all that matters, the comparison between h_i and h_j turns entirely on the likelihood ratio $\text{p}(e|h_i)/\text{p}(e|h_j)$.

9. Maximizing expected content

However, if we are interested in our data (say e) merely as partial evidence for a global theory h, the situation is quite different. Here we are not so much interested in maximizing $\text{transinf}(h|e)$ as maximizing in some sense the information of h itself. Especially when h is a general statement, we are likelier to be interested in the substantive information it yields than in its surprise value. (Trying to maximize substantive information is typically an indication of serious global theorizing.) To maximize this directly means simply to opt for the least likely theory without considering any kind of evidential support, which is obviously unrealistic. The natural course in this case is therefore to consider the expected value of this substantive information as a result of the adoption of the hypothesis (theory) h. If h is true, we gain the (substantive) information $\text{cont}(h)$ by adopting h. If h is false, we loose the information which we could have gained by opting for $\sim h$, rather than h. According to what was just said, our net utility in this case is therefore $-\text{cont}(\sim h)$. The expected value of our information gain is thus

$$\text{p}(h|e)\cdot\text{cont}(h) - \text{p}(\sim h|e)\cdot\text{cont}(\sim h), \tag{22}$$

---

[28] In view of what was said above of regularity and maximum likelihood, this is not incompatible with saying that general laws are involved in historical explanations, too, provided these general laws are taken to be of a very unproblematic character – so unproblematic, indeed, that if they are known to apply in one case, they can be applied to all the others. This is not entirely unlike what the defenders of "covering-law" explanations in history have been led to say of the generalizations involved in historical explanations.

which simplifies as

$$p(h|e) - p(h). \tag{23}$$

This is simply the increase in the probability of h which has been brought about by the evidence e. If expected information is used as a measure of the acceptability of a theory, this acceptability does not depend on a priori or a posteriori probability alone, but on the effect of evidence – on "how well the theory has stood up to the test of experience".[29]

It has been shown elsewhere that a policy of maximizing (23) when one is carrying out a generalization (i.e. choosing h among all the available general statements) results in certain interesting cases in a sound method of inductive generalization.[30]

On the basis of what was said above it is not surprising that it is just in the case of inductive generalization that this strategy succeeds.

Hempel has proposed that we use the relative measure $\text{cont}_{\text{add}}(h|e) = \text{cont}(e \supset h)$ rather than the absolute one $\text{cont}(h)$.[31] The most straightforward way of doing so fails, however, for if we identify the utility of the correct adoption of h with $\text{cont}_{\text{add}}(h|e)$ and the disutility of an incorrect adoption with $\text{cont}_{\text{add}}(\sim h|e)$ (i.e. with the utility which we could have gained by adopting $\sim h$ instead of h), the expected value of our utility will be

$$p(h|e)\,\text{cont}_{\text{add}}(h|e) - p(\sim h|e)\,\text{cont}_{\text{add}}(\sim h|e) =$$
$$= p(h|e)\,p(\sim h\,\&\,e) - p(\sim h|e)\,p(h\,\&\,e) = 0. \tag{24}$$

This result may have been instrumental in leading Hempel to adopt a different measure of the disutility of an incorrect adoption of h.

An attempt to use $\text{cont}_{\text{cond}}$ instead of cont_{add} does not help, for

$$p(h|e)\,\text{cont}_{\text{cond}}(h|e) - p(\sim h|e)\,\text{cont}_{\text{cond}}(\sim h|e) =$$
$$= p(h|e)(1 - p(h|e)) - (1 - p(h|e))\,p(h|e) = 0.$$

The use of (23) as a function to be maximized derives further support from other considerations. It lies close at hand to suggest that we should maximize, not the expected absolute content $\text{cont}(h)$ of a hypothesis h, but rather the

---

[29] The similarity between this characteristic of (23) and what Popper says of his notion of corroboration might prompt one to offer (23) as a possible explication of corroboration. Good has in effect done this, in the highly interesting paper GOOD [1960]. Actually, there is also a rather close connection between (23) and a slightly different notion of POPPER's [1954], called explanatory power. (See below, p. 329.)

[30] HINTIKKA and PIETARINEN [1966].

[31] HEMPEL [1962] especially pp. 153–156; HEMPEL [1960].

content it has relative to the subject matter of the conjunction of all evidential statements e, or $\text{transcont}_{\text{add}}(h|e)$. The expected value of this is, according to the principles already used in obtaining (22),

$$p(h|e)\,\text{transcont}_{\text{add}}(h|e) - p(\sim h|e)\,\text{transcont}_{\text{add}}(\sim h|e). \qquad (25)$$

Substituting for $\text{transcont}_{\text{add}}(h|e)$, which by symmetry is $\text{transcont}_{\text{add}}(e|h)$, the expression $\text{cont}(h) - \text{cont}_{\text{add}}(h|e)$ we obtain from (25)

$$[p(h|e)\,\text{cont}(h) - p(\sim h|e)\,\text{cont}(\sim h)] +$$
$$- [p(h|e)\,\text{cont}_{\text{add}}(h|e) - p(\sim h|e)\,\text{cont}_{\text{add}}(\sim h|e)].$$

Here the second term is (24), and hence zero, while the first is (22) and hence identical with (23) or $p(h|e) - p(h)$. Thus we obtain the same result no matter whether we are trying to maximize the expected value of the absolute content $\text{cont}(h)$ of h or the expected value of the content $\text{transcont}_{\text{add}}(h|e)$ of h with respect to the evidence e. This result may seem surprising. It is understood, however, when we realize that the only "boundary condition" which prevents us from maximizing the content of h ad libitum is the requirement that it has to agree with the evidence e we have. Thus the task in both cases is essentially to maximize the content (substantive information) that h gives us concerning our evidence.

Furthermore, (23) is according to (13) precisely $\text{transcont}_{\text{cond}}(e|h)$, that is, the effect of evidence e on the information-carrying status of hypothesis h. In choosing h so as to maximize the expected value of its information-content $\text{cont}(h)$, we are ipso facto choosing h so as to maximize the gain which our evidence e gives us concerning the information h carries. There is a certain partial symmetry between the principle involved here and the maximum likelihood principle. In the latter, we are maximizing the information (in the sense of (11)) which the hypothesis gives us concerning the evidence, whereas in the former we are maximizing the gain in information (change in the information-carrying status) which the given evidence e brings about concerning a hypothesis.

But why maximize $\text{transcont}_{\text{cond}}(e|h)$ and not its expected value? This contrast is empty, for according to the principles used in arriving at (22) the expectation of $\text{transcont}_{\text{cond}}(e|h)$ is

$$p(h|e)\,\text{transcont}_{\text{cond}}(e|h) - p(\sim h|e)\,\text{transcont}_{\text{cond}}(e|\sim h) =$$
$$= p(h|e)\,[p(h|e) - p(h)] - [1 - p(h|e)]\,[1 - p(h|e) - (1 - p(h))] =$$
$$= p(h|e) - p(h) = \text{transcont}_{\text{cond}}(e|h). \qquad (26)$$

In other words, to maximize $\text{transcont}_{\text{cond}}(e|h)$ is to maximize its expected value, giving us for the fourth time the same expression to be maximized.

10. Degrees of "evidential support"

Thus (23) serves as an especially interesting index of the relation of a hypothesis h to the evidence e. In suitable circumstances, it might be considered as an index of the acceptability of h on the basis of e. Measures of such acceptability are sometimes known as indices of "evidential power" of e with respect to h or the "corroboration" that e lends to h.[32] If (23) is used as a measure of evidential power, it may be desirable to normalize it in a suitable way so as to make the bounds of its variation more uniform.

When h and e are independent with respect to the probability measure p, (23) is zero, for then $p(h|e) = p(h)$. When e logically implies h, $p(h|e) = 1$, and (23) reduces therefore to $p(\sim h)$. When e logically implies $\sim h$, (23) reduces to $-p(h)$. It lies here close at hand to multiply (23) by a suitable normalizing factor. Among the available possibilities there are e.g. the following normalizing factors: (a) $1/p(h)\,p(\sim h)$; (b) $1/p(h)$; (c) $p(e)/p(\sim h)$. These give us the following respective values in the two extreme cases mentioned above: (a) $1/p(h)$ and $-1/p(\sim h)$; (b) $p(\sim h)/p(h)$ and -1; (c) $p(e)$ and $-p(e)\,p(h)/p(\sim h)$.

These still depend on h, however. In order to see one way of making them independent of h, let us first use the normalizing factor (a) which is perhaps the most natural one here. The result can easily be rewritten as

$$\frac{p(e|h) - p(e|\sim h)}{p(e)} \tag{27}$$

which now varies between $1/p(h)$ and $-1/p(\sim h)$. An obvious way to "normalize" this so as to vary between $+1$ and -1 is to replace it by

$$\frac{p(e|h) - p(e|\sim h)}{p(e|h) + p(e|\sim h)}. \tag{27*}$$

This always changes in the same direction as (27).

It behaves in an orderly way: it varies between $+1$ and -1 and receives these two extreme values only when $\vdash(e \supset h)$ and $\vdash(e \supset \sim h)$, respectively, as one can readily verify.

Most of the expressions which we have recently mentioned have actually

---

[32] For a possible difference between these two notions, see GOOD [1960].

been proposed by different writers as measures of evidential power. A number of such suggestions have been conveniently summarized by Kyburg.[33] Of the proposals he lists, those by Levi and Carnap amount to (23) itself. (No suggestion to this effect seems to have been actually made by Carnap, however, and Levi therefore appears to have been the first philosopher to use (23) as a measure of acceptability of h relative to e.) The use of the normalizing factor (b) is tantamount to a suggestion by Finch, and the use of (c) to one by Rescher, while (27)* has been proposed by Kemeny and Oppenheim as a measure of the degree of factual support. If we had normalized (23) directly, without first rewriting it as (27), that is to say, if we had replaced it simply by

$$\frac{p(h|e) - p(h)}{p(h|e) + p(h)} \tag{28}$$

we would have obtained Popper's measure of the explanatory power of e with respect to h. (The limits of its variation are $(1-p(h))/(1+p(h))$ and -1, the former of which still depends on h.) From the point of view here adopted, all these proposed definitions thus turn out to be closely related to each other, and also turn out to be partly justifiable in terms of the concept of information. There is thus more uniformity in different philosophers' conceptions of factual support (or explanatory power) than first meets the eye. It is perhaps significant that all the proposals we have mentioned have turned out to be closely connected with the concept of substantive information (the expected value of our cont) rather than with the concept of surprise value (unexpectedness).

11. Possible reasons for preferring one sense of information

I said earlier that scientific inquiry is a multi-goal enterprise and that there cannot therefore be any uniform measure of its success, i.e. any unique measure of how "good" one's hypotheses and explanations are. This does not mean, however, that the choice of our measures of success – which normally prejudges partly our choice of the statistical techniques involved – is arbitrary or a matter of convention. Very often there are some objective guide-lines, and the realization of what one's objectives are and what their

---

[33] See KYBURG [1964], who supplies further references to the relevant literature. It is perhaps worthwhile to note that in Kemeny and Oppenheim an important role is played by the requirement that their measure of factual support must vary between -1 and $+1$. See KEMENY and OPPENHEIM [1952].

realization presupposes can be a matter of considerable urgency. For instance, if a social science aims at a genuine theory, it cannot be satisfied with explanations of the different particular data that it has available, however "rich" these data and these explanations may be. For a discussion of this point in the case of sociology, see Bernard P. Cohen, "On the construction of sociological explanations" (forthcoming).

There is another, much vaguer criterion that might also be worth a closer scrutiny. Often, the best way of describing an inductive situation is to think of it as arising from a second-order probability distribution, that is, from a probability distribution on a class of probability distributions. De Finetti's famous representation (basis) theorem in fact says that this can be done under quite weak conditions. Now it may be the case that we do not know a priori some of the characteristic parameters of this second-order distribution, but have to estimate them on the basis of our evidence. How are we to do this? In some vague sense, it seems that for this purpose the maximum likelihood principle is appropriate even where it is clearly inappropriate for the purpose of estimating the characteristics of the (true) first-order distribution. In so far as this feeling can be rationalized, it seems to turn on the fact that the second-order distribution exhaust our interest in the world. It may often be inappropriate to focus our explanation on one particular set of data, for there may be other sets of data available which we also have to heed in developing a satisfactory overall theory. But in the case of an explanation of the global features of the universe (as it were), there is nothing else we could possibly be interested in, and hence we can be happy if we can explain them to the exclusion of everything else, for there are no other universa which we have to beware of. And this of course means that the maximum likelihood principle is appropriate.[34]

References

ADAMS, E. W., On the nature and purpose of measurement, Synthese 16 (1966) 125–169.
BAR-HILLEL, Y., Language and information, selected essays on their theory and application (Addison-Wesley Publ. Co., Inc., Reading, Mass., 1964).
BAR-HILLEL, Y. and R. CARNAP, Semantic information, Brit. J. Phil. Sci. 4 (1953) 144–157.
CARNAP, R., Continuum of inductive methods (Chicago, University of Chicago Press, 1952).
CARNAP, R. and Y. BAR-HILLEL, An outline of a theory of semantic information, Techn. Report no. 247 (Research Laboratory of Electronics, Massachusetts Institute of Technology, 1952); reprinted in: BAR-HILLEL [1964].

---

[34] It would be interesting to examine whether this is perhaps part of the reason why Reichenbach resorted to higher-order probabilities in his defense of the straight rule; see REICHENBACH [1949].

CHERRY, C., On human communication (The M.I.T. Press, Cambridge, Mass., 1957; second edition, 1966).

COX, R.T., The algebra of probable inference (The John Hopkins Press, Baltimore, 1961).

CRAMÉR, H., Mathematical methods of statistics (Princeton, Princeton University Press, 1946).

DRAY, W., Laws and explanation in history (Oxford, Clarendon Press, 1956).

DUBINS, L.E. and L.J. SAVAGE, How to gamble if you must: inequalities for stochastic processes (New York, McGraw-Hill, 1965).

FISHER, Sir R.A., Statistical methods for research workers (Edinburgh, Oliver and Boyd, 1925).

FISHER, Sir R.A., Statistical methods and scientific inference (Edinburgh, Oliver and Boyd, 1956).

GOOD, I.J., Weight of evidence, corroboration, explanatory power, information and the utility of experiments, J. Roy. Stat. Soc. B 22 (1960) 319–331.

HANNA, J., A new approach to the formulating and testing of learning models, Synthese 16 (1966) 344–380.

HEMPEL, C.G., Deductive-nomological versus statistical explanation, in: Scientific explanation, space and time, Minnesota studies in the philosophy of science, Vol. 3, eds. H. Feigl and G. Maxwell (Minneapolis, University of Minnesota Press, 1962) pp. 98–169.

HEMPEL, C.G., Inductive inconsistencies, Synthese 12 (1960) 439–469; reprinted in: C.G. Hempel, Aspects of scientific explanation and other essays in the philosophy of science (New York, The Free Press, 1965) pp. 53–79.

HINTIKKA, J., Towards a theory of inductive generalization, in: Logic, methodology and philosophy of science, ed. Y. Bar-Hillel (Amsterdam, North-Holland Publ. Co., 1965) pp. 274–288.

HINTIKKA, J., A two-dimensional continuum of inductive logic, in: Aspects of inductive logic, eds. J. Hintikka and P. Suppes (Amsterdam, North-Holland Publ. Co., 1966) pp. 113–132.

HINTIKKA, J., On semantic information, to appear in: Proc. Intern. Colloq. on logic, physical reality and history at the University of Denver, ed. W. Yourgrau (The Plenum Press, New York, 1968).

HINTIKKA, J. and J. PIETARINEN, Semantic information and inductive logic, in: Aspects of inductive logic, eds. J. Hintikka and P. Suppes (Amsterdam, North-Holland Publ. Co., 1966) pp. 96–112.

KEMENY, J.G., A logical measure function, J. Symb. Logic 18 (1953) 289–308.

KEMENY, J.G. and P. OPPENHEIM, Degree of factual support, Phil. of Sci. 19 (1952) 307–324.

KHINCHIN, A.I., Mathematical foundations of information theory (Dover Publications, N.Y., 1957).

KYBURG, H.E., Recent work in inductive logic, Am. Phil. Quart. 1 (1964) 249–287.

PASSMORE, J., A hundred years of philosophy (London, second edition, 1966).

POPPER, K.R., Logik der Forschung (Springer-Verlag, Wien, 1935); transl. with new notes and appendices as: The logic of scientific discovery (Hutchinson and Co., London, 1959).

POPPER, K.R., Degree of confirmation, Brit. J. Phil. Sci. 5 (1954) 143–149. (Correction ibid. 334.)

REICHENBACH, H., The theory of probability (Berkeley and Los Angeles, University of California Press, 1949).

SAVAGE, L.J., The foundations of statistics (New York, John Wiley and Sons, 1954).

SHANNON, C.E. and W. WEAVER, The mathematical theory of communication (The University of Illinois Press, Urbana, Illinois, 1949).

TÖRNEBOHM, H., Information and confirmation, Gothenburg studies in philosophy, Vol. 3 (Stockholm, Almquist and Wiksell, 1964).

TÖRNEBOHM, H., Two measures of evidential strength, in: Aspects of inductive logic, eds. J. Hintikka and P. Suppes (Amsterdam, North-Holland Publ. Co., 1966) pp. 81–95.

EPISTEMOLOGY WITHOUT A KNOWING SUBJECT

K. R. POPPER

University of London, England

Allow me to start with a confession. Although I am a very happy philosopher I have, after a lifetime of lecturing, no illusions about what I can convey in a lecture. For this reason I shall make no attempt in this lecture to convince you. Instead I shall make an attempt to challenge you, and, if possible, to provoke you.

1. Three theses on epistemology and the third world

I might have challenged those who have heard of my adverse attitude towards Plato and Hegel by calling my lecture '*A theory of the Platonic world*', or '*A theory of the objective spirit*'.

The main topic of this lecture will be what I often call, for want of a better name, '*the third world*'. To explain this expression I will point out that, without taking the words 'world' or 'universe' too seriously, we may distinguish the following three worlds or universes: first, the world of physical objects or of physical states; secondly, the world of states of consciousness, or of mental states, or perhaps of behavioural dispositions to act; and thirdly, the world of *objective contents of thought*, especially of scientific and poetic thoughts and of works of art.

Thus what I call 'the third world' has admittedly much in common with Plato's theory of forms or ideas, and therefore also with Hegel's objective spirit, though my theory differs radically, in some decisive respects, from Plato's and Hegel's. It has more in common still with Bolzano's theory of a universe of propositions in themselves and of truths in themselves, though it differs from Bolzano also. My third world resembles most closely the universe of Frege's objective contents of thought.

It is not part of my view or of my argument that we might not enumerate our worlds in different ways, or not enumerate them at all. We might, especially, distinguish more than three worlds. My term 'the third world' is merely a matter of convenience.

In upholding an objective third world I hope to provoke those whom I call *'belief philosophers'*: those who, like Descartes, Locke, Berkeley, Hume, Kant, or Russell, are interested in our subjective beliefs, and their basis or origin. Against these belief philosophers I urge that our problem is to find better and bolder theories; and that *critical preference* counts, but *not belief.*

I wish to confess, however, at the very beginning, that I am a realist: I suggest, somewhat like a naive realist, that there is a physical world and a world of states of consciousness, and that these two interact. And I believe that there is a third world, in a sense which I shall explain more fully.

Among the inmates of my 'third world' are, more especially, *theoretical systems*; but just as important inmates are *problems* and *problem situations*. And I will argue that the most important inmates of this world are *critical arguments*, and what may be called – in analogy to a physical state or to a state of consciousness – *the state of a discussion* or the *state of a critical argument*; and, of course, the contents of journals, books and libraries.

Most opponents of the thesis of an objective third world will of course admit that there are problems, conjectures, theories, arguments, journals and books. But they usually say that all these entities are, essentially, symbolic or linguistic *expressions* of subjective mental states, or perhaps of behavioural dispositions to act; further, that these entities are means of *communication*, that is to say, symbolic or linguistic means to evoke in others similar mental states or behavioural disposition to act.

Against this, I have often argued that one cannot relegate all these entities and their content to the second world.

Let me repeat one of my standard arguments* for the (more or less) *independent existence of the third world.*

I consider two thought experiments:

Experiment (1). All our machines and tools are destroyed, also all our subjective learning, including our subjective knowledge of machines and tools, and how to use them. But *libraries and our capacity to learn from them* survive. Clearly, after much suffering, our world may get going again.

Experiment (2). As before, machines and tools are destroyed, and our subjective learning, including our subjective knowledge of machines and tools, and how to use them. But this time, *all libraries are destroyed also*, so that our capacity to learn from books becomes useless.

---

* The argument is adapted from POPPER [1962] Vol. II; cp. p. 108.

If you think about these two experiments, the reality, significance and the degree of autonomy of the third world (as well as its effects on the second and first worlds) may perhaps become a little clearer to you. For in the second case there will be no re-emergence of our civilization for many millennia.

I wish to defend in this lecture three main theses, all of which concern epistemology. Epistemology I take to be the theory of *scientific knowledge*.

My first thesis is this. Traditional epistemology has studied knowledge or thought in a subjective sense – in the sense of the ordinary usage of the words 'I know' or 'I am thinking'. This, I assert, has led students of epistemology into irrelevancies: while intending to study scientific knowledge, they studied in fact something which is of no relevance to scientific knowledge. For *scientific knowledge* simply is not knowledge in the sense of the ordinary usage of the words 'I know'. While knowledge in the sense of 'I know' belongs to what I call the 'second world', the world of *subjects*, scientific knowledge belongs to the third world, to the world of objective theories, objective problems, and objective arguments.

Thus my first thesis is that the traditional epistemology, of Locke, Berkeley, Hume, and even of Russell, is irrelevant, in a pretty strict sense of the word. It is a corollary of this thesis that a large part of contemporary epistemology is irrelevant also. This includes modern epistemic logic, *if* we assume that it aims at a theory of *scientific knowledge*. However, any epistemic logician can easily make himself completely immune from my criticism, simply by making clear that he does not aim at contributing to the *theory of scientific knowledge*.

My first thesis involves the existence of two different senses of knowledge or of thought: *knowledge or thought in the subjective sense*, consisting of a state of mind or of consciousness or a disposition to behave or to react, and *knowledge in an objective sense*, consisting of problems, theories, and arguments as such. Knowledge in this objective sense is totally independent of anybody's claim to know; also it is independent of anybody's belief, or disposition to assent; or to assert, or to act. Knowledge in the objective sense is *knowledge without a knower*: it is *knowledge without a knowing subject*.

Of thought in the objective sense Frege wrote: 'I understand by a *thought* not the subjective act of thinking but its *objective content*...'.*

The two senses of thought and their interesting interrelations can be illustrated by the following highly convincing quotation from HEYTING [1962] p. 195 who says about Brouwer's act of inventing his theory of the continuum:

---

* Cp. FREGE [1892] p. 32; italics mine.

'If recursive functions had been invented before, he [Brouwer] would perhaps not have formed the notion of a choice sequence which, I think, would have been unlucky.'

This quotation refers on the one hand to some *subjective thought processes* of Brouwer's and says that they might not have occurred (which would have been unfortunate) had the *objective problem situation* been different.

Thus Heyting mentions certain possible *influences* upon Brouwer's subjective thought processes, and he also expresses his opinion regarding the value of these subjective thought processes. Now it is interesting that influences, *qua* influences, must be subjective: only Brouwer's subjective acquaintance with recursive functions could have had that unfortunate effect of preventing him from inventing free choice sequences.

On the other hand, the quotation from Heyting points to a certain objective relationship between the *objective contents* of two thoughts or theories: Heyting does not refer to the subjective conditions or the electrochemistry of Brouwer's brain processes, but to an *objective problem situation in mathematics* and its possible influences on Brouwer's subjective acts of thought which were bent on solving these objective problems. I would describe this by saying that Heyting's remark is about the objective or third-world *situational logic* of Brouwer's invention, and that Heyting's remark implies that the third-world situation may affect the second world. Similarly, Heyting's suggestion that it would have been unfortunate if Brouwer had not invented choice sequences is a way of saying that the *objective content* of Brouwer's thought was valuable and interesting; valuable and interesting, that is, in the way it changed the objective problem situation in the third world.

To put the matter simply, if I say 'Brouwer's thought was influenced by Kant' or even 'Brouwer rejected Kant's theory of space' then I speak at least partly about acts of thought in the subjective sense: the word 'influence' indicates a context of thought processes or acts of thinking. If I say, however, 'Brouwer's thought differs vastly from Kant's', then it is pretty clear that I speak mainly about contents. And ultimately if I say 'Brouwer's thoughts are incompatible with Russell's', then, by using a *logical term* such as '*incompatible*', I make it unambiguously clear that I am using the word 'thought' only in Frege's objective sense, and that I am speaking only about the objective content, or the logical content, of theories.

Just as ordinary language unfortunately has no separate terms for 'thought' in the sense of the second world and in the sense of the third world, so it has no separate terms for the corresponding two senses of 'I know' and of 'knowledge'.

In order to show that both senses exist, I will first mention three subjective or second-world examples:

(1) 'I *know* you are trying to provoke me, but I will not be provoked.'

(2) 'I *know* that Fermat's last theorem has not been proved, but I believe it will be proved one day.'

(3) From the entry 'Knowledge' in *The Oxford English dictionary*: *knowledge* is a 'state of being aware or informed'.

Next I will mention three objective or third-world examples:

(1) From the entry 'Knowledge' in *The Oxford English dictionary*: *knowledge* is a 'branch of learning; a science; an art'.

(2) 'Taking account of the present state of *metamathematical knowledge*, it seems possible that Fermat's last theorem may be undecidable.'

(3) 'I certify that this thesis is an original and significant *contribution to knowledge*.'

These very trite examples have only the function of helping to clarify what I mean when I speak of 'knowledge in the objective sense'. My quoting *The Oxford English dictionary* should not be interpreted as either a concession to language analysis or as an attempt to appease its adherents. It is not quoted in an attempt to prove that 'ordinary usage' covers 'knowledge' in the objective sense of my third world. In fact, I was surprised to find in *The Oxford English dictionary* examples of objective usages of 'knowledge'. (I was even more surprised to find some at least *partly* objective usages of 'know': 'to distinguish, to be acquainted with (a thing, a place, a person); ... to understand'. That these usages may be partly objective will emerge from the sequel*.) At any rate, my examples are not intended as arguments. They are intended solely as illustrations.

My *first thesis*, so far not argued but only illustrated, was that traditional epistemology with its concentration on the second world, or on knowledge in the subjective sense, is irrelevant to the study of scientific knowledge.

My *second thesis* is that what is relevant for epistemology is the study of scientific problems and problem situations, of scientific conjectures (which I take as merely another word for scientific hypotheses or theories), of scientific discussions, of critical arguments, and of the role played by evidence in arguments; and therefore of scientific journals and books, and of experiments and their evaluation in scientific arguments; or, in brief: that the study of a *largely autonomous* third world of objective knowledge is of decisive importance for epistemology.

---

* See section 7.1, below.

An epistemological study as described in my second thesis shows that scientists very often do not claim that their conjectures are true, or that they 'know' them in the subjective sense of 'know', or that they believe in them. Although they do not, in general, claim to know, they do, in their research programmes, act on the basis of guesses about what is and what is not fruitful, and what line of research promises further results in the third world of objective knowledge. In other words, scientists act on the basis of a guess or, if you like, of a *subjective belief* (for we may so call the subjective basis of an action) concerning what is promising of impending *growth in the third world of objective knowledge.*

This, I suggest, furnishes an argument in favour of both my *first thesis* (of the irrelevance of a subjectivist epistemology) and of my *second thesis* (of the relevance of an objectivist epistemology).

But I have a *third thesis.* It is this. An objectivist epistemology which studies the third world can help to throw an immense amount of light upon the second world of subjective consciousness, especially upon the subjective thought processes of scientists; but *the converse is not true.*

These are my three main theses.

In addition to my three main theses, I offer three supporting theses.

The first of these is that the third world is a natural product of the human animal, comparable to a spider's web.

The second and I think an almost crucial thesis is that the third world is largely *autonomous,* even though we constantly act upon it and are acted upon by it: it is autonomous in spite of the fact that it is our product and that it has a strong feed-back effect upon us; that is to say, upon us *qua* inmates of the second and even of the first world.

The third supporting thesis is that it is through this interaction between ourselves and the third world that objective knowledge grows, and that there is a close analogy between the growth of knowledge and biological growth; that is, the evolution of plants and animals.

2. A biological approach to the third world

In the present section of my talk I shall try to defend the existence of an autonomous world by a kind of biological or evolutionary argument.

A biologist may be interested in the behaviour of animals; but he may also be interested in some of the *non-living structures* which animals produce, such as spiders' webs, or nests built by wasps or ants, the burrows of badgers, dams constructed by beavers, or paths made by animals in forests. I will distinguish between two main categories of problems arising from the study of these structures. The first category consists of problems concerned with *the methods used* by the animals, or *the ways the animals behave* when constructing these structures. This first category thus consists *of problems concerned with the acts of production*, and with the relationships between the animal and the product. The second category of problems is concerned with the *structures themselves*. It is concerned with the chemistry of the materials used in the structure; with their geometrical and physical properties; with their dependence upon or their adjustment to special environmental conditions. *Very* important also is the *feed-back relation* from the properties of the structure to the behaviour of the animals. In dealing with this second category of problems – that is with the structures themselves – we shall also have to look upon the structures from the point of view of their biological *functions*. Thus some problems of the first category will admittedly arise when we discuss problems of the second category; for example 'How was this nest built?' and 'What aspects of its structure are typical (and thus presumably traditional or inherited) and what aspects are variants adjusted to special conditions?'.

As my last example of a problem shows, problems of the first category – that is, problems concerned with the production of the structure – will sometimes be suggested by problems of the second category. This must be so, since both categories of problems are dependent upon *the fact that such objective structures exist*, a fact which itself belongs to the second category. Thus the existence of the *structures themselves* may be said to create both categories of problems. We may say that the second category of problems – problems connected with the structures themselves – is more fundamental: all that it presupposes from the first category is the bare fact that the structures are somehow *produced* by some animals.

Now these simple considerations may of course also be applied to products of *human* activity, such as houses, or tools, and also to works of art. Especially important for us, they apply to what we call 'language', and to what we call 'science'.*

The connection between these biological considerations and the topic of my present lecture can be made clear by reformulating my three main theses. My first thesis can be put by saying that in the present problem situation in philosophy, few things are as important as the awareness of the distinction

---

* On these 'artifacts' cp. HAYEK [1967] p. 111.

between the two categories of problems – production problems on the one hand and problems connected with the produced structures themselves on the other. My second thesis is that we should realize that the second category of problems, those concerned with the products in themselves, is in almost every respect more important than the first category, the problems of production. My third thesis is that the problems of the second category are basic for understanding the production problems: contrary to first impressions, we can learn more about production behaviour by studying the products themselves than we can learn about the products by studying production behaviour. This third thesis may be described as an anti-behaviouristic and anti-psychologistic thesis.

In their application to what may be called 'knowledge' my three theses may be formulated as follows.

(1) We should constantly be aware of the distinction between problems connected with our personal contributions to the production of scientific knowledge on the one hand, and problems connected with the structure of the various products, such as scientific theories or scientific arguments, on the other.

(2) We should realize that the study of the products is vastly more important than the study of the production, even for an understanding of the production and its methods.

(3) We can learn more about the heuristics and the methodology and even about the psychology of research by studying theories, and the arguments offered for or against them, than by any direct behaviouristic or psychological or sociological approach. In general, we may learn a great deal about behaviour and psychology from the study of the products.

In what follows I will call the approach from the side of the products – the theories and the arguments – the 'objective' approach or the 'third-world' approach. And I will call the behaviourist, the psychological, and the sociological approach to scientific knowledge the 'subjective' approach or the 'second-world' approach.

The appeal of the subjective approach is largely due to the fact that it is *causal*. For I admit that the objective structures for which I claim priority are caused by human behaviour. Being causal, the subjective approach may seem to be more scientific than the objective approach which, as it were, starts from effects rather than causes.

Though I admit that the objective structures are products of behaviour, I hold that the argument is mistaken. In all sciences, the ordinary approach is from the effects to the causes. The effect raises the problem – the problem to be explained, the explicandum – and the scientist tries to solve it by constructing an explanatory hypothesis.

My three main theses with their emphasis on the objective product are therefore neither teleological nor unscientific.

3. The objectivity and the autonomy of the third world

One of the main reasons for the mistaken subjective approach to knowledge is the feeling that a book is nothing without a reader: only if it is understood does it really become a book; otherwise it is just paper with black spots on it.

This view is mistaken in many ways. A wasp's nest is a wasp's nest even after it has been deserted; even though it is never again used by wasps as a nest. A bird's nest is a bird's nest even if it was never lived in. Similarly a book remains a book – a certain type of product – even if it is never read (as may easily happen nowadays).

Moreover, a book, or even a library, need not even have been written by anybody: a series of books of logarithms, for example, may be produced and printed by a computer. It may be the best and fullest series of books of logarithms – it may contain logarithms up to, say, 50 decimals. It may be sent out to libraries, but it may be found too cumbersome for use; at any rate, years may elapse before anybody uses it; and many figures in it (which represent mathematical theorems) may never be looked at as long as men live on earth. Yet each of these figures contains what I call 'objective knowledge'; and the question of whether or not I am entitled to call it by this name is of no interest.

The example of these books of logarithms may seem far-fetched. But it is not. I should say that almost every book is like this: it contains objective knowledge, true or false, useful or useless; and whether anybody ever reads it and really grasps its contents is almost accidental. A man who reads a book with understanding is a rare creature. But even if he were more frequent, there would always be plenty of misunderstandings and misinterpretations; and it is not the actual and somewhat accidental avoidance of such misunderstandings which turns black spots on white paper into a book, or an instance of knowledge in the objective sense. Rather, it is something more abstract. It is the possibility or potentiality of being understood, the dispositional character of being understood or interpreted, or misunderstood or misinterpreted, which makes of a thing a book. And this potentiality or disposition may exist without ever being actualized or realized.

To see this more clearly, we may imagine that after the human race has perished, some books or libraries may be found by some civilized successors of ours (no matter whether these are terrestrial animals which have become civilized, or some visitors from outer space). These books may be decyphered. They may be those logarithm tables never read before, for argument's sake. This makes it quite clear that neither its composition by thinking animals nor the fact that it has not actually been read or understood is essential for making a thing a book, and that it is sufficient that it can be decyphered.

Thus I do admit that in order to belong to the third world of objective knowledge, a book should – in principle, or virtually – be capable of being grasped (or decyphered, or understood, or 'known') by somebody. But I do not admit more.

We can thus say that there is a kind of Platonic (or Bolzanoesque) third world of books in themselves, theories in themselves, problems in themselves, problem situations in themselves, arguments in themselves, and so on. And I assert that even though this third world is a human product, there are many theories in themselves and arguments in themselves and problem situations in themselves which have never been produced or understood and may never be produced or understood by men.

The thesis of the existence of such a third world of problem situations will strike many as extremely metaphysical and dubious. But it can be defended by pointing out its biological analogue. For example, it has its full analogue in the realm of birds' nests. Some years ago I got a present for my garden – a nesting box for birds. It was a human product, of course, not a bird's product – just as our logarithm table was a computor's product rather than a human product. But in the context of the bird's world, it was part of an objective problem situation, and an objective opportunity. For some years the birds did not even seem to notice the nesting box. But after some years, it was carefully inspected by some blue tits who even started building in it, but gave up very soon. Obviously, here was a graspable opportunity, though not, it appears, a particularly valuable one. At any rate, here was a problem situation. And the problem may be solved in another year by other birds. If it is not, another box may prove more adequate. On the other hand, a most adequate box may be removed before it is ever used. The question of the adequacy of the box is clearly an objective one; and whether the box is ever used is partly accidental. So it is with all ecological niches. They are potentialities and may be studied as such in an objective way, up to a point independently of the question of whether these potentialities will ever be actualized by any living organism. A bacteriologist knows how to prepare such an ecological niche for the culture of certain bacteria or moulds. It may be perfectly adequate for its purpose. Whether it will ever be used and inhabited is another question.

A large part of the objective third world of actual and potential theories and books and arguments arises as an unintended by-product of the actually produced books and arguments. We may also say that it is a by-product of human language. Language itself, like birds' nests, is an unintended by-product of actions which were directed at other aims.

How does an animal path in the jungle arise? Some animal may break through the underwood in order to get to a drinking place. Other animals find it easiest to use the same track. Thus it may be widened and improved by use. It is not planned – it is an unintended consequence of the need for easy or swift movement. This is how a path is originally made – perhaps even by men – and how language and any other institutions which are useful may arise, and how they may owe their existence and development to their usefulness. They are not planned or intended, and there was perhaps no need for them before they came into existence. But they may create a new need, or a new set of aims: the aim-structure of animals or men is not 'given', but it develops with the help of some kind of feed-back mechanism out of earlier aims, and out of results which were or were not aimed at*.

In this way, a whole new universe of possibilities or potentialities may arise: a world which is to a large extent *autonomous*.

A very obvious example is a garden. Even though it may have been planned with great care, it will as a rule turn out partly in unexpected ways. But even if it turns out as planned, some unexpected interrelationships between the planned objects may give rise to a whole universe of possibilities, of possible new aims, and of new *problems*.

The world of language, of expectations, theories and arguments, in brief, the universe of objective knowledge, is one of the most important of these man-created yet at the same time largely autonomous universes.

The idea of *autonomy* is central to my theory of the third world: although the third world is a human product, a human creation, it creates in its turn, as do other animal products, its own *domain of autonomy*.

There are countless examples. Perhaps the most striking ones, and at any

---

* See HAYEK [1967] Ch. 6, esp. pp. 96, 100, n. 12; DESCARTES [1637], cp. [1931] p. 89; POPPER [1960] p. 65; [1966] sect. XXIV.

rate those which should be kept in mind as our standard examples, may be found in the theory of natural numbers.

Pace Kronecker, I agree with Brouwer that the sequence of natural numbers is a human construction. But although we create this sequence, it creates, in its turn, its own autonomous problems. The distinction between odd and even numbers is not created by us: it is an unintended and unavoidable consequence of our creation. Prime numbers, of course, are similar unintended autonomous and objective facts; and in their case it is obvious that there are many facts here for us to *discover*: there are conjectures like Goldbach's. And these conjectures, though they refer indirectly to objects of our creation, refer directly to problems and facts which have somehow emerged from our creation and which we cannot control or influence: they are hard facts, and the truth about them is often hard to discover.

This exemplifies what I mean when I say that the third world is largely autonomous, though created by us.

But the autonomy is only a partial one: the new problems lead to new creations or constructions – such as recursive functions, or Brouwer's free choice sequences – and may thus add new objects to the third world. And every such step will create *new unintended facts*; *new unexpected problems*; and often also *new refutations**.

There is also a most important feed-back effect from our creations upon ourselves; from the third world upon the second world. For the new emergent problems stimulate us to new creations.

The process can be described by the following somewhat oversimplified schema (see my [1966] especially p. 24):

$$P_1 \rightarrow TT \rightarrow EE \rightarrow P_2.$$

That is, we start from some problem P_1, proceed to a tentative solution or tentative theory TT, which may be (partly or wholly) mistaken; in any case it will be subject to error elimination EE which may consist of critical discussion or experimental tests; at any rate, new problems P_2 arise from our own creative activity; and these new problems are not in general intentionally created by us, they emerge autonomously from the field of new relationships which we cannot help bringing into existence with every action, however little we intend to do so.

The autonomy of the third world, and the feed-back of the third world

---

* An example of the latter is Lakatos's 'concept-stretching refutation'; see LAKATOS [1963–64].

upon the second and even the first, are among the most important facts of the growth of knowledge.

Following up our biological considerations, it is easy to see that they are of general importance for the theory of Darwinian evolution: they explain how we can lift ourselves by our own bootstraps. Or in more highbrow terminology, they help to explain 'emergence'.

4. Language, criticism, and the third world

The most important of human creations, with the most important feedback effects upon ourselves and especially upon our brains, are the higher functions of human language; more especially, the *descriptive function and the argumentative function*.

Human languages share with animal languages the two lower functions of language: (1) self-expression and (2) signalling. The self-expressive function or symptomatic function of language is obvious: all animal language is symptomatic of the state of some organism. The signalling or release function is likewise obvious: we do not call any symptom linguistic unless we assume that it can release a response in another organism.

All animal languages and all linguistic phenomena share these two lower functions. But human language has many other functions*. Strangely enough, the most important of the higher functions have been overlooked by almost all philosophers. The explanation of this strange fact is that the two lower functions are always present when the higher ones are present, so that it is always possible to 'explain' every linguistic phenomenon, in terms of the lower functions, as an '*expression*' or a '*communication*'.

The two most important higher functions of human languages are (3) the *descriptive* function and (4) the *argumentative* function**.

With the descriptive function of human language, the regulative idea of *truth* emerges, that is, of a description which fits the facts***.

---

* For example, advisory, hortative, fictional, etc.

** See POPPER [1963] especially chapters 4 and 12, and the references on pp. 134, 293 and 295 to BÜHLER [1934]. Bühler was the first to discuss the decisive difference between the lower functions and the descriptive function. I found later, as a consequence of my theory of criticism, the decisive distinction between the descriptive and the argumentative functions. See also POPPER [1966] section XIV and note 47.

*** One of the great discoveries of modern logic was Alfred Tarski's re-establishment of the (objective) correspondence theory of truth (truth = correspondence to the facts). The present essay owes everything to this theory; but I do not of course wish to implicate Tarski in any of the crimes here committed.

Further regulative or evaluative ideas are content, truth content, and verisimilitude*.

The argumentative function of human language presupposes the descriptive function: arguments are, fundamentally, about descriptions: they criticize descriptions from the point of view of the regulative ideas of truth; content; and verisimilitude.

Now two points are all-important here:

(1) Without the development of an exosomatic descriptive language – a language which, like a tool, develops outside the body – there can be *no object* for our critical discussion. But with the development of a descriptive language (and further, of a written language), a linguistic third world can emerge; and it is only in this way, and only in this third world, that the problems and standards of rational criticism can develop.

(2) It is to this development of the higher functions of language that we owe our humanity, our reason. For our powers of reasoning are nothing but powers of critical argument.

This second point shows the futility of all theories of human language that focus on *expression and communication*. As we shall see, the human organism which, it is often said, is to express itself, depends in its structure very largely upon the emergence of the two higher functions of language.

With the evolution of the argumentative function of language, criticism becomes the main instrument of further growth. (Logic may be regarded as *the organon of criticism*; see my [1963] p. 64.) The autonomous world of the higher functions of language becomes the world of science. And the schema, originally valid for the animal world as well as for primitive man,

$$P_1 \rightarrow TT \rightarrow EE \rightarrow P_2$$

becomes the schema of the growth of knowledge through error elimination by way of systematic *rational criticism*. It becomes the schema of the search for truth and content by means of rational discussion. It describes the way in which we lift ourselves by our bootstraps. It gives a rational description of evolutionary emergence, and of our *self-transcendence by means of selection and rational criticism*.

To sum up, although the meaning of 'knowledge', like of all words, is

---

* See the previous note and POPPER [1962a] especially p. 292; and POPPER [1963] chapter 10 and Addenda.

unimportant, it is important to distinguish between different senses of the word.

(1) Subjective knowledge which consists of certain inborn dispositions to act, and of their acquired modifications.

(2) Objective knowledge, for example, scientific knowledge which consists of conjectural theories, open problems, problem situations, and arguments.

All work in science is work directed towards the growth of objective knowledge. We are workers who are adding to the growth of objective knowledge as masons work on a cathedral.

Our work is fallible, like all human work. We constantly make mistakes, and there are objective standards of which we may fall short – standards of truth, content, validity, and others.

Language, the formulation of problems, the emergence of new problem situations, competing theories, mutual criticism by way of argument, all these are the indispensible means of scientific growth. The most important functions or dimensions of the human language (which animal languages do not possess) are the descriptive and the argumentative functions. The growth of these functions is, of course, of our making, though they are unintended consequences of our actions. It is only within a language thus enriched that critical argument and knowledge in the objective sense become possible.

The repercussions, or the feed-back effects, of the evolution of the third world upon ourselves – our brains, our traditions (if anybody were to start where Adam started, he would not get further than Adam did) our dispositions to act (that is, our beliefs*) and our actions, can hardly be overrated.

As opposed to all this, *traditional epistemology* is interested in the second world: in knowledge as a certain kind of belief – justifiable belief, such as belief based upon perception. As a consequence, this kind of belief philosophy cannot explain (and does not even try to explain) the decisive phenomenon that scientists criticize their theories and so kill them. *Scientists try to eliminate their false theories, they try to let them die in their stead. The believer – whether animal or man – perishes with his false beliefs.*

5. Historical remarks

5.1. *Plato and Neo-Platonism*

For all we know, Plato was the discoverer of the third world. As Whitehead remarked, all Western philosophy consists of footnotes to Plato.

---

* The theory that beliefs may be gauged by readiness to bet was regarded as well known in 1771; see KANT [1778] p. 852.

I will make only three brief remarks on Plato, two of them critical.

(1) Plato discovered not only the third world, but part of the influence or feed-back of the third world upon ourselves: he realized that we try to grasp the ideas of his third world; also that we use them as explanations.

(2) Plato's third world was divine; it was unchanging and, of course, true. Thus there is a big gap between his and my third world: my third world is man-made and changing. It contains not only true theories but also false ones, and especially open problems, conjectures, and refutations.

And while Plato, the great master of dialectical argument, saw in it merely a way leading to the third world, I regard arguments as among the most important inmates of the third world; not to speak of open problems.

(3) Plato believed that the third world of forms or ideas would provide us with ultimate explanations (that is, explanation by essences; see my [1963] chapter 3). Thus he writes for example: 'I think that if anything else apart from the idea of absolute beauty is beautiful, then it is beautiful *for the sole reason* that it has some share in the idea of absolute beauty. *And this kind of explanation applies to everything.*' (PLATO, Phaedo, 100 C.)

This is a theory of *ultimate explanation*; that is to say, of an explanation whose explicans is neither capable nor in need of further explanation. And it is a theory of *explanation by essences*, that is, by hypostasized words.

As a result, Plato envisaged the objects of the third world as something like non-material things or, perhaps, like stars or constellations – to be gazed at, and intuited, though not liable to be touched by our minds. This is why the inmates of the third world – the forms or ideas – became concepts of things, or essences or natures of things, rather than theories or arguments or problems.

This had the most far-reaching consequences for the history of philosophy. From Plato until today, most philosophers have either been nominalists* or else what I have called essentialists. They are more interested in the (essential) meaning of words than in the truth and falsity of theories.

I often present the problem in the form of a table (see the next page).

My thesis is that *the left side of this table is unimportant,* as compared to the right side: what should interest us are theories; truth; argument. If so many philosophers and scientists still think that concepts and conceptual systems (and problems of their meaning, or the meaning of words) are comparable in importance to theories and theoretical systems (and problems of their truth, or the truth of statements), then they are still suffering from

---

* Cp. WATKINS [1965] Ch. VIII, esp. pp. 145f., and POPPER [1959] pp. 420–2; [1963] pp. 18ff., 262, 297f.

Plato's main error*. For concepts are partly means of formulating theories, partly means of summing up theories. In any case their significance is mainly instrumental; and they may always be replaced by other concepts.

IDEAS
that is

DESIGNATIONS *or* TERMS   STATEMENTS *or* PROPOSITIONS
or CONCEPTS   *or* THEORIES
may be formulated in
WORDS   ASSERTIONS
which may be
MEANINGFUL   TRUE
and their
MEANING   TRUTH
may be reduced, by way of
DEFINITIONS   DERIVATIONS
to that of
UNDEFINED CONCEPTS   PRIMITIVE PROPOSITIONS

---

the attempt to establish (rather than reduce) by these means their
MEANING   TRUTH
leads to an infinite regress

Contents and objects of thought seem to have played an important part in Stoicism and in Neo-Platonism: Plotinus preserved Plato's separation between the empirical world and Plato's world of Forms or Ideas. Yet like Aristotle**, Plotinus destroyed the transcendence of Plato's world by placing it into the consciousness of God.

---

* The error, which is traditional, is known as 'the problem of universals'. This should be replaced by 'the problem of theories', or 'the problem of the theoretical content of all human language'. See POPPER [1959] sections 4 (with the new footnote *1) and 25.
Incidentally, it is clear that of the famous three positions – *universale ante rem*, *in re*, and *post rem* – the last, in its usual meaning, is anti-third-world and tries to explain language as expression, while the first (Platonic) is pro-third-world. Interestingly enough, the (Aristotelian) middle position (*in re*) may be said either to be anti-third-world or to ignore the problem of the third world. It thus testifies to the confusing influence of conceptualism.
** Cp. ARISTOTLE, Metaphysics XII (Λ), 7: 1072b21f.; and 9: 1074b15 to 1075a4. This passage (which Ross sums up: 'the divine thought must be concerned with the most divine object, which is itself') contains an implicit criticism of Plato. Its affinity with Platonic ideas is especially clear in lines 25 f.: 'it thinks of that which is most divine and precious, and it does not change; for change would be change for the worse...'. (See also ARISTOTLE, De Anima 429b27ff., esp. 430a4.)

Plotinus criticized Aristotle for failing to distinguish between the First Hypostasis (Oneness) and the Second Hypostasis (the divine intellect). Yet he followed Aristotle in identifying God's acts of thought with their own contents or objects; and he elaborated this view by taking the Forms or Ideas of Plato's intelligible world to be the immanent states of consciousness of the divine intellect.*

5.2. Hegel

Hegel was a Platonist (or rather a Neo-Platonist) of sorts and, like Plato, a Heraclitean of sorts. He was a Platonist whose world of Ideas was changing, evolving. Plato's 'Forms' or 'Ideas' were objective, and had nothing to do with conscious ideas in a subjective mind; they inhabited a divine, an unchanging, heavenly world (super-lunar in Aristotle's sense). By contrast Hegel's Ideas, like those of Plotinus, were conscious phenomena: thoughts thinking themselves and inhabiting some kind of consciousness, some kind of mind or 'Spirit'; and together with this 'Spirit' they were changing or evolving. The fact that Hegel's 'Objective Spirit' and 'Absolute Spirit' are subject to change is the only point in which his Spirits are more similar to my 'third world' than Plato's world of Ideas (or Bolzano's world of 'statements in themselves').

The most important differences between Hegel's 'Objective Spirit' and 'Absolute Spirit' and my 'third world' are these:

(1) According to Hegel, though the Objective Spirit (comprising artistic creation) and Absolute Spirit (comprising philosophy) both consist of human productions, man is not creative. It is the hypostasized Objective Spirit, it is the divine self-consciousness of the Universe, that moves man: 'individuals … are instruments', instruments of the Spirit of the Epoch, and their work, their 'substantial business', is 'prepared and appointed independently of them'. (Cp. HEGEL [1830] paragraph 551.) Thus what I have called the autonomy of the third world, and its feed-back effect, becomes with Hegel omnipotent: it is only one of the aspects of his system in which his theological background manifests itself. As against this I assert that the individual creative element, the relation of give-and-take between a man and his work, is of the greatest importance. In Hegel this degenerates into the doctrine that the great man is something like a medium in which the Spirit of the Epoch expresses itself.

(2) In spite of a certain superficial similarity between Hegel's dialectic and

---

* Cp. PLOTINUS, Enneades II, 4, 4 ([1883] p. 153, 3); III, 8, 11 ([1883] p. 346, 6); V, 3, 2–5; V, 9, 5–8; VI, 5, 2; VI, 6, 6–7.

my evolutionary schema

$$P_1 \to TT \to EE \to P_2$$

there is a fundamental difference. My schema works through error elimination, and on the scientific level through conscious criticism under the
regulative idea of the search for truth.

Criticism, of course, consists in the search for contradictions and in their
elimination: the difficulty created by the demand for their elimination constitutes the new problem (P_2). Thus the elimination of error leads to the
objective growth of our knowledge – of knowledge in the objective sense. It
leads to the growth of objective verisimilitude: it makes possible the approximation to (absolute) truth.

Hegel, on the other hand, is a relativist*. He does not see our task as the
search for contradictions, with the aim of eliminating them, for he thinks
that contradictions are as good as (or better than) non-contradictory theoretical systems: they provide the mechanism by which the Spirit propels
itself. Thus rational criticism plays no part in the Hegelian automatism, no
more than does human creativity**.

(3) While Plato lets his hypostasized Ideas inhabit some divine heaven,
Hegel personalizes his Spirit into some divine consciousness: the Ideas inhabit it as human ideas inhabit some human consciousness. His doctrine is
throughout that the Spirit is not only conscious but a self. As against this,
my third world has no similarity whatever to human consciousness; and
though its first inmates are products of human consciousness, they are
totally different from conscious ideas or from thoughts in the subjective sense.

5.3. *Bolzano and Frege*

Bolzano's statements in themselves and truths in themselves are, clearly,
inhabitants of my third world. But he was far from clear about their relationship to the rest of the world***.

It is, in a way, Bolzano's central difficulty which I have tried to solve by
comparing the status and autonomy of the third world to those of animal
products, and by pointing out how it originates in the higher functions of
the human language.

---

* See POPPER [1963] chapter 15; POPPER [1962] Addendum to vol. ii: 'Facts, Standards and
Truth: A Further Criticism of Relativism'.
** See LAKATOS [1963] p. 234, footnote 1 (Offprint p. 59).
*** BOLZANO [1837] Vol. I, § 19, p. 78, says that statements (and truths) in themselves have
no being ('*Dasein*'), existence, or reality. Yet he also says that a statement in itself is
not merely 'something stated, thus presupposing a person who stated it'.

As to Frege, there can be no doubt about his clear distinction between the subjective acts of thinking, or thought in the subjective sense, and objective thought or thought content *.

Admittedly, his interest in subordinate clauses of a sentence, and in indirect speech, made him the father of modern epistemic logic **. But I think that he is in no way affected by the criticism of epistemic logic which I am going to offer (see section 7 below): as far as I can see, he was not thinking in these contexts of epistemology in the sense of a theory of scientific knowledge.

5.4. *Empiricism*

Empiricism – say, of Locke, Berkeley and Hume – has to be understood in its historical setting: its main problem was, simply, religion *versus* irreligion; or more precisely, the rational justification, or justifiability, of Christianity, as compared to scientific knowledge.

This explains why knowledge is throughout regarded as a kind of belief – belief justified by evidence, especially by perceptual evidence, by the evidence of our senses.

Though their positions with respect to the relation of science and religion differ widely, Locke, Berkeley *** and Hume agree essentially in the demand (which Hume sometimes feels is an unattainable ideal) that we should reject all propositions – and especially propositions with existential import – for which the evidence is insufficient, and accept only those propositions for which we have sufficient evidence: which can be proved, or verified, by the evidence of our senses.

This position can be analysed in various ways. A somewhat sweeping analysis would be the following chain of equations or equivalences most of which can be supported by passages from the British empiricists and even form Bertrand Russell.****

---

* See the quotation in section 1 above from FREGE [1892] p. 32, and FREGE [1894].
** The way leads from FREGE to RUSSELL [1922] p. 19 and WITTGENSTEIN [1922] 5,542.
*** For Berkeley's position compare section 1 of ch. 3 and ch. 6 of POPPER [1963].
**** Cp. RUSSELL [1906–7] p. 45: 'Truth is a quality of beliefs'; RUSSELL [1910]: 'I shall use the words "belief" and "judgment" as synonyms.' (p. 172, footnote); or: '…judgment is … a multiple relation of the mind to the various other terms with which the judgment is concerned.' (p. 180). He also holds that 'perception is always true (even in dreams and hallucinations)' (p. 181). Or cp. RUSSELL [1959] p. 183: '… but from the point of view of the theory of knowledge and of the definition of truth it is sentences expressing belief that are important'. See also RUSSELL [1922] pp. 19f., and Ducasse's *'epistemic attitudes'* in DUCASSE [1940], pp. 701–711. It is clear that both Russell and Ducasse belong to those traditional epistemologists who study knowledge in its subjective or second-world sense. The tradition far transcends empiricism.

p is verified or demonstrated by sense experience = there is sufficient reason or justification for us to believe p = we believe or judge or assert or assent or know that p is true = p is true = p.

One remarkable thing about this position which *conflates the evidence, or proof, and the assertion to be proved*, is that anybody who holds it ought to *reject the law of the excluded middle*. For it is obvious that the situation may arise (in fact, it would be practically the normal situation) that neither p nor not-p can be fully supported, or demonstrated, by the evidence available. Yet it seems that this was not noticed by anybody before Brouwer.

This failure to reject the law of the excluded middle is particularly striking in Berkeley; for if

$$esse = percipi$$

then the truth of any statement about reality can be established only by perception statements. Yet Berkeley, very much like Descartes, suggests in his Dialogues * that we should reject p if there is 'no reason to believe in it'. The absence of such reasons may be compatible, however, with the absence of reasons to believe in non-p.

6. Appreciation and criticism of Brouwer's epistemology

In the present section I wish to pay homage to L. E. J. Brouwer.

It would be presumptuous of me to try to praise and even more presumptuous to try to criticize Brouwer as a mathematician. But it may be permissible for me to try to criticize his epistemology and his philosophy of intuitionist mathematics. If I dare to do so, it is in the hope of making a contribution, however slight, to the clarification and further development of Brouwer's ideas.

In his Inaugural Lecture BROUWER [1912] starts from Kant. He says that Kant's intuitionist philosophy of geometry – his doctrine of the pure intuition of space – has to be abandoned in the light of non-Euclidean geometry. But, Brouwer says, we do not need it, since we can arithmetize geometry: we can take our stand squarely on Kant's theory of arithmetic, and on his doctrine that arithmetic is based upon the pure intuition of time.

---

* See the second dialogue between Hylas and Philonous (BERKELEY [1949] p. 218, lines 15f.): 'It is to me a sufficient reason not to believe the existence of any thing, if I see no reason for believing it.' Compare DESCARTES [1637] Pt. IV (first paragraph): 'Any opinion should be rejected as manifestly false [*'aperte falsa'* in the Latin version] if the slightest reason for doubt can be found in it.'

I feel that this position of Brouwer's can no longer be sustained; for if we say that Kant's theory of space is destroyed by non-Euclidean geometry, then we are bound to say that his theory of time is destroyed by special relativity. For Kant says explicitly that there is only *one* time, and that the intuitive idea of (absolute) simultaneity is decisive for it*.

It might be argued – on lines somewhat parallel to a remark of Heyting's** – that Brouwer might not have developed his epistemological and philosophical ideas about intuitionist mathematics had he known at the time of the analogy between Einstein's relativization of time and non-Euclidean geometry. To paraphrase Heyting, this would have been unfortunate.

However, it is unlikely that Brouwer would have been overmuch impressed by special relativity. He might have given up citing Kant as a precursor of his intuitionism. But he could have retained his own theory of a *personal* time – of a time of our own intimate and immediate experience. (See BROUWER [1949]). And this was in no way affected by relativity, even though Kant's theory was affected.

Thus we need not treat Brouwer as a Kantian. Yet we cannot sever him from Kant too easily. For Brouwer's idea of intuition, and his use of the term 'intuition', cannot be fully understood without analysing its Kantian background.

For Kant, *intuition is a source of knowledge*; and 'pure' intuition ('the pure intuition of space and time') is an unfailing source of knowledge: from it springs *absolute certainty*. This is most important for the understanding of Brouwer who clearly adopts this epistemological doctrine from Kant.

It is a doctrine with a history. Kant took it from Plotinus, St. Thomas, Descartes, and others. Originally, intuition meant, of course, perception: it is what we see, or perceive, if we look at, or if we direct our gaze on to, some object. But at least from Plotinus on, there developed a contrast between *intuition* on the one hand, and *discursive* thinking on the other. Intuition is God's way of knowing everything at a glance, in a flash, timelessly. Discursive thought is the human way: as in a discourse, we argue step by step, which takes time.

Now Kant upheld the doctrine (against Descartes) that we do not possess

---

* In the Transcendental Aesthetic (KANT [1778] pp. 46f; Kemp-Smith's translation, pp. 74f.), Kant stresses under point 1) the *a priori* character of simultaneity; under points 3) and 4) that there can be only *one* time; and under point 4) that time is *not a discursive concept*, but 'a pure form of ... intuition' (or more precisely, *the* pure form of sensual intuition). In the last paragraph before the Conclusion on p. 72 (Kemp-Smith, p. 90) he says explicitly that the intuition of space and time is not an intellectual intuition.

** See the quotation from Heyting in section 1 above.

a faculty of intellectual intuition, and that, for this reason, our intellect – our concepts – remain empty or analytic, unless indeed they are applied to material which is either given to us by our senses (sense intuition), or unless they are *'concepts constructed in our pure intuition of space and time'* *. Only in this way can we obtain synthetic knowledge *a priori*: our intellect is essentially discursive; it is bound to proceed by logic, which is empty – 'analytic'.

According to Kant, sense intuition presupposes pure intuition: our senses cannot do their work without ordering their perceptions into the framework of space and time. Thus space and time are prior to all sense-intuition; and the theories of space and time – geometry and arithmetic – are *a priori* valid. The source of their *a priori* validity is the human faculty of *pure intuition*, which is strictly limited to this field, and which is strictly distinct from the intellectual or discursive way of thinking.

Kant maintained the doctrine that the *axioms of mathematics* were based on pure intuition (KANT [1778] p. 760 f.): they could be 'seen' or 'perceived' to be true, in a non-sensual manner of 'seeing' or 'perceiving'. In addition, pure intuition was involved in *every step of every proof in geometry* (and in mathematics generally)**: to follow a proof we need to look at a (drawn) figure. This 'looking' is not sense-intuition but pure intuition, as shown by the fact that the figure might often be convincing even though drawn in a very rough manner, and by the fact that the drawing of a triangle might represent for us, in *one* drawing, an infinity of possible variants – triangles of all shapes and sizes.

Analogous considerations hold for arithmetic which, according to Kant, is based on counting; a process which in its turn is essentially based on the pure intuition of time.

Now this theory of the sources of mathematical knowledge suffers in its Kantian form from a severe difficulty. Even if we admit everything that Kant says, we are left puzzled. For Euclid's geometry, whether or not it uses pure

---

* See KANT [1778] p. 741: 'To construct a concept means to exhibit this *a priori* intuition [the 'pure intuition'] which corresponds to the concept.' See also p. 747: 'We have endeavoured to make it clear how great the difference is between the discursive use of reason through concepts and the intuitive use through the construction of concepts.' On p. 751, the *'construction of concepts'* is further explained: 'we can determine our concepts in our *a priori* intuition of space and time in as much as we create the *objects themselves* by way of a uniform synthesis'. (The italics are partly mine.)

** Cp. KANT [1778] pp. 741–764. See, for example, the end of p. 762 where he says about proofs in mathematics ('even in algebra'): 'all inferences are made safe ... by placing them plainly before our eyes'. Cp., for example, also the top of p. 745 where Kant speaks of a 'chain of inferences', and 'always guided by intuition'. (In the same passage (p. 748) 'to construct' is explained as 'to represent in intuition'.)

intuition, certainly makes use of intellectual argument, of logical deduction. *It is impossible to deny that mathematics uses discursive thought.* Euclid's discourse moves through propositions and whole books step by step: it was not conceived in one single intuitive flash. Even if we admit, for the sake of the argument, the need for pure intuition *in every single step without exception* (and this admission is difficult for us moderns to make), the step-wise, discursive and logical procedure of Euclid's derivations is so unmistakable, and it was so generally known and imitated (Spinoza, Newton) that it is difficult to believe that Kant can have ignored it. In fact Kant knew all this probably as well as anybody. But his position was forced upon him, by (1) the structure of the *Critique* in which the 'Transcendental Aesthetic' precedes the 'Transcendental Logic', and (2) by his sharp distinction (I should suggest untenably sharp distinction) between intuitive and discursive thought. As it stands, one is almost inclined to say that there is not merely a lacuna here in Kant's exclusion of discursive arguments from geometry and arithmetic, but a contradiction.

That this is not so was shown by Brouwer who filled the lacuna. I am alluding to Brouwer's theory of *the relation between mathematics on the one hand and language and logic on the other.*

Brouwer solved the problem by making a sharp distinction between *mathematics as such* and *its linguistic expression and communication.* Mathematics itself he saw as an extra-linguistic activity, essentially an activity of mental construction on the basis of our pure intuition of time. By way of this construction we create in our intuition, in our mind, the objects of mathematics which afterwards – after their creation – we can try to describe, and to convey to others. Thus the linguistic description, and the discursive argument with its logic, comes after the essentially mathematical activity: it always comes after an object of mathematics – such as a proof – has been constructed.

This solves the problem which we uncovered in Kant's *Critique.* What at first sight appears to be a contradiction in Kant is removed, in a most ingenious way, by the doctrine that we must sharply distinguish between two levels, one level intuitive and mental and essential for mathematical thought, the other discursive and linguistic and essential for communication only.

Like every great theory, this theory of Brouwer's shows its worth by its fertility. It solved three great sets of problems in the philosophy of mathematics with one stroke:

(1) *Epistemological problems* concerning the source of mathematical cer-

tainty; the nature of mathematical evidence; and the nature of mathematical proof. These problems were solved, respectively, by the doctrine of intuition as a source of knowledge; by the doctrine that we can intuitively see the mathematical objects we have constructed; and by the doctrine that a mathematical proof is a sequential construction, or a construction of constructions.

(2) *Ontological problems* concerning the nature of mathematical objects and the nature of their mode of existence. These problems were solved by a doctrine which had two sides: on the one side there was *constructivism*, and on the other there was a *mentalism* which located all mathematical objects in what I call the 'second world'. Mathematical objects were constructions of the human mind, and they existed solely as constructions in the human mind. Their objectivity – their character as objects, and the objectivity of their existence – rested entirely in the possibility of repeating their construction at will.

Thus Brouwer in his inaugural lecture could imply that, for the intuitionist, mathematical objects existed in the human mind; while for the formalist, they existed 'on paper'*.

(3) *Methodological problems* concerning mathematical proofs.

We may quite naively distinguish two main ways of being interested in mathematics. One mathematician may be interested mainly in theorems – in the truth or falsity of mathematical propositions. Another mathematician may be interested mainly in proofs: in questions of the existence of proofs of some theorem or other, and in the character of the proofs. If the first interest is preponderant (which seems to be the case for example with Polya), then it is usually linked with an interest in the discovery of mathematical 'facts' and thus with a Platonizing mathematical heuristic. If the second kind of interest is preponderant, then proofs are not merely means of making sure of theorems about mathematical objects, but they are mathematical objects themselves. This, it seems to me, was the case with Brouwer: those constructions which were proofs were not only creating and establishing mathematical objects, they were at the same time themselves mathematical objects – perhaps even the most important ones. Thus to assert a theorem was to assert the existence of a proof for it, and to deny it was to assert the existence

---

* Cp. the end of the third paragraph of BROUWER [1912]. Brouwer speaks there about the existence not of mathematics but of 'mathematical exactness', and *as it stands*, the passage therefore applies to the problems (1) and (3) even more closely than to the ontological problem (2). But there can be no doubt that it was meant to apply to (2) also. The passage reads in Dresden's translation: 'The question where mathematical exactness does exist is answered differently .... The intuitionist says: in the human intellect. The formalist says: on paper.'

of a refutation; that is, a proof of its absurdity. This leads immediately to Brouwer's rejection of the law of the excluded middle, to his rejection of indirect proofs, and to the demand that existence can be proved only by the actual construction – the making visible as it were – of the mathematical object in question.

It also leads to Brouwer's rejection of 'Platonism' by which we may understand the doctrine that mathematical objects have what I call an 'autonomous' mode of existence: that they may exist without having been constructed by us, and thus without having been proved to exist.

So far I have tried to understand Brouwer's epistemology, mainly by conjecturing that it springs from an attempt to solve a difficulty in Kant's philosophy of mathematics. I now proceed to what I announced in the title of this section – to an appreciation and criticism of Brouwer's epistemology.

From the point of view of the present paper, it is one of Brouwer's great achievements that he saw that mathematics – and perhaps I may add, the third world – is created by man.

This idea is so radically anti-Platonic that it is understandable that Brouwer did not see that it can be combined with a kind of Platonism. I mean the doctrine of the (partial) *autonomy* of mathematics, and of the third world, as sketched in section 3 above.

Brouwer's other great achievement, from a philosophical point of view, was his anti-formalism: his recognition that mathematical objects must exist before we can talk about them.

But let me turn to a criticism of Brouwer's solution of the three main sets of problems of the philosophy of mathematics discussed earlier in the present section.

(1') *Epistemological problems:* Intuition in general, and the theory of time in particular.

I do not propose to change the name 'Intuitionism'. Since the name will no doubt be retained, it is the more important to give up the mistaken philosophy of intuition as an infallible source of knowledge.

There are no authoritative sources of knowledge, and no 'source' is particularly reliable*. Everything is welcome as a source of inspiration, including 'intuition'; especially if it suggests new problems to us. But nothing is secure, and we are all fallible.

---

* I have dealt with this problem at length in my lecture 'On the sources of knowledge and of ignorance' which now forms the Introduction to POPPER [1963].

Besides, Kant's sharp distinction between intuition and discursive thought cannot be upheld. 'Intuition', whatever it may be, is largely the product of our cultural development, and of our efforts in discursive thinking. Kant's idea of one standard type of pure intuition shared by us all (perhaps not by animals in spite of a similar perceptional outfit) can hardly be accepted. For after having trained ourselves in discursive thought, our intuitive grasp becomes utterly different from what it was before.

All this applies to our intuition of time. I personally find Benjamin Lee Whorf's report on the Hopi Indians* and their utterly different intuition of time convincing. But even if this report should be incorrect (which I think unlikely), it shows possibilities which neither Kant nor Brouwer ever considered. Should Whorf be right, then our intuitive grasp of time – the way in which we 'see' temporal relations – would partly depend on our language and the theories and myths incorporated in it: *our own European intuition of time would owe much to the Greek origins of our civilization, with its emphasis on discursive thought.*

At any rate, our intuition of time may change with our changing theories. The intuitions of Newton, Kant and Laplace differ from Einstein's; and the role of time in particle physics differs from that in the physics of continua, especially optics. While particle physics suggests a razor-like unextended instant, a *'punctum temporis'* which divides the past from the future, and thus a time coordinate consisting of (a continuum of) unextended instants, and a world whose 'state' may be given for any such unextended instant, the situation in optics is very different. Just as there are spatially extended grids in optics whose parts co-operate over a considerable distance of space, so there are temporally extended events (waves possessing frequencies) whose parts co-operate over a considerable distance of time. Thus owing to optics, *there cannot be in physics a state of the world at an instant of time.* This argument should, and does, make a great difference to our intuition: what has been called the specious present of psychology is neither specious nor confined to psychology, but is genuine and occurs already in physics**.

Thus not only is the general doctrine of intuition as an infallible source of knowledge a myth, but our intuition of time, more especially, is just as subject to criticism and correction as is, according to Brouwer's own admission, our intuition of space.

---

* Cp. 'An American Indian model of the universe' in WHORF [1956].
** Cp. GOMBRICH [1964] especially p. 297: 'If we want to pursue this thought to its logical conclusion the *punctum temporis* could not even show as a meaningless dot, for light has a frequency.' (The argument can be supported by considering boundary conditions.)

The main point here I owe to Lakatos's philosophy of mathematics. It is that mathematics grows through criticism of guesses and bold informal proofs. This presupposes their linguistic formulation, and their status in the third world. Language, at first merely a means of communicating descriptions of prelinguistic objects, thus becomes an *essential part* of the scientific enterprise, even in mathematics, which in its turn becomes part of the third world. And there are layers, or levels, in language (whether or not they are formalized in a hierarchy of metalanguages).

Were the intuitionist epistemology correct, mathematical competence would be no problem. (Were Kant's theory correct, it would not be understandable why we – or more precisely Plato and his school – had to wait so long for Euclid*.) Yet it is a problem, since even highly competent intuitionist mathematicians can disagree on some difficult points**. It is not necessary for us to enquire which side in the disagreement is in the right. It is sufficient to point out that, once an intuitionist construction can be criticized, the problem raised can only be solved *by using argumentative language in an essential way*. Of course, the essential critical use of language does not commit us to the use of arguments banned by intuitionist mathematics (though there is a problem here, as will be shown). My point at the moment is merely this: once the admissibility of a proposed intuitionist mathematical construction can be questioned – and of course it can be questioned – language becomes more than a mere means of communication which could in principle be dispensed with: it becomes, rather, the indispensible medium of critical discussion. Accordingly it is no longer only the intuitionist construction 'which is objective in the sense that it is irrelevant which subject makes the construction'***; rather, the objectivity, even of intuitionist mathematics, rests, as does that of all science, upon the criticizability of its arguments. But this means that language becomes indispensable as the medium of argument, of critical discussion.****

It is for this reason that I regard Brouwer's subjectivist epistemology, and the philosophical justification of his intuitionist mathematics, as mistaken. There is a give and take between construction, criticism, 'intuition', and even tradition, which he fails to consider.

---

* Cp. the corresponding remark on Kant's aprioristic view of Newton's physics in POPPER [1963] chapter 2, the paragraph to which the footnote 63 is attached.
** Cp. S. C. Kleene's comments in KLEENE and VESLEY [1965] pp. 176–83, on BROUWER [1951] pp. 357–8, which Kleene criticizes in the light of Brouwer's note on page 1248 of BROUWER [1949].
*** Heyting in LAKATOS [1967] p. 173.
**** Cp. LAKATOS [1963–4], especially pp. 229–35.

I am, however, prepared to admit that even in his erroneous view of the status of language Brouwer was partly right. Although the objectivity of all science, including mathematics, is inseparably linked with its criticizability, and therefore with its linguistic formulation, Brouwer was right in reacting strongly against the thesis that mathematics is *nothing but* a formal language game or, in other words, that there are no such things as extra-linguistic mathematical objects; that is to say, thoughts (or in my view, more precisely, thought contents). As he insisted, mathematical talk is *about* these objects; and in this sense, mathematical language is secondary to these objects. But this does not mean that we could construct mathematics without language: there can be no construction without constant critical control, and no critical control without giving our constructs linguistic form and treating them as objects of the third world. Although the third world is not identical with the world of linguistic forms, it arises together with argumentative language: it is a by-product of language. This explains why, once our constructions become problematic, systematized, and axiomatized, language may become problematic too, and why formalization may become a branch of mathematical construction. This, I think, is what Professor Myhill means when he says that '*our formalizations correct our intuitions while our intuitions shape our formalizations*'*. What makes this remark particularly worth quoting is that, having been made in connection with Brouwerian intuitionist proof, it seems indeed to provide a correction of Brouwerian epistemology.

(2') *Ontological problems:* That the objects of mathematics owe their existence partly to language was sometimes seen by Brouwer himself. Thus he wrote in 1924: 'Mathematics is based upon [*"Der Mathematik liegt zugrunde"*] an unlimited sequence of signs or symbols [*"Zeichen"*] or of finite sequences of symbols...'**. This need not be read as an admission of the priority of language: no doubt the crucial term is 'sequence', and the idea of a sequence is based upon the intuition of time, and upon construction based upon this intuition. Yet it shows that Brouwer was aware that signs or symbols were needed to carry out the construction. My own view is that discursive thought (that is, sequences of linguistic arguments) has the strongest influence upon our awareness of time, and upon the development of our intuition of sequential order. This in no way clashes with Brouwer's constructivism; but it does clash with his subjectivism and mentalism. For the objects of mathematics can now become citizens of an objective third world:

---

* J.MYHILL [1967] p. 175 (my italics). Also cp. LAKATOS [963–4].
** BROUWER [1924] p. 244.

though originally constructed by us – the third world originates as our product – the thought contents carry with them their own unintended consequences. The series of natural numbers which we construct creates prime numbers – which we *discover* – and these in turn create problems of which we never dreamt. *This is how mathematical discovery becomes possible.* Moreover the most important mathematical objects we discover – the most fertile citizens of the third world – are *problems*, and new kinds of *critical arguments.* Thus a new kind of mathematical existence emerges: the existence of problems; and a new kind of intuition: the intuition which makes us see problems, and which makes us understand problems prior to solving them. (Think of Brouwer's own central problem of the continuum.)

The way in which language and discursive thought interact with more immediate intuitive constructions (an interaction which, incidentally, destroys that ideal of absolute evidential certainty which intuitive construction was supposed to realize) has been described in a most enlightening way by Heyting. I may perhaps quote the beginning of a passage of his from which I have derived not only stimulation but also encouragement: 'It has proved not to be intuitively clear what is intuitively clear in mathematics. It is even possible to construct a descending scale of grades of evidence. The highest grade is that of such assertions as $2+2=4$. $1002+2=1004$ belongs to a lower grade; we show this not by actual counting, but by reasoning which shows that in general $(n+2)+2=n+4$. ... [Statements like this] have already the character of an implication: "If a natural number n is constructed, then we can effect the construction, expressed by $(n+2)+2=n=4$".'* In our present context, Heyting's 'grades of evidence' are of secondary interest. What is primarily important is his beautifully simple and clear analysis of the unavoidable interplay between intuitive construction and linguistic formulation which necessarily involves us in discursive – and therefore logical – reasoning. The point is stressed by Heyting when he continues: 'This level is formalized in the free-variable calculus.'

A last word may be said on Brouwer and mathematical Platonism. The autonomy of the third world is undeniable, and with it, Brouwer's equation '*esse = construi*' must be given up; *at least* for problems. This may lead us to look anew at the problem of the logic of intuitionism: *without giving up the intuitionist standards of proof*, it may be important for critical rational discussion to distinguish sharply between a thesis and the evidence for it. But this distinction is destroyed by intuitionist logic which

---

* Cp. HEYTING [1962] p. 195.

results from the *conflation of evidence, or proof, and the assertion to be proved* *.

(3′) *Methodological problems:* The original motive of Brouwer's intuitionist mathematics was security: the search for safer methods of proof; in fact, for infallible methods. Now if you want more secure proofs, you must be more severe concerning the admissibility of demonstrative argument: you must use weaker means, weaker assumptions. Brouwer confined himself to the use of logical means which were weaker than those of classical logic **. To prove a theorem by weaker means is (and has always been) an intensely interesting task, and one of the great sources of mathematical problems. Hence the interest of intuitionist methodology.

But I suggest that this holds for proofs only. For criticism, for refutation, we do not want a poor logic. While an organon of demonstration should be kept weak, an organon of criticism should be strong. In criticism we do not wish to be confined to demonstrate impossibilities: we do not claim infallibility for our criticism, and we are often content if we can show that some theory has counter-intuitive consequences. In an organon of criticism, weakness and parsimony is no virtue, since it is a virtue in a theory that it can stand up to strong criticism. (It seems therefore plausible that in the critical debate – the metadebate – of the validity of an intuitionist construction, the use of full classical logic may be admissible.)

7. Subjectivism in logic, probability theory and science

In view of what has been said in section 5, especially on empiricism, it is not surprising that neglect of the third world – and consequently a subjectivist epistemology – should be still widespread in contemporary thought. Even where there is no connection with Brouwerian mathematics there are often subjectivist tendencies to be found within the various specialisms. I will here refer to some such tendencies in logic, probability theory, and physical science.

7.1. *Epistemic logic*

Epistemic logic deals with such formulae as '*a* knows *p*' or '*a* knows that *p*' and '*a* believes *p*', or '*a* believes that *p*'. It usually symbolizes these by

$$\text{'}Kap\text{' or '}Bap\text{'}$$

---

* Cp. section 5.4 above.
** These remarks hold only for the *logic* of intuitionism which is part of classical logic, while intuitionist mathematics is not part of classical mathematics. See especially Kleene's remarks on 'Brouwer's principle' in KLEENE and VESLEY [1965] p. 70.

where '*K*' or '*B*' respectively stand for the relationships of knowing or believing, and *a* is the knowing or believing subject and *p* the known or believed
proposition or state of affairs.

My first thesis in section 1 implies that this has nothing to do with scientific knowledge: that the scientist, I will call him '*S*', does neither know nor
believe. What does he do? I will give a very brief list:

'*S* tries to understand *p*.'
'*S* tries to think of alternatives to *p*.'
'*S* tries to think of criticisms of *p*.'
'*S* proposes an experimental test for *p*.'
'*S* tries to axiomatize *p*.'
'*S* tries to derive *p* from *q*.'
'*S* tries to show that *p* is not derivable from *q*.'
'*S* proposes a new problem *x* arising out of *p*.'
'*S* proposes a new solution of the problem *x* arising out of *p*.'
'*S* criticizes his latest solution of the problem *x*.'

The list could be extended at some length. It is miles removed in character
from '*S* knows *p*' or '*S* believes *p*' or even from '*S* mistakenly believes *p*' or
'*S* doubts *p*'. In fact, it is quite an important point that we may doubt without criticizing, and criticize without doubting. (That we may do so was seen
by Poincaré in *Science and hypothesis*, which may be in this point contrasted
with Russell's *Our knowledge of the external world*.)

7.2. Probability theory

Nowhere has the subjectivist epistemology a stronger hold than in the
field of the calculus of probability. This calculus is a generalization of
Boolean algebra (and thus of the logic of propositions). It is still widely interpreted in a subjective sense, as a *calculus of ignorance, or of uncertain subjective knowledge*; but this amounts to interpreting Boolean algebra, including
the calculus of propositions, as a *calculus of certain* knowledge – of certain
knowledge *in the subjective sense*. This is a consequence which few Bayesians
(as the adherents of the subjective interpretation of the probability calculus
now call themselves) will cherish.

This subjective interpretation of the probability calculus I have combatted for 33 years. Fundamentally, it springs from the same epistemic
philosophy which attributes to the statement 'I know that snow is white' a
greater epistemic dignity than to the statement 'snow is white'.

I do not see any reason why we should not attribute still greater epistemic
dignity to the statement 'In the light of all the evidence available to me I

believe that it is rational to believe that snow is white'. The same could be done, of course, with probability statements.

7.3. *Physical science*

The subjective approach has made much headway in science since about 1926. First it took over quantum mechanics. Here it became so powerful that its opponents were regarded as nitwits who should rightfully be silenced. Then it took over statistical mechanics. Here Szilard proposed in 1929 the by now almost universally accepted view that we have to pay for subjective information by physical entropy increase; which was interpreted as a proof that physical entropy is lack of knowledge and thus a subjective concept, and that knowledge or information is equivalent to physical negentropy. This development was neatly matched by a parallel development in information theory which started as a perfectly objective theory of channels of communication but was later linked with Szilard's subjectivist information concept.

Thus the subjective theory of knowledge has entered science on a broad front. The original point of entry was the subjective theory of probability. But the evil has spread into statistical mechanics, the theory of entropy, into quantum mechanics, and into information theory.

It is of course not possible to refute in this lecture all these subjectivist theories. I cannot do more than mention that I have combatted them for years (most recently in my [1967]). But I do not harbour any illusions. There will be many more years before the tide will turn – if it ever does.

There are only two final points I wish to make.

First, I shall try to indicate what epistemology or the logic of discovery looks like from an objectivist point of view, and how it may be able to throw some light on the biology of discovery.

Secondly, I shall try to indicate, in the last section of this lecture, what the psychology of discovery looks like, from the same objectivist point of view.

8. The logic and the biology of discovery

Epistemology becomes, from an objectivist point of view, the theory of the growth of knowledge. It becomes the theory of problem-solving, or, in other words, of the construction, critical discussion, evaluation, and critical testing, of competing conjectural theories.

I now think that with respect to competing theories it is perhaps better to speak of their 'evaluation' or 'appraisal', or of the 'preference' for one of them, rather than of its 'acceptance'. Not that words matter. The use of 'acceptance' causes no harm as long as it is kept in mind that all acceptance is tentative and, like belief, of passing and personal rather than objective and impersonal significance *.

The evaluation or appraisal of competing theories is partly prior to testing (*a priori*, if you like, though not in the Kantian sense of the terms which means '*a priori* valid') and partly posterior to testing (*a posteriori*, again in a sense which does not imply validity). Also prior to testing is the (empirical) content of a theory, which is closely related to its (virtual) explanatory power, that is to say, its power to solve pre-existing problems – those problems which give rise to the theory, and with respect to which the theories are *competing theories*.

Only with respect to some pre-existing set of problems can theories be (*a priori*) evaluated, and their values compared. Their so-called simplicity too can be compared only with respect to the problems in whose solution they compete.

Content and virtual explanatory power are the most important regulative ideas for the *a priori* appraisal of theories. They are closely related to their degree of testability.

The most important idea for their *a posteriori* appraisal is truth or, since we need a more accessible comparative concept, what I have termed 'nearness to truth', or 'verisimilitude'**. It is important that while a theory without content can be true (such as a tautology), verisimilitude is based upon the regulative idea of truth content; that is to say, on the idea of the amount of interesting and important true consequences of a theory. Thus a tautology, though true, has zero *truth content* and zero verisimilitude. It has of course the probability *one*. Generally speaking, content and testability and verisimilitude*** can be measured by *im*probability.

The *a posteriori* evaluation of a theory depends entirely upon the way it has stood up to severe and ingenious tests. But severe tests, in their turn, presuppose a high degree of a priori testability or content. Thus the *a posteriori* evaluation of a theory depends largely upon its *a priori* value: theories which are *a priori* uninteresting – of little content – need not be tested be-

---

* For instance, I have no objection whatever to Lakatos's use of the terms 'acceptance$_1$' and 'acceptance$_2$' in his 'Changes in the problem of inductive logic', § 3 (LAKATOS [1968]).
** Cp. POPPER [1963] especially chapter 10, section 3, and addendum 6; also POPPER [1962a] especially p. 292.
*** Cp. POPPER, 'A theorem on truth content', in FEYERABEND and MAXWELL [1966].

cause their low degree of testability excludes *a priori* the possibility that they may be subjected to really significant and interesting tests.

On the other hand, highly testable theories are interesting and important even if they fail to pass their test; we can learn immensely from their failure. Their failure may be fruitful, for it may actually suggest how to construct a better theory.

Yet all this stress upon the fundamental importance of *a priori* evaluation could perhaps be interpreted as ultimately due to our interest in high *a posteriori* values – in obtaining theories which have a high truth content and verisimilitude, though they remain of course always conjectural or hypothetical or tentative. What we are aiming at are theories which are not only intellectually interesting and highly testable, but which have actually passed severe tests better than their competitors; which thus solve their problems better; and which, should their conjectural character become manifest by their refutation, give rise to new, unexpected, and fruitful, problems.

Thus we can say that science begins with problems and proceeds from there to competing theories which it evaluates *critically*. Especially significant is the evaluation of their verisimilitude. This demands severe critical tests, and therefore presupposes high degrees of testability, which are dependent upon the content of the theory, and therefore can be evaluated *a priori*.

In most cases, and in the most interesting cases, the theory will ultimately break down and thus raise new problems. And the advance achieved can be assessed by the intellectual gap between the original problem and the new problem which results from the breakdown of the theory.

This cycle can again be described by our repeatedly used diagram:

$$P_1 \to TT \to EE \to P_2;$$

that is: problem P_1 – tentative theory – evaluative elimination – problem P_2.

The evaluation is always *critical*, and its aim is the discovery and *elimination of error*. The growth of knowledge – and thus the learning process – is not a repetitive or a cumulative process but one of error elimination. It is Darwinian selection, rather than Lamarckean instruction.

This is a brief description of epistemology from an objective point of view: the method, or logic, of aiming at the growth of objective knowledge. But although it describes the growth of the third world, it can be interpreted as a description of biological evolution. Animals, and even plants, are problem-solvers. And they solve their problems by the method of competitive tentative solution and error elimination.

The tentative solutions which animals and plants incorporate into their anatomy and their behaviour are biological analogues of theories; and *vice versa*: theories correspond, as do many exosomatic products such as honeycombs, and especially exosomatic tools, such as spider webs, to endosomatic organs and their ways of functioning. Just like theories, organs and their functions are tentative adaptations to the world we live in. And just like theories, or like tools, new organs and their functions, and also new kinds of behaviour, exert their influence on the first world which they may help to change. (A new tentative solution – a theory, an organ, a new kind of behaviour – may discover a new virtual ecological niche and thus may turn a virtual niche into an actual one.) Behaviour or organs may also lead to the emergence of new problems. And in this way they may influence the further course of evolution, including the emergence of new biological values.

All this holds, especially, for sense organs. They incorporate, more especially, theory-like expectations. Sense organs, such as the eye, are prepared to react to certain selected environmental events – to those events which they 'expect', and *only* to those events. Like theories (and prejudices) they will in general be blind to others: to those which they do not understand, which they cannot interpret (because they do not correspond to any specific problem which the organism is trying to solve).*

Classical epistemology which takes our sense perceptions as 'given', as the 'data' from which our theories have to be constructed by some process of induction, can only be described as pre-Darwinian. It fails to take account of the fact that the alleged data are in fact adaptive reactions, and therefore interpretations which incorporate theories and prejudices and which, like theories, are impregnated with conjectural expectations; that there can be no pure perception, no pure datum; exactly as there can be no pure observational language, since all languages are impregnated with theories and myths. Just as our eyes are blind to the unforeseen or unexpected, so our languages are unable to describe it (though our languages can grow – as can our sense organs, endosomatically as well as exosomatically).

This consideration of the fact that theories or expectations are built into our very sense organs shows that the epistemology of induction breaks down even before having taken its first step. It cannot start from sense data or perceptions and build our theories upon them, since there are no such things as sense data or perceptions which are not built upon theories (or expectations, that is, the biological predecessors of linguistically formulated theo-

---

* Cp. my remarks in LAKATOS and MUSGRAVE [1968] p. 163.

ries). Thus the 'data' are no basis of, no guarantee for, the theories: they are not more secure than any of our theories or 'prejudices' but, if anything, less so (assuming for argument's sake that sense data exist and are not philosophers' inventions). Sense organs incorporate the equivalent of primitive and uncritically accepted theories, which are less widely tested than scientific theories. Moreover, there is no theory-free language to describe the data, because myths (that is, primitive theories) arise together with language. There are no living things, neither animals nor plants, without problems and their tentative solutions which are equivalent to theories; though there may well be, or so it seems, life without sense-data (at least in plants).

Thus life proceeds, like scientific discovery, from old problems to the discovery of new and undreamt of problems. And this process – that of invention and selection – contains in itself a rational theory of emergence. The steps of emergence which lead to a new level are in the first instance the new problems (P_2) which are created by the error elimination (EE) of a tentative theoretical solution (TT) of an old problem (P_1).

9. Discovery, humanism and self-transcendence

For a humanist our approach is important for it suggests a new way of looking at the relation between ourselves – the subjects – and the object of our endeavours: the growing objective knowledge, the growing third world.

The old subjective approach of interpreting knowledge as a relation between the subjective mind and the known object – a relation called by Russell 'belief' or 'judgment' – took those things which I regard as objective knowledge merely as *utterances or expressions* of mental states (or as the corresponding behaviour). This approach may be described as an *epistemological expressionism* because it is closely parallel to the expressionist theory of art. A man's work is regarded as the expression of his inner state: the emphasis is entirely upon the causal relation, and on the admitted but overrated fact that the world of objective knowledge, like the world of painting or music, is created by men.

This view is to be replaced by a very different one. It is to be admitted that the third world, the world of objective knowledge (or more generally of the objective spirit) is man-made. But it is to be stressed that this world exists to a large extent autonomously; that it generates its own problems, especially those connected with methods of growth; and that its impact on any one of us, even on the most original of creative thinkers, vastly exceeds the impact which any of us can make upon it.

But it would be a mistake to leave things at that. What I regard as the most important point is not the sheer autonomy and anonymity of the third world, and the admittedly very important point that we always owe almost everything to our predecessors and to the tradition which they created: that we thus owe to the third world especially our rationality – that is, our subjective mind, the practice of critical and self-critical ways of thinking. More important than all this is, I suggest, the relation between ourselves and our work, and what can be gained for us from this relation.

The expressionist believes that all he can do is to let his talent, his gifts, express themselves in his work. The result is good or bad, according to the mental or physiological state of the worker.

As against this I suggest that everything depends upon the give and take between ourselves and our work; upon the product which we contribute to the third world, and upon that constant feed-back that can be amplified by self-criticism. The incredible thing about life, evolution, and mental growth is just this method of give and take, this interaction between our actions and their results by which we constantly transcend ourselves, our talents, our gifts.

This self-transcendence is the most striking and important fact of all life and all evolution, and especially of human evolution.

In its pre-human stages it is of course less obvious, and so it may indeed be mistaken for something like self-expression. But on the human level the self-transcendence can be overlooked only by a real effort. As it happens with our children, so it does with our theories: they tend to become largely independent of their parents. And as it may happen with our children, so with our theories: we may gain from them a greater amount of knowledge than we originally imparted to them.

The process of learning, of the growth of subjective knowledge, is always fundamentally the same. It is *imaginative criticism*. This is how we transcend our local and temporal environment by trying to think of circumstances *beyond* our experience: by criticizing the universality, or the structural necessity, of what may, to us, appear (or what philosophers may describe) as the 'given' or 'habit'; by trying to find, construct, invent, new situations – that is, *test* situations, *critical* situations; and by trying to locate, detect and challenge our prejudices and habitual assumptions.

This is how we lift ourselves by our bootstraps out of the morass of our ignorance; how we throw a rope into the air and then swarm up it – if it gets any purchase, however precarious, on any little twig.

What makes our efforts differ from those of the amoeba is only that our rope may get a hold in a third world of critical discussion: a world of language, of objective knowledge. This makes it possible for us to discard some of our competing theories. So if we are lucky, we may succeed in surviving some of our mistaken theories (and most of them are mistaken), while the amoeba will perish with its theory, its belief, and its habits.

Seen in this light, life is discovery – the discovery of new facts, of new possibilities, by way of trying out possibilities conceived in our imagination. On the human level, this trying out is done almost entirely in the third world, by attempts to represent, in the theories of this third world, our first world, and perhaps our second world, more and more successfully; by trying to get nearer to the truth – to a fuller, a more complete, a more interesting, powerful and relevant truth – relevant to our problems.

What may be called the second world – the world of the mind – becomes, on the human level, more and more the link between the first and the third world: all our actions in the first world are influenced by our second-world grasp of the third world. This is why it is impossible to understand the human mind without understanding the third world, the objective mind or 'spirit'; and why it is impossible either to interpret the third world as a mere expression of the second, or the second as the mere reflection of the third.

There are three senses of the verb 'to learn' which have been insufficiently distinguished by learning theorists: 'to discover'; 'to imitate'; 'to make habitual'. All three may be regarded as forms of discovery, and all three operate with trial and error methods which contain a (not too important and usually much overrated) element of chance. 'To make habitual' contains a minimum of discovery – but it clears the decks for further discovery; and its apparently repetitive character is misleading.

In all these different ways of learning or of acquiring or producing knowledge the method is Darwinian rather than Lamarckian. It is selection rather than instruction. But selection is a two-edged sword: it is not only the environment that selects and changes us – it is also we who select and change the environment. On the human level, we do this by co-operation with a whole new objective world – the third world, the world of objective tentative knowledge which includes objective new tentative aims and values. We do not mould or 'instruct' this world by expressing in it the state of our mind; nor does it instruct us: both, we ourselves and the third world grow through mutual struggle and selection. This, it seems, holds at the level of the enzyme and the gene – the genetic code may be conjectured to operate by selection or rejection rather than by instruction or command – and through all levels, up to the articulate and critical language of our theories.

References

ARISTOTLE, Metaphysics.

ARISTOTLE, De Anima.

BERKELEY, Three dialogues between Hylas and Philonous, in: Works, eds. Luce and Jessop, Vol. II (1949).

BOLZANO, B., Wissenschaftslehre (1837).

BROUWER, L. E. J., Inaugural lecture, 14 October 1912; transl. A. Dresden, Bull. Am. Math. Soc. 20 (1914) 81–96.

BROUWER, L. E. J., Math. Ann. 93 (1924).

BROUWER, L. E. J., Consciousness, philosophy, and mathematics, in: Proc. 10th Intern. Congress of Philosophy (1949) Vol. I, fascicule II.

BROUWER, L. E. J., On order in the continuum, and the relation of truth to non-contradictority, Kon. Ned. Acad. Recht. Wet. Proc. Sect. Sci. 54 (1951).

BÜHLER, K., Sprachtheorie (1934).

DESCARTES, R., Discourse de la methode (1637); transl. E.S. Haldane and G.R.T. Ross, Vol. I (1931).

DUCASSE, C. J., J. Phil. 37 (1940).

FEYERABEND and MAXWELL, editors, Mind, matter and method, essays in philosophy and science in honor of Herbert Feigl (1966).

FREGE, G., Ueber Sinn und Bedeutung, Z. Phil. und phil. Kritik 100 (1892) 25–50.

FREGE, G., Review of HUSSERL [1891], Z. Phil. und phil. Kritik 103 (1894) 313–332.

GOMBRICH, E. H., Moment and movement in art, J. Warburg and Court. Inst. 27 (1964).

GOMPERZ, H., Weltanschauungslehre, Vol. II/1 (1908).

GOMPERZ, H., Über Sinn und Sinngebilde. Verstehen und Erkennen (1929).

HAYEK, F. A., The constitution of liberty (1960).

HAYEK, F. A., Studies in philosophy, politics, and economics (1967).

HEGEL, G. W. F., Enzyklopädie der philosophischen Wissenschaften (third edition, 1830).

HEINEMANN, F., Plotin (1921).

HENRY, P., Plotinus' place in the history of thought, in: Plotinus, the enneads, transl. S. MacKenna (2nd ed., 1956).

HEYTING, A., After thirty years, in: Logic, methodology and philosophy of science, eds. E. Nagel, P. Suppes and A. Tarski (1962) pp. 194 ff.

HEYTING, A., Intuitionism (1966).

HEYTING, A., Informal rigour and intuitionism in: LAKATOS [1967].

HUSSERL, E., Philosophie der Arithmetik (1891).

HUSSERL, E., Logische Untersuchungen, Vol. I (2nd ed., 1913).

KANT, I., Kritik der reinen Vernunft (first edition 1770, second edition 1778).

KLEENE, S. C. and R. VESLEY, The foundations of intuitionistic mathematics (Amsterdam, North-Holland Publ. Co., 1965).

LAKATOS, I., Proofs and refutations, Brit. J. Phil. of Sci. 14 (1963–64).

LAKATOS, I., editor, Problems of the philosophy of mathematics (Amsterdam, North-Holland Co., 1967).

LAKATOS, I., editor, The problem of inductive logic (Amsterdam, North-Holland Publ. Co., 1968).

LAKATOS, I. and A. MUSGRAVE, eds., Problems in the philosophy of science (Amsterdam, North-Holland Publ. Co., 1968).

MYHILL, J., Remarks on continuity and the thinking subject, in: LAKATOS [1967].

PLATO, Phaedo.

PLOTINUS, Enneades, ed. R. Volkmann (1883, 1884).

POPPER, K. R., Logik der Forschung (1934), The logic of scientific discovery (1959 and later editions).

POPPER, K.R., The poverty of historicism (2nd ed., 1960).
POPPER, K.R., The open society and its enemies (fourth ed. 1962 and later editions).
POPPER, K.R., Truth and the growth of knowledge, in: Logic, methodology and philosophy of science, eds. E. Nagel, P. Suppes and A. Tarski (1962a).
POPPER, K.R., Conjectures and refutations (1963 and later editions).
POPPER, K.R., Of clouds and clocks (1966).
POPPER, K.R., Quantum mechanics without 'the observer', in: Quantum theory and reality, ed. Mario Bunge (1967).
RUSSELL, B., On the nature of truth, in: Aristitelian Soc. Proc. 7 (1906–7), pp. 28–49.
RUSSELL, B., Philosophical essays (1910).
RUSSELL, B., Introduction to WITTGENSTEIN's Tractatus (1922).
RUSSELL, B., My philosophical development (1959).
WATKINS, J.W.N., Hobbes's system of ideas (1965).
WHORF, B.L., Language, thought and reality (1956).
WITTGENSTEIN, L., Tractatus logico-philosophicus (1922).

Section 6

Methodology and
Philosophy of Physical Sciences

THINGS, STRUCTURES AND PHENOMENA
IN QUANTUM PHYSICS

B. D'ESPAGNAT

Faculté des Sciences de Paris-Orsay, Paris, France

The question I wish to discuss bears on the interpretation of the general rules of conventional quantum mechanics. This problem, of course, is as old as quantum mechanics itself. For all scientific purposes, it would seem that it has received a fully satisfactory solution, namely that proposed by Bohr and by the Copenhagen School already a long time ago. Still, a number of physicists have in recent times expressed misgivings about this solution and said that, in spite of its scientific success, they could not consider it as being really a definitive solution to the problem. How can that be?

1. "Weak" and "strong" objectivity

Probably one element of the answer lies in the fact that different people are liable to attach different meanings to the word "scientific". For some, the purpose of a scientific investigation is to discover "how things really are". They therefore demand that a description of a physical law or principle should be objective in the sense that it should not refer, not even implicitly, to any specific abilities or inabilities of the "observer" (usually their argument is that the observer is just a physical system, and a very complicated one moreover, and that it would be a manifestation of a poor methodology to make the fundamental principles of physics ultimately rest on some of the most obscure and most accidental properties of a few complicated systems occupying a tiny portion of the universe). This conception of objectivity we will call "strong objectivity" in what follows.

For others, mainly those who have been more or less consciously influenced by the positivist or pragmatist ideas, the purpose of a scientific investigation is only to describe the "phenomena" and to relate them to each other i.e., in the last resort, to find rules that enable one to calculate some probabilities of observations, when the results of earlier observations come to be known. Of course, these results and these predictions should be fully communicable, but this is all that is required so that in this context the word objectivity must be given a new meaning: it now simply means "invariance under any permutation of the observers". This we shall call "weak objectivity" or, equivalently, "intersubjectivity". The difference between strong and weak objectivity is that a statement of physics may be objective in the weak sense and still refer in a decisive way to some abilities of the "observer", if these abilities are common to all observers.

The existence of these two quite different conceptions of the very purposes of physics and of objectivity, reflects itself in the difference of meanings that can be ascribed to the word "structure". It is true that a general agreement seems nowadays to exist among physicists that the aim of their scientific investigation is to discover structural relationships between individual "happenings". As was, for instance, recently stressed by ROMAN [1966], the importance of this realization lies in the fact that it is sufficient to determine both the language and the form of the physical science: the science that deals with structures in themselves is mathematics, therefore the language of physics is mathematics; the fundamental mathematical structures are either topological (analytical) or algebraic, therefore modern theoretical physics mostly uses either analytical theorems or classifications through algebras.

Thus it seems that we have here, at least, an unanimity of purpose and means among the physicists. While this is certainly true in practice – and therefore very important – it is obvious, however, that, philosophically speaking, the words "structural relationships between individual happenings" are ambiguous and will certainly be understood differently by the two families of scientists described above. Is the word "happening" merely a substitute for "phenomenon" i.e., for "communicable observation" or does it mean something which "really happens" in the sense that it would happen also if there were no observer? The modern scientist may, as a scientist, reject the question, stating that it is not a scientific one. He will even probably be quite wise in doing so. But as a layman he cannot reject the following question: "supposing that we are interested in constructing an objective (in the strong sense) description of the world, does there exist a description of this kind that is compatible with the general rules of quantum mechanics?" This is a perfectly sensible question. We know that such a description is possible in the realm of classical physics. We may be interested to know if it is also possible in quantum physics. Moreover, although I do not wish to embark on a philosophical discussion on this point, I would like to mention the fact that such people as the experimental physicists for instance consider the regularity of phenomena – the existence of structural relationships between them if you prefer – as a stricking piece of evidence in favor of the existence of some reality exterior to ourselves. Indeed they are all firmly convinced not only that such a reality exists, but that science is able to discover its properties. It is a sensible question to ask whether such an opinion is tenable or not and instead of discussing this on very general philosophical grounds it is better to ask if and under what conditions it is compatible with modern physics.

2. "Unirealism" and classical systems

The properties of reality (for the sake of discussing the question above we must assume this word may make sense) can be either general properties (such as: the proton has a spin $\frac{1}{2}$) or special configurations (such as: the spin component along O_z of the proton which presently goes through my instrument is $+\frac{1}{2}$; the pointer of your instrument is in the graduation interval no 4). It is, I think, well-known that, as regards the special configurations, quantum physics meets with serious difficulties*. Just to give a simple example, immediately after two spin $\frac{1}{2}$ particles have interacted, it is not in general a correct statement to say that each of them has along an axis, say O_z, a spin component that is definite and whose value we simply happen not to know. If this situation also holds in the case of macroscopic systems, if, in other words, it is not a generally correct statement to say that after interacting with a quantum system, a measurement apparatus has its pointer in some definite position, then obviously we are in trouble, not with the concept of reality, but with the identification of what we see with objectively existing special configurations of it.

It is often said that orthodox quantum mechanics is able to avoid this difficulty by introducing the concept of *classical systems*. For a classical system, statements such as "the pointer is between graduations nos 3 and 4" would, in all circumstances, and with respect to every *conceivable* measurement, be allowable. This concept however requires a discussion. Are there classical systems?

In order to be able to answer this question, we have to distinguish the philosophical viewpoint sometimes called *"unirealism"* (or materialistic

---

* Some of them are discussed in D'ESPAGNAT [1965]. Generally speaking, the author is ashamed that he has to present here without proofs statements which may be unpalatable to many readers. Proofs however exist! They can be found for instance in WIGNER [1963], BELL [1964] and D'ESPAGNAT [1965], [1966].

monism) from all the others (subjectivist, dualist etc.). "Unirealism" means that philosophy for which a) the whole of reality (including therefore consciousness) is purely "physical" i.e. is made exclusively of entities that obey the fundamental quantum principles and b) the macroscopic configurations we see are objective. For the reasons given above, unirealism requires of course that the quantum principles should satisfy "strong objectivity".

Then there are a few results which, for short, we shall simply state. The first of these (WIGNER [1963]) is the following: in the realm of unirealism there is no correct definition of classical systems. Either the definition defines an empty class, or it refers (sometimes in very hidden ways) to some limitations in the possibilities of "observers".

Does there, at least, exist (still in the realm of unirealism) some cases of systems that can be considered as classical ones to within a good approximation? In the specific case of the measuring instrument this question takes the following form. "Let *one* instrument A be given, which interacts with *one* quantum object S that can exist in several quantum states $u_1, u_2, ..., u_i, ...$. Let us say, for the sake of definiteness, that the pointer of A reaches the position g with $g_i < g < g_i + \Delta g_i$ when the initial state of S is u_i. Let us now consider the case when the initial state of S is

$$v = \sum b_i u_i$$

where the b_i are parameters. We already know that it is not correct to say there is a probability $|b_i|^2$ that after the interaction A will exactly be in a state $v_{i,r}$ corresponding to $g_i < g < g_i + \Delta g_i$. Is it, at least, generally possible to say that, for the individual case we are investigating (just one event), there is a probability $\approx |b_i|^2$ that after the interaction A will be in a state $w_{i,s}$ which is a superposition of states $v_{i,r}$ with large amplitudes and of $v_{k,r}$ $(k \neq i)$ with very small amplitudes?"

Here again, it has been demonstrated that the answer to this question is negative. The proof (D'ESPAGNAT [1966]) is based on the logical proposition that if a statement is true all its consequences, however remote, are strictly true. Here a statistical ensemble is considered of systems S + A of the type introduced above. If the statement that the pointer of *each* individual A occupies *approximately* a certain position (in the precise sense I have just described) were an *exact* statement, all its consequences, however remote, should be exactly true for the ensemble considered. They are not*. We conclude there-

---

* Precisely speaking, a fully watertight proof of these statements requires that the density matrix of an ensemble should, in principle, be completely observable. This has been disputed. It may be that, for systems over a certain size or complexity, the

fore that in the realm of "unirealism" and for the discussion of individual cases of interaction (which is obviously necessary since such experiments exist), classical systems, or systems behaving approximately as classical systems, can not be defined. Fortunately, the experiments that could show the non-classical behaviour of macroscopic systems are in nearly all cases practically impossible to perform, so that it is for all practical purposes fully justified to treat most macroscopic systems, and in particular all measuring instruments, as classical. But, of course, when we introduce the word "practical" in a definition of a class of systems which is used in the formulation of first principles, we evade "unirealism".

Since the concept of classical systems is an essential one for the description of quantum physics, we are thus left with the choice of rejecting either the superposition principle of quantum mechanics (at least, as a principle of absolute validity) or unirealism*. In the absence of any experimental evidence against the superposition principle most physicists, I think, will prefer the second alternative. Then again we have a priori a choice as to what constituents of unirealism we shall reject.

Some physicists go very far. They stress the fact that we only know the "phenomena", i.e. our own experience and that of other human beings, and use this as an argument for rejecting as meaningless the very idea of a reality that i) would exist, with its own laws, even if human beings did not exist and that ii) on the other hand, constitutes the subject matter of scientific investigation. For them, therefore, "reality" reduces to "phenomena". As far as I understand it, the very deep and subtle Niels Bohr interpretation of quantum mechanics (whose scientific usefulness we do not question, of course) is essentially based on a reduction of this kind. The physicists who call themselves "positivists" are sometimes even more explicit on these points but essentially follow the same lines. In other words, all the physicists who strictly adhere to the Copenhagen interpretation or to some even more pragmatic modern views on physics are, partly or totally, subjectivists. They have

---

density matrix overcharacterizes the system. A still unanswered (and difficult) question is then however: "when, precisely, does this happen and what about problems of internal consistency when, for instance, the large system is split?". Remember that in the realm of unirealism we are not allowed to base our argumentation on the extreme difficulty or practical impossibility of experiments.

* Since the proof of the incompatibility between "unirealism" and quantum mechanics implies the non-existence of hidden parameters, a third possibility is a hidden parameter theory exactly reproducing the quantum mechanical results, as that of BOHM [1962]. It may be shown quite generally however (BELL [1964]) that such a theory necessarily implies strong and instantaneous interactions at large distances between any components of the Universe.

to be, of course, because of the failure of unirealism to account for physics, mentioned above*. And it should certainly be stressed that they completely avoid the major pittfall of subjectivism, namely solipsism, since on the contrary they all put communication in the foreground. If one likes epithets, that of "intersubjectivists" may suit them better. This, however, being recognized one may perhaps regret that this school of thought is so much impressed by the scientific importance of observation and communication that it refuses to analyse, and, as we said, really explicitely or tacitly rejects the idea of a permanent and (in the strong sense) objective substratum for the structures that science discovers. As regards purely scientific practice it is most probably quite right in doing so, since such a substratum would not be observable. From a more general point of view, however, it may for that reason appear too vulnerable to the criticism of being, under the disguise of scientific universality, an extreme form of humanism: a malevolent philosophical opponent could accuse it of making man's mind not only the measure but, look, apparently the center, if not the very source, of things! A more sober analyst may find insufficient, or even inexistent, the account it gives of the regularity of phenomena**.

3. Further speculations and conclusions

Now we have seen the two extremes. Unirealism, on the one hand, which is a perfectly objective philosophy, in the strong sense, but which comes, apparently, in conflict with quantum principles, and positivism and related theories, which avoid these difficulties but only at the price of making poorly defined and (partly for that reason) probably too considerable concessions to subjectivism. In view of the regularity of phenomena, which seems incomprehensible if the observed structures do not pertain to some independent "reality", it is quite natural that we should wish to incorporate to our descriptions the smallest possible admixture of subjectivism. I sometimes wonder whether, with these motivations at hand, it would not be appropriate (not, perhaps in science, but in philosophical reflexions about science) to give more considerations than has hitherto been done to explicitely dualisict

---

* Relaxing only condition b) (page 380) of unirealism also leads necessarily to *some* admixture of subjectivity. See below.
** The only serious argument of positivists about this point is that if this regularity were absent we would not be there to discuss the matter. This argument is not utterly convincing in that it does not predict that this regularity will maintain itself at the next moment: it makes it even somewhat miraculous that it should!

ideas, meaning by that those theories (e.g. WIGNER [1962]) which consider physical reality and consciousness as two complementary (and mutually irreducible) aspects of reality and which try to describe their relations.

I would like to conclude with very short qualitative comments on the speculations of this latter kind. Several such models can be constructed. Their common advantages are on the one hand that they *do* give a reason for the stability of observed structures by attributing them to a reality external to ourselves and, on the other hand, that they are free from logical inconsistencies with the general principles of quantum mechanics (some arguments to the contrary based on common sense presuppositions can easily be proved false). One feature of them must be accepted, although it looks a priori somewhat unpleasant: none of these models is such that, in a situation where no observer is present, the physical reality already possesses the "special configurations" that common sense would like, even then, to attribute to it. Some of them are led moreover to incorporate the idea that in the reduction process consciousness really acts on the physical reality (although not, of course, in a way that would be offhand experimentally detectable since these theories do not modify the quantum mechanical probabilities). This latter feature however, if taken litterally, is unattractive, so that one may be willing to pay some price in order to avoid it, at least formally. For instance, one may, on this occasion, be tempted to cast into an entirely new mould the old Kantian idea of distinguishing several levels of reality. A crude model along these lines could, e.g., be as follows.

At the lowest level there is a "non-empirical reality" which is not separable, has none of these "special configurations" that can be described in classical language but has the very important rôle of being the support of the observed general properties (e.g. "proton has spin $\frac{1}{2}$") and of the structural relationships. If one likes, a non reduced state-vector V can presumably be put in correspondence to it. Conscious minds can develop in relation with this non-empirical reality without affecting it. The rules of calculation of the various predictions that these minds can make follow the usual prescriptions of quantum mechanics, not, however, applied to V but rather to some reduced state-vectors obtained by applying the usual rules of the quantum evolution in time, including those (reductions) that refer to previous observations. It is convenient to construct the concept of "empirical realities" attached (at various levels) to these reduced state-vectors. On these, the reduction of wave packets through measurements, of course, acts. Finally, for most of the large systems, and particularly for the measuring apparatus, it is convenient to construct still a further idealization, described by the concept of classical objects and by a shift of the moment when the indeterminate evolution is considered as taking place, the convention being made of fixing it, not at the time of perception, but at the earlier time when the quantum system interacted with the instrument. Such a model is still probably much too naïve since its unattractive aspects are apparent. It may however contain some features that could persist in more elaborate attempts.

We may conclude as follows. "Unirealism" is not in accordance with the general laws of quantum mechanics. Relaxing only the condition that the special configurations we observe are objective would already imply that the formation of such images in our "minds" are themselves very remarkable events, not to be accounted for by the other physical laws. Thus, from whatever side we look at the problem, it seems that some departure from "strong objectivity" is unavoidable (at least if one refuses hidden parameters and the non-locality they require). Such a departure is already existent in the conventional interpretation of quantum mechanics. It may however be interesting, from a philosophical point of view, to elaborate further on this point so as to have a theory in which, even if the formation of special configurations is in the last resort governed by a kind of intersubjectivity, still the general structures disclosed by science are perfectly objective in the strong sense, being the properties of a fundamental (and non-empirical) reality.

References

BELL, J.S., Physics 1 (1964) 195.
BOHM, D., Phys. Rev. 85 (1962) 166.
D'ESPAGNAT, B., Conceptions de la physique contemporaine (Paris, Hermann, 1965).
D'ESPAGNAT, B., Nuovo Cimento Suppl. 1 (1966) 828.
ROMAN, P., Symmetry in physics, address to the Boston Colloquium for the philosophy of science, 1966, in: Boston studies in the philosophy of science.
WIGNER, E.P., in: The scientist speculates, ed. I.J. Good (London, Heinemann, 1962).
WIGNER, E.P., Am. J. Phys. 31 (1963) 6.

WHAT DO PHYSICAL MODELS TELL US?

E. MCMULLIN

University of Notre Dame, Notre Dame, USA

The most important single question that modern physical science poses for the philosopher can be simply put: what do the complex postulated structures of the scientist tell us of the world? The scientist appears to be doing two somewhat different things: he first makes use of complex measure-instruments to record certain "facts" about the world. These so-called facts are expressed in specially-constructed concepts, and depend, of course, rather critically on the theory of the instruments used. Having grouped these "facts" in limited generalizations, he then attempts to account for them, to provide an explanatory structure from which they could be derived. It is this rather hazy separation between the descriptive and the explanatory aspects of science, between (if you prefer) the functions of observational terms and of theoretical terms, that has provided the material for much of the recent discussion in philosophy of science.

Three different levels of question can be asked about this, as about any other problem in philosophy of science. It is important to separate these levels, since the techniques used in answering them are significantly different. First, one may take the terms in which the problem is expressed, terms like 'theory', 'model', 'analogy', and try to determine their boundaries. There are, as we shall see in a moment, several different ways in which this might be done. Having done this, the second stage is to explore the formal consequences of the concept-structure one has decided upon. One might, for instance, ask about the logical properties that follow from the definition of 'model' that has been adopted. Or one could try to formalize the notion of confirmation implicit in the complex of concepts, like *evidence, probability, likelihood* which one can already isolate fairly clearly in ordinary scientific practice. The third stage (one, it must be admitted, that is seldom reached, principally because of the seductive complexities of the first two stages) is to return to the original question, now that its linguistic and logical outlines have been satisfactorily clarified, and see if one can answer it. Presumably the point of philosophy of science is not simply to clarify the linguistic usage of terms such as 'model', or to construct an elaborate formalism that reveals the logical implications implicit in this usage, important and indeed indispensable as these two stages are. One must surely go on to ask a further question: what do models, thus defined, tell us about the nature of the "real world"? Are they simple computational devices and no more? Or do they tell us, in some sort of oblique way, about physical structures that we cannot at present validate on the basis of direct observation? This is, of course, the old issue of instrumentalism versus realism. It is all-too-easy to stop short of this issue, deterred by the notable vaguenesses of words like 'real' and 'world', and to content oneself with what is, after all, only the preliminary task of clarifying and exploring the purely logical implications of the scientists' metalanguage. This, as I shall argue, is to stop short of the properly philosophical point of the entire inquiry.

Beginning, however, at the beginning, we have to decide how the terms 'model' and 'theory' are to be used. It is obvious that no clear criteria for their use can be derived from the actual language-habits of scientists. Scientists are usually quite vague as to the relationship between theory and model, or even between model and empirical law; they use these second-order terms in a vague and often inconsistent manner that would play havoc in their science were it to be extended to the first-order terms also. On the other hand, this does not entitle us to construct purely stipulative definitions that happen to lend themselves to elegant logical elaboration. We have to find some half-way house between these lexical and stipulative extremes in the approach we adopt to definition. The aim is to begin from ordinary usage, and when stipulation becomes necessary, to choose those stipulations that will, so far as is possible, support those conceptual distinctions that are latent in actual scientific practice. Thus when two philosophers disagree as to "what a model is", a rather frequent disagreement recently, this is not like two scientists disagreeing as to "what a meson is" or two lexicographers disagreeing as to how the word 'model' is actually used in some language group. The criteria for settling this sort of disagreement are not purely empirical – we cannot go out and find a model and start observing its behavior – nor are they purely lexical, since linguistic usage is not sufficiently definite nor sufficiently well correlated with actual scientific practice, as a rule, to make sharp decisions of this sort possible. The criteria are, it would seem, partially empirical, in that one must scrutinize the actual epistemological structures inherent in current scientific practice and try to find a conceptual system which will articulate as closely as possible with this practice. Thus, if in analyzing scientific method an important distinction emerges, it may be appropriate to use the terms 'theory' and 'model' to convey this distinction, even though this may not exactly correspond with verbal usage among scientists. On the other hand, one cannot depart *too* far from this usage, otherwise one will not illuminate but only confuse. So the criteria are partially lexical also.

In the last analysis, when two philosophers disagree as to "what a physical model is", it may be assumed that each has isolated some element in scientific practice that he considers important and has attached to it the label 'model', a label which in ordinary usage may be only loosely correlated with this element. When A says a model is X, and B says it is not X, one may be misled by the linguistic form of the argument. It sounds as though they are contradicting one another, when in fact what is happening is something far more complex: each is implicitly affirming the superiority of the network of explanatory terms and their correlative distinctions that he has devised to clarify the procedures of science. I have thought it desirable to spend some time on this point of meta-methodology before beginning my topic proper, because the criteria for evaluation of this sort of discussion are so often misunderstood.

There are several senses of 'model' that one can dismiss as of little interest for inquiry into the use of models in physical science. The scale model or the model as an ideal to be imitated are not relevant for us*. But how about the notion of model implicit in the new branch of mathematics called model theory? SUPPES [1961] claims that "the meaning of the concept of model is the same in mathematics and the empirical sciences", though he adds that there is a difference in "their use of the concept". Now a model is defined by the mathematician as "a possible realization in which all valid sentences of a theory are satisfied"**; the "possible realization" in turn is a set-theoretical structure of some sort. Though this has some affinities with the physicist's use of the word, 'model', I am going to argue that the differences between the two uses are at least as important as the similarities, and in particular that assimilating one to the other runs the risk of obscuring the entire function of models in empirical science. I would not agree, therefore, that the "meaning" or formal structure of the concept can be separated off from its "use" in the way that Suppes suggests.

---

* These and other common usages of the term 'model' are discussed by BLACK [1962].
** Tarski, quoted by SUPPES [1961].

The empirical scientist begins by making carefully-controlled general-izations, usually asserting the interrelation of two or more parameters over a certain range and to a certain degree of accuracy. The aim of such a generalization is to *describe* a certain domain, and it will make use only of terms that have some sort of operational definition. However, even apparently simple terms like 'length' are embedded in a complex theory of measurement, involving all sorts of theoretical assumptions about rigid bodies, transport, and so forth. The "facts" are thus "theory-laden" in the sense that a set of theories has gone to defining the concepts in terms of which they are expressed. But, of course, these theories are not ordinarily the same ones that will be put forward to explain the facts themselves. The facts of spectroscopy, for instance, are dependent upon the theory of the spectroscope, but these facts are explained by the Bohr theory of the atom, which is quite a different matter. Thus the logical circularity so much emphasized by Feyerabend of late ordinarily does not arise; it is not as though the expressing of the facts in a particular language takes for granted the very theory which is subsequently put forward to account for the facts expressed.

A theory is thus something put forward to "account for" one or more empirical laws that are already known. It is not just a singular hypothesis, of the sort alluded to in statements like: "the police have a theory as to how the crime was committed". It has some degree of generality. But it is something more than a mere higher-order generalization. To deduce an empirical law from a more general empirical law does not "explain" it, in the strong sense in which I am using this term. (It is possible that an observed regularity might be said to be "accounted for" by deriving it from a com-bination of empirical laws; we speak of this as an "account" presumably because of the ingenuity required to combine the laws properly.) A theory is intended not as a description of what one already has, but as an hypothesis, something that goes beyond the evidence by introducing a postulated physical structure that could provide a causal account of the data to be explained, although it is not (as yet, at least) itself directly observable. The structure here is called a "model"; every theory has a model associated with it, otherwise it could not serve to explain. It would be merely descriptive in intent.

There is no need to think of the model, thus defined, as being more "familiar" than the data to be explained. It often is, and functions most easily when it is, but quite frequently it is not. The positrons posited to explain Anderson's observations of particle tracks in a cloud chamber were not exactly familiar sorts of entities. Neither does the model necessarily involve microstructure; it can be a macrostructure like a galactic wind. Nor does it postulate unobservables, only structures not at present observed. These misunderstandings have been pointed out by HESSE [1953, 1966], ACHINSTEIN [1964, 1965] and others.

The model is frequently evoked by an analogy from some quite different domain. But it is not itself an analogue, as Achinstein correctly reminds us. And in some instances, it may have no analogical dimension of any significant sort associated with it. For instance, when the geophysicist postulates liquid-solid discontinuities at several levels in the core of the earth in order to explain seismographic data, he provides a model of the earth's inner structure which does not depend on analogies with other better-known objects. It is true that the laws of reflection of vibrations at liquid-solid interfaces are known from elsewhere. But the existence of such interfaces in the core of the earth is postulated here for reasons which do not appear to be analogical in character.

The model is the postulated structure, whereas the theory is the set of statements in terms of which this structure is provisionally described. The theory is thus a linguistic and mathematical entity; the model is not. (Here we disagree with Achinstein, who equates the two.) The theory is derived from the model, therefore, not the reverse. Nor is the model simply an interpretation of the theory, as would be the case if one were to use these terms in their mathematical senses. True, the statements of the theory apply correctly to the model. But this is because the theory is about this model, and about nothing else. It cannot be interpreted by some other entity unless some of the terms that allow it to describe *this* model uniquely be dropped.

The frequent misunderstanding of this point comes from taking the theory as an uninterpreted calculus. Some early accounts of the model-theory relation spoke of an empty calculus that could be interpreted either by the structure postulated in the object to be explained or by the analogue which suggested the use of this calculus in the first place. Thus, Bohr's theory was thought of as a mathematical calculus which could be interpreted either in terms of hydrogen atoms or planetary systems. But this is clearly false. Bohr's theory is about hydrogen atoms, and the statements comprising it make use of terms like 'electrical charge', 'electron', which prevent it from also describing planetary systems. It will not do to appeal to an abstract calculus embodying only the algebraic equations occurring in the Bohr theory. Such a calculus is not a theory at all, in the physicist's sense. To "interpret" it is not simply to find entities for which its "statements" will come out as true. There are no physical statements in the calculus, so it would do no good to look round for an entity satisfying the expressions found there. It is necessary first to transform the calculus into a theory by qualifying it with non-formal concepts like *mass* and *energy*, involving the specification of non-formal operations of measurement. Only after this has been done can one go looking for an interpretation of the theory, although this would be a misleading way of putting the matter; rather, one would ask: what does the theory now *describe*?

It is easy to see how this misunderstanding arises. There is no distinction between calculus and theory in mathematics or logic. Interpretation in these fields is a simple matter of applying the calculus directly to a mathematical structure described in set-theoretic terms. There is no need to introduce a new range of concepts to make the calculus meaningful in order that an "interpretant" for it can then be identified. The logician who attempts to formalize the procedures of the scientist has to be reminded frequently of two things which he may easily be tempted to overlook. First, mathematics and physics differ radically in that the symbols of physics are already interpreted and have no physical sense apart from that interpretation. Thus the notion of interpretation developed within mathematics (that used, for example, in model theory) is not properly applicable to the domain of physics. Second, the logician leaves aside the temporal dimension of scientific procedures: it makes no difference to him whether the theory is suggested by the model or the model is an interpretation of the theory, since the purely formal relations will be the same (he argues) in either case. But to the physicist, the temporal order is all-important. Science as an activity is something which goes on in time; timeless inferences and timeless interpretations are legitimate abstractions, but have to be carefully handled if what one is interested in is what really goes on in science.

Do *all* physical theories involve postulated structures, that is differentiated entities whose properties and interrelations are at least partially specified? Dynamic theories seem to constitute a special category. The inverse square "law" of gravitation can be construed as simply *describing* how any given body moves, at a specified distance from the central body. Or it may be taken to *explain* what happens, in terms of a "gravitational force", now regarded as a pervasive causal activity of some sort. Taken in this latter sense, laws of force have played a properly theoretical role in the history of science, so that dynamic models can be included in our discussion, even though the boundaries between explanation and description are much less well-defined in their regard. The so-called "phenomenological" models of the physicist are, however, another matter. The label is used in somewhat different senses, but in general a phenomenological model appears to be an arbitrarily-chosen mathematically-expressed correlation of physical parameters from which the empirical laws of some domain can be derived. For instance, suppose one has a profusion of data about extensive cosmic ray showers, and one believes these showers to be due to nucleon-nucleon collisions in the upper atmosphere. To bring the data into a single convenient array, one may assume a mathematical distribution function of high generality for nucleon collisions, and then try to specify the parameters in the function more exactly in order to fit the data available. If this can be done successfully, one has an expression which summarizes a whole range of evidence in convenient form. Here the model is the expression itself and not an associated physical structure. It differs from a theory in that it is not regarded as an explanation, only as a summary, a summary whose mathematical form may, however, suggest where to look for a proper theoretical explanation. From the purely logical point of view, there is no difference between a theory and a phenome-nological model. Both can be axiomatized; from both, the desired empirical generalizations can be derived.

But for the physicist there is a crucial difference between them. This difference can be put in one or other of two ways. The physical theory makes an assertion about a physical sub-structure which can account for the data; the phenomenological model makes no such assertion. Insofar as the latter goes beyond the descriptive level, it does so merely to obtain greater mathe-matical generality and not because there are physical reasons that suggest such a hypothetical extension to be appropriate.

The difference can, however, be expressed in another way which serves to bring out the major feature of properly physical models. When the physicist introduces one of these, he does so not merely to summarize the data he already has, but primarily in the hope that the model will prove to contain a further "surplus content". A good model will be expected to suggest how the theory should be modified to meet new results, results which cannot be derived from the first simple theoretical formulation. It will suggest possible ex-tensions of the theory to cover ranges of the parameters not comprised under the empirical laws the theory was originally intended to explain. It may suggest possible linkages with physical domains not formerly seen to be related. In a word, a "good" model will contain resources for meeting the varied challenges which the theory based on it will inevitably evoke as new evidence becomes available. To the extent that the model does not show conceptual resilience of this sort, the physicist will tend to distrust it, or to regard it as merely having had *ad hoc* or, if you like "phenomenological", utility in the first place.

In order to anchor these abstractions somewhat more securely, let us look at the history of one of the two most productive physical models of our century, the Bohr model of the atom. In 1911, Rutherford discovered an anomalous scattering effect when α-particles pass through metal foil. The plausible interpretation of the very occasional sharp deflections that occur is to suppose that the mass of the metal atoms is concentrated in a very small nucleus whose charge can be computed from the average size of the deflections produced. It turns out that the positive nuclear charge is equal to the atomic number of the element; in order that the atom as a whole should be neutral we must then postulate the presence elsewhere in the atom of an equal number of negative charges of very small mass, i.e. electrons. But since the positive and negative charges ought to attract one another, how is it that the atom does not collapse? One is immediately reminded of our planetary system, between whose elements there are also forces of attraction, yet which does not collapse. A plausible model of the atom is suggested by this analogy, namely a massive central nucleus around which the electrons circulate in equilibrium orbits. But an immediate difficulty arises. According to classical electrodynamics, such a system ought to radiate energy continuously, in which case it would, of course, collapse. Bohr realized that if the new quantization of energy transfer introduced by Planck were to apply here, only certain orbits would be "permitted", so to speak, since the moment of momentum of the electron will have to be an integral multiple of $h/2\pi$.

What is the original Bohr model of the hydrogen atom then? It is a very simple physical structure in which a single electron revolves around a tiny positively-charged nucleus in which nearly all the mass of the atom is concentrated. It can take up only certain discrete orbits, the lowest of which is completely stable. It can radiate energy only in discrete amounts when it drops from one of the permitted higher-energy outer orbits to an inner orbit. This is the *model*, and the Bohr *theory* is the set of statements describing how such a model would behave in various conditions. It is, of course, the model that gives rise to the theory; there is no way for one to hit upon the theory somehow first.

Bohr was led to this model by a simple analysis of the results of Rutherford on the one hand, and of Planck on the other. But he immediately saw that if he were right, i.e. if the model were a "good" one, it would have far-reaching consequences for the field of spectroscopy, in which vast masses of data had been accumulating for half a century, and where various numerical correlations had been worked out which as yet lacked any sort of theoretical basis. In particular, the spectrum of hydrogen was known to contain several sets of sharp lines, notably the series given by the formula:

$$v = R\left(\frac{1}{2^2} - \frac{1}{k^2}\right) \qquad (k = 3, 4, \ldots).$$

Balmer had given this formula in 1885 as a "phenomenological" model for the lines in the visible and ultraviolet position of the hydrogen spectrum. The Rydberg constant, R, had been measured to an astonishing accuracy of seven figures; it was at the time the most accurately known number in physics. Ritz had already given a quasi-theoretic interpretation of the Balmer series in 1908, his "Principle of combination"; according to it, such a series, being written as the difference between a constant and a variable term, must represent the difference between successive energy levels in the atom, where the constant term represents the "ground" energy. This suggested a generalization of the formula to:

$$v = R\left(\frac{1}{n^2} - \frac{1}{m^2}\right)$$

where $n = 1, 2, 3$ and m is an integer $> n$. And indeed the existence of such a series for $n = 3$ was shown by Paschen (1908), and for $n = 1$ by Lyman (1906).

Bohr was immediately able to derive not only this formula, but a definition of R as being equal to $2\pi^2 me^4/ch^3$. When the known values of the electron parameters were inserted, a value of R was found which agreed with the observed value to three significant figures. This was already striking enough. But then a more careful analysis of the model showed three ways in which the theory would have to be modified. First, it had been assumed that the nucleus remains at rest while the electron revolves around it, which is equivalent to taking the nucleus to be of infinite mass. If, instead, one allows for the motion of nucleus and electron alike around a common center, one is forced to modify the series formula above by multiplying R by $(1 + m/M)$, which has the effect of increasing it very slightly, depending on the proportion of the electron and the nuclear masses. This immediately explained the puzzle of the Pickering series for ionized helium (1897), which ought, according to the simple Bohr theory, give a spectrum similar to that of hydrogen, but in fact showed lines very slightly separated from the Balmer lines of hydrogen. Since the values of m/M for hydrogen and helium differ, the effect of the nuclear motion on the energy levels will differ in the two cases; the correct value for the Pickering separation was immediately given by the revised formula.

Furthermore, there is no reason to restrict the electron to circular orbits, since elliptical orbits are the normal paths for bodies under central forces of this type. This introduces a new degree of freedom, since two parameters are needed to specify the ellipse. But it is found that the original Bohr circle is equivalent in energy to a family of ellipses, or to put this in a different way, that allowing for elliptical orbits will, under ordinary conditions, introduce no new spectral lines. But now suppose we put the atoms in an intense electrical field. Stark discovered in 1913, the same year in which Bohr proposed his original theory, that the hydrogen lines turn out to have a complex "fine structure", whose components are polarized in different ways when the emitting atoms are subjected to a strong electrical field. Three years later, Schwarzchild showed that this is due to a degeneracy in the original solution: the effect of the field is to separate off the energies of different elliptical orbits very slightly, orbits that would give the same energy in the absence of a field. Again, the correct answer was given for the amount of splitting, and for the polarizations involved.

Finally, there was a third simplification in the way the original Bohr theory had represented the model: it had left out of account the relativistic effects due to the rapid motion of the electron. When these were computed, it was found that a double correction had to be made to the original series formula. First, the series factor $1/n^2$ had to be increased by a very small amount, bearing a ratio of about 3×10^{-6} to the whole. Second, there is a very fine splitting into two or more lines, due to a relativistic energy separation between the different elliptical orbits the electron could take up. Thus the apparently sharp lines of the Balmer series ought to show a fine structure, if the precision of measurement could be improved enough. But in actual fact, as early as 1887 Michelson had noted that the first Balmer "line" is, in fact, a doublet whose components are extremely close. Further examination of other lines in the spectra of hydrogen and ionized helium showed precisely the types and amount of splitting predicted from this taking into account of the relativistic dependence of the mass of the electron upon its velocity.

So far, we have seen three ways in which the theory was amended to describe the original model more correctly. It is worth noting that these were *not* changes in the model, strictly speaking. All three of them are suggested by the *original* model, but for simplicity were left out of account in the first formulation of the theory. If one has a two-body system of the sort postulated, one will *have* to have nuclear motion, elliptical orbits and relativistic mass effects, unless the laws of physics, known from elsewhere, are assumed not to apply to the entities of the model.

But now we come to a modification of a different sort. Long before this, in 1896, Zeeman had noted a splitting effect in the H spectrum when the emitting atoms are placed in a magnetic field. Two different sorts of effect were, in fact, discovered: the so-called "normal" Zeeman effect which splits a singlet line into a doublet or triplet, depending on the direction of the force, and the "anomalous" splitting effect for multiplets. This took much longer to handle theoretically. Only in 1926 did Goudsmit and Uhlenbeck suggest an *addition* to the original Bohr model; an electron spin which would make each electron become a tiny precessing magnet in an imposed magnetic field. From this simple physical assumption the correct answers were found for both Zeeman effects, not only in hydrogen but in other types of atom as well.

I have thought it worthwhile to follow this early development of the Bohr theory in some detail, because much may be learnt from it. One notes, first of all, that the original model, though suggested by analogies with the planetary system, was not in fact a planetary system. The force involved was a Coulomb force, not a gravitational one. And the electron (unlike the planet) is a negative charged particle, which is of central importance in explaining both the Stark and the Zeeman effects. Above all, the electron orbits (unlike the planetary ones) are quantized. It would be incorrect, therefore, to suppose that there is some abstract formal calculus of which both the planetary model of Kepler and the atomic model of Bohr are simply different realizations. It is true that the electron does obey equations which are algebraically similar to Kepler's three laws. But there the resemblance ends, and the subsequent history of the model was governed far more by the differences between the two models than their similarities.

This brings me to my final point. The good model has a surplus content which enables the theory based on it to survive challenge and extend in all sorts of unexpected ways. This is why it is false to say that science is no more than a summary of previous experience. If it were no more than this, there would be no surplus content to guide discovery in the way that the Bohr model – and a myriad of other similar examples could have been chosen – actually did.

The presence of this surplus content is our assurance that the model-structure has some sort of basis in the "real world". For what is "reality" if not the reservoir from which such a surplus is drawn? The fact that the

Bohr model worked out so remarkably indicates that the structure it postulated for the H atom had some sort of approximate basis in the real. Only approximate, of course, and by definition the degree of approximation can never be known. Later quantum mechanics would modify this simple model in all sorts of fundamental ways. But a careful consideration of the *history* of the model – and this is one reason why the study of the history of science is indispensable to an adequate philosophy of science – strongly suggests that the guidance it gave to theoretical research in quantum mechanics for an immensely fruitful fifteen years must ultimately have derived from a "fit" of some sort, however complex and however loose it may have been, between the model and the structure of the real it so successfully explained.

References

ACHINSTEIN, P., Models, analogies, and theories, Phil. Science **31** (1964) 328–349.
ACHINSTEIN, P., Theoretical models, Brit. J. Phil. Science **16** (1965) 102–120.
BLACK, M., Models and metaphors (Ithaca, N. Y., 1962).
HESSE, M., Models in physics, Brit. J. Phil. Science **4** (1953) 198–214.
HESSE, M., Models and analogies in science (Notre Dame, Ind., 1966).
SUPPES, P., The meaning and uses of models, in: The concept and the role of the model in mathematics and natural and social science (Dordrecht, 1961) pp. 163–177.

THE ORIGIN OF THE UNIVERSE

D. W. SCIAMA

University of Cambridge, England

It is often said that philosophical problems, by definition, cannot be affected by new scientific results. If this is strictly true then the present paper is entirely irrelevant to a Philosophical Congress and should not be published in its Proceedings. If it is published it means that someone besides myself thinks that philosophical questions concerning the origin of the universe can be illuminated by new observational discoveries in cosmology. In fact the last few years have seen revolutionary new discoveries, thanks mainly to the development of radio astronomy and the concomitant optical observations. We appear to be on the verge of answering some really significant questions about the structure of the universe in space and time.

The main conclusion to be drawn from these new discoveries is that the steady state theory of the universe is probably wrong. It will be recalled that the red shifts in the spectra of galaxies have led to the belief that the universe is expanding. This naturally suggests that the universe was once very much denser than it is today. In fact on the basis of very reasonable assumptions indeed it can be shown that general relativity requires there to have been a physical singularity in the past. (A result mainly due to Dr. S. W. Hawking.) One way of avoiding this singularity is to deny the validity either of general relativity or of the reasonable assumptions just referred to, and to suppose that the universe can be in a steady state despite the expansion, the continual creation of new matter compensating for the recession of the galaxies. Bondi and Gold took the first way out, that is, denied the validity of general relativity. Hoyle, and later Hoyle and Narlikar, took the second way out, by postulating the existence of a field (the creation or C field) which has *negative* energy density associated with it.

There are three main lines of evidence which suggest that the steady state theory is wrong. They are

(i) the radio source counts,

(ii) the red shifts of quasars,

(iii) the excess microwave background.

It would not be appropriate to give a full scientific discussion of this evidence here, but it may be of interest if I indicate what is involved.

1. The radio source counts

It is known from optical identifications that most sources in the radio catalogues which lie in directions away from the plane of our Galaxy are probably extragalactic. The relative number of sources of different measured intensities then tells us something about their distribution in space. The steady state theory makes rather specific predictions for the counts of radio sources, and it has been known for some time, thanks mainly to the work of Sir Martin Ryle and his colleagues, that the observations differ markedly from these predictions. To put it roughly there are too many faint sources. This almost certainly means that there are too many sources at large distances, and therefore at large times in the past (because of the time the radio noise takes to reach us). To explain the discrepancy we have to suppose that radio sources differed in some way in the distant past from those existing to-day. Such intrinsic evolution in the contents of the universe is, of course, forbidden by the steady state theory, but is permitted, perhaps even expected, in evolutionary theories of the universe.

Attempts have been made by several people (including myself) to get round this difficulty, but they have not met with much success. However, the majority of the sources concerned have not yet been optically identified (their extragalactic nature being assumed inferentially from the identifications that have been made). Thus if this were the only evidence I think it should be treated with reserve.

2. The red shifts of quasars

Most astronomers believe that quasars have red shifts because they partake of the expansion of the universe. The known relation between red shift and distance (Hubble's law) then places most of the quasars at very great distances indeed, much greater than those of galaxies. A study of the distribution of the values of the red shift amongst the quasars should then provide a sensitive test of the steady state theory. Dr. M. J. Rees and I have made this test, and we find that the steady state theory is badly wrong. There is a loophole here, however, because a few astronomers maintain that the quasars are close to our Galaxy, their red shifts having nothing to do with the Hubble law, but arising in some other way. This hypothesis seems unlikely at the moment, but really decisive evidence is still lacking.

3. The excess microwave background

This perhaps is the most remarkable evidence of all. It has been found that the intensity of the radio noise arriving at the earth at microwave frequencies (that is wavelengths of a few centimetres) is far greater than was expected, considering the known sources of such radiation. The evidence strongly suggests that the spectrum of this excess radiation is that of a black body. This would mean that the radiation has somehow come into thermal equilibrium (its temperature being about three degrees absolute). The only reasonable explanation that has so far been proposed is that this black body radiation is what is left over from the very high temperature radiation which may have been present when the density of the universe was extremely high. This "hot big bang" theory was actually formulated many years earlier by George Gamow and his associates. The point is that in the early high density stages there would have been ample time for matter and radiation to come into thermal equilibrium, thus guaranteeing a black body spectrum at that time. One can also show that the spectrum of the radiation would remain that of a black body as the universe expands and matter and radiation eventually become more or less decoupled. The effect of the expansion is simply to cool the radiation, and on this theory it has now cooled to a few degrees. (Gamow's prediction was between one and ten degrees.)

This explanation for the observed excess radiation, which has been pressed especially by R. H. Dicke and his colleagues, is an entirely natural one. By contrast, the steady state theory is in great difficulties. One could imagine radiation being created along with the matter, but why it should result in a black body spectrum is quite obscure. Unless a reasonable proposal can be made to deal with this difficulty, the excess radiation is, I think, the best evidence so far against the steady state theory. The loophole in this case is that the evidence in favour of the radiation having a black body spectrum is not yet quite decisive. Further measurements are on the way which are expected to settle this question.

4. Conclusions

I conclude that unless several unlikely contingencies are the case the universe as we know it to-day must have evolved from a much denser configuration. This configuration is sometimes referred to as the creation of the universe, a description which I heartily deprecate. There is no process of creation in the theory as we understand it today. Of course, this theory probably does not apply to the earliest stages of extremely high density, but how the correct theory will handle the singularity we simply do not know. I might add that we also do not know whether the universe is now going to expand forever or whether it will re-contract under its self-gravitation into another singularity, a singularity which I suppose some would call the destruction of the universe. This question will probably become clearer as a result of the observational discoveries of the next few years.

A UNIFIED APPROACH TO BIOLOGICAL
AND SOCIAL ORGANISMS *

N. RASHEVSKY

Mental Health Research Institute,
The University of Michigan, USA

During the first three decades of its recent intensive growth, which began somewhat over forty years ago, the progress of mathematical biology consisted principally in the development of physico-mathematical or more purely formal mathematical models of various biological phenomena. At least implicitly this development was based on the expectation, if not on a firm conviction, that all biological phenomena could be eventually explained in terms of the known phenomena of physics. In 1934 we coined the term "mathematical biophysics" (RASHEVSKY [1934]) to describe this kind of approach. With the introduction of more phenomenological mathematical descriptions of some biological phenomena, descriptions which did not introduce specific physical models, a broader designation, namely "mathematical biology", became more advantageous. Mathematical biophysics is thus included in the broader concept of mathematical biology.

The success of the new field has been remarkable. Hardly a branch of biology was left out from the mathematical approach. A number of quantitative aspects of biology were adequately represented by mathematical theory. In some cases quantitative relations not hitherto observed were predicted by the theory and subsequently confirmed experimentally.

This development led in a natural manner to a possible mathematical approach to social phenomena. Among other biological phenomena mathematical biologists did study various aspects of the behavior of an individual under the influence of different environmental stimuli (RASHEVSKY [1960]). Inasmuch as a very large part of our environment consists of our fellow men,

* This work has been aided by grant GM-12032 of the United States Public Health Service to the University of Michigan.

the above mentioned studies in the mathematical theory of individual behavior led naturally to the theory of the behavior of individuals under the
influence of other individuals, in other words to the theory of some social
interactions (RASHEVSKY [1947], [1959]). Thus, it appeared that biology
might become a branch of physics, while sociology might become a branch
of biology.

An important characteristic of the above mentioned developments of
mathematical biology and mathematical sociology was the very strong emphasis on quantitative aspects. In 1954 we called attention to the circum-
stance that such an approach was too limited to meet the demands of either
biology or sociology. While the quantitative aspects of biology are very
important, there are a number of qualitative, or as we called them, relational
aspects that are at least just as important, if not even more important. There
are a number of facts which seem to indicate that in spite of their importance,
the quantitative, or as we called them, the metric aspects of biology may be
subordinate in their importance to the qualitative or relational aspects. Contrary to physics, we do not have any universal constants in biology. Quantitatively no two biological systems are completely identical. The absolute
numerical values of some quantitative indices of biological phenomena differ
from organism to organism *even within the same species*. What is actually
meaningfully observable in an organism is not the exact numerical characteristics of some quantitative aspects, but rather the general functional form
of the equations involved. This led RASHEVSKY [1938] to the introduction
of the useful and very powerful approximation method in mathematical
biology (RASHEVSKY [1960]). Many important biological phenomena differ
for different organisms, not only in their quantitative aspects, but even in
the physical mechanisms involved although some qualitative relations between the different phenomena in the organism are invariant for all organisms. Thus, for example, the mechanisms of response to some external
stimuli are quite different in a paramecium, an oyster and a man. Similarly,
the mechanism of catching the food, ingesting it, digesting it, are different
in different organisms, as are the mechanisms of locomotion. Yet for all
motile organisms, the sequence: stimulus, locomotion towards food, ingestion
of food, digestion of food, its absorption, is the same. But this sequence is
a simple case of a qualitative relation which thus holds for a very wide
variety of different organisms.

To investigate mathematically such qualitative or relational aspects of
biology some branch of relational mathematics must be chosen. The proto-
type of such a branch of mathematics is found in elementary plane geometry.

With the exception of Pythagoras' Theorem and two or three other theorems, which are of a quantitative or metric character, all theorems of plane geometry are of a relational, non-quantitative nature. The highest development of relational aspects of geometry is, of course, found in topology. Theory of groups, theory of sets, and the general theory of relations are other branches of relational mathematics.

In his first attempt to create a relational mathematical biology, RASHEVSKY [1954] suggested the use of topology, particularly of the theory of graphs for the representation of organisms in their relational aspects. The approach was generalized by ROSEN [1958a], who eventually used a combination of graph theory and of the theory of categories. General metrized and non-metrized topological spaces, as well as the theory of sets were used by RASHEVSKY [1956a, c], [1958 a]. Theory of sets was also eventually used (RASHEVSKY [1958b]). Graph theoretical studies in relational biology were also made by TRUCCO [1956 a, b, c], by ARBIB [1966] and by BRAMSON [1966]. Lately Rosen discussed the connection between sequential machines and organisms. The work of MARTINEZ [1964] must also be mentioned here. The literature on relational mathematical biology is now quite extensive.

The conclusions of all such theoretical studies are not in the form of analytical expressions which describe quantitatively some biological phenomena, but rather in the form of existential propositions which state that the existence of such phenomena, or of specified relations between phenomena follow from the theory (RASHEVSKY [1956a], [1958a]).

The first person to emphasize the relational aspect of biology and to use the theory of relations a quarter of a century earlier than Rashevsky was WOODGER [1937]. His emphasis was, however, in a very different direction than that of Rashevsky, Rosen and the above mentioned authors. However, Woodger is the real father of relational biology.

In a somewhat similar manner as the quantitative aspects of biology led to some quantitative aspects of sociology, the relational aspects of biology led to some relational aspects of sociology (RASHEVSKY [1954]). Here again we find that the relational aspects are just as important as, if not more important than, the quantitative or metric aspects. Social structures may differ widely in their quantitative aspects and yet show pronounced relational similarities, similarities which, as we shall see, sometimes become isomorphisms. The introduction of relational biology seems to emphasize some analogies between biological and social sciences much more strongly than did the quantitative methods.

It is characteristic of relational biology that it studies the relational aspects quite independently from the metric aspects. The question naturally arises as to the mutual relation between the old metric mathematical biology and the newer relational one. How does mathematical biophysics fit into relational biology and *vice versa*? There is no more contradiction between the two aspects of biology than there is between the same two aspects in mathematics. Topology in its pure form is completely relational. However, quantitative aspects appear in topology in the form of Bettis numbers, Eulers index, etc. Topological methods are blended with metrical ones in many problems of the theory of differential equations, a branch of typical quantitative mathematics. While from the topological properties of a surface, say a torus, we cannot deduce anything about its metric properties, yet the knowledge of the metric properties of a surface *at every point* does completely determine its topology. Thus, in principle, it may be hoped that the relational properties of organisms and of societies may sometime be derived from their metric properties. The metric properties of an organism would be all expressible and describable in terms of physical notions because we can perceive an organism, or more generally know about its existence only to the extent that an organism manifests itself as a physical system. We either see the organism, or hear it, or smell it, or feel it, or weigh it, or stick a pair of electrodes into it and observe an electric output, etc. Thus, the expectation mentioned before, namely that we can *describe* all biological phenomena in terms of physics, not only remains in force, but it actually follows from what we just said. All biological phenomena which *we can observe* are physical in their nature and therefore can be described and explained in terms of physics.

This possibility of explaining biological phenomena in terms of physical ones has apparently for a long time been confused with the possibility of *deducing* from the set of physical laws the necessity of existence under certain conditions of biological organisms. The possibility of deducing the existence of biological phenomena from the laws of physics does not, however, follow from the possibility of representing all observable biological phenomena in terms of physical ones. The laws of biology in their relation to the laws of physics may possibly represent an analogy to the undecidable statements in mathematics. Such undecidable statements in mathematics are *representable* in mathematical terms, yet they may not be deduced from a given system of axioms.

Is there any evidence that biological laws are not deducible from, though representable in terms of, the laws of physics? The answer is no, but the possibilities offered by such an assumption are sufficiently interesting to warrant a detailed study of its consequences. What holds for the connection between physics and biology holds also for the connection between biology and sociology. The phenomena of sociology may well be representable in terms of the biology of interaction of two or more individuals because the observable behavior of an individual is the behavior of a biological system. It does not follow from this that from the postulates of biology we can deduce the existence of social phenomena.

If we accept the above point of view, then there still remains the possibility of *representing* ultimately the phenomena of biology and sociology in terms of physics. But this is no longer a complete reductionism because the three basic sets of postulates of the three sciences may not necessarily be deducible one from another. In particular, we must face the possibility that the relational aspects of biology and sociology are not consequences of the metric aspects of physics.

As we already remarked, the relational aspects of biology and sociology bring the two sciences much closer together than do their metric aspects. In biological and social sciences the relational aspects appear to be more basic than the metric aspects. In physics the metric aspects seem to be the more basic ones although relational aspects are not lacking in quantum mechanics, and especially in the theory of elementary particles. The part played by relational aspects in physics is, however, very small compared to the part which they play in biological and social sciences. This seems to make the distance between physics, on one hand, and biology and sociology, on the other, much greater than the distance between biology and sociology. We shall, therefore, restrict ourselves here to the study of the interrelation between biology and sociology.

Similarities between organisms and societies have been noted since the days of Herbert Spencer. There has been a great deal of discussion as to whether societies are organisms and vice versa. Unless we have a precise definition of an organism and of a society, such discussions are rather fruitless. Yet the similarities just mentioned cannot be easily dismissed. There is a close intertwining of biological and sociological, or even economic, concepts. The biologist speaks of the division of labor between cells (as well as within cells), of specialization of cells or organs, etc. These are fundamentally socio-economic concepts.

If, as we surmise, the existence of societies cannot be deduced from the postulates of biology, and if at the same time we observe a great many similarities between biological and social phenomena, then the natural thing is to seek for an abstract conceptual superstructure which has the properties *common* to both biological and social phenomena. Those two sets of phenomena will then be consequences of the more general theory which describes the superstructure. In a recent publication (RASHEVSKY [1967a]) we have suggested such a conceptual superstructure which we call the theory of organismic sets. We shall now briefly discuss some aspects and conclusions of the approach.

Any society, whether human or animal, is a set of the individuals of which it is composed. It is, however, much more than such a set. A mere collection of individuals which in no way interact with each other would hardly be called a society. The individuals in a society interact both with the environment and with each other and the results of these interactions are various products of the individuals' activities, which are essential for the continued maintenance of those activities and interactions. Our modern, highly developed societies would not be characterized completely without enumerating our means of communication, transportation, industrial production, etc. In primitive societies these results of interactions are less numerous and simpler, still even a primitive society is characterized by hunting or agricultural tools, etc. A similar thing holds for animal societies. A collection of bees without bee hives or ants without anthills is hardly an animal society.

Let us now look at a multicellular organism. It is a set of cells, but also more than a mere set of cells. A suspension of bacteria is not an organism. In a multicellular organism the cells interact with each other. The results of those interactions, such as endocrine secretions for instance, are essential for the continued maintenance of the interactions.

A unicellular organism at first does not seem to present the same picture. Actually it does. Every constituent part of a cell is the result of activity of some gene or genes, and it is necessary for a continued activity of the genes. Thus, a cell may be considered as a set of genes plus the products of their activities.

Another important characteristic common to both biological organisms and to societies is the gradual specialization of activities by either the cells or by the individuals. In the early stages of development of a multicellular organism the cells are at first pluripotent and multifunctional. Gradually *some* functions of each type of cell are lost and the cell *specializes* in only one or relatively few biological functions. A similar situation holds for individuals in a developing society. The only exception to this seems to be the society of genes which form a cell. According to Beadles principle of "one gene–one enzyme" each gene is completely specialized and performs only one activity.

The basic idea of the theory of organismic sets is to study sets the elements of which stand in certain relations to each other, those relations being suggested by the relational aspects common to both biological and social sciences. Like any definitions, the definitions which specify an organismic set are arbitrary. They are, however, chosen from what we know about observed relational aspects common to both biology and social sciences.

We therefore define an organismic set S_0 as satisfying the following properties:

1) Each element e_i of the set S_0 of cardinality n $(i=1,2,...,n)$ can *potentially* perform a set $S_i^{(a)}$ of m_i activities $a_{i_1}, a_{i_2}, ..., a_{i_{m_i}}$, and those activities result in a set $S_i^{(p)}$ of $r_i \leqq m_i$ products $p_{i_1}, p_{i_2}, ..., p_{i_{r_i}}$. The word "product" is used here not to denote a mathematical operation, but rather in an economic sense, as in "The radio is the product of electronic industry". The italicized word "*potentially*" is to indicate that in a given fixed environment E_ε each e_i exhibits only a subset $S_{i\varepsilon}^{(a)} \subseteq S_i^{(a)}$ of activities. Furthermore the set $\bigcup_i S_i^{(p)}$ is assumed to be necessary and sufficient for all the elements e_i to exhibit all the activities of the subset $S_{i\varepsilon}^{(a)}$. More narrowly, we may assume that $\bigcup_i S_i^{(p)}$ is necessary and sufficient for all e_i's to exist continually. If any element of $\bigcup_i S_i^{(a)}$ becomes for any reason superfluous for a complete functioning of all the e_i's, it becomes inhibited, in other words the corresponding activity a_{i_k} ceases. The set $\bigcup_i S_i^{(p)}$ is also necessary and sufficient for the replication of at least some of the elements e_i. Finally, each element e_i can function or exist on the average for a time t_i without being supplied with all elements of the set $S_i^{(p)}$.

A glance at the above description of an organismic set shows that in abstracto it describes the behavior of either the individuals in a society, or of cells in a multicellular organism, or of genes in a cell, with the exception that the genes are completely specialized, as we have seen above. Each element e_i of the set S_0 of genes exhibits, therefore, only one activity and produces only one product.

We then introduce a postulate to the effect that the elements of an organismic set gradually, as time goes on, specialize each in either only one activity, or in a few activities. This postulate is again essentially a description of what we observe either in multicellular organisms or in societies.

The requirement that all the elements of the set $\bigcup_i S_i^{(p)}$ are necessary for the normal functioning of each e_i within a time t_i leads to a basic theorem of the theory of organismic sets. In a non-specialized set each of the elements e_i produces the whole set $\bigcup_i S_i^{(p)}$, in other words a complete lack of specialization means that all $S_i^{(p)}$ are identical, so that $\bigcup_i S_i^{(p)} = S_i^{(p)}$. As specialization proceeds, this condition breaks down. In the limit of complete specialization each element will produce only one or a very few p_i. When $\bigcup_i S_i^{(p)} =$

$S_i^{(p)}$, then all p_i's are produced at the site of each element e_i. In case of a complete specialization, each p_i is produced by a different e_i. Inasmuch as each e_i needs all the p_i's, this raises the problem of transport. In human societies the transport is effected by various known means. In multicellular organisms the *main* method of transport is the cardio-vascular system. In single cells the transport is effected either by diffusion or by the so-called "active transport." In any case the transport takes time. Denote by t_{ik} the transport time of the product p_i from e_i to e_k. If $t_{ik} > t_k$, then the element e_k will not function properly and not produce p_k which is necessary for the normal functioning of every other e_j. Thus, when even for a single t_{ik} we have $t_{ik} > t_i$, the organismic set will break down.

Another essential postulate of the theory of organismic sets is the Postulate of Relational Forces (RASHEVSKY [1966a, b], [1967a]). It states that in the absence of long-range repelling physical forces, the elements e_i, if originally separated, will aggregate if this aggregation results in the above-mentioned relations which characterize an organismic set. For societies this postulate is rather obvious. Human beings aggregate if this aggregation results in social interactions which are beneficial for their survival and the maintenance of their normal functions. In biology this postulate represents a hypothesis.

From what we said about the survival of completely differentiated organismic sets for $t_{ik} > t_k$, it follows that if we have a collection of isolated specialized elements e_i ($i = 1, 2, ..., n$), they will *not* aggregate to form an organismic set. One *isolated* specialized element will not produce any p_i's because all the other necessary p_k's will be absent. When brought together they still will not produce any p_i's because the whole set $\bigcup_i S_i^{(p)}$ is necessary for each element to function. Completely undifferentiated elements will, however, aggregate according to the postulate of relational forces because once such an aggregation takes they will not only continue to function, but will undergo a process of specialization.

In societies this means that a society can be formed only when the individuals are not specialized and when, in case of necessity, everyone can perform the tasks that are necessary for his survival. If in our present highly, though not completely, specialized society, all products of industry and all the means of their production were destroyed by some catastrophe, with all the specialized and highly trained individuals surviving, our society would not reconstitute itself without first undergoing a process of "primitivization" or despecialization. Such a partial "primitivization" is familiar to everyone who lived through the Russian Revolution. It may occur also after devastating wars or natural disasters.

The cells of a higher multicellular organism, if separated and dispersed, will not spontaneously reconstitute the organism. But in the earliest stages of development, the undifferentiated cells of a blastula, when dispersed, spontaneously reconstitute the blastula, a phenomenon called "cytotropism" by W. Roux.

The genes being completely specialized will not aggregate to start a formation of a cell. Since at some time such an aggregation occurred, at the earliest beginning of life, the conclusion must be drawn that originally the genes were non-specialized and poly-functional. Such "protogenes" would have been eventually inhibited as "superfluous" after a complete specialization was reached.

All the above holds only if at least one t_{ik} is greater than t_k; with increasing differentiation and complexity of transport this is more likely to happen than not. The conceptual superstructure suggested here, the organismic sets, thus seems to provide a unified approach to biological and social phenomena. It leads to basically verifiable conclusions. It throws light on phenomena of metamorphosis in biology as well as the biogenetic law (RASHEVSKY [1967a]). It also has been shown (RASHEVSKY [1967b]) to contain the principle of biological epimorphism, proposed and developed by us (RASHEVSKY [1960a, b]), which describes the relational invariants of different organisms.

The above discussion leaves, however, an unsatisfactory asymmetry between physics, on the one hand, and biology and sociology on the other. One should like to have a conceptual superstructure from which all three disciplines would derive. How this can be done is discussed in our most recent publication. It falls, however, outside the scope of the present paper.

References

ARBIB, M., Categories of (M, R)-systems, Bull. Math. Biophys. **28** (1966) 511–517.

BRAMSEN, J., A matrix approach to the theory of biotopological mapping, Bull. Math. Biophys. **28** (1966) 107–116.

MARTINEZ, H., Toward an optimal design principle in relational biology, Bull. Math. Biophys. **26** (1964) 351–365.

RASHEVSKY, N., Foundations of mathematical biophysics, Phil. of Sci. **1** (1934) 180.

RASHEVSKY, N., Mathematical biophysics. The physico-mathematical foundations of biology (Chicago, The University of Chicago Press, 1938).

RASHEVSKY, N., Mathematical biology of social behavior (Chicago, The University of Chicago Press, 1951).

RASHEVSKY, N., Topology and life: In search of general mathematical principles in biology and sociology, Bull. Math. Biophys. **16** (1954) 317–348.

RASHEVSKY, N., Some remarks on topological biology, Bull. Math. Biophys. **17** (1955) 207–218.

RASHEVSKY, N., The geometrization of biology, Bull. Math. Biophys. **18** (1956a) 31–56.
RASHEVSKY, N., What type of empirically verifiable predictions can topological biology make? Bull. Math. Biophys. **18** (1956b) 173–188.
RASHEVSKY, N., The geometrization of biology: A correction, Bull. Math. Biophys. **18** (1956c) 233–235.
RASHEVSKY, N., A contribution to the search of general mathematical principles in biology, Bull. Math. Biophys. **20** (1958a) 71–93.
RASHEVSKY, N., A comparison of set-theoretical and graphtheoretical approaches in topological biology, Bull. Math. Biophys. **20** (1958b) 267–273.
RASHEVSKY, N., Mathematical biophysics. The physico-mathematical foundations of biology (New York, Dover Publications, Inc., third and revised edition, 1960).
RASHEVSKY, N., Mathematical principles in biology and their applications (Springfield, Illinois, Charles C. Thomas, Publisher, 1961).
RASHEVSKY, N., Physics, biology and sociology: A reappraisal, Bull. Math. Biophys. **28** (1966a) 283–308.
RASHEVSKY, N., A sociological approach to biology, Bull. Math. Biophys. **28** (1966b) 655–661.
RASHEVSKY, N., Organismic sets: Outline of a general theory of biological and social organisms, Bull. Math. Biophys. **29** (1967a) 139–152.
RASHEVSKY, N., Organismic sets and biological epimorphism, Bull. Math. Biophys. **29** (1967b) 389–393.
ROSEN, R., A relational theory of biological systems, Bull. Math. Biophys. **20** (1958) 245–260.
ROSEN, R., A relational theory of structural changes induced in biological systems by alterations in environment, Bull. Math. Biophys. **23** (1961) 165–171.
TRUCCO, E., A note on Rashevsky's Theorem about point-bases in topological biology, Bull. Math. Biophys. **18** (1956a) 65–85.
TRUCCO, E., A note on the information content of graphs, Bull. Math. Biophys. **18** (1956b) 129–135.
TRUCCO, E., On the information content of graphs: Compound symbols; different states for each point, Bull. Math. Biophys. **18** (1956c) 237–253.
WOODGER, J.H., The axiomatic method in biology (Cambridge, Cambridge University Press, 1937).

Section 8

Methodology and Philosophy of Psychological Sciences

SOME THOUGHTS ON THE USE OF MODELS IN PSYCHOLOGY

B. A. FARRELL

Corpus Christi College, Oxford, England

I. I want to speak about a certain branch, or current, of psychological work in the Anglo-American world, which I happen to know a little about, and which is of some philosophical interest.

Let me begin with a very quick and crude piece of retrospection. One of the romantic hopes that inspired Anglo-American psychology after World War I was the thought that the application of scientific methods to the behaviour of organisms, human and infra-human, would yield acceptable generalizations, which simply related stimuli and responses. By the end of the 30s it had long become apparent that this hope was a delusion. Whatever the connections were between inputs and outputs – and there obviously *were* a vast and varied range of intimate connections between them – they were not of the simple, straightforward sort that had been previously imagined. By the end of the 30s, what had been clear to common sense (and to workers in the neurological field) also became clear to most psychologists. If the latter wished to arrive at acceptable generalizations about behaviour, they would also have to take into account the internal states of the organism. Well, how was this to be done? The obvious difficulties were that these states could not be identified neuro-anatomically, and hence were unobservable and hypothetical. During the 30s and 40s a pioneering and courageous attempt was developed to deal with these difficulties by HULL [1943]. Hull argued that the postulated, internal and unobservable states of the organism should be tied to antecedent and postcedent observables – just as we do in the natural sciences. So, for example, a postulated internal state like Habit Strength should be tied to antecedent observable conditions like, for example, the number of runs in a maze; and to postcedent observables like, for example, the resistance of the response to extinction training. He argued, moreover, that psychological techniques were strong enough in actual fact to carry out this programme, and to arrive at generalizations that could form part of a large scale theory of organismic functioning.

After World War II the difficulties of the Hulliam answer to the problem became increasingly apparent. It was much more difficult than Hull had thought to tie internal states to observable antecedents and postcedents; and it became evident that it was premature to try to arrive at large generalizations in the context of a large theory of organismic functioning. The romantic age of psychological theory construction was clearly at an end. However, Hull left psychologists certain important legacies. He left them, inter alia, very much clearer about what is involved in attempts to deal with internal states; and he gave them the courage to deal with these without embarrassment and self-apology. At the same time – after World War II – the imaginations of many psychologists were caught by the obvious analogies that could be derived from the new studies of communications engineering, control systems theory, and so on. After the War these several streams came together to produce a certain current or tradition of work in the Anglo-American world. It is this current of work which I want to talk about today.

Psychologists in this current are not concerned to develop large scale theories about the functioning of organisms. Nor are they primarily concerned to establish S–R generalizations – or, as they would put it, generalizations connecting inputs with outputs. They are more concerned to use data about observed inputs and outputs to explore and discover the nature of the internal states of the particular biological systems they are investigating. For this purpose they explicitly construct models to represent what they suppose to be the nature of the internal machinery sufficient to account for the observable input and output. Characteristically they do not interpret these models neuro-physiologically; and do not consider it necessary to do so. But they hold themselves free to indicate possible interpretations when appropriate. However, they are far from free to postulate whatever internal machinery their fancy takes them. For they are constrained in their model building, not only by the data about input and output, but also by the requirement that their models should be testable. They are apt to view their work as a necessary and distinguishable part of a large, many-sided, and world-wide enterprise. This enterprise is the enquiry into the ways in which the nervous systems of organisms really manage to perform the tricks they do.

II. Let me now try to show something of the nature of this psychological work by presenting you, very briefly, with some examples of it. Consider the first, early model produced by SUTHERLAND [1957], [1958] of the visual system of *Octopus vulgaris* Lamarck. It was found that this animal could distinguish vertical and horizontal rectangles, but could hardly distinguish them when presented obliquely. Sutherland suggested that these shapes produced an excitation on the retina, which went to nerve cells in the optic lobes – where the array of excited cells represented a projection of the retina. He suggested that this array, and the subsequent outputs from it, are arranged in the way shown in fig. 1. The cells of each column and each row

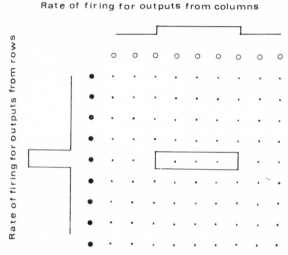

Fig. 1. Dots represent array with horizontal rectangle projected on it. Open circles: cells specific to each column. Filled circles: cells specific to each row. Each cell in the array is connected to the output cell for its own row and the output cell for its own column.

have connections to further cells, which are specific to each column and each row. From this it follows that when a figure is projected on to the array (as shown), the amount of firing from the cells connected with the columns will represent the height of the figure; and the amount of firing from the cells connected with rows will represent the lateral extent of the figure. The amounts of firing for this particular figure are drawn in here – at the top the output from the columns, at the left the output from the rows. With this model it is possible to account for the known facts about the octopus. Vertical and horizontal shapes produce very different patterns of excitation from one another; obliques do not – as we can see in fig. 2.

Sutherland used this model to obtain a number of predictions. For example, consider the excitation patterns produced by a square, by a diamond (that is, a square on one of its corners), and by a triangle. On this model the patterns are more alike for the diamond and the triangle than they are for the square and the triangle (see fig. 3). On testing it was found that the octopus distinguishes a square from a triangle more readily than it distinguishes a diamond from a triangle. In general it is certainly true to say of Sutherland's model that it was a fruitful one.

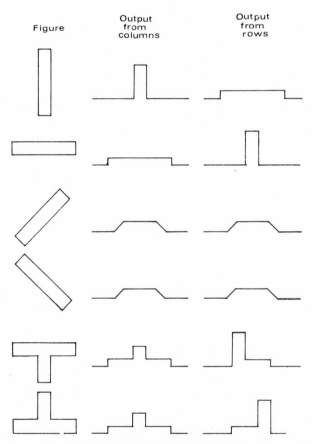

Fig. 2. Figures used for investigating discrimination of orientation, with outputs predicted by theory.

However, as work went on in this field, two developments occurred.

(i) Under the stimulus – in part – of Sutherland's model, YOUNG [1964] tried to discover what actual arrangements in the visual system of the octopus enable it to classify shapes. What he found were, not what the model suggested, but fields of dendrites lying in different orientations. Those fields whose long orientation corresponded to the horizontal axis of the eye were the most plentiful; those whose orientation corresponded to the vertical were less plentiful; and the fewest fields were those corresponding to the oblique axes in the eye. At the same time the work of HUBEL and WIESEL [1962] uncovered findings on orientation that pointed strongly in a related direction.

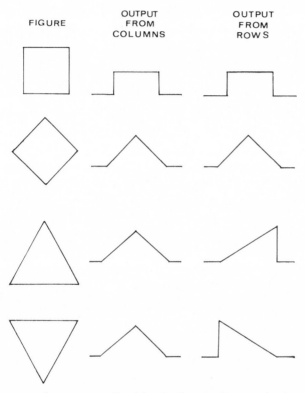

FIGURE   OUTPUT   OUTPUT
                  FROM   FROM
                  COLUMNS   ROWS

Fig. 3. The neuronal patterns predicted by the theory. The second column shows the neuronal firing patterns representing the vertical projection of the figure; the third column shows the neuronal patterns representing the horizontal projection of the figure. In these two columns the height of the diagram represents the strength of firing of cells at a given point in a row of cells.

When therefore we try to interpret Sutherland's first model biologically, we find that it will not do. The visual system of the octopus is not actually organized in the detailed way the model suggests.

(ii) Further psychological work with the model revealed that the octopus was reacting to features of the presented shapes other than their orientation.

The model could not cover these facts. This work suggested that a central idea of the model should be extended further. Instead of thinking of the visual system as concerned only to analyse one dimension of the stimulus (namely, laterality versus verticality), we should think of it as able to analyse an array of features of the stimulus. On this view the visual system would work by means of a set of stimulus analysers, which can be switched on or off, and which are linked to the learning machinery of the organism. These ideas of Sutherland and Mackintosh have been, and still are, of considerable heuristic importance (SUTHERLAND [1964]).

Now let us turn for a quick glance at a part of another model, namely the one developed by BROADBENT [1958]. What were the relevant data Broadbent was concerned to deal with? It had been found, for example, that if a person repeated back a passage of prose heard through one ear, he was unable to report any of the verbal content of another passage presented at the same time through the other ear (CHERRY [1953]). In other words it was found that, if a person has to deal with competing messages, there is a limit at which his performance will break down. The question was then raised: what determines this limit? In particular, is it determined by peripheral conditions, or by central ones? It was found, for example, that similar results were obtained when one message was auditory and the other visual (MOW-BRAY [1953]), which strongly suggests that the limit is determined in part by central conditions. What is more, it was then discovered that this central limit is fixed primarily by the predictability, or information content, of the messages. For example, when dealing with competing call signs, subjects are able to deal correctly with an increasing load when the informational content is low, but are unable to do so when the informational content is high (WEBSTER and THOMPSON [1954]).

Let us look first at the part of Broadbent's model which is designed to handle this data (see fig. 4). He supposes that the messages come from the receptors and pass along different input channels until they reach a selective filter. Here some are blocked, and others are led through to one channel of limited capacity, which has access to a long term memory store. It is in this channel that the organism takes 'a decision' about the input that has been let through the filter (for example, what the verbal content was of the passage just presented); and it is this channel that the appropriate response is determined.

In fact, of course, Broadbent was concerned to handle a much wider range of data than what I have mentioned; and his model as a whole is more complex than the part I have selected. The whole model can be seen in fig. 5. As you see, this contains a unit for short-term memory; there are two feedback arrangements; and in his discussion Broadbent makes it clear just how complex are the relations between the store of conditional probabilities and the rest of the system.

Now it is apparent that this model, as it stands, just amounts to a block diagram, and it has an air of childlike simplicity about it. We may be tempted to think that it is hardly a good enough model to achieve testability. But this is not the case. Consider the relevant part of the model exhibited in fig. 4. According to the model, when messages reach the selective filter, some are blocked and others are allowed to pass. Well, is this true? Does our selective filter work like this or not? If it does, then – as we have seen – the verbal

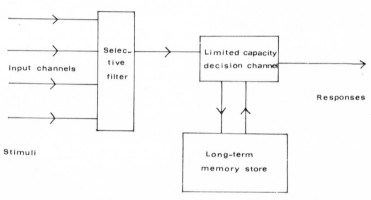

Fig. 4. Broadbent's "filter" and "information flow" model for selective attention (BROADBENT [1958]). The diagram illustrates a model in which man is represented as an information-handling system. The successive parts of the model are discussed in the text.

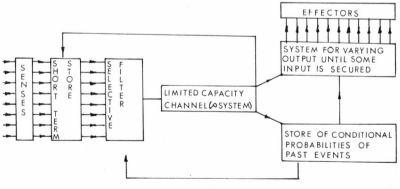

Fig. 5.

content of competing messages will just be blocked and not identified at all. But how then do we account for what happens at the cocktail party? I am straining to hear what my neighbour is saying on my left, when, suddenly, above the din I hear my name mentioned or called on my right. When the cocktail party problem was taken into the laboratory, it was found that there are occasions on which the verbal content of irrelevant messages was identified. This suggests that the Broadbent model is wrong at this point and needs modification. One of the proposed modifications is that the filter does not work by blocking messages, but by attenuating them in a manner which can be analysed in terms of Signal Detection Theory. Of course, this is merely an example of the way in which this apparently naive model can be subjected to test. What is instructive is that it has served as an important heuristic tool in the hands of a number of psychologists. It has been a source of inspiration for quite a considerable body of scientific work. In this way it has paid good dividends; and we have every reason to say that Broadbent has done us a service in offering us this model at the time.

But what is its present status ten years afterwards? It has not yet exhausted its fertility, but, on the other hand, investigation is now focused on the details of the machinery, and it is anybody's guess at present what more general model will emerge next, and how much this will have absorbed and modified Broadbent's model in the process. For one thing, we do seem forced to suppose now that our channel capacity is not only limited in the way that Broadbent emphasized, namely, by unpredictability. It is also limited in other ways – for example, by the meaning of the input to us, which – paradoxically – greatly extends the amount and range of the input we can handle.

A few words now about part of the model of human skill offered by CROSSMAN [1964]. Consider only the effector side of a skill. The facts Crossman tries to cover are familiar ones such as what happens when a person obeys the order "Quick march!", or plays the piano, or sets about serving a ball at lawn tennis. We have to suppose, Crossman argues, that most of the information needed to control muscle action is held in a permanent store that is built up during the acquisition of the skill. "The main theoretical problem", Crossman says, "is how the data are organized in the store and retrieved for use on a given occasion. They cannot be a set of simple space-time patterns like the grooves on records in a juke box, because the detail of a given action varies greatly with circumstances." Hence we have to suppose – he argues – that the human system is organized hierarchically. Therefore the first or initial command (or 'goal' set the system) "is used to retrieve a list or 'programme' of sub-commands, which are obeyed in turn, each sub-command using a further list of sub-commands and so on." However two other facts have also to be taken into account. (i) Consider an example of the first fact. "If a speaker hears his own voice subject to delay of 200 milliseconds through headphones, his speech becomes long drawn out and stuttering." Hence it seems as if "each command, at whatever level, includes a receptor pattern which must appear in the environment before the command is deemed to have been obeyed, and the next one can take over... If this checking signal is late or fails to arrive, the component actions tend to be repeated until it does." (ii) Consider an example of the second fact. In singing, the control of pitch takes place with a rapidity that can only be explained by supposing that the feedback by-passes the central decision machinery. Hence we have to allow for this by-passing feedback from peripherery.

To account for this range of data Crossman proposes the model shown in fig. 6. This is self-explanatory by now. The hierarchical character of the model is shown in the passage from 'main goal' on the left to activating signals on the right. The incoming arrows above the blocks mark the channels for the checking signals that come in at each stage. The peripheral, by-passing feedback from motor action, and its interaction with the task set are shown on the right. (The diagram is actually restricted – quite unnecessarily – to limbic activity.)

It seems evident on inspection that this model is open to testing and elaboration and modification in a way similar to that of Broadbent's. But unlike Broadbent's, it is a comparatively recent offering. When one considers the whole of Crossman's model of skilled performance, it is not clear yet whether it has a heuristic value comparable to Broadbent's, and what its psychological contribution will ultimately turn out to be.

III. Let us now stand back and take a reflective look at this current of psychological work.

First of all, are these models all of the same sort? Or are there differences between them? It is clear that they differ considerably inter se, and in different ways. For example, Sutherland suggests that an optic lobe of the octopus is built like a metal plate with leads going off it in the ways described. Consequently, it contains a good guide to the neuro-anatomist, and others, about what sort of thing to look out for when they actually investigate the optic lobes of this animal. In contrast, Broadbent's model contains a very poor guide to the neuro-anatomist-cum-physiologist when he investigates any

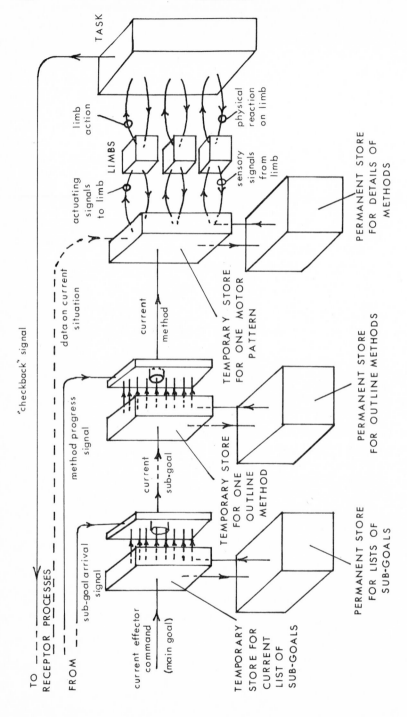

Fig. 6.   Schematic organization of the human effector-system.

actual part of the internal apparatus of the human organism. Neither Sutherland's model nor Broadbent's is given a neural interpretation by their authors. Yet it seems reasonable to say that Sutherland's is much closer to such an interpretation than Broadbent's or Crossman's. There is another obvious contrast between Sutherland's and the other two. The former is concerned to deal with – in some sense – a much smaller range of fact or data than the latter two. Its scope is much smaller. Obviously the scope of the latter two is very large indeed. This makes them in consequence much more vulnerable, and suggests that their role in psychological enquiry will be somewhat different from that of Sutherland's. Then there is a contrast of quite a different sort. Among the data that Broadbent is concerned to explain is the fact that, when a person has to deal with competing messages, there is a limit at which his performance will break down. He explains this fact, in part, by supposing that we each possess a filter that does the trick. Now, it could be argued, this supposition is not a contingent matter, but is a logical consequence of our description of the data to be explained. It follows logically from our saying that there is a limit at which a person's performance will break down, and so on, that the person has a filter. To suggest that he has one is not to put forward a new empirical claim, but simply to state what is entailed, in part, by our description of the facts to be explained. The same thing is even clearer in Crossman's model. A trained soldier knows what he has to do to obey the order "Quick march". Crossman argues that we have to suppose that most of the information the soldier needs to control his muscle action here is held in a permanent store. But it could be maintained that to say "The soldier knows what he has to do here" entails saying that what the soldier knows is held in permanent store. So Crossman is not making an empirical discovery, but, primarily, stating this logical consequence of our description of the facts to be explained. Sutherland's model on the other hands stands in striking contrast here. There is nothing in it that is entailed by his description of the visual performance of the octopus.

I do not propose to examine this last alleged contrast, and to try to determine whether it is real or only apparent. It is obviously a complicated matter; and it is also obvious that, even if the Broadbent-Crossman models do contain entailments, this is not all they contain by a very long chalk. However, it is important that we should take note of this alleged feature of the Broadbent-Crossman models. For in doing this we bring to the surface one of the things that makes us uneasy about them. We bring to the surface our fear that these models may be, in part, a form of faculty psychology in a new guise. But whether the Broadbent-Crossman type of model building is, in part, a new form of faculty psychology, and if it is, whether it is a vicious form of it – all these are questions that I cannot stay to try to answer now.

IV. It is clear from what I said earlier that Sutherland's and Broadbent's models were not sufficient to account for the data; and it is very likely that Crossman's will turn out to be insufficient also. But suppose that we have good grounds to believe that one of these *is* sufficient to cover the existing and the relevant data. What have we then to do, in general, to show that this model is a *necessary* one? In other words, what have we to do in general to obtain the assurance that the data cannot in fact be explained in any other way?

A good case can be made out for the view that it will not be enough for us to discover more and more about inputs and outputs. We shall also have to go inside the organism, and discover how the details of the machinery are actually constituted and function. For this purpose we have to make use of the labour and contribution of anatomists, neurophysiologists, and the like. It is only by making use of the evidence they can produce that we will in fact ever be able to obtain a definitive assurance that the actual machinery of complex organisms contains the elements and works in the way alleged by any psychological models.

This good case, however, has also led unfortunately to some confusion. It has tempted the physio-anatomists to suppose that, because psychological theory and techniques are not strong enough to establish what the actual internal machinery of organisms is like, they are therefore intellectually disreputable in some way or other, not really a necessary part of this whole scientific enquiry, and ultimately due anyhow to be taken over and replaced by physio-anatomy and related studies. Hence physio-anatomists, and the like, are apt to view the whole current of psychological work we are discussing as an unfortunate and passing stage in the history of science. So they do not quite know what to make of their psychological colleagues, and are apt to find them a bit of an embarrassment.

Now this confusion is a complex matter – too complex to deal with adequately. But it is not difficult to see that it *is* a confusion and wholly unnecessary. From the claim that psychological techniques are not strong enough here, we obviously cannot infer that they are disreputable. Nor can we infer that they are unnecessary. What the physio-anatomists overlook is that this current of psychological work is helping to discover the *sorts* of functions and structures that the actual minute machinery subserves. Quite clearly, this is a necessary part of the whole enquiry. The physio-anatomists also overlook another quite crucial matter. If we are to discover that such and such minute machinery subserves such and such organismic functions (e.g. seeing a rectangle, hearing the verbal content of a message), it does not seem possible to do so in practice, and perhaps even in principle, without the use of psychological techniques of enquiry. Hence it is far from certain what the relation will be in the *long* run between psychology and the purely biological studies in this field. We cannot be confident that biologists will be successful in a take-over bid for psychology. In the *short* run, however, it seems reasonable to argue that the macro-theories and techniques of psychological workers and their micro-counterparts in physio-anatomy will complement each other to their mutual advantage. We saw an example of how this can happen in our discussion of Sutherland's work.

V. It is very advisable, therefore, that outsiders, whether laymen or physio-anatomists, should not be tempted to undervalue this psychological work. On the other hand, it is equally advisable that psychologists themselves should not fall into the opposite trap and overvalue it. For psychologists are using models which are built by analogy with other devices, or systems, or what not. Thus, Sutherland supposed that an optic lobe of the octopus is constructed like a metal plate with leads taking away electrical input in certain ways. Broadbent supposed that the nervous system of humans is constructed like a communications-cum-storage device, with a channel capacity limited solely by the amount of information it can carry. Crossman's model is built on a similar analogy. As we have seen, the first two are of value, and the last will almost certainly reveal its worth in due course. But whatever their fertility may be, we can be reasonably certain of one thing. They will exhaust their fertility before they enable us to achieve a reasonably satisfactory account of the aspects of organismic functioning with which they are primarily concerned.

Why is this? It is true, no doubt, that the history of psychology is strewn with models that have exhausted themselves without doing the trick, without cracking the code of organismic functioning. But have we not perhaps reached a turning point in psychology? Current models use the analogy of information processing devices, control systems, and the like. I have presented three examples of them. Is it not perhaps the case that this sort of model is logically different from all previous ones in the psychological field, and really *will* enable us to achieve reasonably satisfactory accounts of organismic functioning? I venture to doubt whether this is the case. I think we can be reasonably sure that the current models will exhaust their fertility without cracking the code, just as other models have failed before them. Why do I say this? What reasons are there to think that this is the case? Let me mention three.

(i) If the three models I have used for illustration are typical or representative – and I think they are – then it is quite obvious that their chief role is exploratory. This is not surprising, as soon as we appreciate that psychology as a whole is still in the stage of being an exploratory science at the present time. So it would be very surprising indeed if any current model were to embody an immense leap forward, and were to bridge the gulfs between exploration and reasonably definitive discovery.

(ii) One of the characteristics of current models is that they are partial and not total in character. They do not attempt to deal with the total organism, but select certain functions only, and then tend to concentrate on certain aspects only of these selected functions. But we have good reason to believe that organisms cannot be split up like this with safety. The function we select for study and modelling is very liable to be affected in its operations by other functions that we are ignoring. The aspects of the function on which we are concentrating is very liable to be affected by aspects we are neglecting. Hence any partial model is liable to be incomplete, and in important respects. Clearly, any model which is built in this way is unlikely to provide us with a good understanding of the function concerned.

(iii) The current models are based on analogies with other devices and systems. But it seems to be a fact that the nervous system of complex organisms is a type of system which is quite unique in its complexity of organization and functioning. If this is so, then it follows that it has no *close* analogies with anything else. From which it seems to follow, in turn, that no models will be sufficient to crack the code of the nervous system. Hence their exploratory power is subject to an inherent limitation here. I confess however, that I am uneasy about this consideration, and uncertain about its implications.

So we may be tempted to fall into two opposing misjudgements about the current of psychological work I have been considering. We may be tempted either to undervalue this work, or to over-value it. I hope I have said enough to warn us against both temptations.

VI. But whatever the scientific worth may be of this type of psychological work, it does produce models of mental functioning that are of some general philosophical interest. Let me conclude by mentioning one respect in which they are of general interest. In current discussions in the philosophy of mind, philosophers have been very apt to presuppose that there are two, and only two, legitimate ways of speaking about mental functioning. The one is ordinary language, safe and hallowed by contact with the mother's breast and knee. The other is the language of the physio-anatomist, safe because it deals with material things – even though they be very minute and a bit messy. When, therefore, I say (to take an arbitrary example): "Smith has a better memory than Jones", what I am saying must be elucidated in either the one way or the other. If we use the former, and stay within ordinary language, then what I am saying has to be elucidated hypothetically. Thus: "What I am saying is that, for example, *if* I were to ask Smith and Jones who won the match yesterday, Smith is more likely to remember than Jones". And so on. The troubles about this answer are well known. For one thing, it is just false. It simply is not the case that, when I say "Smith has a better memory than Jones", I am *merely* asserting a (concealed) string of hypotheticals. I am *also* saying that something is the case about Smith and Jones here and now, even though both may be fast asleep in their beds. But what something else can this be? Now if we are caught within the fashionable presupposition of much philosophy of mind (that there are only two legitimate ways of talking here), we will not know what to say. Clearly, the something else cannot consist in statements about the physio-anatomical differences between Smith and Jones. For these are not contained within the meaning of our statement in ordinary language about memory; and in any case we have only a faint idea at present as to what these physio-anatomical differences may be. So we are now caught in a trap. The subject matter of the philosophy of mind is largely and obviously the conduct, behaviour and mental functioning of human *organisms*, of *embodied* persons. The trap in which we have been caught in recent years has contributed to keep much philosophy of mind somewhat remote from its subject matter, and very remote from the scientific study of the human organism.

One of the interesting things about current model construction in psychology is that it points to a possible way out of this trap. There is another, a third way, of speaking about mental functioning which is neither ordinary language nor physio-anatomy. This is the way developed by the current of psychology we have been considering. We can speak about the *sort* of internal state or states that an organism must possess for it to exhibit memory and intelligence and so on; and we can speak about the differences between these that give Smith a better memory than Jones.

This alternative suggestion raises some interesting possibilities. It may be that this way of talking will help to free us from our present submission to the hypothetical in the philosophy of mind, and free us from our fear of the categorical import of statements about mental powers and functioning. It may also help to bring the philosophy of mind into a closer and more fruitful relation with the scientific enterprise. And, in my view, this would be a good thing!

I wish to thank Dr. Mackintosh for his helpful criticisms.

References

BROADBENT, D., Perception and communication (Pergamon, 1958).
CHERRY, E.C., J. Acoust. Soc. Am. **25** (1953) 975.
CROSSMAN, E.R.F.W., Brit. Med. Bull. **20** (1964) 32.
HUBEL, D.H. and T.N. WIESEL, J. Physiol. **160** (1962) 106.
HULL, C., Principles of behaviour (Appleton, 1943).
MOWBRAY, G.H., J. Exp. Psychol. **45** (1953) 365.
SUTHERLAND, N.S., Nature **179** (1957) 11.
SUTHERLAND, N.S., Quart. J. Exp. Psychol. **10** (1958) 40.
SUTHERLAND, N.S., Brit. Med. Bull. **20** (1964) 54.
WEBSTER, J.C. and P.O. THOMPSON, J. Acoust. Soc. Amer. **26** (1954) 396.
YOUNG, J.Z., A model of the brain (Oxford, Oxford University Press, 1964).

PERCEPTION AS A FUNCTION OF BEHAVIOUR

J. G. TAYLOR

Piper's Croft, Bovingdon, England

While I fully agree with Gibson's contention that perception involves the discovery of invariants, I maintain that what he has offered us is not a theory but a description of perception. He has failed to disclose any mechanism by which invariants of perception are generated to reflect the invariants of the environment. He seems to think that the required invariants are embedded in the flux of information that pours into the receptor system, and that a simple search is all that is needed to reveal them.

I have two major quarrels with this formulation. First, the process of discovering invariants appears to be itself a kind of perceptual activity, so that what Gibson is trying to do is to explain perception by an appeal to a more primitive kind of perception. My second objection is that there are in fact no invariants to be discovered in the information delivered to the receptor system.

Consider any stationary object, and let us confine our attention to its position in space, neglecting any other properties we may perceive. The input to the eyes from this object varies with every movement of the eyes, and, because the projection of the retinal image on the striate area of the cortex is non-linear, the events in the projection area vary in a complex manner with the position of the image on the retina. In other words, there is a one-many relation between the position of the external object and the input to the receptor apparatus, so that an event in the striate area carries no intrinsic information concerning either the position or the shape of an object in the external field. Yet this one-many relation seems to generate an invariant of perception. We perceive this object as remaining in a fixed position. That is to say, there is a one-to-one correspondence between the positions of objects in environmental space and their perceived positions.

Let me state the problem in mathematical form. I define a set, A, whose elements specify the coordinates of objects in a space whose axes are anchored in the body of a seated observer; a set, B, whose elements specify events in the observer's visual apparatus; and a set, C, whose elements are the perceived positions of the objects. There is a one-many relation between A and B, but a one-one relation between A and C. The crucial question concerns the mechanism whereby A is mapped into C via B, and it is at once evident that this mapping cannot be effected unless there is further information specifying the positions of the eyes, the head and the trunk. This means that the receptor information must be understood as including, in addition to the elements of B, the elements of other sets of proprioceptive events, as determined by the momentary orientation of the receptor surfaces. If we define $P_1, P_2, ..., P_{n-1}$ as sets of proprioceptive events determined by the positions of the eyes, head and trunk, we may define another set, D, as a set each of whose elements is an n-tuple including an element of B and elements of $P_1, P_2, ..., P_{n-1}$. That is,

$$D = [(b,\ p_1,\ p_2,\ ...,\ p_{n-1})].$$

Alternatively, we may say that the elements of D are points in a multidimensional receptor space. It is evident that corresponding to each element of A there is a subset of D, containing a large number of elements.

The problem can now be stated. Since the elements of A are not directly given to the observer, the problem is to discover a mechanism, or programme, whereby the elements of the multidimensional set, D, can be made to generate elements of the three-dimensional set, C, so as to reflect, with a substantial measure of accuracy, the elements of the set A. If the elements of D could be expressed in numerical form they could be fed into a computer, and it would be a trivial exercise to write a programme that would yield, as output, a close approximation to the elements of A. What kind of programme does the living organism have to effect the mapping from D to C?

There seem to be two possible answers to this question. The first is that the programme is incorporated in the genetic code. This would imply that the one-one relation between A and C is the result not of interaction between the individual organism and its environment, but of the happy chance that certain genes, selected millions of years ago, determine a programme that maps the elements of D into C in such a manner that C is a reasonably close representation of A. If this were the true answer, it would follow that any transformation applied to B, such as a reversal of the retinal image along the horizontal or vertical axis, or both, would leave the organism permanently impaired. But in fact the impairment is temporary, and the genetic answer must therefore be rejected.

The second answer is that there is no programme at the beginning of life, and each organism has to construct its own programme. This is done by the conditioning of motor responses directed to the objects specified by A. For example, the infant learns very quickly to reach for near objects, and to do so in spite of the one-many relation between A and D. That is, each of the elements of D, including an element of B determined by an external object, is conditioned to a response that establishes contact with the object whose position is specified by an element of A.

Since an element of B is jointly determined by the position of the object and the orientation of the receptors, it is evident that an element of D is sufficient to generate a unique response, carrying the hand to the position in space occupied by the object. Hence we may say that the conditioning process generates behavioural invariants that correspond to the invariants A, so that we have a mechanism that may well provide a basis for the one-one relation between A and C.

But we have not yet arrived at our goal, because the positions of objects are given in C without any need for motor responses. If motor responses were necessary, we could perceive the position of only one object at a time. But in fact we perceive a whole array of objects. How can the existence of behavioural invariants generate simultaneous perception of many objects?

My answer is that the learning process builds up a vast number of links in the brain, connecting elements of D to the motor area. If any of these links, or engrams, gets free access to the motor system, a response occurs; but if the final common path is not available, this does not prevent the engram from being activated. That is, all the conditions for evoking a specific response are satisfied except the availability of the motor apparatus. The activity of the engram may be described as constituting a state of readiness for the appropriate response. Now there is nothing to prevent a myriad of engrams being active simultaneously. When this happens, there is a state of multiple simultaneous readiness for responses adapted to the positions of numerous objects, and the goals of these responses remain invariant despite changes in the relevant elements of D.

Now the properties of simultaneity and invariance that characterise this state of multiple readiness are matched by similar properties in the conscious field of perception, so that it now seems reasonable to assert that perception and multiple simultaneous readiness for action are one and the same thing. If you insist that perception is something different from, and independent of the state of efferent readiness, the onus is on you to show how this independent perception is generated, and how its properties come to match so closely those of the state of readiness.

So far the only responses I have talked about are motor responses directed to the positions of objects in space. But it is evident that these are not the only responses that can be conditioned to the elements of D. There are, for example, the ocular responses that serve to bring specific features of objects into the centre of the visual field; there are responses involving the manipulation of objects, including the innumerable skills of artists and artisans; and, in the human organism, there are verbal responses that serve to describe what is in the environment. I suggest that readiness for all these is included in the state of multiple simultaneous readiness, so that perception includes a great many components in addition to space. It follows then that perception is enriched whenever a new set of skills is acquired. And it also follows that when the set B is altered by a transformation applied to the ocular input, there will be disturbances of both behaviour and perception. But the errors of behaviour are subject to correction, and we can now infer that as this correction proceeds, there will be a corresponding correction of the errors of perception.

It should be noted that if I am right in identifying perception with a state of readiness for *all* the responses that have been conditioned to the elements of the set D, then a transformation experiment will not result in a restoration of veridical perception unless an opportunity is given to correct all the behavioural errors induced by the transformation. There are many experiments whose results appear to contradict my thesis, but invariably the experimental conditions have been so arranged that only a limited class of responses is subject to correction. My thesis then mediates the deduction that the subjects of such experiments remain in a state of readiness for innumerable erroneous responses, and there is therefore only a limited reduction of perceptual distortion.

Let me illustrate the point by reference to one of the experiments of Erismann and Kohler in Innsbruck. The subject, Dr. Kottenhoff, wore spectacles that reverse right and left for seven weeks continuously, but failed to report the correction of the right-left ordering of the perceptual field which had been reported by two other subjects in Innsbruck, and was subsequently reported by my own subject, Dr. Papert, in Cape Town. Kottenhoff's motor responses were just as well adapted to the reversed input as those of the other three subjects. Why then was the perceptual outcome different? I questioned him closely about his actions in response to the reversed input, and he revealed that he had adopted a strategy that ensured that his verbal responses descriptive of the right-left ordering of the field would remain unchanged throughout the experiment. What he did was to note that the image of an object on the right appeared to be close to his left temple, and he got into the habit of describing the positions of objects in relation to this frame of reference. The result was that his verbal responses, as brought out in daily laboratory tests, remained at variance with his motor responses. The other three subjects recognised that their verbal responses, no matter how correct they might be as descriptions of what was happening in themselves, were erroneous as descriptions of the positions of objects in the external field, and consequently made no attempt to prevent the correction of those errors. At the end of the experiment there was virtually complete congruity between verbal and motor behaviour. From this I concluded that to rectify the perception of right-left ordering it was necessary that all the behavioural systems affected by the transformation should be corrected so as to reflect the true positions of objects in space.

This conclusion has been heavily criticised by HOWARD and TEMPLETON [1966], who apparently think that the perception of right-left and up-down ordering is innately determined by the structure of the visual apparatus, from retina to striate area, and is therefore immutable. They are particularly scornful of my claim that the correction of verbal behaviour can tip the balance in favour of veridical perception. But recently some interesting evidence has appeared to support me.

Prompted by Sperry's investigations of the effects of splitting the brains of monkeys, some surgeons in California have split the brains of patients suffering from intractable epilepsy. The operation involved transection of the corpus callosum and other commissures, but the optic chiasma was left intact. In some cases there was a dramatic decrease in both the frequency and the violence of epileptic seizures, and those patients were subjected to extensive tests designed to discover the psychological effects of brain-splitting. This work has been described by GAZZANIGA [1967].

In one test the subject fixated a point in the middle of a screen, and he was asked to report on spots of light flashed on the screen for a tenth of a second. When the spots were to the right of the fixation point the subject reported them accurately; when they were to the left he denied seeing them. Apparently the right hemisphere is blind. But when the subjects were asked to *point* at a momentarily presented stimulus, they did so with equal ease whether the spot was to the right or the left. The right hemisphere retained unimpaired its ability to direct motor responses. But it could not initiate verbal responses, because the speech centre is in the left hemisphere, and the relevant links between the two hemispheres had been severed.

Now let me apply my own terminology to this situation. When information is relayed to the right hemisphere, states of readiness for a variety of motor and manipulatory responses are generated, but there is no readiness for verbal responses. The total state of readiness is diminished by the exclusion of one of its important components; and this diminished state of readiness is not equivalent to normal perception. In fact Gazzaniga's observations have established the important principle that if a human subject is not in a state of readiness to make a verbal statement about the character and position of an object, he has no subjective awareness of the object. Gazzaniga speaks of the right hemisphere as having a limited kind of "perception", but if we decide to restrict the term to conscious phenomena, we cannot accept this. The reports of the subjects must be regarded as conclusive on this point.

The blindness of the right hemisphere was revealed only when stimuli were presented momentarily in the left visual field. When the eyes were free to move there was no evidence of hemianopsia. I suggest that this can be explained by assuming that when an object is presented in the right visual field, engrams mediating verbal responses are aroused to activity, and their activity is maintained for a few seconds through the agency of reverberating circuits in the left hemisphere. It follows that when an eye movement transfers the object to the left visual field, the relevant verbal engrams continue to be active, so that the full state of efferent readiness remains, and perception of the object is therefore not lost.

In another publication (TAYLOR [1962]) I have applied this principle to account for a very interesting property of the visual world discussed by GIBSON [1950]. He pointed out that the visual world is unbounded, in spite of the fact that the retina is bounded. When we turn a camera so that a particular object is no longer represented on the film, it does not appear in the photograph. But when we turn our eyes so that there is no longer a retinal image of the object, we continue to perceive it for a short time. This is quite intelligible if we are willing to interpret perception as a state of behavioural readiness; but it must remain a profound mystery if we adhere to the classical doctrine that the striate area is the birthplace of visual perception.

References

GAZZANIGA, M.S., The split brain in man, Sci. Am., August 1967.
GIBSON, J.J., Perception of the visual world (Boston, Houghton Mifflin, 1950).
HOWARD, I.P. and W.B. TEMPLETON, Human spatial orientation (London, Wiley, 1966).
TAYLOR, J.G., The behavioral basis of perception (New Haven, Yale University Press, 1962).

Methodology and Philosophy of Social Sciences

ON JUDGING THE PLAUSIBILITY OF THEORIES

H. A. SIMON*

Carnegie-Mellon University, Pittsburgh, Pennsylvania, USA

1. It is a fact that if you arrange the cities (or, alternatively, the metropolitan districts) of the United States in the order of their population in 1940, the population of each city will be inversely proportional to its rank in the list (see fig. 1). The same fact is true of these cities at other census dates – back to the first census – and for the cities of a number of other countries of the world.

It is a fact that if you arrange the words that occur in James Joyce's Ulysses in the order of their frequency of occurrence in that book, the frequency of each word will be inversely proportional to its rank in the list (see fig. 2). The same fact is true of the other books in English whose word frequencies have been counted (except, possibly, *Finnegan's wake*), and it is true of books in most other languages (although not books in Chinese).

What do I mean when I say these are "facts"? In a way, it seems incorrect to speak in this way, since none of my "facts" is literally and exactly true. For example, since there were 2034 cities over 5000 population in the United States in 1940, the alleged "fact" would assert that there were therefore one half as many, 1017, over 10000 population. Actually, there were 1072. It would assert that there were one tenth as many, 203, over 50000 population; actually, there were 198. It would assert that the largest city, New York, had a population just over ten million people; actually, its population was seven and one half million. The other "facts" asserted

* This work was supported in part by Public Health Service Research Grant MH-07722 from the National Institutes of Mental Health.

I should like to dedicate this essay to the memory of Norwood Russell Hanson, in acknowledgment of my debt to his *Patterns of discovery*. His work did much to reestablish the notion that the philosophy of science must be as fully concerned with origins of scientific theories as with their testing – indeed that the two are inextricably interwoven. His reconstruction of Kepler's retroduction of the laws of planetary motion will long serve as a model of inquiry into the history and philosophy of science.

above, for cities and words, hold only to comparable degrees of approximation.

At the very least, one would think, the statements of fact should be amended to read "nearly inversely proportional" or "approximately inversely proportional" rather than simply "inversely proportional". But how near is "nearly", and how approximate is "approximately"? What degree of deviation from the bald generalization permits us to speak of an approxi-

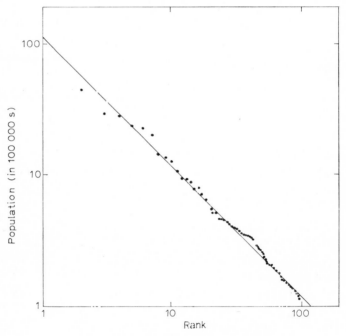

Fig. 1.　Hundred largest U.S. cities, 1940
(ranked in order of decreasing size).

mation to the generalization rather than its disconfirmation? And why do we prefer the simple but approximate rule to the particular but exact facts?

2. It is well known – at least among mathematical statisticians – that the theory of statistical tests gives us no real help in choosing between an approximate generalization and an invalid one.[1] By imbedding our

---

[1] For a brief, but adequate statement of the reasons why "literally to test such hypotheses ... is preposterous", see SAVAGE [1954] pp. 254–256. Since such tests are still reported frequently in the literature, it is perhaps worth quoting SAVAGE [1954] p. 254 at slightly greater length: "The unacceptability of extreme null hypotheses is perfectly well known; it is closely related to the oftenheard maxim that science disproves, but never proves,

generalization in a probability model, we can ask: If this model describes the real "facts" what is the probability that data would have occurred at least as deviant from the generalization as those actually observed? If this probability is very low – below the magic one per cent level, say – we are still left with two alternatives: the generalization has been disconfirmed, and is invalid; or the generalization represents only a first approximation to the true, or "exact" state of affairs.

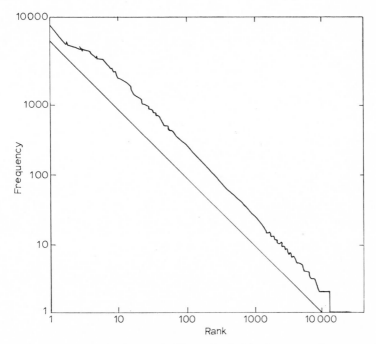

Fig. 2. Words occurring in Joyce's Ulysses (ranked by frequency of occurrence).

Now such approximations abound in physics. Given adequate apparatus, any student in the college laboratory can "disconfirm" Boyle's Law – i.e., can show that the deviations of the actual data from the generalization that the product of pressure by volume is a constant are too great to be dismissed as "chance". He can "disconfirm" Galileo's Law of Falling Bodies even

hypotheses. The role of extreme hypotheses in science and other statistical activities seems to be important but obscure. In particular, though I, like everyone who practices statistics, have often 'tested' extreme hypotheses, I cannot give a very satisfactory analysis of the process, nor say clearly how it is related to testing as defined in this chapter and other theoretical discussions".

more dramatically – the most obvious way being to use a feather as the falling body.

When a physicist finds that the "facts" summarized by a simple, powerful generalization do not fit the data exactly, his first reaction is *not* to throw away the generalization, or even to complicate it by incorporating additional terms. When the data depart from $s = \frac{1}{2}gt^2$, the physicist is not usually tempted to add a cubic term to the equation. (It took Kepler almost ten years to retreat from the "simplicity" of a circle to the "complexity" of an ellipse.) Instead, his explorations tend to move in two directions: (1) toward investigations of his measurement procedures as possible sources of the discrepancies; and (2) toward the identification of other variables associated with the deviations. These two directions of inquiry may, of course, be interrelated.

In his concern with other variables, the physicist is not merely or mainly concerned with "control" in the usual sense of the term. No amount of control of air pressure, holding it, say, exactly at one atmosphere, will cause a feather to obey Galileo's Law. What the physicist must learn through his explorations is that as he decreases the air pressure on the falling body, the deviations from the law decrease in magnitude, and that if he can produce a sufficiently good vacuum, even a feather can be made to obey the law to a tolerable approximation.

In the process of producing conditions under which deviations from a generalization are small, the scope of the generalization is narrowed. Now it is only claimed to describe the facts "for an ideal gas", or "in a perfect vacuum". At best, it is asserted that the deviations will go to zero in the limit as the deviation of the actual experimental conditions from the "ideal" or "perfect" conditions goes to zero.

At the same time that the breadth of the empirical generalization is narrowed by stating the conditions, or limiting conditions, under which it is supposed to hold, its vulnerability to falsification is reduced correspondingly. Since this is a familiar feature of theorizing in science, I will not elaborate on the point here.

Occasionally, an empirical generalization is abandoned, after innumerable attempts to tidy it up have failed. Bode's Law, that the successive distances of the planets from the Sun constitute an approximate geometric series, is an example of a regularity now regarded as perhaps "accidental", through failure to discover limiting conditions that would regularize it, or underlying processes that would account for it. Newton's Laws are *not* an example, for they were saved (a) by limiting them to conditions where velocities are low relative to the velocity of light, and (b) by showing that just under those conditions they can be derived in the limit from the more general laws of Relativity.

From these, and many other examples, we can see what importance the physical and biological sciences attach to finding simple generalizations that will describe data approximately under some set of limiting conditions. Mendel's treatment of his sweet-pea data, as reflecting simple ratios of 3 to 1 in the second-generation hybrids, is another celebrated illustration; as is Prout's hypothesis (uneasily rejected by chemists for several generations until its exceptions were explained by the discovery of isotopes) that all atomic weights are integral multiples of the weight of the hydrogen atom. All of these examples give evidence of strong beliefs that when nature behaves in some unique fashion – deals a hand of thirteen spades, so to speak – this uniqueness, even if approximate, cannot be accidental, but must reveal underlying lawfulness.

3. Let us return to city sizes and word frequencies. We have described the law-finding process in two stages:

(1) finding simple generalizations that describe the facts to some degree of approximation;

(2) finding limiting conditions under which the deviations of facts from generalization might be expected to decrease.

The process of inference from the facts (the process called "retroduction" by Peirce and Hanson[2]) does not usually stop with this second stage, but continues to a third:

(3) explaining why the generalization "should" fit the facts. (Examples are the statistical-mechanical explanation for Boyle's Law or Boyle's own "spring of the air" explanation, and Newton's gravitational explanation for Galileo's Law.)

Before we go on to this third stage, we must consider whether we have really been successful in carrying out the first two for the rank-size distributions.

Does the generalization that size varies inversely with rank really fit the facts of cities and words even approximately? We plot the data on double log paper. If the generalization fits the facts, the resulting array of points will (1) fall on a straight line, (2) with a slope of minus one.

Since we earlier rejected the standard statistical tests of hypotheses as inappropriate to this situation, we are left with only judgmental processes

---

[2] HANSON [1961] pp. 85–88.

for deciding whether the data fall on a straight line. It is not true, as is sometimes suggested, that almost *any* ranked data will fall on a straight line when graphed on doubly logarithmic paper. It is quite easy to find data that are quite curvilinear to the naked eye (see fig. 3). Since we are not committed to exact linearity but only approximate linearity, however, the conditions we are imposing on the data are quite weak, and the fact that they meet the conditions is correspondingly unimpressive. We may therefore find the evidence unconvincing that the phenomena are "really" linear in the limiting cases. The phenomena are not striking enough in this respect to rule out coincidence and chance. Should we believe the data to be patterned?

It has often been demonstrated in the psychological laboratory that men – and even pigeons – can be made to imagine patterns in stimuli which the experimenter has carefully constructed by random processes. This behavior is sometimes called "superstitious", because it finds causal connections where the experimenter knows none exist in fact. A less pejorative term for such behavior is "regularity-seeking" or "law-seeking". It can be given a quite respectable Bayesian justification. As JEFFREYS and WRINCH [1921] have shown, if one attaches a high a priori probability to the hypothesis that the world is simple (i.e., that the facts of the world, properly viewed, are susceptible to simple summarization and interpretation); and if one assumes also that simple configurations of data are sparsely distributed among all logically possible configurations of data, then a high posterior probability must be placed on the hypothesis that data which appear relatively linear in fact reflect approximations to conditions under which a linear law holds.

The reason that apparent linearity, by itself, does not impress us is that it does not meet the second condition assumed above – the sparsity of simple configurations. A quadratic law, or an exponential, or a logarithmic, are almost as simple as a linear one; and the data they would produce are not always distinguishable from data produced by the latter.

What is striking about the city size and vocabulary data, however, is not just the linearity, but that the slope of the ranked data, on a log scale, is very close to minus one. Why this particular value, chosen from the whole non-denumerable infinity of alternative values? We can tolerate even sizeable deviations from this exact slope without losing our confidence that it must surely be the limiting slope for the data under some "ideal" or "perfect" conditions.

We might try to discover these limiting conditions empirically, or we might seek clues to them by constructing an explanatory model for the limiting generalization – the linear array with slope of minus one. In this way we combine stages two and three of the inference process described at the beginning of this section. Let us take this route, confining our discussion to city size distributions.

4. To "explain" an empirical regularity is to discover a set of simple mechanisms that would produce the former in any system governed by the latter. A half dozen sets of mechanisms are known today that are capable of producing the linear rank-size distribution of city populations. Since they are all variations on one or two themes, I will sketch just one of them (SIMON [1955]).

We consider a geographical area that has some urban communities as well as rural population. We assume, for the urban population, that birth rates and death rates are uncorrelated with city size. ("Rate" here always means "number per year per 1 000 population".) We assume that there is migration between cities, and net emigration from rural areas to cities (in addition to net immigration to cities from abroad, if we please). With respect to all migration, we assume: (1) that out-migration rates from cities are uncorrelated with city size; (2) that the probability that any migrant, chosen at random, will migrate to a city in a particular size class is proportional to total urban population in that class of cities. Finally, we assume that of the total growth of population in cities above some specified minimum size, a constant fraction is contributed by the appearance of new cities (i.e., cities newly grown to that size). The resulting steady-state rank-size distribution of cities will be approximately linear on a double log scale, and the slope of the array will approach closer to minus one as the fraction of urban population growth contributed by new cities approaches zero.

When we have satisfied ourselves of the "reasonableness" of the assumptions incorporated in our mechanism, and of the insensitivity of the steady-state distribution to slight deviations from the assumptions as given, then we may feel, first, that the empirical generalization can now be regarded as "fact"; and, second, that it is not merely "brute fact" but possesses a plausible explanation.

But the explanation does even more for us; for it also suggests under what conditions the linearity of the relation should hold most exactly, and under what conditions the slope should most closely approximate to one. If the model is correct, then the rank-size law should be best approximated in geographical areas (1) where urban growth occurs largely in existing cities, (2) where all cities are receiving migration from a common "pool"; and (3) where there is considerable, and relatively free, migration among all the cities. The United States, for example, would be an appropriate area to fit the assumptions of the model; India a less suitable area (because of the relatively weak connection between its major regions); Austria after World War I a still less suitable area (because of the fragmentation of the previous Austro-Hungarian Empire, see fig. 3). I do not wish to discuss the data here beyond observing that these inferences from the model seem generally to be borne out.

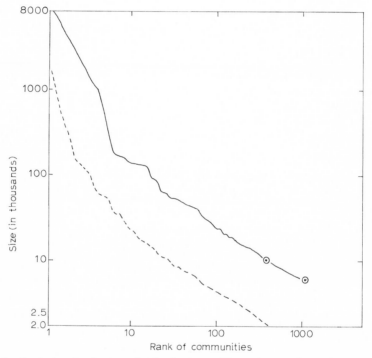

Fig. 3.   Rank-size distribution of cities in Austro-Hungarian Empire, 1910 (——) and in Austria, 1934 (-----).

5. In our account thus far, the simplicity of the empirical generalization has played a central role. Simplicity is also an important concept in POPPER [1961][3] but Popper treats simplicity in a somewhat different way than we have done. Popper (on p. 140) equates simplicity with *degree of falsifiability*. A hypothesis is falsifiable to the degree that it selects out from the set of all possible worlds a very small subset, and asserts that the real world belongs to this subset.

---

[3] Especially Chapter VII.

There is a strong correlation between our intuitive notions of simplicity (e.g., that a linear relation is simpler than a polynomial of higher degree) and falsifiability. Thus, among all possible monotonic arrays, linear arrays are very rare. (They would be of measure zero, if we imposed an appropriate probability measure on the set of all monotonic arrays.) Linear arrays with slope of minus one are even rarer.

No one has provided a satisfactory general measure of the simplicity

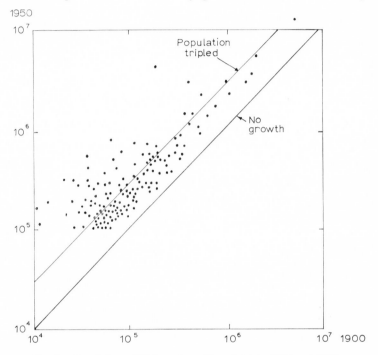

Fig. 4.   Population of U.S. metropolitan districts, 1900 and 1950.
(Only districts over 100000 population in 1950 are shown.)

or falsifiability of hypotheses. In simple cases, the concepts have an obvious connection with degrees of freedom: the fewer the degrees of freedom, or free parameters, the simpler and more falsifiable the hypothesis. I shall not undertake to carry the formalization of the concepts beyond this intuitively appealing basis[4].

---

[4] The most serious attempts at formalization are those undertaken by JEFFREYS and WRINCH [1921], and GOODMAN [1958]. I must note in passing that in his discussion of the former authors POPPER [1961] does not do justice to their technical proposal for introducing prior probabilities based on simplicity.

Notice, however, that our use of simplicity is quite different from POPPER's [1961]. Popper's argument runs like this: it is desirable that hypotheses be simple so that, if they are false, they can be disconfirmed by empirical data as readily as possible. Our argument (apparently first introduced by JEFFREYS and WRINCH [1921]) runs: a simple hypothesis that fits data to a reasonable approximation should be entertained, for it probably reveals an underlying law of nature. As Popper himself observes (POPPER [1961] p. 142, footnote*2), these two arguments take quite opposite positions with respect to the "probability" or "plausibility" of simple hypotheses. He regards such hypotheses as describing highly particular, hence improbable states of the world, and therefore as readily falsified. JEFFREYS and WRINCH [1921] (and I) regard them as successfully summarizing highly unique (but actual) states of the world, therefore as highly plausible.

Which of these views is tenable would seem to depend on which came first, the generalization or the data. If I construct generalizations, with no criterion to guide my choice except that they be simple, and subsequently apply them to data, then the simpler the generalization the more specific their description, and the less likely that they will stand up under their first empirical test. This is essentially Popper's argument.

But the argument does not apply if the generalization was constructed with the data in view. The rank-size hypothesis arises because we think to plot the data on double log paper, and when we do, it appears to be linear and to have a slope of minus one. There is no thought of using the data to falsify the generalization, for the latter has come into being only because it fits the data, at least approximately.

Now one can cite examples from the history of science of both of these alternative sequences of events. It is probably true, however, that the first sequence – generalization followed by data – seldom occurs except as a sequel to the second. The Special Theory of Relativity, for example, led to the prediction of the convertibility of mass into energy. But Special Relativity itself was based on a generalization, the Lorentz-Fitzgerald equation, that was derived to fit facts about the behavior of particles in very intense fields of force, as well as other facts about electromagnetics and the "luminiferous ether". Special Relativity did not commend itself to Einstein merely because of its "simplicity" independently of the facts to be explained (the Galilean transformations would be thought by most people to be simpler than the Lorentz).

If the generalization is just that – an approximate summary of the data – then it is certainly not falsifiable. It becomes falsifiable, or testable, when

(a) it is extended beyond the data from which it was generated, or (b) an explanatory theory is constructed, from which the generalization can be derived, and the explanatory theory has testable consequences beyond the original data.

With respect to the city size data, case (a) would arise if the rank size generalization were proposed after examining the data from the 1940 U.S. Census, and then were extrapolated to earlier and later dates, or to the cities of other countries. Case (b) would arise if we were to note that the explanatory theory of Section 4, above, has implications for patterns of migration that could be tested directly if data on points of origin and destination of migrants were available.

It should be evident that the mechanisms incorporated in the explanatory theory were not motivated by their falsifiability. They were introduced in order to provide "plausible" premises from which the generalization summarizing the observed data could be deduced. And what does "plausible" mean in this context? It means that the assumptions about birth and death rates and migration are not inconsistent with our everyday general knowledge of these matters. At the moment they are introduced, they are already known (or strongly suspected) to be not far from the truth. The state of affairs they describe is not rare or surprising (given what we actually know about the world); rather their subsequent empirical falsification would be rather surprising. What is *not* known at the moment they are introduced is whether they provide adequate premises for the derivation of the rank-size generalization.

Explaining the empirical generalization, that is, providing a set of mechanisms capable of producing it, therefore reintroduces new forms of testability to replace those that were lost by accepting the approximation to the data. Even without data on migration, the mechanism proposed to explain the city rank-size law can be subjected to new tests by constructing the transition matrix that compares the sizes of the same cities at two points of time (taking the 1900 population, say, as the abcissa, and the 1950 population as the ordinate (see fig. 4)). The explanatory mechanism implies that the means of the rows in this matrix fall on a straight line through the origin (or on a straight line of slope $+1$ on a log-log scale). The result (which we will expect to hold only approximately) is equivalent to the proposition that the expected growth rates are independent of initial city size.

6. In the preceding sections a model has been sketched of the scientific activities of hypothesis-generation and hypothesis-testing. The model suggests that there are several distinct processes that lead to hypotheses being formulated, judged with respect to plausibility, and tested. One of these processes, the generation of simple extreme hypotheses from the "striking" characteristics of empirical data, fits closely the idea of JEFFREYS and WRINCH [1921] that simple hypotheses possess a high plausibility. A second process, the construction of explanations for these extreme hypotheses, takes us back to POPPER's [1961] idea that simple hypotheses entail strong and "improbable" consequences, hence are readily falsified (if false). There is no contradiction between these two views.

To elucidate further this model of the scientific process, and to reveal some additional characteristics it possesses, the remaining sections of this paper will be devoted to the analysis of a second example, this one of considerable interest to the psychology of learning and concept formation. An important question in psychology during the past decade has been whether learning is to be regarded as a sudden, all-or-none phenomenon, or whether it is gradual and incremental. One value in stating the question this way is that the all-or-none hypothesis is a simple, extreme hypothesis, hence is highly falsifiable in the sense of POPPER [1961].

The experiments of ROCK [1957] first brought the all-or-none hypothesis into intense controversy. His data strongly supported the hypothesis (even under rather strict limits on the degree of approximation allowed). Since his generalization challenged widely-accepted incrementalist theories, his experiment was soon replicated (seldom quite literally), with widely varying findings. The discussion in the literature, during the first few years after Rock's initial publication, centered on the "validity" of his data – i.e., whether he had measured the right things in his experiment, and whether he had measured them with adequate precision.

Only after several years of debate and publication of apparently contradictory findings was some degree of agreement reached on appropriate designs for testing the hypothesis. Still, some experimenters continued to find one-trial learning, others incremental learning. After several more years, the right question was asked, and the experiments already performed were reviewed to see what answer they gave[5]. The "right question", of course, was: "Under what conditions will learning have an all-or-none character?" The answer, reasonably conformable to the experimental data, commends itself to common sense. Oversimplified, the answer is that one-trial learning is likely to occur when the time per trial is relatively long, and when the

---

[5] POSTMAN [1963], UNDERWOOD [1964].

items to be learned (i.e., associated) are already familiar units[6]. There are the "ideal" or "perfect" conditions under which one-trial learning can be expected to occur.

7. Meanwhile, the all-or-none hypothesis was also being applied to concept attainment experiments. Important work was done in this area by Estes, by Bourne, and by Bower and Trabasso, among others. I will take as my example for discussion a well-known paper by Bower and Trabasso that Gregg and I have analysed in another context[7].

The experiments we shall consider employ an N-dimensional stimulus with two possible values on each dimension, and having a single relevant dimension (i.e., simple concepts). On each trial, an instance (positive or negative) is presented to the subject; he responds "positive" or "negative"; and he is reinforced by "right" or "wrong", as the case may be.

Bower and Trabasso obtain from the data of certain of their experiments an important empirical generalization: the probability that a subject will make a correct response on any trial prior to the trial on which he makes his last error is a constant. (In their data, this constant is always very close to one half, but they do not incorporate this fact in their generalization as they usually state it.) Since the generalization that the probability of making a correct response is constant is an extreme hypothesis, the standard tests of significance are irrelevant. We must judge whether the data fit the generalization "well enough". Most observers, looking at the data, would agree that they do (see fig. 5).

But Bower and Trabasso go a step further. They derive the empirical generalization from a simple stochastic model of the learning process – they explain it, in the sense in which we used that term earlier. The explanation runs thus: (1) the subject tries out various hypotheses as to what is the correct concept, and responds on individual trials according to the concept he is currently holding; (2) if his response is wrong, he tries a new concept. Two important empirical quantities are associated with

---

[6] As a matter of history, I might mention that in 1957, prior to ROCK's [1957] publication of his experiment, a theory of rote learning, designed especially to explain data that were in the literature prior to World War II (the serial position curve, the constancy of learning time per item, some of E. Gibson's experiments on stimulus similarity) had been developed by E. Feigenbaum and the author. This theory, EPAM, was sufficiently strong to predict the conditions under which one-trial learning would occur. It was not widely known among psychologists at that time, however, and had little immediate influence on the controversy. (But see GREGG, CHENZOFF and LAUGHERY [1963], also, GREGG and SIMON [1967b].)

[7] BOWER and TRABASSO [1964]; GREGG and SIMON [1967a].

the model: The probability of making a correct response prior to the last error; and the probability that any particular trial will be the trial of last error.

Now there are in fact *two* distinct all-or-none generalizations that can be formulated in terms of these two empirical quantities. The first, already mentioned, is the generalization that the probability of making a *correct response* is constant as long as the subject holds the wrong hypothesis about the concept (i.e., up to the trial of his last error). The second, quite different, is the generalization that the probability of switching to the *correct hypothesis* about the concept does not change over trials (i.e., that the probability is constant that each trial will be the trial of last error).

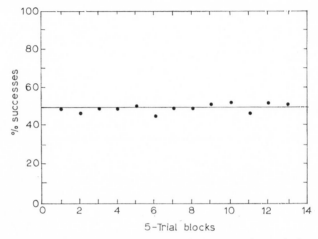

Fig. 5.   Concept experiment: percentage of successes prior to the last error (from Bower and Trabasso).

To test the first (correct response) all-or-none generalization, we have one datum from each subject for each trial prior to his last error – a considerable body of data to judge the approximation of the error rate to a constant. To test the second (correct hypothesis) all-or-none generalization, we have only one datum from each subject – the trial on which he made his last error. Hence, trial-to-trial changes in the probability of switching to the right concept are confounded with differences in that probability among subjects. If, for any single subject, this probability increases with trials, the increase is counterbalanced by the fact that the subjects with lowest average probability will tend to learn last. Thus (as Bower and Trabasso are careful to point out) the data to test the second generalization directly are scanty and inadequate.

8. The Bower-Trabasso stochastic model is an explanation of the observed constancy of the error rate. But it is a very bland model, making rather minimal assumptions about the process that is going on. We can pursue the goal of explanation a step further by constructing a more detailed model of the cognitive processes used by subjects in concept attainment, then using this detailed model to subject the theory to further tests. (As Gregg and I have shown in our previous paper on this topic (GREGG and SIMON [1967a]), Bower and Trabasso do, in fact, employ such a process model, but only informally.)

There are two important differences between the summary stochastic model and the more detailed process model. The process model, but not the stochastic model, spells out how the experimenter selects (on a random basis) the successive instances, how the subject responds, and how he selects a new concept when his current one is found wrong. The stochastic model, but not the detailed model, contains two free parameters, one specifying the probability that the subject's response will be (fortuitously) correct when he does not hold the correct concept; the other specifying the probability that he will select the correct concept as his new one when his current concept is found wrong.

The stochastic model and process model can be formalized by stating them in a computer programming language (GREGG and SIMON [1967a]). When this is done, it is found that the stochastic model requires 15 statements – i.e., simple computer instructions – for its formulation, the detailed process model 27. Against this parsimony of the stochastic model must be balanced the fact that that model contains two free numerical parameters, the process model none. Which model is the simpler?

If we apply Popper's criteria of simplicity – the simpler theory being the one that is more highly falsifiable – then the question has a definite answer. The detailed process model is simpler than the stochastic model (see GREGG and SIMON [1967a] pp. 271–272). For, by a straightforward aggregation of variables, the stochastic model, with particular values for the free parameters, can be derived deductively from the process model. Hence, the process model is a special case of the stochastic model. (The process model predicts an error rate of about 0.5 per trial prior to the trial of last error. It also predicts the probability that the last error will occur on a particular trial, but this probability depends on the structure of the stimuli – the number of attributes they possess, and the number of values of each attribute.)

The additional detail incorporated in the process model's assumptions also provides additional opportunities for subjecting the model to empirical test. The hypotheses held by the subject as to the correct concept do not appear explicitly in the stochastic model; hence data relating to these hypotheses (obtained, say, by asking the subject on each trial what concept he holds, as was done by FELDMAN [1964], or obtained by indirect procedures developed by LEVINE [1966]) cannot be used to test that model, but can be used to test the process model.

If parsimony refers to the brevity with which a theory can be described, then the stochastic model is the more parsimonious (fifteen statements against twenty-seven). But lack of parsimony, so defined, must not be confused with degrees of freedom. We have seen in this case that the less parsimonious theory is the simpler (by POPPER's [1961] criterion), and by far the more falsifiable.

Testing the detailed process theory raises all the problems mentioned earlier with respect to extreme hypotheses. If the error rate on guessing trials deviates from 0.5 should the theory be rejected? How much of a deviation should be tolerated? In how many cases can a subject report he is holding a concept different from that predicted by the theory before we reject the latter? I have given my reasons earlier for thinking that these questions are judgmental, and for concluding that the theory of statistical tests offers no help in answering them. A judgmental answer is that the theory should be rejected only if it turns out to be "radically" wrong. Otherwise, deviations should lead to a search for variables to account for them, and for the "ideal" limiting case in which they would disappear.

Justice Holmes once said: "Logic is not the life of the law". I would paraphrase his aphorism by saying: "Statistics is not the life of science". No existing statistical theory explains what scientists do (or should do) to retroduce, develop, test, and modify scientific theories.

9. Just as statistically significant deviations of data from a generalization should not always, or usually, lead us to abandon the generalization, so we should not be unduly impressed by excellent statistical fits of data to theory. More important than whether the data fit is why they fit – i.e., what components in the theory are critical to the goodness of fit. To answer this question, we must analyse the internal structure of the theory.

For example, under the conditions where all-or-none learning can be expected to take place, the learning trials can generally be divided into two parts: an initial sequence prior to learning, during which the subject can only guess at the correct answer; a terminal sequence, during which the subject knows the correct concept, and makes no new mistakes. Let us suppose that the boundary between these two segments can be detected (as it can in the concept-learning experiments by the trial on which the last error is made).

Under these conditions, no important conclusions can be drawn about psychological characteristics of the subjects by examining the statistical structure of their responses prior to learning. For the statistics of these responses are simply reflections of the experimenter's randomization of the sequence of stimuli. In one experiment, ESTES [1959], for example, employed three different conditions differing only with respect to the number of alternative responses (2, 4 and 8, respectively) available to the subject (see SIMON [1962]). He found that the relative number of errors per trial made in these three conditions could be represented by the formula, $A(N-1)/N$, where A is a constant and N is the number of alternative responses.

The data on relative numbers of errors fit this formula with great accuracy – a clearcut case of success for an extreme hypothesis of the kind we have been commending in this paper. However, the hypothesis that was being tested was not a generalization about psychology, but a well-known generalization about the laws of probability: that in drawing balls at random from an urn containing white and black balls in the ratio of 1 to $(N-1)$, on the average $(N-1)/N$ of the balls drawn will be black. This is true regardless of whether the subjects themselves, prior to learning, thought they were simply guessing or thought they were responding in selective, patterned ways to the stimuli. By randomizing the sequence of stimuli presented, the experimenter guaranteed the applicability of the laws of probability to the subject's errors, independently of the systematic or "random" character of the subject's behavior.

As I have pointed out elsewhere, a number of other excellent fits of simple generalizations to data can be attributed to the random presentation of stimuli, rather than to characteristics of the subjects (SIMON [1957], SIMON [1962], GREGG and SIMON [1967a]). This does not imply that it is useless to extract the underlying regularities from the data; but we must be careful to provide the regularities with a correct explanation. To do so, we must examine the internal structure of the theories that lead to the successful generalization.

10. Throughout this paper, considerable stress has been placed on the close interaction between hypotheses and data in the building and testing of theories. In most formal theories of induction, particularly those that belong to the genus "hypothetico-deductive" or "H-D", hypotheses spring full-blown from the head of Zeus, then are tested with data that exist, timelessly and quite independently of the hypotheses[8]. Theories as otherwise divergent as Popper's and Carnap's share this common framework.

It was one of Norwood Hanson's important contributions to challenge this separation of hypothesis from data, and to demonstrate that in the history of science the retroduction of generalizations and explanations from data has been one of the central and crucial processes. In making his point, Hanson was careful not to revert to naive Baconian doctrines of induction. To look at a series of size-rank distributions, approximately log-linear with slopes of minus one; then to conclude that *all* such distributions share these properties, is Baconian. To look at the raw data, and conclude that they can be described adequately by the log-linear function with slope of minus one is not Baconian. It is the latter form of derivation of generalizations from data with which Hanson was primarily concerned, and to which he (following Peirce) applied the name "retroduction".

One of my principal theses here has been that hypotheses retroduced in this way are usually highly plausible, and not highly improbable, as POPPER [1961] would insist. We have already resolved part of the apparent paradox. The "improbability" to which Popper refers is improbability of the very special state of nature described by the empirical generalization, not improbability of the generalization itself. But it remains to understand how the scientist can ever be lucky enough to discover the very special generalizations that describe these a priori improbable (but actual) states of nature.

Fortunately, considerable light has been cast on this question by progress in the past decade in our understanding of the theory of human problem solving (SIMON [1966]). If the scientist had to proceed by searching randomly through the (infinite) space of possible hypotheses, comparing each one with the data until he found one that matched, his task would be hopeless and endless. This he does not need to do. Instead, he extracts information from the data themselves (or the data "cleaned up" to remove some of the noise), and uses this information to construct the hypothesis directly, with a modest amount of search.

Let us consider a concrete example (BANET [1966]). Suppose we are presented with the sequence: $\frac{9}{5}, \frac{4}{3}, \frac{25}{21}, \frac{9}{8}, \ldots$. What simple generalization can we discover to fit this sequence? We note that all the numerators are

---

[8] For a criticism of this view, see SIMON [1955]. In that paper I was concerned specifically with the relative dating of theory and data, and while I still subscribe to the general position set forth there – that this dating is relevant to the corroboration of hypotheses by data – I would want to modify some of my specific conclusions about the form of the relevance, as various paragraphs in the present paper will show.

squares, that the first and third denominators are four less than their numerators, the second and fourth denominators are one less. We notice that the sequence appears to be monotone decreasing, and to approach a limit – perhaps unity. Nine is 3^2, 25 is 5^2. Suppose we number the terms 3, 4, 5, 6. The corresponding squares are 9, 16, 25, 36. Let's multiply numerator and denominator of the second and fourth terms by four, getting: $\frac{9}{5}, \frac{16}{12}, \frac{25}{21}, \frac{36}{32}, \ldots$. Now the empirical generalization is obvious: the general term of the sequence is $n^2/(n^2 - 4)$. Physicists will recognize this as the well known Balmer series of the hydrogen spectrum, and what we have done is to reconstruct hypothetically part of Balmer's retroduction. (He probably followed a somewhat different path, and we have only considered the last half of his problem of getting from data to generalization, but this partial and somewhat unhistorical example will serve to illustrate our central point. For the actual history, see BANET's [1966] interesting paper.)

However great a feat it was for Balmer to extract his formula from the data, the process he used was certainly not one of generating random hypotheses, then testing them. It is better described as a process of searching for the pattern in the data. It can be shown, for a considerable class of patterns that are of practical importance, in science, in music, and in intelligence tests, that the range of relations the searcher must be prepared to detect is quite small. It may be that these are the sole relations from which the simplicity of nature is built; it may be they are the only relations we are equipped to detect in nature. In either event, most of the patterns that have proved important for science are based, at bottom, on these few simple relations that humans are able to detect.

11. In this paper, I have examined several aspects of the problem of testing theories, and particularly those important theories that take the form of extreme hypotheses. In part, my argument has been aimed at a negative goal – to show that when we look at realistic examples from natural and social science, statistical theory is not of much help in telling us how theories are retroduced or tested.

As an alternative to standard probabilistic and statistical accounts of these matters, I have proposed that we take into account a whole sequence of events:

(1) The enterprise generally begins with empirical data, rather than with a hypothesis out of the blue.

(2) "Striking" features of the data (e.g., that they are linear on a log scale with slope of minus one) provide for a simple generalization that summarizes them – approximately.

(3) We seek for limiting conditions that will improve the approximation by manipulating variables that appear to affect its goodness.

(4) We construct simple mechanisms to explain the simple generalizations – showing that the latter can be deduced from the former.

(5) The explanatory theories generally make predictions that go beyond the simple generalizations in a number of respects, and hence suggest new empirical observations and experiments that allow them to be tested further.

"Testing" theories, as that process is generally conceived, is only one of the minor preoccupations of science. The very process that generates a theory (and particularly a simple generalization) goes a long way toward promising it some measure of validity. For these reasons, histories of science written in terms of the processes that discover patterns in nature would seem closer to the mark than histories that emphasize the search for data to test hypotheses created out of whole cloth.

References

BANET, L., Evolution of the Balmer series, Am. J. Phys. **34** (1966) 496–503.

BOWER, G. H. and T. R. TRABASSO, Concept identification, in: Studies in mathematical psychology, ed. R. C. Atkinson (Stanford, Stanford University Press, 1964) pp. 32–94.

ESTES, W. K., Growth and functions of mathematical models for learning, in: Current trends in psychological theory (Pittsburgh, University of Pittsburgh Press, 1959) pp. 134–151.

FELDMAN, J., Simulation of behavior in the binary choice experiment, in: Computers and thought, eds. E. A. Feigenbaum and J. Feldman (New York, McGraw-Hill, 1964) pp. 329–346.

GOODMAN, N., The test of simplicity, Science **176** (1958) 1064–1069.

GREGG, L. W. and H. A. SIMON, Process models and stochastic theories of simple concept formation, J. Math. Psych. **4** (1967a) 246–276.

GREGG, L. W. and H. A. SIMON, An information processing explanation of one-trial and incremental learning, J. Verbal Learning and Verbal Behavior **6** (1967b) 780–787.

GREGG, L. W., A. P. CHENZOFF and K. LAUGHERY, The effect of rate of presentation, substitution and mode of response in paired-associate learning, Am. J. Psych. **76** (1963) 110–115.

HANSON, R. N., Patterns of discovery (Cambridge, The University Press, 1961).

JEFFREYS, H. and D. WRINCH, On certain fundamental principles of scientifique inquiry, Phil. Magazine **42** (1921) 369–390.

LEVINE, M., Hypothesis behavior by humans during discrimination learning, J. Exper. Psych. **71** (1966) 331–338.

POPPER, K. R., The logic of scientific discovery (New York, Science Editions, 1961).

POSTMAN, L., One-trial learning, in: Verbal behavior and learning, eds. C. F. Cofer and B. S. Musgrave (New York, McGraw-Hill, 1963) pp. 295–321.

ROCK, I., The role of repetition in associative learning, Am. J. Psych. **70** (1957) 186–193.

SAVAGE, L. J., The foundations of statistics (New York, Wiley, 1954).

SIMON, H. A., Prediction and hindsight as confirmatory evidence, Phil. Sci. **22** (1955) 227–230.

SIMON, H. A., On a class of skew distribution functions, Biometrika, **42** (1955) 425–440; reprinted in: Models of man (New York, Wiley, 1957) pp. 145–164.

SIMON, H. A., Amounts of fixation and discovery in maze learning behavior, Psychometrika **22** (1957) 261–268.

SIMON, H. A., A note on mathematical models for learning, Psychometrika **27** (1962) 417–418.

SIMON, H. A., Scientific discovery and the psychology of problem solving, in: Mind and cosmos, ed. R. Colodny (Pittsburgh, University of Pittsburgh Press, 1966) pp. 22–40.

UNDERWOOD, B. J. and G. KEPPEL, One-trial learning, J. Verbal Learning and Verbal Behavior **3** (1964) 385–396.

Section 10

Methodology and Philosophy
of Linguistics

THE LOGIC OF QUESTIONS*

J. J. KATZ

*Department of Humanities and Research Laboratory of Electronics,
Massachusetts Institute of Technology, Cambridge, Massachusetts, USA*

1. Introduction

If, like other titles, the title of this paper tells what the paper is about, then it might be claimed that this paper is not about anything. That is, as far as our hopes for acquiring knowledge are concerned, the title could just as well be "an exposé of the life and loves of the barber who shaves all and only those who do not shave themselves".

This claim might be argued as follows: what admits of truth and falsity are statements, which are true when what they assert is the case and false otherwise. Since questions do not assert anything, but instead request information, truth and falsity cannot be properties of questions. Since this is so, it makes no sense to speak of deductive connections between questions, of one question logically implying another. Hence, there cannot be a logic of questions.

But this conclusion does not follow from the fact that questions do not have truth-values. It is compatible with the premises of this argument that there are deductive connections between questions; only, if there are, then the truth-functional interpretation of deductive connections in the case of statements – that truth is inherited under them – does not apply to such connections in the case of questions. Hence, the conclusion that there can be no logic of questions follows only if we grant a further premiss, one to the effect that logic is solely concerned with those relations between the premises and conclusion of arguments on which the formers' truth necessitates the latter's. Unless some such further premiss is added, there is no valid infer-

* This work was supported principally by the U.S. Air Force (Electronic Systems Division) under Contract Af 19(628)–2487; and in part by the Joint Services Electronics Program (Contract DA36-039-AMC-03200(E)), the National Science Foundation (Grant GK-835), the National Institutes of Health (2PO1 MH-04737-06), and the National Aeronautics and Space Administration (Grant NsG-496).

ence to the impossibility of a logic of questions. As it stands, nothing in the argument precludes the possibility that questions have genuine logical properties and relations under some non-truth-functional interpretation of deductive connections.

One purpose of this paper is to establish the falsity of this further premiss, and thus to provide a foundation for the logic of questions. To achieve this purpose, we must show, first, that deductive connections hold between entities that do not bear a truth value, that questions have logical properties and relations; and second, that there is a motivated and well-defined non-truth-functional interpretation for deductive connections between questions. The former will be shown by appropriate examples, ones that are fully on a par with those that have long served to establish that statements have logical properties and relations. The latter will be shown by constructing a non-truth-functional interpretation of validity on the basis of definitions from semantic theory[1] and demonstrating that these definitions and the interpretation based on them explain the examples is an acceptable manner. This type of demonstration will be essentially the same as the one on which the truth-functional interpretation of validity rests.

However, there is another purpose of this paper. My more pervasive interest, of which my interest in the logic of questions is a part, is the development of semantic theory, and the elaboration of its philosophical consequences.[2]

The present paper further develops semantic theory in two ways. First, it extends the range of semantic concepts that the theory can successfully define by adding definitions for the logical properties and relations of questions to the definitions already given for semantic properties and relations such as *semantic anomaly, semantic ambiguity, synonymy, antonymy, analyticity, contradiction, entailment*, etc. Second, it increases the empirical support for semantic theory by showing that the conceptual apparatus of semantic theory – the machinery of semantic markers, readings, projection rules, selection restrictions, semantically interpreted underlying phrase markers, definitions of semantic properties and relations, etc. – explains the logical properties and relations in questions.[3]

---

[1] Cf. KATZ [1966], [1967a].

[2] Cf. KATZ [1965], [1966], [1967a] and [in press].

[3] Note that this conceptual apparatus was not devised ad hoc to handle questions, but is part of semantic theory already, having been developed to deal with other semantic problems. Hence, its application to the logic of questions shows the explanatory power of semantic theory in much the same way that the application of the laws of mechanics for macro-objects to molecular phenomena shows their explanatory power.

This paper also elaborates further my approach to the philosophy of language. The approach, in essence, is to seek solutions to philosophical problems, or pieces of their solutions, on the basis of the theoretical constructions found in linguistic theory. Elsewhere[4], I have tried to show that some of the problems concerning analyticity, semantic categories, innate ideas, linguistic analysis, and logical form can be represented as questions about the nature of language and, so represented, can be solved by theoretical constructions from linguistic theory. Here, I will try to show that the theoretical constructions in semantic theory, which is a part of linguistic theory, enable us to solve certain crucial problems about the possibility of a logic of questions and about the nature of logic in general.

2. Examples of logical properties and relations of questions

Logic is commonly regarded as the science of necessary inference. Its aim is the formulation of truths about the conditions under which a step of passing from one proposition to another in an argument is a necessary one. Accordingly, to show that questions have logical properties and relations, we must provide examples, on the one hand, of questions that are parallels for a statement whose truth can be inferred without any premises, and on the other, of questions that are parallels for a pair of statements where one member is true just in case the other is. That is, there must be questions with a property analogous to analyticity and pairs or *n*-tuples of questions between which a relation analogous to entailment holds.

As examples of questions of the former sort, there are what are sometimes called "joke-questions", questions of the "Who's buried in Grant's tomb?" variety, made famous by Groucho Marx (as a way of giving booby-prizes to deserving contestants on his quiz program). Consider these examples of the who's-buried-in-Grant's-tomb type question:

(1) Is a spinster female?
(2) Is a spinster male?
(3) Who killed the man who was killed by John?
(4) What is the color of the red wagon?
(5) Where is the hat that is on my head?
(6) What time is it at exactly twelve midnight?

Less familiar, but in this context directly suggested by (1)–(6) are the following parallels to entailments.

---

[4] In particular, KATZ [1966] and [1965].

(7) Is John a bachelor?
     Is John male?
(8) Who stole a cat?
     Who stole an animal?

Such "question-arguments" are parallels to arguments from the assertion of one statement or set of statements to the assertion of another, just as (1)–(6) are parallels to statements that can be asserted without premises. Except for (2), whose status will be discussed below, the analytic statements and statement-arguments to which (1)–(8) are directly parallel can be gotten simply by converting each of these interrogatives into its obvious declarative counter-part, e.g. (1) into "Spinsters are female", (3) into "The color of my red wagon is red", (8) into the argument from "Someone stole a cat" to "Someone stole an animal", and so on.

We should note also "mixed-arguments", i.e. arguments involving both questions and statements, like

(9) Who killed Cock Robin?
     Cock Robin is dead

where on the occasions when the premiss-question makes a request for information the conclusion-statement must be true. Such examples are interesting because they illustrate an inherent involvement of the logic of questions and the logic of statements.

I will not bother arguing that these examples are clear-cut illustrations that questions have logical properties and relations. It is quite uncontroversial that they are. Examples (1)–(6) are certainly as clear-cut as their analytic parallels, and examples (7) and (8) are as clear-cut as their entailment parallels. Of course, some philosophers have their qualms about the parallels in the case of statements, but I have replied to them elsewhere. [5] Thus, I shall take the existence of such examples as establishing the existence of deductive relations among questions (and between questions and statements) and shall try to explicate them.

3. The two basic questions for the logic of questions

To explain these examples, it is necessary to answer two questions. First, what is the property that questions like (1)–(6) possess by virtue of

---

[5] KATZ [1967b].

which they stand as parallels to analytic statements? How can the property they have be like analyticity without conferring truth on cases that have it? Second, what is the relation between the questions in pairs like (7) or (8)? Also, what is the relation between the question and statement in pairs like (9)? If valid arguments with statements preserve truth, what do valid question arguments preserve? Since they do not preserve truth, how is it that, in cases such as (9), the truth of a statement can be inferred from a question?

4. Linguistic background

Before attempting to answer these questions, it will be necessary to review certain aspects of linguistic theory that will enter into the answers that will be proposed.

The underlying phrase marker for an interrogative sentence is like the underlying phrase marker for a declarative except that its first (left-most) terminal symbol is Q and that it contains one or more noun-phrases (i.e. substrings of the string of terminal symbols that are dominated by the symbol "NP") to which an occurrence of the symbol *wh* is attached. [6] Q is the

---

[6] Interrogatives are closely related to imperatives, and may even be a form of the imperative type. Postal and I (KATZ and POSTAL [1965] pp. 79–120) took interrogatives to be semantically related to imperatives. We took them both as expressing propositions of the same semantic type, i.e. as expressing requests – requests for a certain kind of linguistic object (i.e. an answer) in the case of questions, and requests for behavior of some sort in the case of requests expressed by ordinary imperatives. We formulated this view in terms of suitable lexical readings for the Q and I morphemes. However, some evidence suggests that the relation may go deeper, that there is also a syntactic connection between imperatives and interrogatives. This evidence suggests that interrogatives might even be imperatives of some special sort. Consider the following: The sentences (i) and (ii)

(i) $\begin{Bmatrix} \text{You} \\ \text{John} \end{Bmatrix}$, what is the capital of France?

(ii) What is the capital of France, $\begin{Bmatrix} \text{You} \\ \text{John} \end{Bmatrix}$?

are both grammatical, but (iii) and (iv)

(iii) * $\begin{Bmatrix} \text{he} \\ \text{she} \\ \text{it} \\ \text{they} \\ \text{one} \end{Bmatrix}$, what is the capital of France?

(iv) * What is the capital of France, $\begin{Bmatrix} \text{he} \\ \text{she} \\ \text{it} \\ \text{they} \\ \text{one} \end{Bmatrix}$?

are ungrammatical. Moreover, the sentences (v) and (vi)

question morpheme. It makes the application of question transformations obligatory. *wh* is a scope indicator for *Q*. Its attachment to a noun-phrase indicates that that noun-phrase is questioned: syntactically, that that noun-phrase is transformed into an interrogative pronoun which may receive a high intonation. In general, the noun-phrases to which *wh* can be attached are pro-forms such as "someone", "something", "sometime", "someplace", "someway", etc., and their corresponding interrogative pronouns occurring in the phonetic or orthographic realization of a sentence are "who", "what", "when", "where", "how", etc.

For example, the underlying phrase marker for

(10) What did John eat?

is

(11)

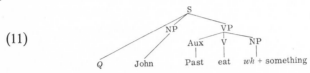

The superficial phrase marker which specifies the interrogative form of the sentence that (11) underlies is simply

(12)

(12) is transformationally derived from (11) by formal operations characteristic of the generation of interrogatives. *Q* is deleted and the constituent "*wh* + something" is moved to the position vacated by *Q*. The constituent dominated by "Aux" is inserted between "*wh* + something" and the subject noun-phrase "John". An occurrence of "do" is introduced immediately preceding the constituent dominated by "Aux". Then "do + Past" is converted into "did" and "*wh* + something" is converted into the inter-

---

(v) * You, the capital of France is Paris
(vi) * The capital of France is Paris, you.
are also ungrammatical. Thus, the restriction on the subject of ordinary imperatives, which is characteristic of this sentence type, is found also in questions. This, of course, is not conclusive, but its implication shouldn't be ignored.

rogative pronoun "what". [7] (12) is operated on by phonological rules which provide its phonetic shape.

Other types of interrogatives like

(13) Who did John eat with?
(14) When did John eat?
(15) Where did John eat?
(16) How did John eat?

or rather their superficial phrase markers, are each transformationally derived from an underlying phrase marker of the general form described above by such operations of deletion, permutation, and addition. These underlying phrase markers are each appropriately different from the others in a way that reflects the differences between the interrogatives they underlie. That is, although each contains Q and occurrences of *wh* attached to noun-phrases, different noun-phrases in each have *wh* attached to them and these noun-phrases occur in constituents of different syntactic types. For example, in (13) the *wh*-ed noun-phrase is the noun-phrase "some one" in the prepositional phrase "with some one"; in (14) it is the noun-phrase "some time" in the temporal adverbial "at some time"; in (15) it is the noun-phrase "some place" in the locative adverbial "at some place"; and in (16) it is the noun-phrase "some way" in the manner adverbial "in some way". The pattern of variation on the interrogative theme is thus clear: each distinct type of interrogative arises, transformationally, from a different *wh* + ed noun-phrase forming part of a different, but for its type, characteristic syntactic category. *Which-interrogatives, how-much-interrogatives, why-interrogatives, whoever-interrogatives,* and other types also fall into place in this pattern. [8]

Jespersen and other grammarians distinguish interrogatives of the sort considered above from what are commonly referred to as "yes/no-questions". Jespersen writes:

---

[7] Notice that the *wh* morpheme functions somewhat like bracketing in a quantification formula, in that it determines which noun-phrases in the terminal string of an underlying phrase marker are 'captured' by the question-morpheme Q. For just as not all occurrences of a particular variable need be in the scope of a given quantifier, so not all noun-phrases need be questioned, nor even all pro-forms, in an interrogative. Consider the interrogatives "Who did something to John?", "Who did what to Howard?", and "Who did what to whom?".

[8] For a more detailed and complete discussion, cf. KATZ and POSTAL [1965] pp. 144–147 and pp. 177–184.

There are two kinds of questions: "Did he say that?" is an example of the one kind, and "What did he say?" and "Who said that?" are examples of the other. In the former kind – *nexus-questions* – we call in question the combination (nexus) of a subject and a predicate. ... In questions of the second kind we have an unknown quantity x, exactly as in an algebraic equation; we may therefore use the term *x-questions*. The linguistic expression for this x is an interrogative pronoun or pronominal adverb.[9]

Semantically, this is a crucial distinction, but, syntactically, nexus-interrogatives, like the different cases of x-interrogatives that we have been discussing, are just another variant in the pattern. They also arise from a specific constituent belonging to a distinct syntactic category falling in the scope of the question morpheme Q. This may not at first glance seem right because of the important semantic difference Jespersen mentions, yet it can be shown that nexus-interrogatives are also derived from wh + ed constituents.

wh-interrogatives, regardless of type, appear as embedded questions in almost their standard interrogative form. For example,

(17) John asked which Mary went

(18) John asked where Mary went

(19) John asked when Mary went

(20) John asked how Mary went

(21) John asked why Mary went

(22) John asked who went

But so do nexus-interrogatives. For example,

(23) John asked whether Mary went

This and other evidence establishes that there is a wh–ed constituent underlying the word "whether" whose morphemic shape is "wh + either".

But to show that all nexus-interrogatives are derived from wh-ed constituents in their underlying phrase marker, it must also be shown that when a nexus-interrogative occurs by itself as a full sentence – rather than an embedded question within another sentence – its underlying phrase marker contains a wh-ed constituent. That is, it must not only be shown that a "wh + either" occurs in the underlying phrase marker for an interrogative like (23) but must also be shown that a "wh + either" occurs in the underlying phrase marker for an interrogative like

---

[9] JESPERSEN [1933] pp. 304–305.

(24) Did Mary go?

One of the things that makes it necessary to say that "*wh* + either" is found in the underlying phrase marker for interrogatives like (24) whose phonetic shape does not contain "whether" is that such nexus-interrrogatives are derived from underlying phrase markers that are disjunctive in form. Consider:

(25) Did Mary go or didn't Mary go?
(26) Did Mary go or didn't she?
(27) Did Mary go or not?
(28) Did Mary or didn't Mary go?

Clearly, the underlying phrase markers for (25)–(28) are disjunctive in form.[10] Consequently, if (24) has the same underlying phrase marker as any of these nexus-interrogatives, its underlying phrase marker too will be disjunctive in form. Now, the nexus-interrogatives (25)–(28) are synonymous with each other, and moreover, (24) is equivalent in meaning to them. Each of the cases (24)–(28) questions the truth of the statement that Mary went. These synonymy relations cannot be accounted for on a strictly semantic basis, since unlike

(29) John is a bachelor

and

(30) John is an unmarried adult male

they do not hold between sentences with different morphemic content which through semantic interaction express the same meaning. Hence, these synonymy relations must be explained on the grounds that (24)–(28) have the *same* underlying phrase marker. Any sentences with the same underlying phrase marker are paraphrases of one another, since, insofar as the semantic component operates exclusively on underlying phrase markers, [11] such sentences must receive the same semantic interpretation.

The underlying phrase marker for (24)–(28) is:

---

[10] Also, contrast these with: * who went or not?
[11] This expresses the fact that transformations make no contribution to the meaning of a sentence. Cf. KATZ and POSTAL [1965] and CHOMSKY [1966].

(31)

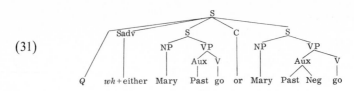

(24)–(28) (or rather their superficial phrase markers) are each derived transformationally from (31) by a familiar ellipsis pattern in which repeated elements can be deleted.[12] This derivation is not only an explanation of the syntactic and semantic relations between (24)–(28) but much else as well. For one thing, it explains the synonymy of (23) and (32).

(32) John asked whether Mary went or not

And for another, it explains why nexus-interrogatives like

(33) Didn't Mary go?

express the same question as interrogatives like (24) even though the former are negatives of the latter.[13] Finally, on this treatment, when a nexus-interrogative occurs by itself, as a full sentence, "*wh* + either" is phonetically realized in the form of a stressed initial occurrence of "do" and *tense* (or "will", "can", "should", "be", "have", etc. and *tense*, as the case may be).

In terms of this conception of the grammar of interrogatives, in particular the treatment of their underlying syntactic structure, it is possible to define the semantic relations (i) *x is the presupposition of the question q*; (ii) *x is a possible answer to the question q*; (iii) *x is an answer to the question q*; (iv) *x is an evasion of the question q*; and (v) *x is a rejection of the question q*. These definitions are not only important in their own right, but they have added significance here, since they will be ingredients in our definitions for the logical properties and relations upon which the logic of questions depends.

The presupposition of a question is a sentence, or, better, the statement it expresses, which must be true if the question is to express a genuine request

---

[12] Cf. CHOMSKY [1966] pp. 144–147 and pp. 177–184.

[13] Of course, even though the negative and positive forms of a nexus-interrogative ask the same question, they are normally appropriate in different contexts. The latter is used in cases where it is reasonable for the speaker to presume that the person referred to did not do the thing in question. Hence, the secondary use of negative forms, as in the case where a husband and wife are going out and the wife is taking her time dressing, so the husband says "Aren't you coming?". Thus, this case of positive and negative forms of nexus-questions is like the case of "rabbit" and "bunny", which are synonymous but used in different contexts, the latter being appropriate when conversing with children. Cf. also JESPERSON [1933] p. 304.

for information. The classic case of such is the presupposition of the question

(34) When did you stop beating your wife?

viz., the statement expressed by

(35) You have beaten your wife at some time

(when used under the same utterance conditions as (34)). The notion of the presupposition of a question is parallel to the notion of a presupposition of a statement except that in the latter case the truth of the presupposition is a necessary condition for the sentence to express an assertion (rather than a request). Thus, the fact that the presupposition of

(36) The man who invented the perpetual motion machine is Polish

viz., the statement expressed by

(37) Some man invented the perpetual motion machine

is false means that (36) makes no assertion about anyone being Polish nor indeed any assertion at all. As a parallel, we propose the following definition for (i):

(38) A sentence x (expresses the statement which) is the presupposition of the question q just in case (a) the underlying phrase marker of x is the same as that for q except for the absence of Q and occurrences of wh, or (b) x is a paraphrase of (on the appropriate sense, i.e. has the same reading as) some sentence satisfying (a).

On the basis of (31), the presupposition of (10) is:

(39) John ate something

or, by virtue of condition (b) of (38):

(40) Something was eaten by John[14]

Similarly, the presuppostions of (13)–(16) are, respectively:

(41) John ate with somebody
(42) John ate at some time
(43) John ate at some place
(44) John ate in some manner

---

[14] That is, (40) is just the passive of (39) and passives are synonymous with their active counter parts. Cf. KATZ and POSTAL [1965] pp. 72–74, and KATZ and MARTIN [1967].

The presupposition of the nexus-interrogative (24) and its paraphrases (25)–(28) and (33) is:

(45) (Either) Mary did go or Mary did not go

Of course the presupposition in this type of nexus-interrogative is vacuous since it is an instance of a logical truth, but this is not the case for all types of nexus-interrogatives. The case

(46) Did Mary go home or did Mary go to school?

has the non-vacuous presupposition

(47) (Either) Mary went home or Mary went to school

The notion of a possible answer is analogous to the notion of a *lawlike statement*.[15] Just as a lawlike statement is a statement that has all the characteristics of a law except for possibly being false, so a possible answer has all the characteristics of an answer except for possibly being false. True lawlike statements are genuine laws, and analogously, true possible answers are genuine answers. Accordingly, the notion of a possible answer is that of a sentence (or the statement it expresses) that would satisfy the request for information if it were true.

Our definition of this notion treats nexus-interrogatives and x-interrogatives differently, in the manner *suggested* by Jespersen's remarks, i.e. semantically, the questions expressed by the former request information as to the truth or falsity of a statement (or set of statements, as in (46)) while those expressed by the latter request information about some unknown x. Thus:

(48) A sentence x (expresses the statement which) is a possible answer to the question q just in case (a) q is a nexus-interrogative and x's underlying phrase marker is the same as one of the two proper-parts of the underlying phrase marker for q whose top-most node is labeled 'S' and is directly dominated by the top-most node in that phrase marker; (b) q is an x-interrogative and x's underlying phrase marker is the same as that of the presuppostion of q (cf. condition (a) of (38)) except that, for each noun-phrase NP_i in the latter corresponding to a *wh*-ed noun-phrase in the former, NP_i is replaced in the semantically interpreted underlying phrase marker for x by a

---

[15] This is a familiar notion in the philosophy of science, e.g. cf. the discussions of GOODMAN [1965] p. 22.

noun-phrase NP_j such that the reading for NP_j has more semantic markers than the reading for NP_i; or (c) x is a paraphrase of (on the appropriate sense, i.e. has the same reading as) some sentence satisfying either (a) or (b).

By this definition, in both the case of nexus-interrogatives and x-interrogatives, a possible answer provides information beyond what is contained in the meaning of the questioned constituent(s). However, in the former case this information is provided by a choice from among the disjuncts in the question. Jespersen put the matter in terms of questioning "the combination (nexus) of a subject and predicate". But since questioning the combination actually takes the form of posing alternatives, one of which expresses its correctness and the other its incorrectness, if a possible answer is a particular choice from among the alternatives posed in the question it will express a claim about the correctness of a predication. Accordingly, the questioning of a sentence-adverbial requests information beyond what is given in the reading of the disjunction of sentences. The reading of one (in certain cases more than one) of the disjuncts provides this information. Thus, possible answers to (24) are:

(49) Mary did go
(50) Mary did not go

"yes" is a stylistic variant of possible answers such as (49), and "no" is a stylistic variant of possible answers such as (50), but only when the superficial form of the interrogative is that represented in (24). Such variants of cases like (49) and (50) – including the bureaucratic uses of "affirmative" and "negative" – cannot be possible answers when the superficial form of the interrogative is like that represented in (25)–(28) or when its underlying form is like that represented in (46).

In the case of x-interrogatives, the questioning of a noun-phrase requests information beyond that given in the reading of the noun-phrase questioned. Thus, a possible answer must provide the further information. (48) (b) captures this in its requirement that the appropriate noun-phrases in a possible answer have a reading that contains more semantic markers than appear in the reading for their corresponding wh-ed noun-phrases in the question. These additional semantic markers in the relevant noun-phrases of a possible answer provide the further information requested. Thus, continuing Jespersen's algebraic analogy, such semantic markers are the analogues of expressions, such as "y^2", "17", "$5y + 8z^3$", etc., which "x" may equal in an equation. Accordingly, possible answers to (10) are

(51) John ate sticks and some stones

(52) John ate food

(53) John ate something he had in his pocket

and so forth.

Knowing already the relation of an answer to a possible answer, it is an easy matter to define the notion of an answer to a question:

(54) A sentence x (expresses the statement which) is an answer to the question q just in case x is a possible answer to q and x is true (expresses a true statement) or x is a paraphrase of such a sentence.

Thus, the answer to the question expressed by

(55) Who is president of the U.S.A.?

is the statement expressed by

(56) Lyndon Johnson is president of the U.S.A.

but not that expressed by

(57) Paul Goodman is president of the U.S.A.

though both are possible answers to (55).

(54) explains the nature of the request embodied in the asking of a question: that the person addressed by the speaker supply him with an answer in the sense of (54).[16]

Possible answers and answers must, however, be distinguished from two closely related things, *evasions* and *rejections* of questions. Thus:

(58) A sentence x (expresses the statement which) is an evasion of the question q just in case x is a presupposition of q.

(59) A sentence x (expresses the statement which) is a rejection of the question q just in case x is inconsistent with (on the appropriate sense) the presupposition of q.[17]

---

[16] Cf. KATZ and POSTAL [1965] pp. 85–91.

[17] Let P_1 and P_2, respectively, be the semantically interpreted underlying phrase markers for x and the presupposition of q. If the reading of the subject of P_1 is the same as the reading of the subject of P_2 and the reading of the predicate of P_2 contains at least one semantic marker M_i such that there is a semantic marker M_j in the reading for the predicate of P_1 ($M_i \neq M_j$) and M_i belongs to the same antonymous n-tuple of semantic markers as M_j, then x and the presupposition of q are inconsistent. Cf. KATZ [1964] pp. 519–543.

By (58) the sentences[18]

(60) John ate something
(61) John ate something eatable
(62) John ate things eatable

are merely evasions when given as answers to (10). By (59), the cases

(63) John did not eat anything
(64) (John ate) nothing

are rejections of the question expressed by (10). Similarly

(65) Mary did go or Mary didn't go

is an evasion of (24) while

(66) Mary did not go home and Mary did not go to school

is a rejection of (47).

However, simple nexus-interrogatives like (24) always produce legitimate questions if the noun-phrases in them that occur in a referential position succeed in denoting something in the context where they are used. That is, they cannot be rejected on the basis of a true statement. We can account for this too. If the appropriate noun-phrases do not succeed in denoting, then there cannot be a true, or for that matter even a false, rejection, since these noun-phrases in the putative rejection will also fail to denote (in that context). On the other hand, if they succeed in denoting, then the putative rejection must, by (59), be logically false, since it is inconsistent with the presupposition of a simple nexus-interrogative and, as we observed earlier, such presuppositions are logical truths.

Note, finally, that the notion of answer we have defined is that of *direct* answer. We might define an *indirect* answer as any true statement that entails a (direct) answer. Similarly, we might define indirect versions of the other notions defined in this section.[19]

---

[18] Cf. the discussion of the semantic marker (Selector) in KATZ and POSTAL [1965] pp. 81–84 for an explanation of why the three sentences (60)–(62) are paraphrases, i.e. why "eatable" is redundant in (61) and (62).

[19] Thus, an *indirect* (a) possible answer, (b) evasion, (c) rejection, and (d) presupposition might be defined as a sentence that is not contradictory and (a) entails a sentence that is a possible answer, (b) is entailed by an evasion, (c) entails a rejection, and (d) is entailed by the presupposition.

5. Answers to the two basic questions

Let us begin with the first of the two questions posed in Section 3. Cases like (1)–(6) are direct analogues of sentences that have a linguistically determined truth-value. A case such as (1) is the analogue of an analytic sentence, thus of one whose truth is linguistically determined, while a case such as (2) is the analogue of a contradictory sentence, thus of one whose falsehood is linguistically determined. But, clearly, (1), (3), (4), (5) and (6) cannot be taken as analytic themselves since, being questions, they express requests for information, not true assertions; and likewise, (2) cannot be taken as contradictory since, being a question, it makes no assertion, and hence no false one. Nevertheless, as is intuitively quite clear, they are very much like linguistically determined truths and falsehoods. Their similarity to and difference from sentences that have a linguistically determined truth-value can be put as follows. Just as analytic and contradictory sentences express assertions whose truth and falsity is guaranteed by their meaning, so such interrogatives express questions whose affirmative answer, negative answer, or answer is given by their meaning. Since such questions are parallel to statements with a linguistically determined truth-value, let us call them *linguistically answered questions.*

We have to show here how the property of being a linguistically answered question can be defined in semantic theory. This amounts to explaining how the meanings of the morphemes in an interrogative sentence can determine the answer to the question it expresses, analogously to the manner in which the meanings of the morphemes in a declarative sentence can determine the truth of the statement it expresses. [20]

Since a question is either a nexus-question or an x-question, we have only to define the notions *linguistically answered nexus-question* and *linguistically answered x-question*. Let us consider the former case first. A nexus-question, as the comparison of (1) and (2) shows, can be *linguistically answered in the affirmative* or *linguistically answered in the negative*. Accordingly,

(67) A nexus-question *q* is linguistically answered just in case *q* is linguistically answered in the affirmative or linguistically answered in the negative.

---

[20] It might be asked why a question like "Who saw the man who was seen by John?" is not linguistically answered whereas (3) is. My answer is that, like "Who's buried in Grant's tomb?", "Who saw the man who was seen by John?" is ambiguous. Just as Groucho Marx's question can be taken either to mean *who is buried in the tomb known as the place*

There are two types of nexus-questions, ones like (24), which we may call *simple nexus-questions*, and ones like (46), which we may call *complex nexus-questions*. The former have underlying phrase markers of the form:

(68)

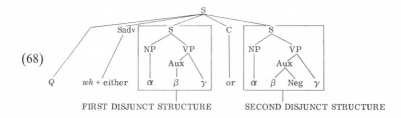

while the latter have underlying phrase markers of the form:

(69)

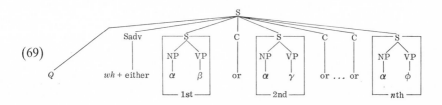

To simplify matters, I will introduce the terms "first disjunct-structure", "second disjunct-structure", and in the case of complex nexus-questions, "third disjunct-structure", "fourth disjunct-structure", and so on. A disjunct-structure is a proper part of an underlying phrase marker for a nexus-interrogative, as shown in (68) and (69), whose top-most node is labeled 'S' and is directly dominated by the top-most node in the whole underlying phrase marker and whose terminal string is bounded by occurrences of the morpheme "or" or in the case of the first and *n*th, respectively, by "*wh* + either" and "or" and by "or" and the sentence boundary "#". The left-most such proper-part is referred to as the "first disjunct-structure", the next, as the "second disjunct-structure", and so forth. We can define the operative notions in the definition (67) as follows:

(70) A nexus-question *q* is linguistically answered in the affirmative just in case (a) *q* is a simple nexus-question and the reading of the subject of the first disjunct-structure contains every semantic marker in the

of Grant's interment or to mean *who is buried in the tomb where Grant himself is interred*, so the latter question can mean *who else (besides John) saw the man who was seen by John* or simply *who saw him*.

reading of the predicate of that disjunct-structure (in the semantically interpreted underlying phrase marker for q) or (b) q is a complex nexus-question and there is one disjunct-structure the reading of whose subject contains every semantic marker in the reading of its predicate (in the semantically interpreted underlying phrase marker for q). [21]

(71) A nexus-question q is linguistically answered in the negative just in case (a) q is a simple nexus-question and the reading of the subject of the first disjunct-structure contains a semantic marker M_i from the same antonymous n-tuple of semantic markers as a semantic marker M_j in the reading of the predicate of that disjunct-structure and $M_i \neq M_j$ or the predicate contains two such semantic markers, or (b) q is a complex nexus-question and each of its disjunct-structures meet the condition in (a). [22]

For simple nexus-questions, (70) and (71) say that such a question is, respectively, linguistically answered in the affirmative and linguistically answered in the negative if and only if the sentence represented by its first disjunct-structure is, in the former case, analytic, and in the latter, contradictory. Thus, (1) is marked linguistically answered affirmatively and (2) is marked linguistically answered negatively. By (67), both are marked linguistically answered. For complex nexus-questions, like

(72) Is a spinster female or unmarried?
(73) Is a spinster female or male?
(74) Is a spinster male or married?
(75) Is a spinster male or rich?

(70) and (71) say that such a question is, respectively, linguistically answered in the affirmative and linguistically answered in the negative if and only if one disjunct-structure represents a sentence that is analytic and every disjunct-structure represents a sentence that is contradictory. Thus, (72) and (73) are marked linguistically answered in the affirmative and (74) but not (75) is marked linguistically answered negatively. (72), (73) and (74) but not (75) are marked as linguistically answered questions by (67).

---

[21] This definition is to some extent a simplification, cf. KATZ (1964] and [1966].

[22] Same comment as in previous footnote. Roughly, antonymous n-tuples of semantic markers reconstruct the relation of logical incompatibility between the members of a set of related concepts by formal distinctions in the semantic markers representing the concepts.

Now we turn to linguistically answered *x*-questions. We can simplify our discussion here by introducing the terms *matrix-structure* and *constituent-structure*. The matrix-structure of an underlying phrase marker is the whole phrase marker minus the subtrees in it that are dominated by an occurrence of 'S' which is dominated by 'NP'. Such subtrees are constituent-structures. Thus:

(76) An *x*-question is linguistically answered just in case its semantically interpreted underlying phrase marker contains a matrix-structure which has the form of an underlying phrase marker for a question *q'* and a constituent-structure which has the form of an underlying phrase marker for a possible answer to the question *q'*.

Since the underlying phrase markers for (3) and (4) are

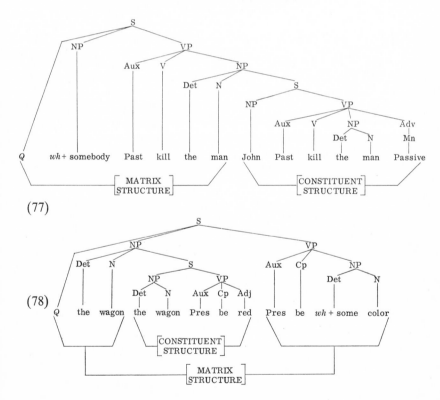

(77)

(78)

(3) and (4) are marked as linguistically answered questions.

But beyond simply marking questions as linguistically answered or not, these definitions also explain why questions so marked have the property of being linguistically answered. For nexus-questions the explanation is as follows. As we have observed, such questions query the truth of a statement, e.g. (24) asks about the truth of the statement that Mary went. The first disjunct-structure of such nexus-questions represents the statement whose truth is asked about in the asking of the question (and the second helps state the query by posing its denial as an alternative). Thus, if a nexus-question is marked linguistically answered in the affirmative, the first disjunct-structure in its underlying phrase marker will represent an analytic statement. So, by virtue of the fact that the statement whose truth is queried is a linguistic truth, the query is answered. If a nexus-question is marked linguistically answered in the negative, the first disjunct-structure in its underlying phrase marker will represent a contradictory statement. So, by virtue of the fact that the statement whose truth is queried is a linguistic falsehood, the query is again answered. In either case, then, the query is answered.

In the case of x-questions, the explanation is this. If an x-question is linguistically answered, then the constituent-structure in its underlying phrase marker represents a possible answer to the question represented in the matrix-structure of that underlying phrase marker (cf. (48) (b)). This possible answer is also part of the presupposition of the whole question (cf. (38)). If the use of such an interrogative sentence expresses a request for information, its presupposition must be true, since the truth of the presupposition of an interrogative is a necessary condition for it to express a question. Consequently, this possible answer – being part of the pre-supposition – must itself be true. But since a true possible answer is a (genuine) answer (cf. (54)), this possible answer is an answer to the question of which it is a part. Therefore, the whole question gives its own answer. Its request for information is made and met in one and the same breath.

Since there is a parallel to analytic statements in the case of questions, we should naturally try to push the analogy further. We *can* carry the analogy further and, by so doing, uncover another interesting logical property of questions: the property of being *linguistically unanswerable*, which can be thought of as the parallel of contradictory statements.

In the case of declarative sentences, semantic theory distinguishes two types of non-anomalous sentences, i.e. two sorts of senses that such sentences can have. The contrast is exemplified by

(79) The rich queen is unhappy
(80) The male queen is unhappy

Briefly [23], the idea is this. (79) can be used to express a statement because there can be an individual for the expression "rich queen" to designate. The statement is true if the individual identified by this expression is unhappy and false if she is happy. In contrast, (80) can never be used to make a statement, since there cannot be anyone to whom the contradictory expression "male queen" refers. Moreover, if we allowed (80) to count as capable of expressing a statement in the manner of (79), then so would

(81) The male queen is female.

But this would produce a contradiction, since (81) would be both analytic and contradictory and hence be both true and false. Accordingly, it is necessary to say that sentences like (79) and (80) belong to different categories and that the category to which (80) and (81) belong is disjoint with respect to the category that includes the subcategories of analytic, contradictory, and synthetic sentences. We can accomplish this required categorization by defining sentences whose subject has a reading containing two distinct semantic markers from the same antonymous n-tuple as *indeterminable sentences*, by defining other sentences as *determinable sentences*, and by making the categories of analytic, contradictory, synthetic, etc. subcategories of the category of determinable sentences. [24]

Interrogatives like

(82) Is the male queen rich?
(83) Who did the living corpse fall on?

express linguistically unanswerable questions. They can no more express answerable questions than their declarative counterparts can express true or false statements. The presupposition of (82) is that the male queen is either rich or not rich and the presupposition of (83) is that something that is both living and a corpse fell on someone. Both these presuppositions are indeterminable sentences, and hence neither can be true. Since the truth of the presupposition of an interrogative is a necessary condition for it to express a request for information, no token of an interrogative type such as (82) or (83) can express such a request, for there is nothing for its answer to be about.

Another kind of linguistically unanswerable question is illustrated by the interrogative

---

[23] For more detail, cf. KATZ [1966] pp. 211–220.
[24] Cf. KATZ [1966] pp. 211–220.

(84) Who will kill the corpse?

In this case, although there can be something for the question and its answer to be about, nonetheless, the condition under which an interrogative expresses a question having an answer cannot, in principle, be met. For the condition is that its presupposition, that someone will kill the corpse, be true, and this condition cannot be met because the presupposition is contradictory.

To cover both types of cases, we give the definition:

(85) A question q is linguistically unanswerable just in case the presupposition of q is either indeterminable or contradictory. [25]

Since linguistically answered questions are the parallel of analytic statements and linguistically unanswerable questions are the parallel of contradictory statements, there should be a further category of questions, namely, *linguistically answerable questions*, which is the parallel of synthetic statements. Accordingly,

(86) A question q is linguistically answerable (but not linguistically answered) just in case q is not semantically anomalous and satisfies neither (67) nor (85).

This completes our answer to the first of the two basic questions underlying the logic of questions. In short, parallel to statements that are validly assertable without premisses are linguistically answered questions, questions that are answered without an independent answer being required.

We now turn to the second of these two questions, the problem of what property is preserved in valid question arguments. Or to put the problem another way: what sense does it make to say that the premisses in cases like (7) and (8) entail their conclusion?

In the case of arguments involving statements, a conclusion that can be validly asserted on certain premisses is so assertable because its relation to its premisses is one that always preserves truth. Since the parallel of linguistically determined truth, which is what makes a statement assertable without premisses or on any premisses, is linguistically determined answerhood, by analogy, in the case of arguments involving questions, the property preserved ought to be *sameness of answer* or simply *answerhood*. We shall now try to show that this analogy does indeed provide the solution to the second problem.

---

[25] In the case of disjunctions or conjunctions, we use the rule that if each disjunct or conjunct is contradictory or indeterminable, then the whole is.

The notion of entailment being developed in semantic theory is an explication of immediate – or one-step – inferences, whose validity depends on semantic relations among the non-logical terms in the premiss and conclusion. Such inferences are not adequately dealt with in the traditional Aristotelian theory of immediate and syllogistic inference; and modern quantification theory, whatever its advantages over the traditional Aristotelian theory, is no improvement over it on this score. Both fail to take into account semantic relations between the non-logical expressions, the nouns, verbs, adjectives, adverbs, and phrases compounded of them, and accordingly, both theories leave indefinitely many clear cases of valid inferences unaccounted for.

Consider the inference from (87) to (88):

(87) Females are dangerous motorists
(88) Spinsters are dangerous motorists

Proceeding in the usual way, each of the non-logical terms, "females", "spinsters", and "dangerous motorists", is represented as the class of all and only those entities to which the unanalyzed term applies, and the relation expressed by the copula is treated as a membership or class-inclusion relation between the extensions of the subject and predicate terms. Thus, we represent (87) by drawing a circle to stand for the class of females inside a circle that stands for the class of dangerous motorists, since the copula of (87) indicates that the former is included in the latter. Next, we draw another circle for the class of spinsters, locating it inside the circle standing for the class of dangerous motorists, since this is dictated by the copula of (88). But since nothing constrains us to represent the extension of "spinsters" as included within the extension of "females", the extensional account of this inference is:

(89)
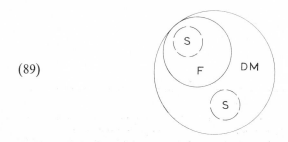

Thus, the inference from (87) to (88) cannot be shown to be valid.

But since what actually constrains us to say that spinsters are females is just what makes "Spinsters are females" analytic, namely, the semantic relation between "spinsters" and "females", it is necessary to formulate the definition of entailment in a way that takes such semantic relations into account. Accordingly, this definition must be framed in terms of intension or meaning.

Roughly, this definition may be given as follows:

> (90) A sentence s_1 entails another sentence s_2 just in case (a) both are universal and the reading of s_2's subject contains every semantic marker in the reading of the subject of s_1 and the reading of s_1's predicate contains every semantic marker in the reading of the predicate of s_2 or (b) both are particular and the reading of s_1's subject contains every semantic marker in the reading of the subject of s_2 and the reading of s_1's predicate contains every semantic marker in the reading of the predicate of s_2.[26]

The inference from

> (91) Some bachelors are rich

to

> (92) Some males are rich

and the inference from

> (93) Some bachelors are kings

to

> (94) Some males are monarchs

and from

> (95) John is a bachelor

to

> (96) John is a male

are marked as entailments by (90) (b). The inference from (87) to (88) and

---

[26] A few comments need to be made here. First, this definition is a simplification, cf. the references cited in footnote 21. Second, it is an extension of previous treatments, insofar as it treats both universals and particular sentences, cf. footnote 9 in KATZ [1967b]. Third, it does not treat cases where one sentence is universal and the other is particular because of the question of existential import of universal propositions. Finally, here by subject and predicate in the case of nexus-questions we mean subject and predicate of the first disjunct structure.

the inferences from

(97) Females are geniuses

to

(98) Spinsters are intelligent

and from

(99) Principals are spinsters

to

(100) Principals are females

are marked as entailments by (90) (a).

Consider now the following question-arguments (involving nexus-questions) that are, case by case, counterparts of the statement-arguments presented immediately above.

(101) Are some bachelors rich?

Are some males rich?

(102) Are some bachelors kings?

Are some males monarchs?

(103) Is John a bachelor?

Is John a male?

(104) Are females dangerous motorists?

Are spinsters dangerous motorists?

(105) Are females geniuses?

Are spinsters intelligent?

(106) Are principals spinsters?

Are principals females?

Clearly, by (90) each of the arguments (91)–(106) are entailments, just as their statement-argument counterparts are, for the definition (90) is given for sentences, not declaratives, and in each case, the entailment in the question-argument and its counterpart statement-argument is based on the same semantic relation.

What is preserved in a valid question-argument involving nexus-questions is *affirmative answerhood*. That is to say, if A is an affirmative answer to the premiss question Q_1 and Q_1 entails Q_2, then A is necessarily an affirmative answer to Q_2. For example, an affirmative answer to the premiss of (101), say

(107) (Yes) Some bachelors are rich

is necessarily also (implies) an affirmative answer to the conclusion of (101). Moreover, corresponding to the fact that in a valid deduction from one statement to another the falsity of the conclusion implies the falsity of at least one of the premisses, if N is a negative answer to Q_2, then N is necessarily also (implies) a negative answer to Q_1. For example, a negative answer to the conclusion of (101)

(108) (No) No males are rich

is a negative answer to the premiss of (101). Notice, however, that a negative answer to the premiss in a valid nexus-question argument is not an answer to the conclusion. For example, a negative answer to the premiss of (103) is not an answer to its conclusion. This can be shown quite easily. Both

(109) Is John unmarried?

and the conclusion of (103) are entailed by the premiss of (103). Yet, given that the answer to the premiss of (103) is negative, these two questions can have opposite answers, i.e. the answer to one can be affirmative and the answer to the other negative. Furthermore, an affirmative answer to the conclusion of a valid nexus-question argument is not an answer to the premiss, since, for example, the answer to the conclusion in (103) can be affirmative while the answer to the premiss in (103) is negative.

   In valid arguments involving x-questions like (8), answerhood is preserved in the direct sense that anything that is an answer to the premiss question is itself an answer to the conclusion question. For example, if

(110) The little old lady stole a cat

is the answer to (8)'s premiss question, it is the answer to (8)'s conclusion question as well. But, of course, an answer to a conclusion question in such arguments is not necessarily an answer to the premiss question.

   Finally, in valid arguments from questions to statements such as (9), we can say that if the premiss question has an answer then the conclusion is true. But, of course, the truth of the conclusion in such cases does not imply that the premiss question has an answer. Thus, Cock Robin might have died of natural causes, so assuming that it is true that Cock Robin is dead, it does not follow that someone killed Cock Robin, which, as the presupposition of the premiss of (9), must be true if this question is to have an answer.

   In the discussion in this section we have formulated the property that the conclusion of a valid question-argument inherits from its premiss:

affirmative answerhood in the case of nexus-questions, and answerhood in the case of x-questions. Moreover, we have offered an explanation of the formal conditions under which such arguments are valid – under which they preserve answerhood – namely, that given in (90) and in the semantic theory on which (90) depends.

6. A proposal for a question calculus

Other logical relations can also be defined for questions, parallel to other logical relations of statements. As examples, we give the relations of *contrary* and *contradictory* for nexus-questions.

If a nexus-question is the contrary of another, then an affirmative answer to one implies a negative answer to the other. The questions

(111) Is your benefactor a spinster?

and

(112) Is your benefactor married?

are contraries: saying yes to one implies no to the other. But it is not the case that saying no to one of two contrary questions implies saying yes to the other. A negative answer to (111) can be given when the benefactor in question is male and married.

If a nexus-question is the contradictory of another, then an affirmative answer to one implies a negative answer to the other and a negative answer to one implies an affirmative answer to the other. (111) and

(113) Is your benefactor a bachelor?

constitute an example of contradictory nexus-questions.

We can define these notions as follows:

(114) A nexus-question q_1 is the contrary of a nexus-question q_2 just in case their subject readings are identical and their predicate readings are such that each contains a distinct semantic marker from the same antonymous n-tuple of semantic markers.[27]

(115) A nexus-question q_1 is the contradictory of a nexus-question q_2 just in case they are contraries and for any semantic marker M_i in the reading of q_1's predicate that is not also in the reading of q_2's

---

[27] Cf. last comment in footnote 26.

predicate, there is a distinct semantic marker from the antonymous n-tuple to which M_i belongs in the reading for q_2's predicate and for any semantic marker M_j in the reading of q_2's predicate that is not in the reading for q_1's predicate, there is a distinct semantic marker from the antonymous n-tuple to which M_j belongs in the reading of q_1's predicate. That is, the readings of two subjects are the same and the readings of the two predicates are the same except for antonymous semantic markers. [28]

Given (115), we can develop a system of logic for nexus-questions that is parallel to the propositional calculus. (115) provides an interpretation for the connective '$\sim$'. That is, it tells us what the semantic relation between two questions must be in order for us to express them in the form 'q' and '$\sim q$'. Thus, it enables us to interpret the relation between 'q' and '$\sim q$' by the condition that a negative answer or positive answer to one implies the opposite answer to the other. Moreover, we can interpret '$q_1 \& q_2$' as the question whose answer is an answer to 'q_1' and an answer to 'q_2', and we can interpret '$q_1 \vee q_2$' as the question whose answer is either an answer to 'q_1' or an answer to 'q_2'. These interpretations can be justified on the basis of the meanings of "and" and "or" and can be built into their dictionary entries. With this much, it is an easy matter to take any standard system of propositional calculus and convert it into a question calculus, since '$q_1 \supset q_2$' could be defined as the disjunction of the contradictory of 'q_1' and 'q_2'. But this would be a trivial sort of question calculus, and one that failed to do justice to question-arguments. Accordingly, we want to go further and interpret implication in terms of (90) and equivalence in terms of synonymy. This leads to a question calculus with many interesting features, one well worth examining in more detail. [29]

7. Applications: practical and theoretical

The practical application of the logic of statements needs no demonstration. We are continually arguing with others on behalf of our statements,

---

[28] Cf. last comment in footnote 26.

[29] Notice that even in this system, where implication is rendered not as material conditional but as entailment in the semantic sense of (90), a contradiction still implies anything. For although a contradiction such as "John is a married bachelor" or "John is a bachelor and John is not a bachelor" does not entail "Russell is the Pope", the latter can be inferred from the former on the basis of the meaning of "or" by the usual steps of simplification and disjunctive syllogism.

trying to refute theirs, and so on. But the question arises whether there is a practical application of the logic of questions, i.e. cases of arguing from one question to another that might be taken as what is explicated by a logic of questions, parallel to the manner in which everyday statement-arguments are taken to be explicated by a logic of statements. Are there cases for which a logic of questions can serve as a standard of acceptable inference?

I do not wish to claim extensive applications for the logic of questions, not here anyway. But it is necessary for me to show that there are *some* applications. The following as a typical example. Consider a cross-examination in the course of a trial. Suppose the prosecuting attorney were to ask the witness

(116) Did the victim murmur anything before dying?

and the defense attorney were to object that the witness need not answer this question on the grounds that it is entailed by a previous question, namely

(117) Did the victim utter any sound before dying?

which, as the transcript shows, the witness answered negatively. We could regard the logic of questions as providing an explication of the defense attorney's inference that the prosecuting attorney's question had already been answered, since (116) is marked as entailing the previously (negatively) answered question (117), so that, by the interpretation of deductive connections between questions, the answer to (116) is already determined, without the witness needing to reply.

The theoretical application I wish to discuss concerns the nature of logic in general. The conception of logic that makes the notion of a logic of questions seem paradoxical is the view that the proper domain of logic is restricted to entities that bear a truth-value. "Logic", as Quine succinctly puts it, "studies the bearing of logical structure [of statements] upon truth and falsity". [30] The business of logic, on this view, is to construct a theory of logical structure that sorts out those statements that are true just by virtue of their logical form from those that are not. [31] But, although this conception of the nature of logic is more precise than the definition of logic as the science of necessary inference, it is also less accurate.

We have shown that logic concerns the logical properties and deductive

[30] QUINE [1941] p. 1.
[31] QUINE [1959] p. xi, cf. first paragraph.

relations of questions as well as statements. We have shown, further, that there is a suitable non-truth-functional interpretation of validity for question-arguments that parallels the truth-functional interpretation of validity for statement-arguments. Accordingly, it can be no more correct to say that logic studies the bearing of logical structure on truth than it would be to say that logic studies the bearing of logical structure on answerhood. Logic studies both. Truth is what is preserved in valid statement-arguments and answer-hood is what is preserved in valid question-arguments. Neither by itself is what is common to all and only cases of necessary inference.

If it were argued that the logic of statements is basic, and the logic of questions derivative from it, so that, once we have a logic of statements, we can define logical relations between questions indirectly in terms of a one-one mapping given by the grammar of declaratives onto interrogatives, it could easily be replied that the logic of questions can make the same claim to priority. Once we have a logic of questions, we can define logical relations between statements indirectly in terms of the same one-one grammatically determined mapping of interrogatives onto declaratives. That is, if someone were to claim that there is a one-one mapping M that pairs arguments such as that from (95) to (96) with arguments such as (103) and that, therefore, we can characterize a valid question-argument as one whose image under M is a valid statement-argument, that is, one that perserves truth, then it can be replied to this claim that we can also proceed the other way around. We can characterize a valid statement-argument as one whose image under M is a valid question-argument, that is, one that perserves answerhood. Thus, the complete symmetry that obtains here leads to the conclusion that neither truth nor answerhood by itself should occupy the privileged position of being the basis for a definition of logic.

Once again. The entailment relation explicated in (90), as well as the property of redundant predication explicated in the definitions of an analytic statement and a linguistically answered question, are sufficiently general to be features of both the meaning of declaratives and the meaning of interrogatives, and so they are independent of the different interpretations of validity for statements and questions.

Therefore, the doctrine that this entire discussion implies is that what is common in all and only cases of necessary inference, the common element in logic in any of its forms, are the semantic structures defined in the definitions of an optimal semantic theory of natural language. Accordingly, what properly defines logic are the definitions of analyticity, contradiction, entailment, metalinguistic truth, etc. together with definitions expressing the rules of propositional logic and quantification, insofar as these are broad enough to represent all the logical aspects of the meanings of connectives like "or", "and", etc. and quantifiers like "all", "some", etc. as well as ones like "many", "exactly one", etc. The semantic structures characterized in these definitions, determine necessary truth and inherited truth, on the one hand, and necessary answerhood and inherited answerhood, on the other. Logic, on this hypothesis, is the study that attempts to give a systematic definition of the semantic structures that abstractly represent valid inferences, with respect to all interpretations that say what is necessary or necessarily inherited under them.

References

CHOMSKY, N., Aspects of the theory of syntax (Cambridge, M.I.T. Press, 1966).

GOODMAN, N., Fact, fiction, and forecast (New York, The Bobbs-Merrill Company, Inc., 1965).

JESPERSEN, O., Essentials of English grammar (New York, Henry Holt and Co., Inc., 1933).

KATZ, J.J., The relevance of linguistics to philosophy, J. Phil. **62** (1965) 590–602.

KATZ, J.J., The philosophy of language (New York, Harper and Row, Inc., 1966).

KATZ, J.J., Recent issues in semantic theory, Found. of Language **3** (1967a) 124–194.

KATZ, J.J., Some remarks on Quine and analyticity, J. Phil. **64** (1967b) 36–52.

KATZ, J.J., Analyticity and contradiction in natural language, in: The structure of language: Readings in the philosophy of language, eds. J.A. Fodor and J.J. Katz (Englewood Cliffs, N.J., Prentice-Hall, Inc., 1964) 519–543.

KATZ, J.J., The underlying reality of language and its philosophical import, in: The Harper guide to philosophy, ed. A. Danto (New York, Harper and Row, Inc., in press).

KATZ, J.J. and E. MARTIN Jr., The synonymy of actives and passives, Phil. Rev. Vol. LXXVI, No. 4, October 1967, 476–491.

KATZ, J.J. and P. POSTAL, An integrated theory of linguistic descriptions (Cambridge, M.I.T. Press, 1965).

QUINE, W.V., Elementary logic (Boston, Ginn and Company, 1941).

QUINE, W.V., Methods of logic (New York, Henry Holt and Co., Inc., 1959).

EXISTENCE, LOCATION, POSSESSION AND TRANSITIVITY

J. LYONS

University of Edinburgh, Edinburgh, U.K.

In this paper, we shall be concerned mainly with four classes of sentences: existential, locative, possessive and perfective-transitive. They may be illustrated by means of the following examples from English:

(1) EXISTENTIAL: (a) Lions exist
                       (b) There are lions (in Africa)
(2) LOCATIVE: (a) The book is on the table
                       (b) There is a book on the table
(3) POSSESSIVE: (a) The book is John's
                       (b) John has a book
(4) PERFECTIVE-TRANSITIVE: John has read the book.
Throughout the paper I would ask you to keep in mind the following well-known facts.

(i) In some languages (e.g. Turkish) the possessive is structurally similar to the existential; in others (e.g. Chinese, Hindi, Russian, Gaelic, Swahili) the possessive is structurally similar to the locative; in others (e.g. English, Greek, Latin) the existential is structurally similar to the locative.

(ii) The expression of 'possession' (to use the traditional, but quite unsatisfactory, term) by means of a quasi-transitive verb (cf. English *have*) with the 'possessor' as its subject and the 'possessed thing' as its object is relatively uncommon throughout the languages of the world. Far more common is a construction in which 'being possessed', rather than 'possessing' is what is predicated.

(iii) There is a structural similarity in many languages (including English) between the possessive and the perfective-transitive construction (cf. the 'verb' *have* in sentences (3b) and (4) given above).

As I have said, these facts are well-known. Various attempts have been made to account for them by linguists, both in the past and in a number of recent and forthcoming publications. Of the works I have seen, the most interesting in this connexion are those by ALLEN [1964], ANDERSON [1968], BACH [1965], [1967], BENDIX [1966], BENVENISTE [1960], FILLMORE [1966], [forthcoming], GRAHAM [1967], HALLIDAY [1967], HUANG [1966], KAHN [1966], LANGENDOEN [1966a, b], SMITH [1964] and STAAL [1967]. In a forthcoming article and book, I have myself put forward the hypothesis that in many, and perhaps in all, languages existential and possessive constructions derive (both synchronically and diachronically) from locatives: cf. LYONS [1967], [1968] chapter 8. This hypothesis is not wholly original. Many of the points made in the argument have, to my knowledge, been made before; and the others may have been. Following KURYŁOWICZ [1931], I have also proposed that the English possessive with *have* (e.g. *John has a book*) is diachronically related to the perfective-transitive with *have* (e.g. *John has read a book*) by means of a principle (which is still operative in English), the effect of which was to bring the 'person interested in the state of affairs' into the subject-position: cf. LYONS [1968] § 8.4.6. (For a rather different, but related, suggestion: cf. CLOSS [1965]; VISSER [1963] pp. 93–138.)

I do not wish simply to repeat here what I have said elsewhere. I will, therefore, give only the briefest account of what the hypothesis is, without recapitulating the evidence, from various languages, upon which it is based. I will then discuss some of the implications of the hypothesis from a more general point of view.

I am taking for granted the distinction between deep structure and surface structure that is currently drawn in transformational syntax: cf. CHOMSKY [1965], [1966]. I also assume that, 'although the Surface Structures of different languages are enormously varied, there is no reason to believe that their Deep Structures are not highly similar' (cf. POSTAL [1966] p. 97). At the same time, I should point out that the hypothesis that I am putting forward does not rest upon the prior acceptance of any particular transformational model of syntax. Indeed, it could also be stated within the framework of certain alternative approaches to syntactic analysis which are normally described as non-transformational: e.g., those associated with the names of HALLIDAY [1967] or LAMB [1967]. But the closest connexion is probably with FILLMORE's [forthcoming] version of transformational grammar.

Like BACH [1967], FILLMORE [forthcoming] and LAKOFF [1965], though independently of them (cf. LYONS [1966]), and unlike CHOMSKY [1965] and HALLIDAY [1967] pp. 66–71, I am of the opinion that there is no categorial distinction in deep structure between what are traditionally called 'verbs' and 'adjectives' and that the copula is a purely grammatical element which 'carries' distinctions of tense, mood and aspect in the surface-structure of sentences which do not contain a 'full verb'. For example, I assume that the underlying constituent-structure of the following two sentences, (5) and (6), is identical

(5) The girl dances

(6) The girl is beautiful.

Both *dance* and *beautiful* belong to the same major syntactic category in English. This category is appropriately called 'verbs', in the earliest and wider sense of this term – the sense in which Plato employed the Greek equivalent (cf. LYONS [1966]). The difference between *dance* and *beautiful*, from a syntactic point of view, is this: *dance* is what I will call a 'full verb', *beautiful* is not. In particular (for there are many ways in which 'full verbs' differ from the various subclasses of 'non-full verbs' in English) *beautiful* is characterised by the following two important properties, or 'features': (a) it is stative; and (b) it does not take the temporal and aspectual inflexions of English. The first of these is connected with the fact that a sentence like *The girl is being beautiful* is unusual, if not ungrammatical (it can be interpreted by 'recategorizing' *beautiful* as nonstative, or dynamic: cf. LYONS [1968] § 8.4.7; the second is connected with the fact that one says *The girl was beautiful*, rather than **The girl beautifulled*. (These two properties, although they are normally associated with 'adjectives', are independent. The distinction of 'verbs' and 'adjectives' is quite inadequate for the description of the deep structure of English: cf. LYONS [1968] chapters 7 and 8.)

The 'dummy verb' *be* is generated by the grammar of English to 'carry' the past-tense and perfective-aspect inflexions whenever a word like *beautiful* occurs as the head of the predicate: cf. JAKOBS and ROSENBAUM [1967] p. 43. Presumably, it is the same rule which inserts *be* before the 'present participle' to form the progressive aspect (e.g. *The girl is dancing*) and before the 'past participle' to form the perfective passive (e.g. *The window is broken*). Similarly with the locative and possessive sentences, (2a) and (3a), given above – *The book is on the table* and *The book is John's*. The underlying predicate of the former is the locative phrase *on the table*, and of the latter what for the moment we may call the 'possessive phrase' *John's*. Once again, the 'dummy verb' *be* is generated by the grammatical rules of English to serve as the 'locus' for tense, mood and aspect in surface structure. There are other languages in which a quite different copula is used for possessive and locative sentences from that which is used (if there is one) in what we may refer to as 'attributive' sentences (e.g. *The girl is beautiful*).

Each of the five types of sentences to which we have referred so far in connexion with the distribution of the 'verb *to be*' in English is related to a corresponding noun-phrase in which the predicate is transformed to ad-nominal position: cf. *the beautiful girl, the dancing girl, the broken window, the book on the table, John's book*. Standard transformational treatments of English generate such phrases – rather counter-intuitively, to my mind – via relative-clauses: cf. LEES [1960], SMITH [1961], BACH [1965], JAKOBS and ROSENBAUM [1967]. We need not go into this question here.

So far so good. Let us now turn to (2b) and (3b) – *There is a book on the table* and *John has a book*. At first sight, these sentences would seem to be quite different structurally. It is obvious that the only deep-structure differ-ence between (2a) *The book is on the table* and (2b) *There is a book on the table* is that in (2a) the subject is definite, whereas in (2b) it is indefinite. In other words, (2b) is an alternative (and more common) version of *A book is on the table* or *On the table is a book*. (For this 'expletive' function of *there*, cf. FILLMORE [forthcoming] § 3.5. It may be compared with the 'expletive' *it* studied by LANGENDOEN [1966a, b].) But (3a) *The book is John's* differs from (3b) *John has a book* in the same way that (2a) differs from (2b). *John has a book* is the obligatory version of the ungrammatical *A book is John's*. It will be observed that, in both locative and possessive sentences, the in-definite subject is 'demoted', as it were, from a position of prominence in surface-structure. The 'expletive' *there* and the verb *have* serve the same function in the syntax of modern English: they bring the locative, in the one case, and the 'possessor', in the other, into the 'topic'-position in surface structure (for the 'topic'-'comment' distinction: cf. HOCKETT [1958] p. 201, CHOMSKY [1965] p. 221, HALLIDAY [1967], GRUBER [1967]). It is worth pointing out that these two syntactic 'devices' are employed in many other types of sentences: *There's a window broken, There's a man coming to inspect the premises, We have guests coming to lunch, I had my car stolen*, etc. I shall not go further into this question, except to point out one fact. Everyone is aware that sentences like *The window is broken* are ambiguous (or, if you wish, 'neutral') as between perfective and habitual aspect. It is also well known that the explicit occurrence of an agentive *by*-phrase makes them habitual (as also does the occurrence of certain adverbials, e.g. *regularly* – but that is irrelevant to the present point). It is not always realized that the corresponding agentive form of the perfective *The window is broken* is in fact the active *X has broken the window*. The English perfect with *have*, like the possessive with *have*, and like such sentences as *John has a book on the table* (cf. *There is a book on the table*), originated under the operation of the principle to which we have already referred – a principle which brings the 'person interested in the state of affairs' into the subject-position in surface structure. I believe that transitive-perfective sentences occupy a double position, as it were, in the grammar of modern English: one may generate them as one generates the intransitive perfectives (and this is the method favoured by most generative grammarians since the publication of CHOMSKY [1957]); or one may generate them from the 'simple' passive perfectives like *The window* + (*be*) *broken*. But I will not argue this point here: cf. LYONS [1968] § 8.4.6. I must now move on to the more hypothetical part of my thesis (for I am almost inclined to say that so far I have been asserting matters of fact).

This is, you will recall, that both existential and possessive sentences, are 'derived' from locatives (I put the word 'derived' in quotation marks to remind us that we must come back to ask what is meant by 'derived' in this context). There is no need to stress the diachronic connexion between existential and locative sentences: the use of a locative (and deictic particle) in English and in various other European languages – cf. *there* in *There are lions* (*in Africa*) – is sufficient evidence of this. In fact, the 'existential' *be*-copula does not normally occur in English (or in other languages with which I am acquainted) without a locative complement. It might seem reasonable to say that all existential sentences are at least implicitly locative (the term 'locative' being understood to include both temporal and spatial reference). Kahn has argued this point for Greek, to my mind quite convincingly; and he has pointed out that for the Greeks (and the 'absolute' use of the 'existential' εἶναι was fairly common in Greek – hence the importance of the problem of 'being' and 'becoming' in Western philosophy: cf. LYONS [1963] p. 115) it was taken as axiomatic that 'whatever is, is somewhere; whatever is nowhere is nothing'; cf. KAHN [1966] p. 258. This would suggest, as I said in my earlier paper [1967], that the Platonic, Aristotelian and Scholastic account of 'being' depended upon a tacit or acknowledged application of the 'analogical' mode of reasoning by way of what the Scholastics called the 'via negativa' – by abstracting from the spatiotemporal implications of 'normal' existential statements. That is to say *God exists* or *There is a God* is understood 'analogically' with reference to such sentences as *Lions exist* or *There are lions* – the deep structure of the latter sentences being, as it were, *lions* + *somewhere* (cf. *book* + *on the table*). I also suggested that this analysis of 'existential' sentences was 'in accord with the views of a number of twentieth-century empirical philosophers, who would say that existential statements are logically equivalent to pointing, or deixis' (i.e. *lions exist* is reducible to *lions there*). I was thinking of such philosophers as Russell and

Ayer (in my now rather hazy recollections of reading them some years ago). Professor J. F. Staal [personal communication] suggested that I would do better to compare the thesis 'to be is to be somewhere' with Quine's slogan that 'to be is to be the value of a variable'. All I can say on this topic – and I am reluctant to say even this in a gathering of specialists – is that, whereas there seems to me to be good evidence in natural language for the connexion between existential and deictic (or 'ostensive') sentences, I am not aware of any syntactic evidence that would lead the linguist to dispense with a category of 'names' (or nouns) in the syntactic analysis of any natural language, cf. LYONS [1966] p. 232. But I am well aware that is a very amateurish reply. I therefore pass the question on to the philosophers and logicians, and turn instead to the relationship between locative and possessive sentences.

The first point that must be made is that the traditional term 'possessive' is far too narrow. The majority of English sentences of the form $NP_1 – have – NP_2$, or phrases of the form NP_1's NP_2 have nothing whatsoever to do with possession, or ownership. And it is quite wrong to assume that this is the primary, or central, meaning of *have* (or the 'genitive') in all sentences (or phrases) which will support this interpretation: e.g. *John has a book* or (*John's book*): cf. BENDIX [1966] pp. 37ff. The second point is that in many languages, as I mentioned at the beginning of this paper, what we will translate into English as 'possessive' sentences are quite clearly locatives (using a locative case, preposition or postposition): and it is interesting to note that, in default of any contextual information, our decision is usually influenced by the classification of the locative-noun as animate or inanimate (cf. BENDIX [1966] pp. 85, 110). In other words, *book* + (*be*) *table* + '*locative*' would be translated as 'The book is on the table' and *book* + (*be*) *John* + '*locative*' as 'John has the book'. Finally, in many languages the case or preposition of the 'indirect object' ('dative') is identical with that of 'motion towards'. *Give the book to me* is related to *I have the book* as *Bring the book here* (or *Put the book here*) is related to *The book is here*: in the former case we say that *to me* is the 'indirect object', in the latter that *here* is 'directional' (or locative). But *to me* cannot be classified as either 'indirect object' or 'directional', to the exclusion of the other, in *Bring the book to me*. My hypothesis, therefore, is that the distinction between locatives and possessives, in languages like English in which there is a distinction, is a secondary surface-structure distinction based, largely, on the distinction between animate and inanimate nouns. *John has a book* is the surface-structure 'realization' of what might be represented as *A book (be) at-John*. (For further discussion I must refer you to my earlier paper; for a fuller account of the theoretical framework,

I refer you to my forthcoming book: cf. LYONS [1968].) I now want to discuss the general implications of the hypothesis that I have put forward.

I have suggested that both existential and possessive sentences are derived from locatives. I must now explain what 'derivation' means in this context, since the term 'derivation' can be interpreted in at least four ways (apart from the more particular sense in which it opposes 'inflexion').

The first, and most obvious, distinction is between synchronic and diachronic derivation. Not so very long ago, it was quite common for linguists to object to the use of 'process-terminology' in the synchronic analysis of languages: cf. especially HOCKETT [1954]; discussed by TEETER [1964]. One or two linguists still maintain this attitude: cf. LAMB [1964]. But I should imagine that the majority now accept that considerations of simplicity or economy will frequently favour the derivation of one form from another in the synchronic description of a language. Since the advent of generative grammar, synchronic derivation has been given a clear interpretation in terms of the ordering of the rules in the system. We assume, therefore, that the notion of synchronic derivation is legitimate and reasonably well-understood.

Every recent textbook of linguistics lays stress upon the necessity of making the synchronic description of languages independent of diachronic considerations (including LYONS [1968] § 1.4.5). This does not mean, however, that there is no connexion between synchronic and diachronic derivation. It has long been clear that the Saussurian dichotomy between diachronic and synchronic analysis can only be drawn 'macroscopically' (i.e. with respect to *états de langue* that are relatively far-removed in time). Any speech-community at any one time includes speakers of different ages, of different geographical and social backgrounds; and their speech reflects these differences. Despite these differences, they are generally able to communicate successfully with one another. The fact that they can communicate with one another is no doubt explained in part by the relatively high degree of redundancy in natural languages. But it may also be the case that what Hockett has called the 'common core' [1958] pp. 331ff. – the overlap in the grammatical, phonological and semantic systems of different speakers – is more 'central', or 'basic'; and this may also be true, in general, of two diachronically-distinct *états de langue*.

This hypothesis forms part of a theory of language-change recently proposed by Halle, who has suggested, following Chomsky, 'that language acquisition by a child may best be pictured as a process of constructing the simplest (optimal) grammar capable of generating the set of utterances, of which the utterances heard by the child are a representative sample' (HALLE [1962] p. 64). He goes on to conjecture that the changes in the speech of adult speakers are accounted for by the addition or elimination of a few 'low-level' rules, but that the child who 'constructs his own optimal grammar by induction from the utterances to which he has been exposed' (HALLE [1962] p. 65), will not necessarily arrive at the same grammar as that which his parents have 'internalized'. He may simplify it by, *inter alia*, re-ordering the rules. I do not wish to express any opinion about the validity of particular details of Halle's theory of language-change, because I do not consider myself sufficiently competent in the field of phonology, to which it has so far been applied: but cf. CLOSS [1965]. But it does seem to me to have at least a *prima facie* plausibility, and it has inspired some interesting work in the comparison of dialects (cf. KEYSER [1963], SAPORTA [1965], VASILIU [1966]).

My point is simply that we should not be surprised, but rather should expect, that there should be some correlation between synchronic and diachronic derivation. It is for this reason that I adduced both kinds of evidence in support of the hypothesis I put forward in my earlier paper. At the same time, I would emphasize that these are in principle empirical questions. Where we have the historical evidence – and we have at least some of this in the case of the constructions I have been referring to – we can compare the diachronic order of development with the order of the rules in the synchronic description of the language at a particular period.

The third sense in which the term 'derivation' might be interpreted has to do with what has been called the 'ontogeny' of language (cf. BRAINE [1963]) – the acquisition of language by children. A good deal of research is now being devoted to this question: cf., for example, MCNEILL [1966], KLIMA and BELLUGI [1966], and papers in SMITH and MILLER [1966], and LENNEBERG [1964]. As HALLE [1962] has pointed out (with an apt quotation from Meillet), the theory of language-change cannot be treated in isolation from a theory of the acquisition of language by children. It seems reasonable to assume (although this assumption has been challenged) that the order in which young children learn more complex constructions will reflect their decreasing 'centrality' in the language which they eventually come to speak. It would be interesting to know, therefore, whether there is any evidence of this nature for the hypothesis that existential and possessives derive from locatives. Once again, this seems to me to be an empirical question.

The fourth sense of 'derivation' is one that I will merely mention: this has to do with the development of human language from something that was not human language – if, in fact, it did 'develop' from some non-human system of communication. Much as I should like to, I doubt whether I can legitimately call upon those working in the field of animal-communication for evidence to support my hypothesis! I must be content with the notions of synchronic, diachronic and 'ontogenetic' derivation. I have assumed that there will be a considerable degree of convergence in the evidence that might be brought forward from these areas of linguistic (and psycholinguistic) research.

References

ALLEN, W.S., Transitivity and possession, Language 40 (1964) 337–343.

ANDERSON, J.M., Ergative and nominative in English, J. of Linguistics 4 (1968).

BACH, E., On some recurrent types of transformations, in: Monograph series on language and linguistics, Vol. 18, ed. Ch. W. Kreidler (Washington, D.C., Georgetown University Press, 1965) pp. 1–18.

BACH, E., *Have* and *be*, Language 43 (1967).

BACH, E. and R. HARMS eds., Proc. Texas Symp. on Language universals (New York, Holt, Rinehart and Winston, forthcoming).

BENDIX, E.H., Componential analysis of general vocabulary: The semantic structure of a set of verbs in English, Hindi and Japanese (Bloomington, Indiana University and The Hague, Mouton and Co., 1966).

BENVENISTE, E., "Etre" et "Avoir", Bull. Soc. de Linguistique de Paris, 55; Reprinted in: Problèmes de Linguistique Générale (Paris, Gallimard, 1966) pp. 187–207.

BRAINE, M.D.S., The ontogeny of English phrase structure: the first phase, Language 39 (1963) 1–13.

CHOMSKY, N., Syntactic structures (The Hague, Mouton and Co., 1957).

CHOMSKY, N., Aspects of the theory of syntax (Cambridge, Mass., M.I.T. Press, 1965).

CHOMSKY, N., Cartesian linguistics (New York, Harper and Row, 1966).

CLOSS, Elizabeth, Diachronic syntax and generative grammar, Language 41 (1965) 402–415.

FODOR, J.A. and J.J. KATZ eds., The structure of language: Readings in the philosophy of language (Englewood Cliffs, N.J., Prentice-Hall, Inc. 1964).

FILLMORE, C.J., Towards a modern theory of case, in: Project on linguistic analysis, Report No. 13 (Columbus, Ohio, Ohio State University Research Foundation, 1966).

FILLMORE, C.J., The case for case, in: E. Bach and R. Harms eds. (forthcoming).

GRAHAM, A.C. (1967), "Being" in Classical Chinese', in: The verb 'be' and its synonyms, Part 1, ed. J.W.M. Verhaar (D. Reidel, Dordrecht, Holland, 1967); Foundations of Language, Supplementary Series, 1.

GRUBER, J.S., Topicalization in child language, Found. of Language 3 (1967) 37–65.

HALLE, M., Phonology in generative grammar, Word 18 (1962) 54–72; Reprinted in: J.A. Fodor and J.J. Katz eds., pp. 334–352.

HALLIDAY, M.A.K., Notes on theme and transitivity in English, Part 1, J. of Linguistics 3 (1967) 37–81.

HOCKETT, C.F., Two models of grammatical description, Word 10 (1954) 210–233; Reprinted in: M. Joos ed., Readings in linguistics (Washington, D.C., American Council of Learned Societies, 1957, and Chicago and London, Chicago University Press, 1966) pp. 386–399.

HOCKETT, C.F., A course in modern linguistics (New York, MacMillan, 1958).

HUANG, Shuan F., Subject and object in mandarin, in: Project on linguistic analysis, Report No. 13 (Columbus, Ohio, Ohio State University Research Foundation, 1966).

JAKOBS, R.A. and P.S. ROSENBAUM, Grammar 2 (Boston, Mass., Ginn and Co., 1967).

KAHN, C. H., The Greek verb "to be" and the concept of being, Found. of Language 2 (1966) 245–265.

KEYSER, S. J., Review of: Kurath and McDavid, The pronunciation of English in the Atlantic states, Language 39 (1963) 303–316.

KLIMA, E. S., Relatedness between grammatical systems, Language 40 (1964) 1–20.

KLIMA, E. S. and Ursula BELLUGI, Syntactic regularities in the speech of children, in: J. Lyons and R. J. Wales eds. (1966) pp. 183–219.

KURYLOWICZ, J., Les temps composés du Roman, Prace Filologiczne 15 (1931) 448–453; Reprinted in: Esquisses linguistiques (Wroclaw and Kraków, 1963).

LAKOFF, G., On the nature of syntactic irregularity, Report No. NSF-16, Mathematical linguistics and automatic translation (Cambridge, Mass., Harvard University Computational Laboratory, 1965).

LAMB, S. M., On alternation, transformation, realization and stratification, in: Monograph series on languages and linguistics, Vol. 17, ed. C. I. J. M. Stuart (Washington, D.C., Georgetown University Press, 1964) pp. 105–122.

LAMB, S. M., Outline of stratificational grammar (Washington, D.C., Georgetown University Press, 1966).

LANGENDOEN, D. T., Some problems concerning the English expletive "it", in: Project on linguistic analysis, Report No 13 (Columbus, Ohio, Ohio State University Research Foundation, 1966a).

LANGENDOEN, D. T., The syntax of the English expletive "it" in: Monograph series on language and linguistics, Vol. 19, ed. F. P. Dinneen (Washington, D.C., Georgetown University Press, 1966b) pp. 207–216.

LYONS, J., Structural semantics (Oxford, Blackwell, 1963); Publications of the Philological Society, 20.

LYONS, J., Towards a "notional" theory of the "parts of speech", J. of Linguistics 2 (1966) 209–236.

LYONS, J., A note on possessive, existential and locative sentences, Found. of Language 3 (1967) 390–396.

LYONS, J., Introduction to theoretical linguistics (London and New York, Cambridge University Press, 1968).

LYONS, J. and R. J. WALES, Psycholinguistics papers: Proc. Edinburgh Conf. 1966 (Edinburgh, Edinburgh University Press, 1966).

LENNEBERG, E. H. ed., New directions in the study of language (Cambridge, Mass., M.I.T. Press, 1964).

MCNEILL, D., The creation of language by young children, in: Lyons and Wales eds. (1966) pp. 99–132.

POSTAL, P. M., Review of R. E. Longacre, Grammar discovery procedures, Intern. J. Am. Linguistics 32 (1966) 93–98.

SAPORTA, S., Ordered rules, dialect differences and historical processes, Language 41 (1965) 218–224.

SMITH, Carlota S., A class of complex modifiers in English, Language 37 (1961) 342–365.

SMITH, Carlota S., Determiners and relative clauses in a generative grammar of English, Language 40 (1964), 37–52.

SMITH, F. and G. A. MILLER eds., The genesis of language: In children and animals (Cambridge, Mass., M.I.T. Press, 1966).

STAAL, J. F., Some semantic relations between sentoids, Found. of Language 3 (1967) 66–88.

TEETER, K. V., Descriptive linguistics in America: Triviality versus irrelevance, Word 20 (1964) 197–207.

VASILIU, E., Towards a generative phonology of Daco-Rumanian dialects, J. Linguistics 2 (1966) 79–98.

VISSER, F. Th., An historical syntax of the English language, Part 1 (Leiden, Brill, 1963).

Section 11

History of Logic, Methodology and Philosophy of Science

LEIBNIZ ON POSSIBLE WORLDS

B. MATES

University of California, Berkeley, USA

When defining logical truth in terms of interpretations or models, logicians frequently make reference to the Leibnizian idea that a proposition is a necessary truth if and only if it is true of all possible worlds. The same idea is usually mentioned in discussions of the semantics of modal logics. As soon as one looks a bit further into the matter, however, it becomes apparent that the concepts of 'possible world' employed by modern investigators are quite different from that of Leibniz himself; and although perhaps this is all to the good, there may be some interest in considering what the effect would be if a more strictly Leibnizian approach were followed.

The present paper describes certain features of the Leibnizian conceptual framework and attempts to incorporate them in the semantics of a formalized language. Specifically, the formal system to be discussed will be a first order monadic predicate calculus with identity and necessity, and also with individual constants that do not in all cases denote. A similar system without the modal operator will be considered in an auxiliary way.

Although in presenting Leibniz's views I have done my best to stick to the strict historical truth, the reader who is unfamiliar with the subject should be warned that for the most part we are working not from treatises but rather from a large number of notes and other bits and pieces, written over a long period of time and apparently not intended for publication. It is unreasonable to expect such fragments to present a complete and coherent doctrine. There are Leibnizian statements that I do not know how to reconcile with the interpretation here offered; where I am aware of these I mention them in footnotes or other references. It also should be mentioned at the outset that clearly the formalized language toward which Leibniz was moving would have been more like that of Lesniewski than like the Fregean systems employed by most logicians today, and inevitably a certain amount of distortion is involved in attempting to apply his ideas to a type of language he never considered. Nevertheless I believe that such application is not without interest.[1]

I

1. The general outlines of Leibniz's doctrine of possible worlds are well known to every philosopher. Especially striking is the way in which matters of logic, metaphysics, and theology are interwoven. Leibniz tells us that the actual, existent world is only one of infinitely many possible worlds that *could* have existed (G II 40).[2] It is, indeed, the *best* of these possible worlds, in the sense that any alteration whatsoever, taken together with all its ramifications, would be a change for the worse; and of course that is why God chose to make actual this particular world rather than one of the others. The distinction between the actual world and the various other possible worlds is associated with certain philosophically significant classifications of statements or sentences. Instead of employing a simple dichotomy between truth and falsehood, Leibniz in effect relativizes these concepts to possible worlds. Given a sentence and a possible world, the sentence is said to be true or false *of* that possible world. Thus, the sentences, 'Caesar crossed the Rubicon' and 'Adam was the first man', are true of the actual world but false of infinitely many other possible worlds. (In fact, it turns out that they are true of the actual world *only*, as will be discussed in the sequel.) On the other hand, the sentence, 'Either Caesar crossed the Rubicon or he didn't', in the sense that either it is or it is not the case that he did, is true not only of the actual world but of all possible worlds. Such sentences are called by Leibniz *necessary truths* ('truths of reason', 'eternal truths', cp. C 18, NE 714). Sentences true of the actual world but not of all possible worlds are *contingent truths* ('truths of fact').[3]

Following the usage of Russell (R 32), we say that a sentence is true or false *of* a possible world rather than *in* it. The truth value of a sentence relative to a possible world does not depend upon what would have happened to the language, or to that sentence in particular, if the given possible world had been made actual. Thus the sentence, 'there are no sentences', is

---

[1] For reasons of space I have not attempted to make clear in detail the relevance of my discussion to the recent literature on the same subject. In the biliography, however, I have listed a number of books and papers that set forth ideas to which the views of Leibniz are highly germane.

[2] To decipher the citations, see the bibliography.

[3] Usually, however, Leibniz *defines* a necessary truth as 'one the contradictory of which involves a contradiction' (e.g., at S 480).

presumably true of some possible worlds (though not *in* one); and although no sentence is itself a necessarily existent substance or has a necessarily fixed sense, some sentences are true of all possible worlds.

2. Attributes and concepts

If, seeking to come to closer quarters with the subject, we now raise the heuristically useful (though in other ways suspect) question, "What, exactly, *is* a possible world?", difficulties appear at once. Leibniz's stock answer seems to be that a possible world is a collection of individuals. But of course the only actually existing individuals (i.e., the only individuals) are the ones that constitute the actual world, and thus we seem led to the unsatisfactory conclusion that the number of nonactual possible worlds is either 1 or 0. Many philosophers try to restore the desired multiplicity by saying that in addition to the actual individuals, which exist, there are also some entities called 'possible individuals', which 'subsist'. Upon occasion Leibniz himself talks this way and gives the appearance of believing the associated doctrine (cp. G III 573). It seems to me, however, that his metaphysics offer him another and somewhat more satisfactory method of handling the problem.

Consider, for example, a name like 'Adam', which denotes an individual existing in the actual world, and compare it with a name like 'Pegasus', which does not (but for which there *could* have been a corresponding individual). Associated with the name 'Adam' there is, according to Leibniz, not only Adam himself but also the so-called *complete individual concept of Adam*, which is said to 'involve' all of Adam's attributes, including everything that has ever happened to him and everything that will happen to him, as, for example, that he will have such and such progeny (G II 42, G II 131, G IV 437, S 475, S 477).[4] With the word 'Pegasus', on the other hand, there is associated a complete individual concept but no corresponding individual (cf. C 53). The concept of Pegasus (and it will be noticed that here and at other essential points in this discussion we are forced to quantify or abstract into oblique contexts) contains all the attributes Pegasus would have

---

[4] In connection with this we may note that if essentialism is the doctrine that distinguishes 'some traits of an object as essential to it ... and other traits of it as accidental' (QUINE [1963] p. 104), then Leibniz is no essentialist. It seems that in effect he chooses the alternative of regarding *every* trait of an object as essential to it, and what saves the contingency of synthetic truths about the object is only the fact that the object might not have existed at all.

had if he had existed.[5] Leibniz seems to hold that corresponding to every significant proper name [6] there is a complete individual concept, which is such that it *might* be exemplified by an individual. Usually he limits the attributes under consideration to what he calls 'simple' attributes – i.e., to attributes that cannot be 'analyzed' or 'explicated' in terms of other attributes. Thus a complete individual concept is a set of (or an attribute composed of) simple attributes jointly satisfiable by exactly one individual; it is 'complete' in the sense that it contains every simple attribute such an individual would have. Since all the attributes of an individual substance are presumed to be analyzable, or resolvable, into simple ones, a complete individual concept is complete also in the sense that every attribute a corresponding individual would have is 'deducible' from the set of attributes constituting the concept (G IV 432, S 475, S 478).

All simple attributes are 'positive', while complex attributes are composed of the simples by negation and (possibly infinite) conjunction (cp. C 35). Leibniz says further, 'all purely positive terms are compatible inter se' (S 480, G VII 195, R 20n). It is not easy, if this is true, to see how there can be more than one complete individual concept. But Leibniz seems worried by a different difficulty. When he speaks of the 'compatibility' of positive attributes, he evidently has in mind something more like their independence; he cannot understand how one object's having a positive attribute P can logically imply or exclude another object's having a positive attribute Q. He decides that this is one of those mysteries understandable by God but not by man.[7]

Some of these details are irrelevant to the exegetical suggestion I wish to make here, which is only that we interpret the term 'possible world' as referring for Leibniz to a set of individual concepts, and not to a set of individuals. In that way he can avoid introducing a shadowy realm of 'possible individuals' in addition to the abstract entities (i.e., the attributes and concepts) already involved in his metaphysics.[8] We may note that since in the case of the actual world there is a 1–1 correspondence between the

---

[5] Or, perhaps, all the attributes an object must have if it is properly to be called 'Pegasus', where the word 'properly' carries such a metaphysical load that only Pegasus can *properly* be called 'Pegasus'.

[6] Apparently this does not apply to names of mathematical objects, which latter are considered by Leibniz to be 'abstract' and 'nonreal' (cf. C 8).

[7] One is reminded of the problem faced by Professor Carnap when, endeavoring (in *Meaning and necessity*) to explicate logical connections (including logical independence) in terms of his L-concepts, he found that in defining these L-concepts he had to stipulate explicitly that the atomic sentences of his language were *inter se* logically independent.

[8] There is a considerable amount of indirect textual support for this interpretation.

individual concepts and objects exemplifying them, there will sometimes be no harm in speaking of that world as though it were a collection of individuals (cf. G VII 303).

3. Compossibility

Individual concepts are said to be *compossible* if they are capable of joint realization. Thus, on the interpretation here proposed, a possible world is a set of mutually compossible complete individual concepts. It is 'maximal' in the sense that it contains every complete individual concept that is compossible with the ones it contains. We are told explicitly that, just as there are infinitely many possible worlds, so there are infinitely many elements in each possible world (T 128, T 267, but cf. C 360) and infinitely many attributes in each individual concept (G IV 432, G V 268, NE 309).

Distinctively Leibnizian is the view that in the actual world, and in every other possible world, each individual concept is interlocked with each of the other individual concepts in that world; each 'mirrors' all the others (G II 112, G II 40, R 132, R 205, NE 716, C 15, C 19). Making the same point in another way, Leibniz says that each individual of the actual world is related to all of the others, and every relation is 'grounded' in simple properties of the things related; the other possible worlds are similarly constructed (T 128).

Thus, for example, consider again the individual concept of Adam. Contained in this concept are one or more simple properties that are the ground (as concerns Adam) of the truth of the proposition, 'Adam was the father of Cain' (cp. G II 37). If Adam had not been the father of Cain, Adam would not have been the same Adam; more exactly, Adam would not have existed (T 128). Similarly, if Cain had not been the son of Adam, *he* would not have existed. Putting the matter in still another way, any concept that does not contain the simple attributes that are the basis of Adam's being the father of Cain is not the concept of Adam. The concepts of Adam and Cain are connected in this manner; so are those of Cain and Abel; and the same is true of every other collection of concepts in every possible world (cf. G II 42 ff., T 168).

One sees, therefore, that the relation of compossibility between individual concepts, unlike that of consistency between sentences or propositions, is transitive;[9] since it is also reflexive and symmetrical it is an equivalence

---

[9] This crucial point was explicitly noted for the first time, so far as I know, by RESCHER (*Philosophy of Leibniz*, p. 17).

relation. As noted above, the possible worlds are 'maximal' or 'closed' with respect to this relation; so they are just the equivalence classes into which the relation of compossibility partitions the entire class of complete individual concepts. Thus, each such concept belongs to one and only one possible world (G III 573, R 66, T 371, but cf. G VII 194, T 146), and two concepts are compossible if and only if they belong to the same possible world.

As is well known, Leibniz believed these matters to possess important theological aspects. He argues that in creating the actual world God did not have a choice as to whether Judas should be a betrayer, but only whether Judas-who-was-going-to-be-a-betrayer should exist. Otherwise expressed, the point is that there are not two possible worlds, in one of which Judas betrays Christ and in the other of which he does not. God cannot be charged with having decided that Judas should sin. He did decide, however, that *Judas peccaturus* should nevertheless exist, "since He saw that this evil would be immensely outweighed by greater goods and that there was no better way" (C 24). "If the smallest evil that comes to pass in the world", Leibniz says in another place, "were missing in it, it would no longer be this world; which, with nothing omitted and all allowance made, was found the best by the Creator who chose it" (T 128, T 10). [10]

The point under discussion is also relevant to God's omniscience. Since "all things are connected in each one of the possible worlds" and "the universe, whatever it may be, is all of one piece, like an ocean: the least movement extends its effect there to any distance whatsoever" (T 128) – since this is so, "God sees in each portion of the universe the whole thing ... He is infinitely more discerning than Pythagoras, who judged the height of Hercules by the size of his footprint" (T 341). This capacity of God's is but the limit of a similar property Leibniz thought he had noticed in men: "the wiser a man is, the less detached intentions he has, and the more the views and intentions he does have are comprehensive and interconnected" (G II 19).

There is also a grammatical aspect to the matter. It seems evident that for Leibniz the plausibility of his doctrine on this point is intimately connected with a certain grammatical transformation that in most cases is permissible in Latin but seems to have no simple counterpart in English.

---

[10] On the other side, Diodorus's view, that everything possible happens, is put down by Leibniz as due to a confusion of *possible* with *compossible with what exists* (G III 572 ff., E 654).

In general, he tells us (C 375), to say

$$A \text{ est } B$$

is the same as to say

$$AB \text{ est existens};$$

e.g., to say

$$\text{Petrus est abnegans}$$

is to say

$$\text{Petrus abnegans est existens.}$$

Thus every simple question about an individual is transformed into a question of existence. Note, for future reference, that as a special case

$$A \text{ est } A$$

is transformed into

$$AA \text{ est existens,}$$

i.e., into

$$A \text{ est existens.}$$

It is worth noting that there is a lack of symmetry between the ways in which individuals and attributes of individuals are treated, as concerns the question whether their identity is preserved from one possible world to another. According to Leibniz it is not possible that a given individual should have had attributes other than the ones he does have. But it is possible that a given attribute should have characterized individuals other than the ones it does characterize. Thus, although no individual concept is part of two possible worlds, the attributes that constitute concepts are the same from one world to another. (Indeed, Leibniz sometimes talks as though every attribute is part of some individual concept in each possible world.) This seems to imply that an attribute may characterize an individual or belong to his concept without itself having the (an) attribute of characterizing that individual or belonging to his concept. Adam is a man, so Adam's concept involves the attribute of manhood, but the attribute manhood does not have the attribute of being involved in Adam's concept. If it did, then manhood would not be the same in any possible world to which the concept of Adam did not belong. In other words, no men could have existed other than the ones who do.

(In this regard classes appear to fare like individuals and differently from attributes. If Adam had not existed, the class of men would not have been the same, although the attribute presumably would have been unaffected. We can say intelligibly, "Suppose that there had been fewer men than there are", and metaphysicalize this into, "Suppose that the attribute of manhood had belonged to fewer objects than it does". But if we say, "Suppose that the class of men had contained fewer elements than it does", our remark hardly can be understood in the sense of "Suppose that this very class, which has so-and-so many elements, had had fewer elements". It seems intelligible only when taken in the sense of, "Suppose that the attribute of manhood had belonged to fewer objects and so that the class determined by this attribute had had fewer elements than the class it actually does determine".)

4. We come next to the principle, *Nihili nullae proprietates sunt* ("Nothing has no properties"), a Scholastic maxim asserted by Leibniz on many occasions. It does not mean, of course, that there is something called 'nihil' and which has the remarkable property of having no properties at all. Nor, I believe, is its force brought out by rephrasing it as, "Everything has some property", for that seems to be as completely trivial a metaphysical proposition as will ever be found. The point is rather that Leibniz's advocacy of this principle amounts in practice to a decision to regard as false every atomic sentence that contains a nondenoting name. Since, for him, existence is a predicate (NE 401), so that $\ulcorner A$ exists $\urcorner$, where A is a name, is an atomic sentence, this in turn amounts to asserting the following:

A singular name N is non-denoting if and only if every atomic sentence containing N is false. (Here cf. C 393 ⧣ 153, S 478, C 252, S 474, NE 516.)

Other formulations of the principle and discussions of it substantiate the proposed interpretation. For example, in one place it appears in the form, *Non entis nulla sunt attributa*, i.e., "what does not exist has no properties". And at nearly every occurrence it is found in some such context as:

Suppose that ... N is not A, N is not B, N is not C, etc.: then N is called *Nothing*. From this definition there follows the common saying that Nothing has no attributes' (S 472, cf. C 252, C 356, S 474). [11]

---

[11] As the passage just quoted shows, the simple sentences Leibniz has in mind are of the form $\ulcorner A$ is $B\urcorner$, where the argument positions may be occupied by singular or general terms. The formal system toward which he was moving was probably more like that of Lesniewski than like the Fregean-style predicate calculi employed by most logicians today. When he says $\ulcorner N$ is Nothing $\urcorner$ he means in effect not only that N denotes nothing at all if N is a singular term (like 'Pegasus'), but also that N denotes the empty set if N is a general term (like 'man twenty feet tall') (cf. Couturat [1901] p. 348 n2). Consequently, it would be more accurate to say that *part* of the point of *Non entis nulla attributa sunt*, as understood by Leibniz, is that a singular name is nondenoting if and only if every atomic sentence containing it is false.

Leibniz explicitly rejects the possibility of saying that atomic sentences containing nondenoting terms are neither true nor false. In one place, where the context shows that only atomic sentences are under consideration, he states:

In order, namely, to keep (the principle) that every proposition is true or false, (I consider) as false every proposition that lacks an existent subject or real term (C 393).

Leibniz also makes it clear that although such atomic sentences are false, their negations and many other compounds containing them are true. He goes on to say that while such a procedure may not be consonant with ordinary usage, there is no reason for him to care about *that*, for he is engaged in finding a suitable notation (*propria signa*), not in trying to establish the application of existing terminology (*recepta nomina*) (*loc. cit.*, cf. C 188, C 272, 273).

The idea of considering atomic sentences false if they contain singular terms that fail to name has of course occurred to many other philosophers and logicians.[12] No doubt the most obvious objection to this procedure is based upon the consideration that what is expressed by an atomic sentence in one language may be expressed by a complex sentence in another. Or, even in the same language, there may be cases in which an atomic sentence seems synonymous with a sentence that is not atomic. Thus it might be felt awkward to declare that 'Zeus is bald' is false while at the same time insisting that 'Zeus does not have hair on his head' is true. Probably Leibniz's reply to this sort of objection would be to reiterate his view[13] that in the realm of thought, as in that of language, there is a complex and a simple, and that the ideal language he is seeking will associate signs with thoughts in such a way that signs for complex thoughts will be composites of the signs for their parts. "The law of expressions is this", he says, "that the expression for a given thing shall be composed of the signs of those things the ideas of which compose the idea of the given thing". So the point is that in an ideal language, to which alone Leibniz intends his considerations strictly to apply, atomic sentences express the 'atomic thoughts', and hence difficulties of the type mentioned above cannot arise.[14]

However, COUTURAT (*loc. cit.*) is surely mistaken in supposing that by 'nihil' Leibniz *always* meant the empty set and hence should have defined it as 'the term that is included in every term'. Couturat also argues mistakenly that for Leibniz *non-ens* means *the impossible*; on this cf. Parkinson, *Papers*, p. lvii.

[12] Cf., e.g., QUINE, *Logical Point of View*, pp. 166–7.

[13] A view that is as unintelligible as it is common.

[14] Also, Leibniz thought that the more perfect a language is, the more of its inferences will be formal; from this point of view he says he prefers binary notation in arithmetic,

Note that once again we have the consequence that if the singular term A fails to name, then the sentence $\ulcorner A$ is $A \urcorner$ is false.

5. Identity

Leibniz's views on identity are central to his entire metaphysics. His most widely known pronouncement on this topic is his principle, "Things are the same if it is possible to substitute one for the other everywhere *salva veritate*" or "That A is the same as B means that the one may be substituted for the other in any proposition whatsoever *salva veritate*". It is usual to point out that these (and other) formulations given by Leibniz seem to involve a confusion of sign and object (cp. C 35, C 72, C 240, NE 279 ff.). [15] Perhaps he should have said something like one of the following:

(1) For any names N and N': the sentence $\ulcorner N = N' \urcorner$ is true if and only if N and N' are everywhere interchangeable *salva veritate*: or

(2) For any objects A, B: A is identical with B if and only if A and B have all their attributes in common; or

(3) For any objects, A, B: A is identical with B if and only if every predicate expression that is true of A is true of B and conversely.

In connection with the features of Leibnizian philosophy under discussion here, the seemingly slight differences among these three formulations are by no means without important effect. Principle (1) leads to the result that every sentence of the form $\ulcorner N = N \urcorner$ is true, whether or not N denotes an object existing in the actual world, i.e., an object. (And it is reasonably clear that for Leibniz not all names denote.) On this basis 'Pegasus = Pegasus' would be true of the actual world even though Pegasus does not exist. The initial quantifiers of formulations (2) and (3), on the other hand,

---

because e.g. '$3 \times 3 = 9$' can be demonstrated by

$$\begin{array}{r} 11 \\ 11 \\ \hline 11 \\ 11 \\ \hline 1001 \end{array}$$

cf. KNEALE and KNEALE, *Development*, pp. 327 ff.

[15] See also QUINE, *Word and Object*, pp. 116, 117. Quine mentions formulations by Aristotle and Aquinas. Cf. also Sextus Empiricus, *Hyp. Pyrrh.* II, p. 229. The question whether Leibniz was in fact guilty of a use-mention confusion is not quite easy, since it could be argued that he was defining the identity of concepts (not objects) in terms of some sort of 'interchangeability' of these in propositions (not sentences). At NE 379 ff., Leibniz inveighs against 'confusing words and things'.

run over (existent) objects; thus these forms of the principle yield no conclusions about the truth or falsity of sentences such as the one just mentioned.
As indicated earlier, other statements by Leibniz suggest that he was inclined
to regard these identity sentences as *false* of the actual world, and, in general,
to think that $\ulcorner N = N \urcorner$ is to count as false of any possible world not containing
the concept associated with N. Indeed, this follows (as he notes) from the
doctrine of the previous section plus the plausible assumption that self-
identity is a simple attribute. Furthermore, at several places Leibniz explicitly interprets '$AB \neq AB$' as 'AB does not exist' (C 393; cf. K 181). It
must be acknowledged, however, that on one occasion he adds the curious
remark, "When everything is taken into consideration, though, it is perhaps
better to say that we can indeed always *write* $A = A$ but that when A does not
exist nothing useful can be concluded therefrom".

Often the identity of things and the identity of their concepts seem im-
perfectly distinguished by Leibniz, and I am inclined to think that this is
because his doctrine implies that individuals (of the actual world) are
identical if and only if their corresponding individual concepts are identical.
In a very interesting passage he writes:

    ... Thus 'Alexander the Great' and 'King of Macedonia' and 'Con-
queror of Darius' are intersubstitutable, and so are 'triangle' and 'trilateral'.
Furthermore, such identities can always be demonstrated by resolution ...
Suppose that A and B are terms, and that the definition of each is substituted for it, and the definitions of (resulting) parts are substituted for
them, and so on until primitive, simple terms are reached; then if one
comes out formally the same as the other, A and B *coincide* or are *virtually
identical* ... For changes made by substituting a definition for what is
defined, or vice versa, preserve truth ... So A coincides with B if it is
possible to substitute one in place of the other *salva veritate*, or if when
one analyzes each by substituting values or definitions in place of the
terms the same thing (where 'same' is meant formally) results in both
cases (C 362).

Part of the point of this appears to be that two terms A and B are interchangeable *salva veritate* just in case they can be resolved into one another
by substitutions of a sort that preserve truth when made in sentences (e.g.,
by substituting definiens for definiendum, or vice versa). For any such
interchange could be accomplished also by the same sequence of substitutions
that carries A into B. Assuming that A and B can be resolved into one another
in the way described just in case the associated concepts are identical, then
this is still another indication that for Leibniz individuals of the actual

world are identical if and only if their concepts are identical (cf. S 307).[16]

As an alternative to his definition of identity in terms of substitutivity *salva veritate* Leibniz often defines it as follows: *A* is the same as *B* if and only if *A* is *B* and *B* is *A* (C 382, S 479). We noted earlier that as Leibniz uses variables the substituends include both singular and general terms (this is, of course, syntactically easier in Latin than in English). Thus he applies the just-mentioned definition not only in cases like

Octavianus et Augustus idem est,

but also in cases like

Felix et pius idem est.

In dealing with the latter sentence he plainly takes

Pius est felix et felix est pius

to be equivalent with

Omnis pius est felix et omnis felix est pius.

I am convinced that this ambiquity (if we may somewhat incorrectly call it that) in Leibniz's use of variables is partially responsible for his ambivalent attitude toward $\ulcorner A$ is $A \urcorner$ as a law of logic. When *A* is general, this proposition has for him no existential import, amounting to $\ulcorner$Whatever is A is $A \urcorner$. When A is singular, on the other hand, Leibniz is inclined to deny $\ulcorner A$ is $A \urcorner$ if A fails to name, on the ground that what does not exist has no attributes, including, presumably, the attribute of self-identity. In setting up the formal calculus embodying Leibnizian ideas we shall let the sentence $\beta \equiv \beta$ come out false for nondenoting β, but at the same time we shall make recompense by including as valid such sentences as $\bigwedge \alpha(\alpha \equiv \beta \leftrightarrow \alpha \equiv \beta)$ and $\bigwedge \alpha(\theta\alpha \leftrightarrow \theta\alpha)$ (cf. NE 404 ff., 'Everything is what it is ... A is A', S 472, C 266, C 186).

Before we leave the topic of identity it is interesting to observe in passing that Leibniz himself drew attention to the kinds of cases in which what we now call 'Leibniz's Law' fails, namely those involving oblique or referentially opaque contexts. He puts it this way:

> If *A* is *B* and *B* is *A*, then *A* and *B* are called *the same*. Or, *A* and *B* are the same if they can be substituted for one another everywhere (*excepting*, however, those cases in which not the thing itself but the manner of conceiving the thing, which may be different, is under discussion; thus

---

[16] The favorite example, that no two eggs are in all respects alike (cf., e.g., S 476) may be found also in Sextus Empiricus, *Adv. Math.* VII 409.

Peter and the Apostle who denied Christ are the same, and the one term may be substituted for the other, unless we are considering the matter in the way some people call 'reflexive': e.g., if I say 'Peter, insofar as he was the Apostle who denied Christ, sinned', I cannot substitute 'Peter' and say 'Peter, insofar as he was Peter, sinned') (S 475). [17]

The analysis here offered by Leibniz is, in its essentials, very much like that of Frege, who said, "in indirect discourse we talk about the *senses* of the words", and that the sense of a word "contains the manner and context of presentation" of the designated object. Leibniz's expressions *de re* and *de modo concipiendi* also suggest the medieval distinction of modalities *de dicto* and *de re*, a distinction with which he was doubtless familiar.

Another, somewhat less clear, statement to the same effect is the following.

$A \infty B$ means that A and B are the same or may be substituted for one another everywhere (unless this is not permissible, which happens in those cases in which a term is presented for consideration in a certain respect; e.g., granted that Triangle and Trilateral are the same, still if you say 'A triangle, as such, has (an angle-sum of) 180 degrees' it is not permissible to substitute 'trilateral', since part of the content lies in that (way of saying it) (C 261)).

6. Relations

In a passage that if often quoted, Leibniz says:

You will not, I believe, admit an accident which is in two subjects at once. Thus I hold, as regards relations, that paternity in David is one thing, and filiation in Solomon is another, but the relation common to both is a merely mental thing, of which the modifications of singulars are the foundation (G II 486).

This remark usually is taken to mean that according to Leibniz there is not, in addition to individual substances and their attributes, a third category of metaphysically fundamental entities called 'relations'. The doctrine seems to be that the truth of each true sentence of the form $\ulcorner A$ is $B \urcorner$, where A is a singular term and B expresses a simple attribute, depends in almost a pictorial way upon the existence of an extralinguistic complex consisting of an individual substance's 'having' that attribute (C 241), and that the truth of all other kinds of sentences is to be reduced somehow to the truth of these.

---

[17] My delight in finding this passage is somewhat mitigated by the fact that, according to what I am propounding as 'standard' Leibnizian doctrine, Peter wouldn't have been Peter if he hadn't sinned.

In the case of negations, conjunctions, generalizations (cp. C 252), and even modalizations built up out of such materials it is not too difficult to make a plausible guess about how the reduction would be accomplished. And presumably if B expresses a complex attribute analyzable into simple attributes $B_1, B_2, ..., B_n, ...$ the truth of $\ulcorner A$ is $B \urcorner$ would be the same as that of some combination, possibly very complicated but hopefully truth-functional, of the sentences $\ulcorner A$ is $B_i \urcorner$. But sentences of the form $A \mathscr{R} B$, with A and B singular terms and $\mathscr{R}$ a relational expression, seem to cause particular difficulty for Leibniz. He is not content to take the trivial way out that just rereads or redescribes the sentence

David is the father of Solomon,

for example, as ascribing the attribute 'father of Solomon' to David and the attribute, 'having David as father', to Solomon; it is clear, to use some more recent terminology, that he would not be inclined to accept every open sentence with one free variable as expressing an attribute.

We know very little about how Leibniz did propose to explicate relational sentences in terms of the sentences for which he supplied fundamental metaphysical counterparts. For a few special cases we have analyses or hints. He says that

Peter is similar to Paul

is reducible to

Peter is now A and Paul is now A,

for some A, and he uses this 'reduction' [18] to explain how the former has as a consequence the sentence

Paul is similar to Peter (C 244).

In line with the definition of identity in terms of substitutivity, the truth of an identity sentence, like

Paris = Alexander

presumably would depend upon whether all sentences of the form $\ulcorner$Paris is $A \urcorner$, with A expressing a simple attribute, have the same truth values as the corresponding sentences with 'Paris' replaced by 'Alexander' (plus, as argued above, the condition that 'Paris' denotes). Further there are

---

[18] Of course, unless the quantifier is understood as part of the analysans, no reduction has been given. By using a free variable, Leibniz leaves us guessing.

indications that sentences of the form

A is the one and only *B*

were to be analyzed as

A is *B* and, for every *C*, if *C* is *B* then *A* is *C* and *C* is *A* (C 239).

Leibniz's treatment of the sentence

Paris loves Helen

is especially significant. It shows that he contemplated making essential use of non truth-functional operators in his reductions. For this sentence he offers

Paris loves, and by that very fact (*eo ipso*)
Helen is loved (C 287).

For the still more complicated case

Titius is wiser than Caius

he produces the remarkable (multiply opaque) analysis:

Titius is wise, and *qua* wise is superior insofar as
(*quatenus*) Caius *qua* wise is inferior (C 280).[19]

It is difficult for a nonmetaphysician to appreciate Leibniz's motivation for these linguistic contortions, but at any rate one can see that he hoped to analyze relational sentences by means of sufficiently complex (and not in general truth-functional) combinations of the sentences he accepted as atomic.

7. Summary

According to the present interpretation, then, possible worlds are maximal sets of mutually compossible complete individual concepts, and a complete individual concept is a maximal set of (or a 'maximal' attribute composed of) compatible simple attributes. How two such concepts can fail to be compossible is a great mystery, according to Leibniz, but he clearly holds that there *are* infinitely many possible worlds, each of which contains infinitely many concepts. All the concepts of a given possible world are interlocked

---

[19] Leibniz proposes to eliminate adverbs in a similar way: 'Petrus stat pulchre = Petrus est pulcher quatenus est stans' (C 242). 'Omnis *B* est *C*' is analyzed as 'Si *A* est *B* etiam *A* est *C*' (C 252).

with one another; each concept belongs to exactly one possible world. Each significant singular term is associated with a complete individual concept. A sentence of the form ⌜A is B⌝, with singular A, is true of a possible world W if and only if the individual concept associated with A belongs to W and contains the attribute expressed by B (C 85, S 474). Thus in particular, if the individual concept associated with A does not belong to W, then the sentence is false ("what does not exist has no attributes"). Even ⌜A is A⌝, with singular A, is false of possible worlds to which the individual concept associated with A does not belong. An identity sentence ⌜$A = B$⌝, i.e., ⌜A is B and B is A⌝, with A, B singular, is true of a possible world if and only if the individual concepts associated with A and B are the same and belong to that possible world; otherwise it is false. A generalization is true of a possible world if and only if all of its instances, with singular terms for concepts belonging to that world, are true of that world.[20] And a sentence is a necessary truth if and only if it is true of all possible worlds.

II

8. On this basis we can go some distance toward constructing a Leibnizian semantics for a system of quantified modal logic with identity and individual constants. As a first step we briefly describe a nonmodal system that in most respects is like ordinary systems of predicate logic but does not assume that every interpretation assigns a denotation to each individual constant. In this system an atomic sentence is false under a given interpretation if it contains an individual constant to which that interpretation assigns no object as denotation.

For definiteness, let the formalism be the result of adding individual constants to the formalism of TARSKI [1965]. Thus an *atomic formula* is the concatenation of a predicate of rank $n \geqslant 1$ with an n-termed sequence of individual symbols, i.e., variables and/or individual constants; the class of *formulas* is the smallest class including the atomic formulas and containing $\neg\phi$, $(\phi \rightarrow \psi)$, and $\bigwedge \alpha\phi$ whenever it contains ϕ and ψ, for any expressions ϕ, ψ and variable α. A formula in which no variable occurs free is called a *sentence*. For any formula ϕ, variable α, and individual symbol β, $\phi\alpha/\beta$ is the result of replacing all free occurrences of α in ϕ by occurrences of β.

An *interpretation* is an ordered pair $\langle K, \Phi \rangle$, where K is a nonempty set and Φ is a function that assigns to each predicate of rank n a subset of ^nK

---

[20] I thought I had textual support for this, but I can no longer find it.

(and to the identity predicate, in particular, the identity relation among elements of K), and to each individual constant either *nothing at all* or an element of K.

Given an arbitrary sentence ϕ and an interpretation $\mathscr{I} = \langle K, \Phi \rangle$, ϕ will be *true* or *false* relative to that interpretation ($\mathscr{I}$-true or $\mathscr{I}$-false). These notions are defined as follows. Let ψ, χ be formulas, α a variable, and β the first (in some fixed ordering) individual constant not occurring in ϕ.

(1) If ϕ is atomic, then ϕ is $\mathscr{I}$-true iff ϕ assigns elements of K to all individual constants occurring in ϕ and these elements (when taken in the order in which their corresponding constants occur in ϕ) are related by the relation that ϕ assigns to the predicate of ϕ;

(2) If ϕ is $\neg \psi$, then ϕ is $\mathscr{I}$-true iff ψ is not $\mathscr{I}$-true;

(3) If ϕ is $(\psi \rightarrow \chi)$, then ϕ is $\mathscr{I}$-true iff either ψ is not $\mathscr{I}$-true or χ is $\mathscr{I}$-true, or both;

(4) If ϕ is $\wedge \alpha \psi$, then ϕ is $\mathscr{I}$-true iff $\psi \alpha / \beta$ is $\mathscr{I}'$-true for every β-variant $\mathscr{I}'$ of $\mathscr{I}$.

Further, ϕ is $\mathscr{I}$-false iff ϕ is not $\mathscr{I}$-true.

(Where β is any individual constant, an interpretation $\mathscr{I}'$ is a β-variant of $\mathscr{I}$ iff $\mathscr{I}'$ makes an assignment to β and $\mathscr{I}$ and $\mathscr{I}'$ are the same or differ at most in not assigning the same thing to β. Note that 'is a β-variant of' is not symmetrical.)

A sentence ϕ is *universally valid* if ϕ is $\mathscr{I}$-true for every interpretation $\mathscr{I}$.

Complete sets of axioms for the universally valid sentences of this system are not hard to find. One such set may be obtained by making relatively minor modifications in the elegant set for the system Σ_5 of KALISH and MONTAGUE [1965] (cf. TARSKI [1965]) for ordinary predicate logic with identity. Namely, for all formulas ϕ, ψ, χ, variables α, and individual symbols β, γ we take all universal closures of the following as axioms:

(1) $(\phi \rightarrow \psi) \rightarrow ((\psi \rightarrow \chi) \rightarrow (\phi \rightarrow \chi))$;

(2) $(\neg \phi \rightarrow \phi) \rightarrow \phi$;

(3) $\phi \rightarrow (\neg \phi \rightarrow \psi)$;

(4) $\wedge \alpha (\phi \rightarrow \psi) \rightarrow (\wedge \alpha \phi \rightarrow \wedge \alpha \psi)$;

(5) $\phi \rightarrow \wedge \alpha \phi$, where α does not occur free in ϕ;

(6) $\neg \wedge \alpha \neg \alpha \equiv \beta$, where β is a variable;

(7) $\beta \equiv \gamma \rightarrow (\phi \rightarrow \psi)$, where ϕ, ψ are atomic and ψ is like ϕ except for containing an occurrence of γ where ϕ contains an occurrence of β;

(8) $\phi \rightarrow \neg \wedge \alpha \neg \alpha \equiv \beta$, where ϕ is atomic and β is an individual constant occurring in ϕ.

The single rule of inference is *modus ponens*.

The essential differences between this set and the set for the system Σ_5 are the addition of axiom-schema (8) and the restriction of the axioms (6) to those cases in which β is a variable. If '$\neg \bigwedge \alpha \neg \alpha \equiv \beta$' is read '$\beta$ exists', it will be seen that the former of these changes reflects the Leibnizian principle that "What does not exist has no properties" and that the latter expresses our decision not to presuppose that every individual constant denotes.

Completeness may be proved along the lines of Henkin's proof, as formulated e.g. in MATES [1965]. Relative to that formulation the principal change is that ω-completeness must be redefined in such a way that a set of sentences Γ is ω-complete iff, for every formula ϕ and variable α, if $\neg \bigwedge \alpha \neg \phi$ belongs to Γ then there is an individual constant β such that $\phi\alpha/\beta$ and $\beta \equiv \beta$ belong to Γ. This leads to the result that, if Γ is maximal d-consistent and ω-complete, then $\bigwedge \alpha\phi \in \Gamma$ iff $\phi\alpha/\beta \in \Gamma$ for every individual constant β such that $\beta \equiv \beta \in \Gamma$.

Comparison of the foregoing axioms with the axioms for the Kalish-Montague system Σ_5 shows that (i) every individual-constant-free theorem of ordinary predicate logic with identity is a theorem of the present system, and (ii) every theorem of this system is a theorem of ordinary predicate logic with identity. From the semantic characterization of the theorems it is evident that the rule of substitution for predicates does not hold; for example

$$Fa \to \neg \bigwedge x \neg Fx$$

is a theorem, but

$$\neg Fa \to \neg \bigwedge x \neg \neg Fx$$

is not. Intuitively, if the individual a has the property F, then something has F, but if it is not the case that the individual a has F, the reason might be that a does not exist at all.

9. One could construct a more-or-less Leibnizian system of predicate logic by adding modal operators to the foregoing revised quantification theory, in the manner suggested in KRIPKE [1963,2], p. 89n. But in order to stay somewhat closer to the Leibnizian framework we shall formulate our semantics in terms of attributes and concepts, abandoning (partially) the relatively secure basis of sets.

For this second system the formalism will be the same as for the system described above, except that (i) a necessity-symbol $\square$ is added, and (ii) all predicates other than the identity predicate are of rank 1.

A *complete individual concept* is a set of simple properties satisfiable by exactly one thing and containing all the simple properties that would belong to that one thing if it existed. The set of all complete individual concepts and the set of all simple properties are denumerably infinite. *Compossibility* is an equivalence relation in the former set, partitioning it into equivalence classes, called *possible worlds*. There are denumerably infinitely many possible worlds, each containing infinitely many concepts. The nonlogical contants of our language are interpreted, once and for all, as follows: (i) the set of individual constants is mapped onto the set of complete individual concepts; (ii) the set of singulary predicates is mapped onto the set of simple properties. (If β is an individual constant, let $C(\beta)$ be the complete individual concept associated with β; if θ is a singulary predicate, let $C(\theta)$ be the simple property associated with θ.)

We define the relation *true of*, for any sentence ϕ and possible world W, as follows. Let ψ, χ be formulas, α a variable, β, γ individual constants, θ a predicate other than the identity predicate.

(1) If ϕ is $\theta\beta$, then ϕ is true of W iff $C(\theta) \in C(\beta)$ and $C(\beta) \in W$;

(2) If ϕ is $\beta \equiv \gamma$, then ϕ is true of W iff $C(\beta) = C(\gamma)$ and $C(\beta) \in W$;

(3) If ϕ is $\neg\psi$, then ϕ is true of W iff ψ is not true of W;

(4) If ϕ is $(\psi \to \chi)$, then ϕ is true of W iff either ψ is not true of W or χ is true of W, or both;

(5) If ϕ is $\wedge \alpha\psi$, then ϕ is true of W iff $\psi\alpha/\beta$ is true of W for every individual constant β such that $C(\beta) \in W$;

(6) If ϕ is $\square\psi$, then ϕ is true of W iff ψ is true of every possible world W'.

A sentence ϕ is a *necessary truth* iff ϕ is true of all possible worlds.

Due to the open-endedness and perhaps the vagueness of the foregoing semantics, there can be no question of constructing a complete set of axioms for the system. For example, nothing that has been said would determine in a particular case whether $\phi \to \psi$, with ϕ, ψ atomic sentences, was a necessary truth or not. [21] We *are* able, however, to characterize certain large classes of necessary truths syntactically and to provide counterexamples for various principles (e.g., for the so-called 'Barcan formula' – MARCUS [1946] – and its converse) that have sometimes been proposed as laws of modal quantification theory. Note that such counterexamples can always be made 'intuitive' – relative to Leibniz's philosophical outlook, at least – via the definition of 'true of' given above. [22]

---

[21] Thus, for each individual constant β there are infinitely many predicates θ such that $\beta \equiv \beta \to \theta\beta$ is a necessary truth (cf. NE 309) and infinitely many for which it is not a necessary truth.

[22] As Mrs. Marcus (MARCUS [1963]) has said, "... the polemics of modal logic are perhaps best carried out in terms of some explicit semantical construction".

A. Some classes of necessary truths.

(1) All the universally valid sentences of the earlier system that are sentences of the Leibnizian system are necessary truths; and in fact all sentences derivable by *modus ponens* from sentences of types (1)–(8), with ϕ, ψ, χ now taken as arbitrary formulas of the Leibnizian system, are necessary truths.

(2) For any formulas ϕ, ψ: all universal closures of (i) $\Box\phi\rightarrow\phi$, (ii) $\Box(\phi\rightarrow\psi)\rightarrow(\Box\phi\rightarrow\Box\psi)$, and (iii) $\neg\Box\phi\rightarrow\Box\neg\Box\phi$ are necessary truths, and if ϕ is a necessary truth, so is $\Box\phi$. Therefore, the Leibnizian system includes the Lewis system S5, cf. PRIOR [1962] p. 312.

(3) All theorems of the 'quantified M' system of KRIPKE [1963, 2] are necessary truths.

(4) For any formulas ϕ, ψ and individual constants β, γ: all universal closures of $\beta\equiv\gamma\rightarrow\Box(\phi\rightarrow\psi)$ are necessary truths, where ψ is like ϕ except for having occurrences of γ at one or more places where ϕ has occurrences of β.[23]

(5) For any individual constants β, γ and possible world W: $\beta\equiv\gamma$ is true of W iff $\neg\wedge\alpha\neg\alpha\equiv\beta$ is true of W and all sentences $(\theta\beta\leftrightarrow\theta\gamma)$ are true of W for all singulary predicates θ.

(6) Where $\Diamond, \not\equiv, \&,$ and $\leftrightarrow$ are defined in the usual manner:

(i) For every individual constant β, $\Diamond\,\beta\equiv\beta$ is a necessary truth.

(ii) For every pair of individual constants β, γ,

$\Diamond(\beta\equiv\beta\,\&\,\gamma\equiv\gamma)\rightarrow\Box(\beta\equiv\beta\leftrightarrow\gamma\equiv\gamma)$ is a necessary truth.

(iii) For any individual constants $\beta_1,\ldots,\beta_n$

$\Diamond(\beta_1\not\equiv\beta_1\,\&\,\beta_2\not\equiv\beta_2\,\&\ldots\&\,\beta_n\not\equiv\beta_n)$ is a necessary truth.

(iv) For any variables $\alpha_1,\ldots,\alpha_n$,

$\bigvee\alpha_1\ldots\alpha_n(\alpha_1\not\equiv\alpha_2\,\&\ldots\&\,\alpha_1\not\equiv\alpha_n\,\&\ldots\&\,\alpha_{n-1}\not\equiv\alpha_n)$ is a necessary truth.

B. Counterexamples, etc.

(1) Specification, of course, does not hold; e.g., $\wedge\alpha\theta\alpha\rightarrow\theta\beta$ is not in general a necessary truth, for variable α, individual constant β, and singulary predicate θ.

(2) Generalization on individual constants does not hold; i.e., it is *not* the case that for every formula ϕ, variable α, and individual constant β, if $\phi\alpha/\beta$ is a necessary truth and β does not occur in ϕ, then $\wedge\alpha\phi$ is a necessary truth. Counterexample: let individual constants β, β' and possible worlds

---

[23] It seems that paradoxes like the one about '$(9 > 7)$' can best be handled in this sort of system (expanded to include nonlogical predicates of rank greater than 1) by adding a Russellian theory of descriptions with scope always taken as innermost.

W, W', be such that $C(\beta)\in W$, $C(\beta')\in W'$, $W\neq W'$. Then $\Diamond(\beta\not\equiv\beta\,\&\,\beta'\equiv\beta')$ is a necessary truth, but $\wedge\alpha\Diamond(\beta\not\equiv\beta\,\&\,\alpha\equiv\alpha)$ is not, since it is not true of W. Thus

Adam doesn't exist but Pegasus does

is true of a possible world, and so

$\Diamond$ (Adam doesn't exist but Pegasus does)

is true of the actual and all other possible worlds, i.e., is a necessary truth. But

$\wedge x \Diamond$ (Adam doesn't exist but x does)

is false of the actual world because Adam is one of the values of the variable; thus the specific case is a necessary truth but the generalization is not.

(3) The so-called Barcan formulas $\wedge\alpha\,\Box\phi\rightarrow\Box\,\wedge\alpha\,\phi$ are not in general necessary truths. If $C(\beta)\in W$, then $\wedge\alpha\,\Box(\alpha\equiv\alpha\leftrightarrow\beta\equiv\beta)$ is true of W, but $\Box\,\wedge\alpha\,(\alpha\equiv\alpha\leftrightarrow\beta\equiv\beta)$ is not true of any W. E.g., it is true of the actual world that every object in it exists in those and only those possible worlds in which Adam exists, but it is not true of the actual world that in every possible world all the objects exist if and only if Adam exists. The converses of the Barcan formulas fail, too: $\Box\,\wedge\alpha\,\alpha\equiv\alpha$ is a necessary truth but $\wedge\alpha\,\Box\alpha\equiv\alpha$ is not; i.e., in each possible world everything is self-identical, but nothing in the actual world is self-identical in any other world, since it does not even exist in any other world. There is in general no commutativity of quantifiers with modal operators.

(4) $\beta\equiv\gamma\rightarrow\Box\beta\equiv\gamma$, for individual constants β, γ is not a necessary truth, nor are its generalizations.

Although, as mentioned above, there can be no question of axiomatizing the set of necessary truths (since 'necessary truth' has been not defined exclusively in terms of the logical form of the expressions concerned), we could introduce a set of 'formally necessary truths' or 'truths that are necessary by virtue of their form' and ask whether axioms can be found for that totality. One could say, for example, that ϕ is a *formally* necessary truth if and only if ϕ is a necessary truth and every result of replacing distinct nonlogical constants in ϕ by distinct nonlogical constants is again a necessary truth. I do not know how or even whether axioms can be found for this subset, but clearly the sentences 6 (i)–(iv) above (which seem collectively to express the crucial facts that every individual concept belongs to some possible world, no individual concept belongs to more than one possible world, there are infinitely many possible worlds, and each possible world contains infinitely many individual concepts) are among the promising candidates.[24]

References

Abbreviations are indicated in parentheses. I have included in this bibliography various items which are not explicitly cited in my text but which constitute an important part of the literature of the subject under discussion.

CARNAP, R., Modalities and quantification, *Journal of Symbolic Logic* **11** (1946) pp. 33–64.

COUTURAT, Louis, *La logique de Leibniz d'après des documents inédits* (Paris 1901).

(C)   *Opuscules et fragments inédits de Leibniz* (Paris 1903).

DÜRR, K., *Neue Beleuchtung einer Theorie von Leibniz* (Darmstadt 1930).

(E)   ERDMANN, J.D., *G. G. Leibnitii Opera Philosophica* (Berlin 1840).

(G)   GERHARDT, C.I., *Die philosophischen Schriften von G. W. Leibniz*, I–VII (Berlin 1875–1890).

HINTIKKA, J., Existential presuppositions and existential commitments, *The Journal of Philosophy* **56** (1959) pp. 125–37.

Modality and quantification, *Theoria* **27** (1961) pp. 119–28.

Studies in the logic of existence and necessity, *The Monist* **50** (1966) pp. 55–76.

KALISH, D. and R. MONTAGUE, On Tarski's formalization of predicate logic with identity, *Archiv für mathematische Logik und Grundlagenforschung* **7** (1965) pp. 81–101.

KANGER, S., The Morning Star paradox, *Theoria* **23** (1957) pp. 1–11.

(K)   KAUPPI, R., *Über die Leibnizsche Logik* (Helsinki 1960).

Einige Bemerkungen zum Principium Identitatis Indiscernibilium bei Leibniz, *Zeitschrift für philosophische Forschung* **11** (1966) pp. 497–506.

KNEALE, W. and M. KNEALE, *The Development of Logic* (Oxford 1962).

KRIPKE, S.A., Semantical analysis of modal logic I, *Zeitschrift für mathematische Logik und Grundlagen der Mathematik* **9** (1963) pp. 67–96.

Semantical considerations on modal logic, *Acta Philosophica Fennica* **16** (1963) pp. 83–94.

LEBLANC, H. and T. HAILPERIN, Nondesignating singular terms, *The Philosophical Review* **68** (1959) pp. 239–43.

(NE)   LEIBNIZ, G.W., *New Essays*, tr. A. G. Langley, Chicago, 1916.

(T)   *Theodicy*, tr. E. M. Huggard, New Haven, 1952.

MARCUS, (Mrs.) Ruth Barcan, A functional calculus of first order based on strict implication, *The Journal of Symbolic Logic* **11** (1946) pp. 1–16.

Modal Logics I: Modalities and Intensional Languages, *Boston Studies in the Philosophy of Science* (Dordrecht, Holland 1963) pp. 77–96.

MONTAGUE, R., Logical necessity, physical necessity, ethics, and quantifiers, *Inquiry* **4** (1960) pp. 259–68.

Syntactical treatments of modality, with corollaries on reflexion principles and finite axiomatizability, *Acta Philosophica Fennica* **16** (1963) pp. 153–67.

PARKINSON, G.H.R., *Leibniz: Logical Papers* (Oxford 1966).

Logic and reality in Leibniz's metaphysics (Oxford 1965).

PRIOR, A.N., *Formal Logic* (second edition, Oxford 1962).

---

[24] Research for this paper was supported by National Science Foundation Grant No. GS-180.

QUINE, W.V.O., Comments (see MARCUS [1963]), *Boston Studies in the Philosophy of Science* (Dordrecht, Holland 1963) pp. 97–104.

From a logical point of view (Cambridge, Mass., 1961).

Three grades of modal involvement, *Proceedings of the XIth International Congress of Philosophy* (Amsterdam 1953) Vol. XIV, pp. 65–81.

QUINE, W.V.O., *Word and Object* (New York 1960).

RESCHER, N., *The philosophy of Leibniz* (Englewood Cliffs, New Jersey 1967).

(R)   RUSSELL, B.A.W., *A critical exposition of the philosophy of Leibniz* (London 1900).

(S)   SCHMIDT, F., *Gottfried Wilhelm Leibniz: Fragmente zur Logik* (Berlin 1960).

TARSKI, A., A simplified formalization of predicate logic with identity, *Archiv für mathematische Logik und Grundlagenforschung* 7 (1965) pp. 61–79.

GAṄGEŚA ON THE CONCEPT OF UNIVERSAL PROPERTY
(KEVALĀNVAYIN)

B. K. MATILAL

University of Toronto, Toronto, Canada

Inference in Indian logic can be described as the establishment of an object through another already known object by establishing a connection between these two. That which we are going to prove by inference will be called probandum (*sādhya*), while the object by which we are going to prove it will be called probans (*hetu*). And the connection or association between these two objects is empirically established by the inductive method. We can define the class of agreeing instances (*sapakṣa*) as the class α of all objects x such that the probandum is present in x. In symbols: $\hat{x}$ (x possesses the probandum). Similarly the class of disagreeing instances (*vipakṣa*) can be defined as class β of all objects x such that the probandum is absent from x. In symbols: $\hat{x} - (x$ possesses the probandum). Thus, any member of α is a *sapakṣa*[1] and any member of β is a *vipakṣa*. Now, the probans as a property can be present in all, some or no members of α. Similarly, the probans can be present in all, some or no members of β. Combining these two sets of cases we get nine possibilities, of which only two cases are cases of valid inference[2].

---

[1] There is, however, one difficulty here. The *pakṣa*, i.e., the subject of inferential conclusion, possesses also the probandum, if the inference is a valid one. Thus, *pakṣa* should also be a member of α. But to avoid a *petitio principii*, the *pakṣa* should be considered as being in a twilight zone during the process of inference. In other words, we are not sure whether the probandum is present in the *pakṣa* or not. Diṅnāga defined *pakṣa* as: *sādhyatvenepsitaḥ pakṣo viruddhārthānirākṛtaḥ* (quoted by VĀCASPATI [1925] p. 273). In his system, *pakṣa* differs from *sapakṣa* in that in the latter the probandum is already established while in the former the probandum is *not yet* established. See DIṄNĀGA [1965] Chapter III, verse 18cd and the *vṛtti*; Kanakavarman (fol. 130a–130b), Vasudhararakṣita (fol. 45a). I owe this information to my friend Prof. M. Hattori. Navya-nyāya tackled this problem by its doctrine of *pakṣatā*. See MAṆIKAṆṬHA [1953] pp. 109–115; GAṄGEŚA [1926] p. 1079–1176.

[2] The second and the eighth in Diṅnāga's table are valid forms of inference. In one case the probandum and the probans are equal in extension, in the other case the class of probans is included under the class of probandum. See next note.

The above is a rough sketch of Diṅnāga's system of logic as found in his *Hetucakraḍamaru* (c.A.D. 500).[3] For our purpose it is important to note here that one of the nine possibilities demands that the probans be present in all members of α as well as β. Now, if α and β are taken to be two complementary classes in the sense that taken together they exhaust the whole universe of discourse, then the probans in the above case will be a universal property which is present everywhere. UDDYOTAKARA [1915] (c.A.D. 580) argued that in some cases of inference even our probandum can be a universal, i.e. everpresent, property. This implies that with regard to certain cases of inference class β may be a null class, class α being a universal class[4].

In Navya-nyāya school, however, the concept of everpresent property appears to have been taken very seriously. Navya-nyāya writers like Vallabha, Maṇikaṇṭha and Gaṅgeśa, rejected all such definitions of *vyāpti* (invariable concomitance between the probans and the probandum) as were based on the notion of nondeviation (*avyabhicaritatva*) because such definition would be inapplicable to cases of inference with an everpresent property as the probandum[5]. The *siddhāntalakṣaṇa* 'conclusive definition' of *vyāpti* is formulated in such a way that it becomes logically applicable to all cases of inference including those in which some everpresent property is the probandum[6]. Although there had been important and significant developments in logical theories (in India) during the period between Diṅnāga and Gaṅgeśa (c.A.D. 1325), my main concern in this paper will be with the position of Gaṅgeśa.

First, let me point out that an everpresent property, in the sense I am using it here, cannot be identified with the notion of universal class for the following reason. Using the convention of modern class logic we can say that

---

[3] This is a very short but illuminating manual of logic written by Diṅnāga. It consists of a table of nine forms of inference and only 17 explanatory verses. The Sanskrit original is lost but the Tibetan translation is available.

[4] I am using the term "everpresent" to translate the Sanskrit "*kevalānvayin*" although there is a touch of neologism here. "Omnipresent" and "ubiquitous" are not acceptable for this purpose because they express just the opposite sense. The physical space, for instance, is omnipresent or ubiquitous because everything exists in space, but it is not *kevalānvayin*. "*Kevalānvayin*" means a property which is present in everything. "Unnegatable" (used by Ingalls) may be all right inspite of the periphrasis, but I fear that it is more suitable to be an adjective of "term" rather than of "property". I refrain from using "universal property" in order to avoid confusion with "universal class".

[5] Thus see VALLABHA [1927–1934] (c.A.D. 1175) p. 500, line 1; MAṆIKAṆṬHA [1953] (c.A.D. 1300) pp. 45–46; and GAṄGEŚA [1926] p. 141. For an English version of the argument see INGALLS [1951] pp. 61–62, 86 and 151.

[6] See MAṆIKAṆṬHA [1953] p. 62; and GAṄGEŚA [1926] p. 391. Ingalls gave a rough idea about the structure of this definition (INGALLS [1951] p. 62).

classes with same members are identical. Thus, '$\omega = \omega''$' may be written as a convenient abbreviation of '$(x)(x\varepsilon\omega \cdot \equiv \cdot x\varepsilon\omega')$'. But a property or an attribute, in its non-extensional sense, cannot be held to be identical with another attribute even if they are present in all and only the same individuals [7]. Properties are generally regarded by the Indian logicians as nonextensional inasmuch as we see that they do not identify two properties like *anityatva* (noneternal-ness) and *kṛtakatva* (the property of being produced or caused) although they occur in exactly the same things [8]. In Udayana's system, however, such properties as are called *jāti* (generic characters) are taken in extensional sense because Udayana (c.A.D. 1025) identifies two *jāti* properties only if they occur in the same individuals [9].

Following the older tradition of the Nyāya school (noted in Uddyotakara), Gaṅgeśa classified the types of inference as follows [10]: 1. *kevalānvayin*, cases in which the probandum is an everpresent property, 2. *kevalavyatirekin*, cases in which the probandum is a property *unique* to the subject (*pakṣa*) so that no agreeing instances are available, 3. *anvaya-vyatirekin*, cases in which the probandum is a property present in some examples but absent from others. The third type includes the commonest forms of inference where both classes α and β (i.e., *sapakṣa* and *vipakṣa*) are neither universal class nor null class. We shall be concerned here mainly with the first type, in which there cannot be any *vipakṣa*, i.e., class β is a null class.

Uddyotakara's example (taken from Diṅnāga's [11]) of *anvayin* inference (corresponding to the first type here) was "Sound is noneternal because it is a product (*anityaḥ śabdaḥ kṛtakatvāt*)". Here the probandum noneternalness will be a universal property for those thinkers who hold to the doctrine that everything is noneternal. Note here that the universe of discourse in this case will include only noneternal things and hence class β will be a null

---

[7] See QUINE [1961] p. 107. Particularly significant is the remark of Quine [1963] p. 2, "If someone views attributes as identical always when they are attributes of the same things, he should be viewed as talking rather of classes".

[8] Those familiar with the Western logic may recall Carnap's excellent illustration of the distinction between class and property: the class of humans and the class of featherless bipeds are identical but the property humanity is distinct from the property of being a featherless biped. See CARNAP [1956] p. 18.

[9] This is the significance of the condition called *tulyatva* (equipollence) found in the list of six *jāti-bādhakas* (impediments to generic characters) mentioned by UDAYANA [1885–1919] p. 33, lines 7–8.

[10] GAṄGEŚA [1926] p. 1326. See in this connection UDDYOTAKARA [1915] p. 46.

[11] Diṅnāga anticipated the possibility of *kevalānvayin* inference and discussed the issue in DIṄNĀGA [1965] Chapter III, verse 20. See Kanakavarman (fol. 131a–131b); Vasudhararakṣita (fol. 45a). But this created little problem in Diṅnāga's system. According to him, 'to be absent from *vipakṣa*' can conveniently be interpreted as 'absence of *vipakṣa*'.

class. Vācaspati (c.A.D. 950) cited a better example of this type of inference: *Viśeṣa* (particularity) is namable because it is knowable. In a slightly modified form, this example was accepted as a paradigm in later Nyāya school: The pot is namable because it is knowable.

Gaṅgeśa defined this kind of inference as one where there is no disagreeing instances (*vipakṣa*). Since everything in the universe of discourse is (at least, theoretically) namable or expressible in language, the property namability (*abhidheyatva*) is a universal property and in no individual is there an absence of namability. To cite an instance where namability is absent is *ipso facto* to demonstrate that this instance is not inexpressible. If, however, the opponent does not cite such an instance where namability is absent, but, nevertheless, believes it to be existent, then as far as the logicians' inference is concerned it is as good as non-existent, since inferential procedure demands the use of language. The opponent may argue that although a disagreeing instance in this case is not expressible in language, it can still be a communicable concept in the sense that it is *conveyed* by the meaning of some linguistic expression. But this would run counter to the Nyāya premiss that there cannot be any instance which is not namable.

Besides, Gaṅgeśa argued from the opponent's viewpoint, the notion of everpresent property invites the following paradox. If *p* is asserted to be an everpresent property then one can infer validly from this premiss that *p* is not everpresent. It is observed that each property (*dharma*) is such that it is legitimate (according to the Indian theory of induction) to assert that each property is such that it is absent from something. Using quantificational notations and interpreting '*Fx*' as '*x* is a property' and '*Oxy*' as '*x* is present in *y*' we may represent this premiss as:

$$(x)(\exists y)(Fx \supset - Oxy).$$

Now, since *p* is a property (which we have assumed to be everpresent), it follows (by universal instantiation and truth-functional tautology) that *p* is such that it is *absent* from something. In other words, the conclusion is '$(\exists y) - Opy$'. This implies that there is an instance *y* where *p* (i.e., knowability) is *not* present. Thus, our original assumption that *p* is an everpresent property is contradicted.

Gaṅgeśa tried to answer this objection as follows. If the property 'to be absent from something', i.e. the property represented by the propositional function '$(\exists y) - Opy$', is said to be a property which is not absent from anything then the same property becomes everpresent. If, however, this property (i.e., 'to be absent from something') happens to be *not* present in something

x then that x becomes, in fact, everpresent[12]. Let us try to understand the implication of this argument. Let class ω be defined as $\hat{x}(\exists y) - Oxy$. Now, if we assume $-(\omega\varepsilon\omega)$, it means that the statement '$(\exists y) - O\omega y$' is false, i.e., '$-(\exists y) - O\omega y$' is true. This implies that the classproperty of ω is something which is not absent from anything, i.e., everpresent. In an indirect way, this means that ω is a universal class. If, on the other hand, we assume $\omega\varepsilon\omega$ then the statement '$(\exists y) - O\omega y$' becomes true. This means that there is something y from which the class-property ω is absent. But to deny the class-property ω of something y means to admit y as an everpresent property.

Gaṅgeśa's argument was exactly similar to this, although he did not use the notion of class. Instead, he used his notion of constant absence (*atyantābhāva*) and its counterpositive-ness (*pratiyogitā*). A constant absence is arrived at by hypostatizing the negation illustrated in the matrix 'there is no x in y' or 'x is not present in y'. Thus, y is said to be the locus which possesses constant absence of x, and x is said to be the counterpositive of an absence which is present in locus y.[13] In fact, the constant absence of x may conveniently be regarded as a class-property of the class which is defined as $\hat{y}(\exists x)$ (x is not present in y). The mutual absence of x (illustrated by the matrix 'y is not x') may likewise be regarded as a class-property of the class which is defined (using usual symbols for identity and negation) as $\hat{y}(\exists x)$ ($x \neq y$). This interpretation of absences in terms of the class-concept of modern logic gets indirect support from the fact that Navya-nyāya, in most cases, identifies two absences which occur in the same loci[14].

Thus, Gaṅgeśa argued as follows. If the property of being the counterpositive of a constant absence does not become the counterpositive of any constant absence then the same property can be taken to be everpresent. And if, on the other hand, that property is regarded as the counterpositive of some constant absence (say, the constant absence of x in locus y) then the locus y where such a constant absence resides becomes itself an everpresent property. The upshot of Gaṅgeśa's argument is that if something x is a property it does not necessarily follow that there is something else y where-

---

[12] This argument may remind one of the famous class-paradox, viz., if the class of all classes which are not members of themselves is a member of itself, then it is not a member of itself. But note that Gaṅgeśa's philosophical motivation was different.

[13] For the notions of counterpositive and constant absence, see INGALLS [1951] p. 54–58. They have also been explained in detail in my book, see MATILAL [1968] pp. 52–61, 94–95.

[14] Thus the prevailing view of Navya-nyāya writers is that the two absences which are *samaniyata* (equipollent) are identical.

from x will be absent because there are everpresent properties also. An everpresent property can now be defined as:

D1. x is an everpresent property if and only if x is not the counterpositive of any constant absence[15].

To develop the next point in Gaṅgeśa's discussion we have to understand what Navya-nyāya calls a non-pervasive (avyāpyavṛtti) property. A property is called non-pervasive if and only if it occupies only a part of the locus such that in remaining parts of the locus there is the constant absence of that property[16]. Thus, properties like a pot or contact-with-a-monkey (in fact, almost all properties except certain abstract ones like cow-ness), with respect to their loci, such as a piece of ground or a tree, behave as non-pervasive properties. Now, the constant absence of a property p is regarded as another property, say q, which is present in all things except where p is present. But the constant absence of any non-pervasive property, it may be argued, will become an everpresent property simply because such an absence is not only present in all loci except where the non-pervasive property in question is present but also in locus where the same non-pervasive property is present. This follows from the very definition of non-pervasive property. But Gaṅgeśa pointed out that as soon as we introduce the notion of delimitors (avacchedaka) in our discourse the constant absence of a non-pervasive property (say, a pot) can no longer be, strictly speaking, an everpresent property. Thus, a pot cannot be said to be constantly absent from the locus ground as delimited by the counterpositive (pratiyogin) pot. In simple language, this only means that right in the space of the ground occupied by the pot there cannot be any constant absence of the pot. Hence, such a constant absence is not everpresent. Note that the notion of delimitor here serves to dispel the vagueness of ordinary uses of 'locus (adhikaraṇa)' and 'occurrence (vṛtti)'.

---

[15] MAṆIKAṆṬHA [1953] gave a similar definition of everpresent property "tatrātyan-tābhāvāpratiyogī dharmaḥ kevalānvayī" (p. 126). Maṇikaṇṭha's three-fold classification of parāmarśa corresponds to Gaṅgeśa's three-fold classification of inference. But there seems to be a difference. Maṇikaṇṭha seems to consider the nature of the probans while Gaṅgeśa, as he has been explained by Raghunātha, considers the nature of the probandum. Thus, an inference with an everpresent property as the probandum and an ordinary (non-everpresent) property as the probans will be included under the first type, i.e., kevalānvayin inference. This is, at least, what Gadādhara seems to think. See Gadādhara's sub-commentary on Raghanātha's commentary on GAṄGEŚA [1926] p. 1327, lines 6–7: "... kevalānvayisādhyaka-vyatirekihetoḥ kevalānvayyanumānatayā ..."

[16] See INGALLS [1951] p. 73. The meaning of "contact-with-a-monkey" has been explained by Ingalls. See also MATILAL [1968] pp. 53, 71–72.

Another suggestion for constructing an everpresent property can be given as follows. The ubiquitous physical space (*gagana*) in the Nyāya-Vaiśeṣika system of categories is held to be a non-occurrent entity in the sense that it does not occur in any locus. All entities of the Nyāya-Vaiśeṣika system are properties (in the sense that they occur in some locus or other) except entities like the ubiquitous space. Thus, since there is no entity where the space might occur as a property, the constant absence of the space becomes everpresent. But this procedure eventually leads to some difficulties. Technically speaking, the constant absence of the space can very well be the counterpositive of another constant absence, viz., the constant absence of the constant absence of the space (which, according to Nyāya, is just identical with the space itself). Thus, the above definition of everpresent property cannot be applied to the constant absence of the space. This eventually landed Gaṇgeśa into the puzzling discussion of the Nayva-nyāya school, viz., what constitutes the absence of an absence?[17]

The constant absence of x is constantly absent from all things except those that have no x. Hence, the constant absence of the constant absence of x is present in all and only those things where x is present. Applying the principle of identification of the indiscernibles, Udayana, and following him Gaṇgeśa, identified the constant absence of the constant absence of x with x on the gound that

A. $(y)(y$ has the constant absence of the constant absence of $x \cdot \equiv \cdot y$ has $x)$.

The mutual absence of pot is constantly absent from all things that are called "pot", i.e., from all things that have pot-ness. Thus, the constant absence of the mutual absence of pot is present in all and only those things that have pot-ness. Therefore, as above, one can identify the constant absence of the mutual absence of pot with pot-ness on the principle that

B. $(y)(y$ has the constant absence of the mutual absence of pot $\cdot \equiv \cdot y$ has pot-ness).[18]

Note that we are identifying here two class-properties on the ground that the corresponding classes are identical by virtue of their having the same members. This indirectly supports my earlier suggestion that absences in

---

[17] See INGALLS [1951] pp. 68, 71–72.
[18] See GAṄGEŚA [1926] p. 1350: *atyantābhāvātyantābhāvaḥ pratiyogy eva; anyonyābhāvātyantābhāvas tu pratiyogivṛttir asādhāraṇo dharma iti.* See UDAYANA [1926] Chapter III, verse 2.

many contexts can conveniently be taken to be class-properties suitably chosen. And properties, in such contexts, are used in their non-intensional sense.

Navya-nyāya, however, regards the constant absence of the ubiquitous space as an everpresent property, and accordingly, Gaṅgeśa developed a technical sense of 'everpresent property' by rephrasing D1 as follows: [19]

D2. x is everpresent if and only if x is not the counterpositive of any occurrent (*vṛttimat*) constant absence.

Although the constant absence of the space *may be* said to be the counterpositive of the constant absence of the constant absence of the space, the second absence is not *occurrent* because it is to be identified with the space and the space is, by definition, not occurrent anywhere. Properties like knowability and namability are *not* the counterpositive of any occurrent constant absence and hence they can be called everpresent. This is one of many possible interpretations of Gaṅgeśa's rephrasing (which was ambiguous in the original). But, according to Raghunātha, this was just Gaṅgeśa's way of being polite to the opponent (cf. *abhyupagamamātram*). Actually, the constant absence of the constant absence of the space cannot be identified with the space because the above principle A is not applicable here. Since in the Nyāya-Vaiśeṣika system there is no entity which *has* the space as a property, we cannot identify it with the constant absence of the constant absence of the space under principle A. The significance of the adjective "occurrent (*vṛttimat*)" was explained by Raghunātha as follows. When something is said to be present in something else, it is present there always through some relation or other. Thus, in speaking of something as ever present one should specify the relation through which it is considered present everywhere:

D3. x is ever present through relation r if and only if r is the delimiting relation of the counterpositive-ness of some constant absence and x is never the counterpositive of such absence [20].

To expose another logical difficulty involved in the notion of everpresent property we have to go back to the definition of *kevalānvayin* inference (type 1 above). First, it is odd to say that the probans does not reside in disagreeing instances, when there is, in fact, no disagreeing instance. It is

---

[19] GAṄGEŚA [1926] p. 1353: *vṛttimad-atyantābhāvāpratiyogitvaṃ kevalānvayitvam.*

[20] Raghunātha comments on GAṄGEŚA [1926] p. 1354: *evaṃ ca yatsambandhāvacchin-napratiyogitākābhāvāpratiyogitvaṃ yasya tasya tena sambandhena kevalānvayitvam iti sūcayituṃ vṛttimad iti.*

further odd to say that there is no disagreeing instance, when "disagreeing instance (*vipakṣa*)" is a mere indesignate or empty (*nirupākhya*) term, for one tends to argue that to make such denials meaningful our acceptance of the existence of such non-entities is in order. Vācaspati puzzled over this problem because, according to the Nyāya theory, each negation, in order to be meaningful, must negate a real entity and must denote an absence which usually behaves as a property occurring in some locus. Thus, an absence is always determined by its counterpositive (i.e., the negatum) on the one hand and by the locus (*ādhāra*) on the other[21]. Vācaspati tried to solve the above puzzle by saying that the prudent course is silence, i.e., not to deny or affirm anything (including existence) of the non-existents. The denial sounds odd because its contradictory, i.e., affirmation, sounds odd too[22]. Udayana suggested a better method of answering such problems. According to him, a statement like

(1) "the rabbit's horns do not exist"

does not affirm or deny existence of anything, but simply expresses an absence *not* of the rabbit's horns *but* of horns, an absence which occurs in a rabbit[23]. Note that having horns is a real property such that one can meaningfully speak of its absence (another real property for the Naiyāyikas). This analysis is related to the epistemological theory of error of the Nyāya school, which is technically known as *anyathākhyāti*. The structure of this analysis may remind one of B. Russell's analysis of similar statements with his theory of description[24]. In quantificational notations, (1) can be analyzed as:

(2) $(x)(x$ is a rabbit $\supset x$ is a locus of the absence of horns) or,
$-(\exists x)(x$ is a rabbit $\cdot x$ is *not* a locus of the absence of horns).

Applying Udayana's principle of analysis, Gaṅgeśa tried to make sense of statements which make use of such indesignate expression as "the absence of an everpresent property like knowability", viz.,

(3) "the absence of knowability is *not* present in y" (a true one).
(4) "the absence of knowability is present in y" (a false one).

---

[21] VĀCASPATI [1925] p. 172: *sadbhyām abhāvo nirūpyate naikena satety uktam.*
[22] See VĀCASPATI [1925] pp. 172–173.
[23] Compare UDAYANA [1957] p. 331: *kas tarhi śaśaśṛṅgaṃ nāstīty asyārthaḥ? śaśe adhika-raṇe viṣāṇābhāvo'stīti.* In UDAYANA [1940] Udayana discussed at length the example *"bandhyā-suto na vaktā* (the son of a barren woman does not speak)" (see pp. 64–73).
[24] See RUSSELL [1919] pp. 168–180.

Note that "the absence of knowability" is, as it stands, an empty term and on par with "the present king of France". According to Gaṅgeśa, we can rephrase (3) and (4) as:

(5) Knowability is not the counterpositive of any absence that may occur in y.

(6) Knowability is the counterpositive of an absence which occurs in y.

Here, (5) predicates of knowability the *absence* of the property of being the counterpositive of any absence occurring in y, while (6) predicates of knowability the counterpositive-ness of an absence occurring in y. Thus, (5) expresses a trivial truth (see D1 before) while (6) expresses a falsehood. Note that "an absence which occurs in y" will denote a real absence occurring in the thing substituted for y and that its counterpositive will be a real entity. Hence the property of being such a counterpositive is also a real property which characterizes certain things (viz., things which are really absent from y) but not knowability.

Gaṅgeśa used this method of analysis in order to make sense of the doubt or uncertainty (*saṃśaya*) of the form "perhaps it is knowable, perhaps it is not". This statement which expresses a doubt can be said to be a meaningful statement if it is rephrased in the above manner so as to avoid the use of any empty term-complex such as "the absence of knowability" (which refers to nothing) as a predicate or even as a subject (as in 4 above). Note that the second part of the statement expressing doubt, viz., "it is not (knowable)", would have contained such an empty term-complex, if it were straight-forwardly analyzed in its logical form: it has the absence of knowability.

It should be noted in this connection that, according to the Navya-nyāya theory of inference, an inference (as an effect, i.e., *kārya*) must be pre-conditioned by what Navya-nyāya calls *pakṣatā* [25]. The condition of *pakṣatā*, according to the view of the old Nyāya, involves in the presence of a doubt or uncertainty which should be expressed in the form "perhaps the subject possesses the probandum, perhaps it does not". This postulate is based upon the simple fact that we do not infer something which we already know with certainty unless we wish to prove it again. Now, if inference of an everpresent property like knowability has to be an actual event, it should be pre-conditioned by an uncertainty of the form described above. Thus, the statement which expresses this uncertainty or doubt must be a meaningful statement so that the required doubt (*saṃśaya*) may, in fact, arise. Gaṅgeśa

---

[25] MAṆIKAṆṬHA [1953] pp. 109–115; and GAṄGEŚA [1926] pp. 1079–1176.

pointed out that when the second part of the statement expressing doubt is interpreted as (6) above we can retain its meaningfulness and avoid using empty terms that refer to nothing[26].

I would like to conclude by remarking that while studying Indian logic, scholars will find themselves concerned with issues of two different kinds. The first are those problems which are bounded by the Indian tradition itself, i.e., those which arise out of the peculiar yet rich tradition of India's scholastic past. They are partly conditioned by the Sanskrit language and partly by the fundamental concepts and philosophical attitudes that Indian logicians inherited. The second set of problems which we face here could be called universal. They are, in essence, the very same problems faced by the Western tradition, though often, because of the parachiol and tradition-bound interests of both sides, this fact has been either ignored or badly misunderstood. I cannot help feeling that a historian would be gratified to learn that many of the problems with which Indian logicians of the 12th and 13th centuries came to grips are very similar to the problems faced by modern analytic philosophers. In judging these medieval logicians we must bear in mind the fact that it is only quite recently that many of these issues have been satisfactorily explained. For students of philosophy in general, and more particularly for historians of philosophy, I find it regrettable that so little of the Indian philosophical materials are available in anything like satisfactory form. The difficulties are not only those of language, but also the peculiar philological problems in translating Sanskrit philosophical texts. Far too many of the existing translations are not only unreadable but also sometimes philosophically absurd. Some of them abound in old-fashioned terminology that is at best misleading, and at worst simply wrong. I make this remarks about the materials, because it seems to me obvious that future historians will increasingly take note of the considerable Indian contributions to the general heritage of philosophy and it is essential that they do so on the basis of careful and valid studies and translations.

References

CARNAP, R., Meaning and necessity (Chicago, University Press, 2nd ed., with supplements, 1956).

DIŃNĀGA, Hetucakraḍamaru. It survives in Tibetan translation (Tibetan Tripiṭaka). Tanjur Mdo; Ce. fols. 193$^b_1$–194$^b_2$ (Narthang edition). Printed with a re-translation into Sanskrit by D.C. Chatterjee in: Indian Historical Quarterly 9 (1933) 266–272.

---

[26] GAŃGEŚA [1926] pp. 1356–1359.

DIṄNĀGA, Pramāṇasamuccayavṛtti. It survives in Tibetan translation (Tibetan Tripiṭaka). Peking edition, Mdo-hgrel XCV, Ce. No. 5701: Vasudhararakṣita. No. 5702: Kanaka-varman. A Japanese translation (from the Tibetan version) of the important portions has been published by H. Kitagawa: A study of Indian classical logic- Diṅnāga's system (Tokyo, 1965). My knowledge of this book (apart from the Sanskrit citations) is derived from the lectures of M. Hattori who used the Japanese translation.

GAṄGEŚA, Tattvacintāmaṇi (Anumāna-khaṇḍa). Edited with the Dīdhiti commentary of Raghunātha and the sub-commentary of Gadādhara (Benares, Chowkhamba Sanskrit Series 42, Chowkhamba Office, 1926).

INGALLS, D. H. H., Materials for the study of Navya-nyāya logic (Cambridge, Mass., Harvard Oriental Series 40, Harvard, 1951).

MAṆIKAṆṬHA, Nyāyaratna. Edited by V. Subrahmanya Sastri and V. Krishnamacharya (Madras, Madras Government Oriental Series 104, Oriental Mss. Library, 1953).

MATILAL, B. K., The Navya-nyāya doctrine of negation (Cambridge, Mass., Harvard Oriental Series 46, Harvard, 1968).

QUINE, W. V. O., From a logical point of view (Cambridge, Mass., Harvard, second revised ed., 1961).

QUINE, W. V. O., Set theory and its logic (Cambridge, Mass., Belknap Press of the Harvard University Press, 1963).

RUSSELL, B., Introduction to mathematical philosophy (London, Allen and Unwin, 1919).

UDAYANA, Ātmatattvaviveka. Edited by Dhundhiraja Sastri (Benares, Chowkhamba Sanskrit Series 84, Chowkhamba Office, 1940).

UDAYANA, (Vaiśeṣikadarśana) Kiraṇāvalī. Edited by Vindheswari Prasad Dube (Dvivedin) (Benares, Benares Sanskrit Series 9, Braj B. Das, 1885–1919).

UDAYANA, Nyāyakusumāñjali. Edited by P. Upadhyaya and Dhundhiraja Sastri (Benares, Kashi Sanskrit Series 30, Chowkhamba Office, 1957).

UDDYOTAKARA, Nyāyavārttika. Edited by Vindheswari Prasad Dvivedin (Benares, Chowkhamba Office, 1915).

VALLABHA, Nyāyalīlāvatī. Edited by Harihara Sastri and Dhundhiraja Sastri (Benares, Chowkhamba Sanskrit Series 64, Chowkhamba Office, 1927–1934).

VĀCASPATI, Nyāyavārttikatātparyaṭīkā. Edited by Rajeswar Sastri (Benares, Kashi Sanskrit Series 24, Chowkhamba Office, 1925).

PROGRAM

3rd INTERNATIONAL CONGRESS FOR LOGIC, METHODOLOGY AND PHILOSOPHY OF SCIENCE

Amsterdam, August 25–September 2, 1967

FRIDAY MORNING, AUGUST 25

9.30 a.m.–11.00 a.m.	**Opening Ceremonies**

Section 5, Chairman: H. B. CURRY

11.15 a.m.–12.00 a.m.	**Invited Hour Address** SIR KARL POPPER, Epistemology and scientific knowledge.

FRIDAY AFTERNOON, AUGUST 25

Section 2, Chairman: A. HEYTING

2.30 p.m.– 3.15 p.m.	**Invited Hour Address** S. FEFERMAN, Autonomous transfinite progressions and the extent of predicative mathematics.

Section 4, Chairman: A. R. ANDERSON

3.30 p.m.– 5.30 p.m.	**Invited Half Hour Addresses**
3.30 p.m.– 4.00 p.m.	D. FØLLESDAL, Interpretation of quantifiers.
4.10 p.m.– 4.40 p.m.	M. A. E. DUMMETT, Platonism.
4.50 p.m.– 5.20 p.m.	A. A. MARKOV, An approach to constructive mathematical logic.
5.30 p.m.	Closure of the session.

Section 1, Chairman: A. BORGERS

3.30 p.m.– 5.50 p.m.	**Contributed Papers**
3.30 p.m.– 3.45 p.m.	S. AANDERAA, A reduction method for special cases of the decision problem.
3.50 p.m.– 4.05 p.m.	J. E. FENSTAD, On the completeness of some recursive progressions of axiomatic theories.
4.10 p.m.– 4.25 p.m.	J. M. DUNN, An algebraic completeness proof for the first degree fragment of entailment.
4.30 p.m.– 4.45 p.m.	R. H. THOMASON, On the strong semantical completeness of the intuitionistic predicate calculus.
4.50 p.m.– 5.05 p.m.	K. BING, A linear system of natural deduction with few restrictions on variables.
5.10 p.m.– 5.25 p.m.	N. M. NAGORNY, About one simplification of the notion "realisation", introduced by S. C. Kleene.
5.30 p.m.– 5.45 p.m.	Y. N. MOSCHOVAKIS, Model-theoretic characterization of search computable and hyperprojective relations.
5.50 p.m.	Closure of the session.

Section 5, Chairman: E. ALBRECHT

3.30 p.m.– 5.30 p.m. **Contributed Papers**
3.30 p.m.– 3.45 p.m. S. J. DOORMAN, Analyticity: its limited role in the philosophy of science.
3.50 p.m.– 4.05 p.m. H. E. KYBURG Jr., The synthetically probable a priori.
4.10 p.m.– 4.25 p.m. M. BLACK, Can experience support induction?
4.30 p.m.– 4.45 p.m. R. HILPINEN, On inductive generalization in binary functional calculus of first order.
4.50 p.m.– 5.05 p.m. H. A. WEISSMAN, Remarks on induction.
5.10 p.m.– 5.25 p.m. H. SMOKLER, Competing concepts of confirmation.
5.30 p.m.   Closure of the session.

SATURDAY MORNING, AUGUST 26

9.30 a.m.–12.30 p.m. Intersectional Symposium 'The role of formal logic in the evaluation of argumentation in natural languages'.
                     Chairman: Y. BAR-HILLEL

Section 5, Chairman: B. JUHOS

9.30 a.m.–12.30 p.m. **Contributed Papers**
9.30 a.m.– 9.45 a.m. D. WAHL, On the theory of experimental method.
10.10 a.m.–10.25 a.m. A. KOSING, Remarks on the concept of science.
10.30 a.m.–10.45 a.m. E. ALBRECHT, The relations between logic, epistemology and methodology.
10.50 a.m.–11.05 a.m. R. BAARS, Logic and the development of science.
11.10 a.m.–11.25 a.m. E. DE GORTARI, Symmetry as a scientific method.
11.30 a.m.–11.45 a.m. B. G. KOUZNETSOV, Einstein et Spinoza.
11.50 a.m.–12.05 p.m. C. JOJA, The concept of nature in the contemporary philosophy of science.
12.10 p.m.–12.25 p.m. R. GENOFRE, Revolutionary discovery of functional mathematics of word and their aesthetico-logical sequences.
12.30 p.m.   Closure of the session.

Sections 4 and 10, Chairman: R. M. MARTIN

9.30 a.m.–12.30 p.m. **Contributed Papers**
9.30 a.m.– 9.45 a.m. R. L. MARTIN, On Grelling's paradox.
9.50 a.m.–10.05 a.m. L. BÜCHLER, Paradoxes, intuitionism and relativity.
10.10 a.m.–10.25 a.m. R. J. ILIC, Identity in mathematics.
10.30 a.m.–10.45 a.m. M. MLEZIVA, Analytische Wahrheit und Fixierung der Extension.
10.50 a.m.–11.05 a.m. K. BERKA, Remarks on the antinomy of the namerelation.
11.10 a.m.–11.25 a.m. M. GROSS, The notion of reference in linguistics.
11.30 a.m.–11.45 a.m. D. P. GORSKI, The problem of meaning (sense) for symbolical expressions as a problem of their understanding.
11.50 a.m.–12.05 p.m. V. A. SMIRNOV, Natural inference and transformational analysis.
12.10 p.m.–12.25 p.m. C. H. HEIDRICH, Models for language production and their relation to the theory of Katz and Postal.
12.30 p.m.   Closure of the session.

SATURDAY AFTERNOON, AUGUST 26

Section 10, Chairman: B. MATES

2.30 p.m.– 3.15 p.m. **Invited Hour Address**
                     J. J. KATZ, The logic of questions.

Section 10, Chairman: J. F. STAAL

3.30 p.m.– 4.15 p.m.	**Invited Half Hour Address**
3.30 p.m.– 4.00 p.m.	J. LYONS, Existence, location, possession and transitivity.
4.15 p.m.	Closure of the session.

4.15 p.m.– 5.30 p.m.	Intersectional Symposium 'The role of formal logic in the evaluation of argumentation in natural languages'. Chairman: Y. BAR-HILLEL.

Section 2, Chairman: A. GRZEGORCZYK

3.50 p.m.– 5.10 p.m.	**Contributed Papers**
3.50 p.m.– 4.05 p.m.	H. LUCKHARDT, Brouwer-Funktionale und Funktionalinterpretation der Analysis.
4.10 p.m.– 4.25 p.m.	H. PFEIFFER, A constructive system of ordinals.
4.30 p.m.– 4.45 p.m.	I. REZNIKOFF, An effective aspect of independent axiomatization.
4.50 p.m.– 5.05 p.m.	H. N. GUPTA, The roles of some axioms in n-dimensional Cartesian spaces over arbitrary ordered fields.
5.10 p.m.	Closure of the session.

Section 5, Chairman: J. A. PASSMORE

3.30 p.m.– 5.10 p.m.	**Contributed Papers**
3.30 p.m.– 3.45 p.m.	P. CAWS, A negative interpretation of the causal principle.
3.50 p.m.– 4.05 p.m.	J. WALLACE, Causality and logical form.
4.10 p.m.– 4.25 p.m.	J. ZEMAN, Das Gefälle-modell in der Ontologie und Erkenntnistheorie.
4.30 p.m.– 4.45 p.m.	S. NOVAKOVIC, Is there a chance for a logic of discovery?
4.50 p.m.– 5.05 p.m.	V. N. SADOVSKY and E. G. JUDIN, On ways of construction of the general system theory.
5.10 p.m.	Closure of the session.

MONDAY MORNING, AUGUST 28

Section 2, Chairman: A. HEYTING

9.30 a.m.–12.30 a.m.	**Symposium 'Foundations of intuitionism'**
9.30 a.m.	J. MYHILL, Formal systems of intuitionistic analysis I, read in the absence of the author by P. C. Gilmore.
10.30 a.m.	S. C. KLEENE, Constructive functions in 'the foundations of intuitionistic mathematics'.
11.30 a.m.	W. W. TAIT, Constructive reasoning.

Section 3, Chairman: S. GORN

9.50 a.m.–12.10 p.m.	**Contributed Papers**
9.50 a.m.–10.05 a.m.	D. M. R. PARK, Computer programs and decision problems.
10.10 a.m.–10.25 a.m.	J. W. THATCHER, A generalization of finite automata theory – connections to programming languages and decision problems.
10.30 a.m.–10.45 a.m.	M. A. HARRISON, On the modeling of programming languages by formal languages.
10.50 a.m.–11.05 a.m.	S. GINSBURG and E. H. SPANIER, Languages generated by restrictions on the use of rewriting systems.
11.10 a.m.–11.25 a.m.	G. T. HERMAN, A definition of simulation for discrete computing systems.
11.30 a.m.–11.45 a.m.	W. A. V. D. MOORE, A formal programming language.

11.50 a.m.–12.05 p.m.	B. MELTZER, Flexible complete strategies in theoremproving by computer.
12.10 p.m.	Closure of the session.

Section 5, Chairman: M. BUNGE

9.30 a.m.–12.30 a.m.	**Contributed Papers**
9.30 a.m.– 9.45 a.m.	G. KRÖBER, Structure of laws.
9.50 a.m.–10.05 a.m.	W. SEGETH, Methodical rules.
10.10 a.m.–10.25 a.m.	M. MARKOVIC, Apodictic universality of scientific laws.
10.30 a.m.–10.45 a.m.	R. WÓJCICKI, On some meaning connections between terms.
10.50 a.m.–11.05 a.m.	B. S. GRJASNOV, Logical analysis of the concept 'object of scientific research'.
11.10 a.m.–11.25 a.m.	R. J. HEASTON, The development of a general methodology of analysis from conservation equations.
11.30 a.m.–11.45 a.m.	V. V. MSHVENIERADZE, Objective foundations of scientific methodology.
11.50 a.m.–12.05 p.m.	K. LEHRER, The theoretician's dilemma: a solution.
12.10 p.m.–12.25 p.m.	D. J. SCHULZ, Paradoxes of confirmation and symmetries of language.
12.30 p.m.	Closure of the session.

MONDAY AFTERNOON, AUGUST 28

Section 3, Chairman: A. VAN WIJNGAARDEN

2.30 p.m.– 3.15 p.m.	**Invited Hour Address**
	H. HIŻ, Computable and noncomputable elements in syntax.

Section 2, Chairman: A. HEYTING

3.30 p.m.– 5.30 p.m.	**Symposium 'Foundations of Intuitionism'**
3.30 p.m.	A. S. TROELSTRA, Theory of choice sequences.
4.30 p.m.	G. KREISEL, Functions, ordinals, species.

Section 11, Chairman: J. F. STAAL

4.10 p.m.– 5.30 p.m.	**Invited Half Hour Addresses**
4.10 p.m.– 4.40 p.m.	B. MATES, Leibniz on possible worlds.
4.50 p.m.– 5.20 p.m.	B. K. MATILAL, Gaṅgeśa on the concept of universal property (kevalanvayin).
5.30 p.m.	Closure of the session.

Section 5, S. KÖRNER

3.30 p.m.– 5.30 p.m.	**Contributed Papers**
3.30 p.m.– 3.45 p.m.	VL. ZEMAN and B. KAZANSKY, Contribution to the theory of operations. (Read by Vl. Zeman.)
3.50 p.m.– 4.05 p.m.	L. TONDL, Some possibilities of reduction in identification procedures.
4.10 p.m.– 4.25 p.m.	R. MATTISON, A syntactically complete set of axioms for the relation 'wholly before' between intervals.
4.30 p.m.– 4.45 p.m.	R. S. MCGOWAN, Extension and defence of the positivist meaning criterion.
4.50 p.m.– 5.05 p.m.	G. A. GEVORKJAN, Scientific theory, its function.
5.10 p.m.– 5.25 p.m.	H. MARGENAU, Philosophical problems connected with the concept of measurement.
5.30 p.m.	Closure of the session.

TUESDAY MORNING, AUGUST 29

	Section 3, Chairman: H. Hiż.
9.30 a.m.–12.30 p.m.	**Symposium 'Parenthemes'**
	Invited participants: A. Grzegorczyk and Z. Pawlak.

	Section 2, Chairman: S. C. Kleene
9.50 a.m.–12.30 a.m.	**Contributed Papers**
9.50 a.m.–10.05 a.m.	E. Wette, Transfinite computation of the Gödel function P.
10.10 a.m.–10.25 a.m.	B. Scarpellini, A generalisation of Gentzen's second consistency proof.
10.30 a.m.–10.45 a.m.	J. Diller, Computability of certain functionals of higher type.
10.50 a.m.–11.05 a.m.	M. Kühnrich, On ordered pairs, relations and universal algebras.
11.10 a.m.–11.25 a.m.	J. Heidema, Metamathematical ideals and Ω-algebras.
11.30 a.m.–11.45 a.m.	L. Bukovsky, Δ-models and distributivity in Boolean algebras.
11.50 a.m.–12.05 p.m.	A. S. Davis, Postulates for the operations of direct and inverse image.
12.10 p.m.–12.25 p.m.	A. Sochor, Δ-model over generalized Boolean algebra.
12.30 p.m.	Closure of the session.

TUESDAY AFTERNOON, AUGUST 29

	Section 4, Chairman: K. J. J. Hintikka
2.30 p.m.– 3.15 p.m.	**Invited Hour Address**
	M. Dummett, Platonism.

	Section 3, Chairman: F. B. Cannonito
3.30 p.m.– 5.00 p.m.	**Invited Half Hour Addresses**
3.30 p.m.– 4.00 p.m.	J. W. de Bakker, Problems in the theory of programming languages.
4.15 p.m.– 4.45 p.m.	Z. Pawlak, On the notion of a computer.
5.00 p.m.	Closure of the session.

	Section 8, Chairman: J. G. Taylor
3.30 p.m.– 5.30 p.m.	**Invited Half Hour Addresses**
3.30 p.m.– 4.00 p.m.	B. Farrell, Some thoughts on the use of models.
4.10 p.m.– 4.40 p.m.	J. J. Gibson, A study of the stick-in-water illusion with children.
4.50 p.m.– 5.20 p.m.	J. G. Taylor, Perception as a function of behaviour.
5.30 p.m.	Closure of the session.

	Section 11, Chairman: B. Mates
3.30 p.m.– 5.30 p.m.	**Contributed Papers**
3.30 p.m.– 3.45 p.m.	E. Herlitzius, The dialogue in the history of science.
3.50 p.m.– 4.05 p.m.	N. J. Rondy, The history and logic of science.
4.10 p.m.– 4.25 p.m.	A. Joja, The propositions de futuris contingentibus and the Aristotelian concept of truth.
4.30 p.m.– 4.45 p.m.	N. Rescher, The history of the concept of quantity and quality in 'Aristotelian' logic.
4.50 p.m.– 5.05 p.m.	G. Buchdahl, Kant on gravitation: a priori or a posteriori.
5.10 p.m.– 5.25 p.m.	R. E. Butts, The purpose of Kant's talk about purposes.
5.30 p.m.	Closure of the session.

WEDNESDAY MORNING, AUGUST 30

Section 9, Chairman: I. GADOUREK

9.30 a.m.–10.15 a.m. **Invited Hour Address**
H. A. SIMON, On judging the plausibility of theories.

Sections 5 and 6, Chairman: G. NUCHELMANS

10.30 a.m.–12.45 p.m. **Invited Half Hour Addresses**
10.30 a.m.–11.00 a.m. M. B. HESSE, A self-correcting observation language.
11.15 a.m.–11.45 a.m. J. HINTIKKA, The varieties of information and scientific explanation.
12.00 p.m.–12.30 p.m. W. YOURGRAU, Is general relativity theory verified? A critical analysis of Dicke's quadruple-moment hypothesis.
12.45 p.m. Closure of the session.

Section 2, Chairman: K. SCHÜTTE

10.30 a.m.–12.50 p.m. **Contributed Papers**
10.30 a.m.–10.45 a.m. B. BALCAR, Submodels of ultraproduct models.
10.50 a.m.–11.05 a.m. VL. DEVIDÉ, A theorem on partially ordered sets and its applications.
11.10 a.m.–11.25 a.m. P. C. GILMORE, The consistency of a theory of partial sets.
11.30 a.m.–11.45 a.m. W. MAREK and J. ONYSZKIEWICZ, Some independence results in set theory.
11.50 a.m.–12.05 p.m. T. JECH, Non-provability of Souslin's hypothesis.
12.10 p.m.–12.25 p.m. W. GIELEN, A counter-example to a strong intuitionistic form of the continuum-hypothesis.
12.30 p.m.–12.45 p.m. D. PRAWITZ, Hauptsatz for higher order logic.
12.50 p.m. Closure of the session.

Section 5, Chairman: J. B. UBBINK

10.30 a.m.–12.30 p.m. **Contributed Papers**
10.30 a.m.–10.45 a.m. M. V. POPOVICH, Problems of analysis of the language of science.
10.50 a.m.–11.05 a.m. A. J. LYON, A non-deductive logical relation in Wittgenstein's philosophy.
11.10 a.m.–11.25 a.m. L. A. ABRAMJAN, Scientific theory, its function.
11.30 a.m.–11.45 a.m. M. BANKOV, La logique considérée comme méthodologie de la connaissance scientifique.
11.50 a.m.–12.05 p.m. S. OHE, Flexibility in human cognitive behavior toward nature.
12.10 p.m.–12.25 p.m. V. VALPOLA, What is the problem of dispositional predicates?
12.30 p.m. Closure of the session.

WEDNESDAY AFTERNOON, AUGUST 30

Section 1, Chairman: S. FEFERMAN

2.30 p.m.– 5.30 p.m. **Invited Half Hour Addresses**
2.30 p.m.– 3.00 p.m. C. C. CHANG, An infinitely long remark on models generated from indiscernibles.
3.10 p.m.– 3.40 p.m. D. SCOTT, A survey of recent results of the interpolation theorem.
3.50 p.m.– 4.10 p.m. Interval
4.10 p.m.– 4.40 p.m. W. CRAIG, Two complete algebraic theories of logic.
4.50 p.m.– 5.20 p.m. H. J. KEISLER, Models with orderings.
5.30 p.m. Closure of the session.

Sections 8 and 9, Chairman: J. A. PASSMORE

2.30 p.m.– 5.30 p.m.	**Contributed Papers**
2.30 p.m.– 2.45 p.m.	M. G. JAROSHEVSKY, Principle of determinism in the general history of psychology.
2.50 p.m.– 3.05 p.m.	W. MAYS, Probability, psychology and common sense.
3.10 p.m.– 3.25 p.m.	M. DONALDSON and R. J. WALES, On claiming transitions in cognitive development.
3.30 p.m.– 3.45 p.m.	J. B. HUNSDAHL, Problems of relevance in evaluating different methodological approaches to subception.
3.50 p.m.– 4.05 p.m.	B. M. KEDROV, Psychology of scientific creativity.
4.10 p.m.– 4.25 p.m.	H. BARREAU, Psychology and phenomenology.
4.30 p.m.– 4.45 p.m.	J. H. GREIDANUS, Merger of physics and psychology.
5.10 p.m.– 5.25 p.m.	J. L. FISHER, Value and objectivity in the social sciences.
5.30 p.m.	Closure of the session.

WEDNESDAY EVENING, AUGUST 30

8.00 p.m.	General Assembly, Division of Logic, Methodology and Philosophy of Science of the International Union of History and Philosophy of Science.

THURSDAY MORNING, AUGUST 31

Section 2, Chairman: S. C. KLEENE

9.30 a.m.–11.50 a.m.	**Invited Half Hour Addresses**
9.30 a.m.–10.00 a.m.	P. VOPENKA, Ultraproduct, submodels and their extensions.
10.10 a.m.–10.40 a.m.	R. O. GANDY, Generalizations of recursion theory.
10.50 a.m.–11.10 a.m.	Interval.
11.10 a.m.–11.40 a.m.	S. A. KRIPKE, Recursion on ordinals and models of sub-systems of analysis.
11.50 a.m.	Closure of the session.

Section 9, Chairman: I. GADOUREK

9.50 a.m.–12.30 a.m.	**Contributed Papers**
9.50 a.m.–10.05 a.m.	Ju. A. LEVADA, Mathematical methods in sociology.
10.10 a.m.–10.25 a.m.	C. HAYASHI, One-dimensional quantification and multidimensional quantification.
10.30 a.m.–10.45 a.m.	R. TUOMELA, An analysis of the application process of a social psychological theory.
11.10 a.m.–11.25 a.m.	J. M. BROEKMAN, Social time as a tool for social analysis.
11.30 a.m.–11.45 a.m.	M. BLEGVAD, Problems of integration in social science.
11.50 a.m.–12.05 p.m.	W. J. BRANDENBURG, From survey-to action-research as a way from community to the individual learning child.
12.10 p.m.–12.25 p.m.	J. PASSMORE, Philosophy of education and educational science.
12.30 p.m.	Closure of the session.

Section 11, Chairman: E. STENIUS

9.30 a.m.–12.30 p.m.	**Contributed Papers**
9.30 a.m.– 9.45 a.m.	N. S. YULINA, Exact methods, scientism and value-orientation in philosophical knowledge.
10.50 a.m.–11.05 a.m.	M. RIESER, Kazimierz Ajdukiewicz (1890–1963).
11.10 a.m.–11.25 a.m.	H. L. MULDER, Ludwig Wittgenstein comments on the pamphlet 'Wissenschaftliche Weltauffassung der Wiener Kreis'.

11.30 a.m.–11.45 a.m.	C. EISELE, The problem of mathematical continuity in the thought of Charles S. Peirce.
11.50 a.m.–12.05 p.m.	I. LAKATOS, What caused the downfall of the infinitesimals?
12.10 p.m.–12.25 p.m.	W. K. WILSON, Correlations, essences, and Carnap's use of 'enumerative definition'.
12.30 p.m.	Closure of the session.

THURSDAY AFTERNOON, AUGUST 31

3.30 p.m.	Session in commemoration of A. I. Malcev. Speaches by A. TARSKI and Yu. L. ERSHOV.

Sections 1 and 2, Chairman: P. C. GILMORE

4.10 p.m.– 5.30 p.m.	**Invited Half Hour Addresses**
4.10 p.m.– 4.40 p.m.	K. SCHÜTTE, On simple type theory with extensionality.
4.50 p.m.– 5.20 p.m.	G. TAKEUTI, Formalization principle.
5.30 p.m.	Closure of the session.

Section 4, Chairman: D. FØLLESDAL

2.30 p.m.– 5.30 p.m.	**Contributed Papers**
2.30 p.m.– 2.45 p.m.	E. M. BARTH, Modal logic and natural deduction.
2.50 p.m.– 3.05 p.m.	R. M. MARTIN, On objective intensions and Frege's Sinne.
3.10 p.m.– 3.25 p.m.	L. O. KATTSOFF, On existence in mathematics.
3.30 p.m.– 3.45 p.m.	E. STENIUS, On the semantical status of laws of logic.
3.50 p.m.– 4.05 p.m.	S. E. LEVY, Syntactical contiguity in the sentential calculus.
4.10 p.m.– 4.25 p.m.	A. J. UEMOV, Objects identity and validity of analogy-conclusions.
4.30 p.m.– 4.45 p.m.	E. AGAZZI, About limitations in the validity of the exclude third.
4.50 p.m.– 5.05 p.m.	J. TUCKER, Methodology and the foundations of mathematics.
5.10 p.m.– 5.25 p.m.	J. FANG, What is, and ought to be, philosophy of mathematics?
5.30 p.m.	Closure of the session.

Section 6, Chairman: P. G. BERGMANN

2.30 p.m.– 5.10 p.m.	**Contributed Papers**
2.30 p.m.– 2.45 p.m.	W. K. BURTON, Justifiable physical theories.
2.50 p.m.– 3.05 p.m.	M. STRAUSS, The Huygens-Leibniz-Mach criticism in the light of present knowledge.
3.10 p.m.– 3.25 p.m.	B. JUHOS, Limit forms of empirical knowledge.
3.30 p.m.– 3.45 p.m.	C. MARE, Causality and duration.
3.50 p.m.– 4.05 p.m.	F. QUELON, Matter and arithmetical exactness.
4.10 p.m.– 4.25 p.m.	J. A. AKCHURIN, Informational capacity and microworld.
4.30 p.m.– 5.05 p.m.	O. ONICESCU, Mouvement et structure mécanique et relativité.
5.10 p.m.– 5.40 p.m.	A. POLIKAROV, A new conception of the relationship between the macro-world and the submicro-world.
5.45 p.m.	Closure of the session.

FRIDAY MORNING, SEPTEMBER 1

Section 7, Chairman: Chr. P. RAVEN

10.00 a.m.–12.15 p.m.	**Invited Half Hour Addresses**
10.00 a.m.–10.45 a.m.	J. H. WOODGER, Aspects of biological methodology.
11.00 a.m.–11.15 a.m.	Interval.
11.15 a.m.–12.00 a.m.	N. RASHEVSKY, A unified approach to biological and social organism.
12.15 p.m.	Closure of the session.

Section 1, Chairman: A. A. MARKOV

9.30 a.m.–12.30 p.m.	**Contributed Papers**
9.30 a.m.– 9.45 a.m.	A. MENNE, Zur Transitivität der Implikation.
9.50 a.m.–10.05 a.m.	A. OBERSCHELP, On the interpolation theorem of the predicate calculus.
10.10 a.m.–10.25 a.m.	G. C. MOISIL, Sur le calcul des propositions d'ordre supérieur.
10.30 a.m.–10.45 a.m.	R. SUSZKO, Algebraic treatment of translatability and of non-creativity in extending of theories.
10.50 a.m.–11.05 a.m.	F. VON KUTSCHERA, Interpretation of classical logic in constructive semantics.
11.10 a.m.–11.25 a.m.	K. ŠEPER, A remark on monotone functions of many-valued logic.
11.30 a.m.–11.45 a.m.	A. KRON, Causal ordering in first order theories.
11.50 a.m.–12.05 p.m.	W. FELSCHER, On criteria of definability.
12.10 p.m.–12.25 p.m.	A. L. DARZINS, The 'unambiguous' characterization problem: more complex cases.
12.30 p.m.	Closure of the session.

Section 6, Chairman: H. J. GROENEWOLD

9.30 a.m.–12.30 p.m.	**Contributed Papers**
9.30 a.m.– 9.45 a.m.	M. BUNGE, On physical meaning.
9.50 a.m.–10.05 a.m.	B. C. VAN FRAASSEN, On Beth's semantics of physical theories.
10.10 a.m.–10.25 a.m.	H. SCHLEICHERT, On the application of semantics to physics.
10.30 a.m.–10.45 a.m.	C. G. G. VAN HERK, Primitive physical concepts.
10.50 a.m.–11.05 a.m.	J. D. SNEED, Theoretical terms in set-theoretic axiomatizations of physical theories.
11.10 a.m.–11.25 a.m.	R. M. ROSENBERG, On axiomatics of Newtonian particle mechanics.
11.30 a.m.–11.45 a.m.	H. J. TREDER, On the structure of physical laws.
11.50 a.m.–12.05 p.m.	A. KOSLOW, The structure and significance of the law of inertia.
12.10 p.m.–12.25 p.m.	H. R. POST, Logic of theory-construction in physics.
12.30 p.m.	Closure of the session.

FRIDAY AFTERNOON, SEPTEMBER 1

Section 6, Chairman: W. YOURGRAU

2.30 p.m.– 5.30 p.m.	**Invited Half Hour Addresses**
2.30 p.m.– 3.00 p.m.	D. W. SCIAMA, The origin of the universe.
3.10 p.m.– 3.40 p.m.	D. FINKELSTEIN, Logical consequences of complementarity.
3.50 p.m.– 4.10 p.m.	Interval.
4.10 p.m.– 4.40 p.m.	B. D'ESPAGNAT, Objets et phénomènes en physique quantique.
4.50 p.m.– 5.20 p.m.	E. MCMULLIN, What do physical models tell us?
5.30 p.m.	Closure of the session.

Section 1, Chairman: R. O. GANDY

2.30 p.m.– 5.30 p.m.	**Contributed Papers**
2.30 p.m.– 2.45 p.m.	M. A. TAICLIN, Finitely generated commutative subgroups.
2.50 p.m.– 3.05 p.m.	S. Ju. MASLOV, Algorithms of logic inference search, based on the inverse method.
3.10 p.m.– 3.25 p.m.	A. GRZEGORCZYK, Assertions depending on time and corresponding logical calculi.
3.30 p.m.– 3.45 p.m.	H. KAMP, Expressibility in tense logic.
3.50 p.m.– 4.05 p.m.	I. RUZSA, A new formal system of deontic logic.

4.10 p.m.– 4.25 p.m.	B. Chendow, A theory of modalities.
4.30 p.m.– 4.45 p.m.	K. Potthoff, Some results concerning non-standard models of arithmetic.
4.50 p.m.– 5.05 p.m.	M. Richter, Applications of direct and inverse limit to elementary classes.
5.10 p.m.– 5.25 p.m.	C. G. McKay, Some results on intermediate propositional logics.
5.30 p.m.	Closure of the session.

Section 7, Chairman: N. Rashevsky

2.30 p.m.– 4.50 p.m.	**Contributed Papers**
2.30 p.m.– 2.45 p.m.	J. F. Frolov, Dialectics and methodology of biological knowledge.
2.50 p.m.– 3.05 p.m.	F. G. Asenjo, Mathematical organisms.
3.10 p.m.– 3.25 p.m.	A. Lindenmayer, An axiom system for the development of filamentous organisms.
3.30 p.m.– 3.45 p.m.	H. Ley, The conception of models in biology.
3.50 p.m.– 4.05 p.m.	S. R. Mikulinski, The history of biological science and contemporary problems.
4.10 p.m.– 4.25 p.m.	P. Lüth, Monadology and general system theory. Some aspects of the philosophy of Leibniz and the 'Wissenschaftslehre' of Ludwig van Bertalanffy.
4.30 p.m.– 4.45 p.m.	M. Jeuken, Models in biology.
4.50 p.m.	Closure of the session.

SATURDAY MORNING, SEPTEMBER 2

Section 1, Chairman: A. Tarski

| 9.30 a.m.–10.15 a.m. | **Invited Hour Address** |
| | A. Mostowski, The descriptive set theory and some problems of logic. |

Section 1, Chairman: D. Scott

10.30 a.m.–12.30 p.m.	**Invited Half Hour Addresses**
10.30 a.m.–11.00 a.m.	H. Gaifman, Types of elements in non-standard models of Peano's arithmetic.
11.10 a.m.–11.40 a.m.	R. M. Montague, A generalization of recursion theory.
11.50 a.m.–12.20 p.m.	Yu. L. Ershov, Numbered fields.
12.30 p.m.	Closure of the session.

Section 4, Chairman: R. M. Martin

10.30 a.m.–12.30 p.m.	**Contributed Papers**
10.30 a.m.–10.45 a.m.	P. Tichý, Analyticity in terms of Turing machines.
10.50 a.m.–11.05 a.m.	A. A. Zinov'ev, Theory of logical inference.
11.10 a.m.–11.25 a.m.	P. Weingartner, Towards a far reaching calculus of systems.
11.30 a.m.–11.45 a.m.	P. Braffort, Lindenbaum's problem: Present situation and possible developments.
11.50 a.m.–12.05 p.m.	A. A. Subbotin, Algebraic semilattices and formal logic.
12.10 p.m.–12.25 p.m.	H. P. Jochim, Note on intuitionism and the 'modality scandal'.
12.30 p.m.	Closure of the session.

Section 6, Chairman: R. M. Rosenberg

| 10.30 a.m.–12.30 p.m. | **Contributed Papers** |
| 10.30 a.m.–10.45 a.m. | L. S. Polak, Problems of models in physics. |

10.50 a.m.–11.05 a.m.	M. E. OMELJANOVSKI, Philosophical aspects of the measurement problem in quantum theory.
11.10 a.m.–11.25 a.m.	N. F. OFCHINNIKOW, Principles of conservation.
11.30 a.m.–11.45 a.m.	B. ROGERS, The possibility of non-continuous physical space.
11.50 a.m.–12.05 p.m.	S. T. MELJUKIN, Some methodological problems of the unity of scientific knowledge.
12.10 p.m.–12.25 p.m.	M. S. ASIMOV, About a correlation between philosophical and physical notions of matter.
12.30 p.m.	Closure of the session.

SATURDAY AFTERNOON, SEPTEMBER 2

2.00 p.m.– 3.00 p.m.	**Closing Session.**

AUTHOR INDEX

FALVEY MEMORIA'
VILLANOVA UN